Preparation for Precalculus Math 115

Selected Material from Understanding Intermediate Algebra

FIFTH EDITION

Lewis Hirsch | Arthur Goodman

CENGAGE
Learning™

Australia • Brazil • Japan • Korea • Mexico • Singapore • Spain • United Kingdom • United States

CENGAGE
Learning™

**Preparation for Precalculus Math 115
Selected Material from Understanding
Intermediate Algebra
FIFTH EDITION**

Lewis Hirsch | Arthur Goodman

Executive Editors:
Michele Baird

Maureen Staudt

Michael Stranz

Project Development Manager:
Linda deStefano

Senior Marketing Coordinators:
Sara Mercurio

Lindsay Shapiro

Senior Production / Manufacturing Manager:
Donna M. Brown

PreMedia Services Supervisor:
Rebecca A. Walker

Rights & Permissions Specialist:
Kalina Hintz

Cover Image:
Getty Images*

* Unless otherwise noted, all cover images used
by Custom Solutions, a part of Cengage
Learning, have been supplied courtesy of Getty
Images with the exception of the Earthview
cover image, which has been supplied by the
National Aeronautics and Space Administration
(NASA).

For product information and technology assistance, contact us at
Cengage Learning Customer & Sales Support, 1-800-354-9706
For permission to use material from this text or product,
submit all requests online at **cengage.com/permissions**
Further permissions questions can be emailed to
permissionrequest@cengage.com

ISBN-13: 978-0-534-65192-3

ISBN-10: 0-534-65192-5

Cengage Learning
5191 Natorp Boulevard
Mason, Ohio 45040
USA

Cengage Learning is a leading provider of customized learning solutions with
office locations around the globe, including Singapore, the United Kingdom,
Australia, Mexico, Brazil, and Japan. Locate your local office at:
international.cengage.com/region

Cengage Learning products are represented in Canada by Nelson Education, Ltd.

For your lifelong learning solutions, visit **custom.cengage.com**

Visit our corporate website at **cengage.com**

Printed in the United States of America

Table of Contents

Chapter 1 The Fundamental Concepts
1.3   Algebraic Expressions   2

     Review Exercises   11

Chapter 2 Equations and Inequalities
2.1   Equations as Mathematical Models   16

Chapter 3 Graphing Straight Lines and Functions
3.1   The Rectangular Coordinate System and Graphing Straight Lines   28
3.2   Graphs and Equations   40
3.3   Relations and Functions: Basic Concepts   53
3.4   Function Notation   70
3.5   Interpreting Graphs   78

     Chapter 3 Summary   90
     Chapter 3 Review   93
     Chapter 3 Practice Test   98

Chapter 4 Equations of a Line and Linear Systems in Two Variables
4.1   Straight Lines and Slope   100
4.2   Equations of a Line and Linear Functions as Mathematical Models   118
4.3   Linear Systems in Two Variables   132
4.4   Graphing Linear Inequalities in Two Variables   147

     Chapter 4 Summary   149
     Chapter 4 Review Exercises   152
     Chapter 4 Practice Test   155

Chapter 5 Polynomial Expressions and Functions
5.1   Polynomial Functions as Mathematical Models   158
5.2   Polynomials: Sums, Differences, and Products   165
5.3   General Forms and Special Products   171
5.4   Factoring Out the Greatest Common Factor   179
5.5   Factoring Trinomials   184
5.6   Solving Polynomial Equations by Factoring   193
5.7   Polynomial Division   201

Chapter 5 Summary   204
Chapter 5 Review Exercises   205
Chapter 5 Practice Test   207

Chapter 6 Rational Expressions and Functions

6.1   Rational Functions   208
6.2   Equivalent Fractions   213
6.3   Multiplication and Division of Rational Expressions   218
6.4   Sums and Differences of Rational Expressions   222
6.5   Mixed Operations and Complex Fractions   229
6.6   Fractional Equations and Inequalities   235
6.7   Literal Equations   241
6.8   Applications: Rational Functions and Equations as Mathematical Models 245

Chapter 6 Summary   260
Chapter 6 Review Exercises   262
Chapter 6 Practice Test   266
Chapter 4–6 Cumulative Review   267
Chapter 4–6 Cumulative Practice Test   271

Chapter 7 Exponents and Radicals

7.1   Natural Number and Integer Exponents   274
7.3   Rational Exponents and Radical Notation   287
7.4   Simplifying Radical Expressions   298
7.5   Adding and Subtracting Radical Expressions   305
7.6   Multiplying and Dividing Radical Expressions   308

Chapter 7 Summary   313
Chapter 7 Review Exercises   316
Chapter 7 Practice Test   318

Chapter 8 Quadratic Functions and Equations

8.1   Quadratic Functions ad Mathematical Models   320
8.2   Solving Quadratic Equations: The Factoring and Square Root Methods 328
8.3   Solving Quadratic Equations: Completing the Square   340
8.4   Solving Quadratic Equations: The Quadratic Formula   344
8.5   Equations Reducible to Quadratic Form (and More Radical Equations) 351

Chapter 8 Review Exercises   359

Answers to Selected Exercises and Chapter Tests   361

Queens College
Department of Mathematics
Project PROMISE

- Elementary Algebra - <u>VIDEOTAPES</u>

1. Introduction to Algebra: Algebraic Notation and
    Order of Operations (30 minutes)
2. Addition of Signed Numbers (35 minutes)
3. Subtraction of Signed Numbers (32 minutes)
4. Multiplication and Division of Signed Numbers (34 minutes)
5. Introduction to Exponents and the Distributive Law (26 minutes)
6. Simplifying Algebraic Expressions (31 minutes)
7. Solving Simple Equations (First Degree, One Variable) (33 minutes)
8. Solving Simple Inequalities (30 minutes)
9. Multiplication and Division of Fractions (34 minutes)
10. Addition and Subtraction of Fractions (36 minutes)
11. Solving Simple Fractional Equations (28 minutes)
12. Rules for Exponents (33 minutes)
13. Zero and Negative Exponents (27 minutes)
14. Scientific Notation (33 minutes)
15. Addition, Subtraction & Multiplication of Polynomials (35 minutes)
16. Factoring (27 minutes)
17. More Factoring (32 minutes)
18. Polynomial Long Division (28 minutes)
19. Reducing Fractions to Lowest Terms Using Factoring (18 minutes)
20. More Multiplication and Division of Fractions (18 minutes)
21. More Addition and Subtraction of Fractions (26 minutes)
22. More Fractional Equations (26 minutes)
23. Solving Formulas (15 minutes)
24. Graphing Straight Lines (50 minutes)
25. Solving Two Equations in Two Variables (31 minutes)
26. Square Roots (26 minutes)
27. Simplest Radical Form (26 minutes)
28. Addition and Subtraction of Radicals (23 minutes)
29. Multiplication and Division of Radicals (25 minutes)
30. Solving Quadratic Equations by Factoring (26 minutes)
31. Solving Quadratic Equations by Extracting Roots (18 minutes)
32. Solving Quadratic Equations by Completing the square (40 minutes)
33. The Quadratic Formula (30 minutes)

<u>Geometry</u>

Geometry 1: Lines and Angles (33 minutes)
Geometry 2: Triangles (30 minutes)
Geometry 3: Quadrilaterals and Area (48 minutes)
Geometry 4: Similar Triangles and the Pythagorean Theorem (40 minutes)
Geometry 5: Circles (27 minutes)
Geometry 6: Review of Geometry (45 minutes)

CONTINUED ON NEXT PAGE

Verbal Problems

34. Introduction to Verbal Problems I (37 minutes)
        [Prerequisite: Tape 7]
35. Introduction to Verbal Problems II (27 minutes)
        [Prerequisite: Tape 7]
36. Coin and Similar Word Problems (25 minutes)
        [Prerequisite: Tape 7]
37. Distance Problems (34 minutes)
        [Prerequisite: Tape 7]
38. Miscellaneous Word Problems (41 minutes)
        [Prerequisite: Tape 30]

Review Tapes

39. Review of Tapes 1 - 7: Computations using Signed Numbers,
    Simplifying Algebraic Expressions, Solving Equations (42 minutes)
40. Review of Tapes 9 - 11: Fractions [of Monomials] (43 minutes)
41. Review of Tapes 12 - 14: Integer Exponents (25 minutes)
42. Review of Tapes 15 - 19: Polynomials; Factoring (45 minutes)
43. Review of Tapes 20 - 23: Fractions [of Polynomials] (35 minutes)
44. Review of Tapes 8, 24, 25: Inequalities; Lines; and
                                Systems of Equations (29 minutes)
45. Review of Tapes 26 - 29: Radicals (28 minutes)
46. Review of Tapes 30 - 33: Quadratic Equations (37 minutes)

47. Elementary Algebra Final Exam Review, Part I (56 minutes)
48. Elementary Algebra Final Exam Review, Part II (56 minutes)

Chapter Reviews

Goodman, Chapter 1: The Integers (47 minutes)
Goodman, Chapter 2: Algebraic Expressions (50 minutes)
Goodman, Chapter 3: First Degree Equations and Inequalities (44 min.)
Goodman, Chapter 4: Rational Expressions (52 minutes)
Goodman, Chapter 5: Exponents and Polynomials (56 minutes)
Goodman, Chapter 6: Factoring (52 minutes)
Goodman, Chapter 7: More Rational Expressions (56 minutes)
Goodman, Chapter 8: Graphing, and Systems of Linear Equations (57 min)
Goodman, Chapter 9: Radical Expressions (55 minutes)
Goodman, Chapter 10: Quadratic Equations (48 minutes)

Queens College
Department of Mathematics
Project PROMISE

- Intermediate Algebra

VIDEOTAPES

1. Review of Signed Numbers and Order of Operations (37 minutes)
2. Solving First Degree Equations and Inequalities (35 minutes)
3. Absolute Value Equations (25 minutes)
4. Absolute Value Inequalities (32 minutes)
5. Addition and Subtraction of Polynomials (21 minutes)
6. Multiplication and Division of Polynomials (32 minutes)
7. Factoring (29 minutes)
8. More Factoring (38 minutes)
9. Multiplication and Division of Rational Expressions (26 minutes)
10. Addition and Subtraction of Rational Expressions (34 minutes)
11. Complex Fractions (24 minutes)
12. Solving Fractional Equations (32 minutes)
13. Integer Exponents I: Rules and Definitions (27 minutes)
14. Integer Exponents II: Examples (35 minutes)
15. Rational Exponents (39 minutes)
16. Simplifying and Combining Radical Expressions (38 minutes)
17. Multiplication and Division of Radical Expressions (25 minutes)
18. Quadratic Equations: Solutions by Factoring (36 minutes)
19. Solving Radical Equations (32 minutes)
20. Quadratic Equations: Solutions by Completing the Square (36 min.)
21. The Quadratic Formula (35 minutes)
22. Rectangular Coordinate System, & Graphing Linear Equations (30 min)
23. The Slope of a Line (36 minutes)
24. Equations of Straight Lines (40 minutes)
25. Graphing Linear Inequalities (22 minutes)
26. Variation (28 minutes)
27. Solving Systems of Linear Equations in 2 Variables (31 minutes)
28. Solving Systems of Linear Equations in 3 Variables (21 minutes)

Geometry

Geometry 1: Lines and Angles (33 minutes)
Geometry 2: Triangles (30 minutes)
Geometry 3: Quadrilaterals and Area (48 minutes)
Geometry 4: Similar Triangles and the Pythagorean Theorem (40 minutes)
Geometry 5: Circles (27 minutes)
Geometry 6: Review of Geometry (45 minutes)

CONTINUED ON NEXT PAGE

Verbal Problems

29. Word Problems Resulting in One 1st Degree Equation (26 minutes)
    [Prerequisite: Tape 2]
30. Word Problems Resulting in One Rational Equation (24 minutes)
    [Prerequisite: Tape 12]
31. Word Problems Resulting in One 2nd Degree Equation (30 minutes)
    [Prerequisite: Tape 21]
32. Word Problems Resulting in Two Linear Equations (23 minutes)
    [Prerequisite: Tape 27]

Review Tapes

33. Review of Tapes 1 - 4: Equations, Inequalities,
                                 and Absolute Value (28 minutes)
34. Review of Tapes 5 - 8: Polynomials and Factoring (43 minutes)
35. Review of Tapes 9 - 12: Rational Expressions (44 minutes)
36. Review of Tapes 13 - 14: Integer Exponents [Scien. Nota.] (25 min)
37. Review of Tapes 15 - 17: Rational Exponents & Radicals (37 min.)
38. Review of Tapes 18 - 21: Quadratic Equations (47 minutes)
39. Review of Tapes 22 - 26: Lines/[In]Equations. Variation (40 min.)
40. Review of Tapes 27 - 28: Systems of Equations (42 minutes)

41. Intermediate Algebra Final Exam Review, Part I (57 minutes)
42. Intermediate Algebra Final Exam Review, Part II (57 minutes)

Chapter Reviews

Hirsch, Chapter 1: Fundamental Concepts (46 minutes)
Hirsch, Chapter 2: Equations and Inequalities (55 minutes)
Hirsch, Chapter 3: Polynomials (58 minutes)
Hirsch, Chapter 4: Rational Expressions (56 minutes)
Hirsch, Chapter 5: Exponents (53 minutes)
Hirsch, Chapter 6: Radical Expressions (44 minutes)
Hirsch, Chapter 7: Second Degree Equations and Inequalities (55 min.)
Hirsch, Chapter 8: Graphing Linear Equations and Inequalities (57 min)
Hirsch, Chapter CS: Conic Sections (55 minutes)
Hirsch, Chapter SE: Systems of Equations (53 minutes)

Queens College
Department of Mathematics
Project PROMISE
Math Lab -- Kiely Hall 331

Math 122 - Pre-Calculus

VIDEOTAPES

1. Review of Signed Numbers and Order of Operations (37 minutes)
2. Solving First Degree Equations and Inequalities (35 minutes)
3. Absolute Value Equations (25 minutes)
4. Absolute Value Inequalities (32 minutes)
13. Integer Exponents I: Rules and Definitions (27 minutes)
14. Integer Exponents II: Examples (35 minutes)
15. Rational Exponents (39 minutes)
16. Simplifying and Combining Radical Expressions (38 minutes)
17. Multiplication and Division of Radical Expressions (25 minutes)
5. Addition and Subtraction of Polynomials (21 minutes)
6. Multiplication and Division of Polynomials (32 minutes)
7. Factoring (29 minutes)
8. More Factoring (38 minutes)
9. Multiplication and Division of Rational Expressions (26 minutes)
10. Addition and Subtraction of Rational Expressions (34 minutes)
11. Complex Fractions (24 minutes)
A. Relations and Functions (43 minutes)
B. Functional Notation and Operations on Functions (35 minutes)
22. Rectangular Coordinate System and Graphing Linear Equations (30 minutes)
23. The Slope of a Line (36 minutes)
24. Equations of Straight Lines (40 minutes)
27. Solving Systems of Linear Equations in 2 Variables (31 minutes)
28. Solving Systems of Linear Equations in 3 Variables (21 minutes)
25. Graphing Linear Inequalities (22 minutes)
C. Extracting Functions from Geometric Figures (27 minutes)
18. Quadratic Equations: Solutions by Factoring (36 minutes)
20. Quadratic Equations: Solutions by Completing the Square (36 minutes)
21. The Quadratic Formula (35 minutes)
E. Quadratic Inequalities (29 minutes)
F. Graphing Parabolas (39 minutes)
G. The Circle (35 minutes)
H. Ellipses and Hyperbolas (41 minutes)
I. Graphing Review (33 minutes)
J. Solving Non-Linear Systems of Equations (40 minutes)
12. Solving Fractional Equations (32 minutes)
K. Graphing Rational Functions and Radical Functions (40 minutes)
19. Solving Radical Equations (32 minutes)
L. Inverse Functions (48 minutes)
M. Logarithms and Exponents (40 minutes)
N. Properties of Logarithms (26 minutes)
O. Exponential Equations (14 minutes)
P. Types of Functions: Graphing Review (26 minutes)

CONTINUED ON NEXT PAGE

LIST OF VIDEOTAPES (Continued)

Trigonometry

Q. Angles, Degrees, and Radians (30 minutes)
R. Definitions of the Trigonometric Functions and Some Identities (20 minutes)
S. Trigonometric Functions of Some Basic Angles, and Graphs of y=sin(x) and y=cos(x) (42 minutes)
T. Trigonometric Functions of Second, Third, and Fourth Quadrant Angles (32 minutes)
U. Some More Trigonometric Identities (41 minutes)
V. Half Angle and Double Angle Formulas, and Proving Identities (27 minutes)
W. Solving Triangles and Trigonometric Equations (37 minutes)
X. Polar Coordinates and Graphing Polar Equations (36 minutes)

Verbal Problems

29. Word Problems Resulting in One 1st Degree Equation (26 minutes)
       [Prerequisite: Tape 2]
32. Word Problems Resulting in Two Linear Equations (23 minutes)
       [Prerequisite: Tape 27]
31. Word Problems Resulting in One 2nd Degree Equation (30 minutes)
       [Prerequisite: Tape 21]
30. Word Problems Resulting in One Rational Equation (24 minutes)
       [Prerequisite: Tape 12]

Review Tapes

33. Review of Tapes 1 - 4 (28 minutes)
36. Review of Tapes 13 - 14 (25 minutes)
37. Review of Tapes 15 - 17 (37 minutes)
34. Review of Tapes 5 - 8 (43 minutes)
35. Review of Tapes 9 - 12 (44 minutes)
 Y. Review of Tapes A - B (31 minutes)
39. Review of Tapes 22 - 25 (40 minutes)
40. Review of Tapes 27 - 28 (42 minutes)
38. Review of Tapes 18 - 21 (47 minutes)
 Z. Review of Tapes F - I (36 minutes)
AA. Review of Tapes M - O (39 minutes)
BB. Review of Tapes Q - W (49 minutes)

41. Intermediate Algebra Final Exam Review, Part I (57 minutes)
42. Intermediate Algebra Final Exam Review, Part II (57 minutes)
CC. Pre-Calculus Final Exam Review, Part I (60 minutes)
DD. Pre-Calculus Final Exam Review, Part II (57 minutes)

1.3 Algebraic Expressions

Suppose you deposit $5,000 in a bank that pays interest at the effective rate of 7.5% simple yearly interest, and you want to determine how much money you will have in the bank at the end of the year. You may approach this problem by first computing the interest you would earn after 1 year, and then adding this interest to the original amount you deposited (called the *principal*) as follows:

$$
\begin{aligned}
\text{Amount in the bank at the end of the year} &= \text{Principal} + \text{Interest} \\
&= \text{Principal} + \text{Principal} \times \text{Rate} \\
&= \$5{,}000 + \$5{,}000 \times 0.075 \\
&= \$5{,}000 + \$375 \\
&= \$5{,}375
\end{aligned}
$$

So if you deposited $5,000 in this bank, you would have $5,375 at the end of the year.

Notice the number of computations you had to perform to come up with your answer. Is there a simpler way to compute the amount you would have after 1 year?

Let's look at this process using symbolic notation. If we let P stand for the principal, then we can rewrite the amount at the end of the year as

$$\text{Amount in the bank at the end of the year} = \text{Principal} + \text{Interest}$$
$$= \text{Principal} + \text{Principal} \times \text{Rate}$$
$$= P + P \times 0.075$$
$$= P + 0.075P$$

The distributive property allows us to factor out P to get

$$= (1 + 0.075)P$$
$$= 1.075P$$

This says that to answer the question, all we need to do is multiply the principal by 1.075. Note that our use of symbolic notation has not only given us a more convenient (simpler) way to compute the answer, but also has given a general way to compute that answer for *any* principal. The expression $1.075P$ is an elementary example of what we intend to discuss for the remainder of this section: *simplifying* very basic algebraic expressions.

A *variable* is a symbol, usually a letter, that stands for a number (or set of numbers). In algebra, there are primarily two ways variables are used. One use of a variable is to represent a particular number (or set of numbers) whose value(s) need to be found. Equations are examples of this type of variable use.

A second use of variables is to describe a general relationship involving numbers and/or arithmetic operations, such as in the commutative property:

$$a + b = b + a$$

Variables represent unknown quantities. A *constant,* on the other hand, is a symbol whose value is fixed, such as 2, –6, 8.33, or π.

DEFINITION	An *algebraic expression* is an expression consisting of constants, variables, grouping symbols, and symbols of operations arranged according to the rules of algebra.

Our goal in this section is to review how to simplify algebraic expressions. That is, given a basic set of guidelines and the real number properties, we will take algebraic expressions and change them into simpler equivalent expressions. By *equivalent expressions,* we mean expressions that represent the same number for all valid replacements of the variables in the expression. For example, the expression $3x + 7x$ is equivalent to the expression $10x$ because when we substitute any number for x, the computed value of $3x + 7x$ will be the same as the computed value of $10x$.

Products

Recall the definition of exponential notation:

$$x^n = x \cdot x \cdot \cdots \cdot x \qquad \textit{The factor } x \textit{ occurs } n \textit{ times.}$$

The natural number n is called the *exponent,* x is called the *base,* and x^n is called the *power.* Thus,

$$5a^4b^2 = 5aaaabb \qquad (-3x)^3 = (-3x)(-3x)(-3x)$$

DEFINITION	The numerical factor of a term is called the *numerical coefficient* or simply the *coefficient.*

For example:

The coefficient of $3x^2y$ is 3.

The coefficient of $-5a^4b^2$ is -5.

The coefficient of z^3y is understood to be 1.

We will call the nonnumerical factors in a term the *literal part.* For example:

The literal part of $3x^2y$ is x^2y.

To multiply two powers with the same base, such as $x^5 \cdot x^4$, we can write out the following:

$$x^5 \cdot x^4 = (x \cdot x \cdot x \cdot x \cdot x)(x \cdot x \cdot x \cdot x) \qquad \textit{Write } x^5 \textit{ and } x^4 \textit{ without exponents.}$$
$$= x \cdot x \cdot x \cdot x \cdot x \cdot x \cdot x \cdot x \cdot x \qquad \textit{Then count the x's.}$$
$$= x^9$$

We can see that multiplying two powers with the same base is a matter of counting the number of times x appears as a factor. This gives us the first rule of exponents.

The First Rule of Exponents	$x^n x^m = x^{n+m}$

Thus, to *multiply* two powers of the *same base*, we simply keep the base and *add* the *exponents.*

The first rule can be generalized to include more than two powers. For example,

$$x^p x^q x^r x^m = x^{p+q+r+m}$$

When asked to *simplify* an expression involving exponents, we should write the expression with bases and exponents occurring as few times as possible.

EXAMPLE 1

Simplify each of the following.

(a) $x^2 x^7 x$ (b) $(-2)^3(-2)^2$

Solution

(a) $x^2 x^7 x = x^{2+7+1} \qquad \textit{Remember that } x = x^1.$

$$= \boxed{x^{10}}$$

(b) $(-2)^3(-2)^2 = (-2)^{3+2}$

$$= \boxed{(-2)^5} \qquad \textit{Evaluated, this answer is } \boxed{-32}. \qquad \blacksquare$$

To find a product such as $(3x^3y)(-4xy^2)$, *we could* proceed as follows:

$(3x^3y)(-4xy^2)$

$= (3)[(x^3y)(-4x)](y^2) \qquad \textit{Associative property of multiplication (Notice that only the grouping symbols were changed.)}$

$= (3)[(-4x)(x^3y)](y^2) \qquad \textit{Commutative property of multiplication}$

$= (3)(-4)(x \cdot x^3)(y \cdot y^2) \qquad \textit{Associative property of multiplication}$

$= -12x^4y^3 \qquad \textit{Multiplication and the first rule of exponents}$

We stated above that we *could* proceed in this way; however, we usually do *not* proceed in this manner unless we need to *prove* that $(3x^3y)(-4xy^2)$ is equal to $-12x^4y^3$.

Actually, to find a *product* such as $(3x^3y)(-4xy^2)$ quickly, we can ignore the original order and grouping of the variables and constants. Therefore, we just multiply the coefficients and then multiply the powers of each variable using the first rule of exponents.

(c) $4xy^2 - 4y^2x + 3x^2y = (4 - 4)xy^2 + 3x^2y$ *Note that $xy^2 = y^2x$ by the*

$\qquad\qquad\qquad\qquad\quad = 0xy^2 + 3x^2y$ *commutative property and*

   they are therefore "like"

   terms.

$\qquad\qquad\qquad\qquad\quad = \boxed{3x^2y}$ *Since $0xy^2 = 0$*   ∎

In summary, to combine "like" terms, add their numerical coefficients.

Removing Grouping Symbols

If we wanted to compute a numerical expression such as $7(9 + 4)$, we would evaluate it as follows:

$$7(9 + 4) = 7(13) = 91$$

We perform the operations within parentheses first.

However, in multiplying algebraic expressions with variables, as in the product $3x(x + 4)$, we cannot simplify within the parentheses. Instead, we multiply using the distributive property:

$$a(b + c) = ab + ac \quad \text{or} \quad (a + b)c = ac + bc$$

Verbally stated, multiplication distributes over addition.

Multiplication distributes over subtraction as well:

$$a(b - c) = ab - ac$$

For example,

$$7(9 + 4) = 7 \cdot 9 + 7 \cdot 4 = 63 + 28 = 91 \qquad \textit{Note that we still arrive at}$$
$$\textit{the same answer as } 7(13).$$

$$3x(x + 4) = (3x)(x) + (3x)(4) = 3x^2 + 12x$$

$$-2(x + y - 3) = (-2)x + (-2)y + (-2)(-3) = -2x - 2y + 6$$

When a negative sign immediately precedes a grouping symbol, as in

$$-(x + 4 - 3y)$$

we may interpret this as the negative of the quantity $x + 4 - 3y$. In the previous section, we found that we can rewrite $-a$ as $(-1)a$. We do the same to $-(x + 4 - 3y)$ to remove the grouping symbol:

$$-(x + 4 - 3y) = (-1)(x + 4 - 3y) \qquad \textit{Since } -a = (-1)a$$
$$\textit{Then we use the distributive property.}$$

$$= (-1)(x) + (-1)(4) + (-1)(-3y)$$

$$= -x - 4 + 3y$$

Thus, we can interpret $-(x + 4 - 3y)$ as multiplying the quantity $x + 4 - 3y$ by -1. When subtracting a quantity within grouping symbols, change the sign of *each term* within the grouping symbols.

If a positive sign precedes a grouping symbol, as in

$$+(x + 4 - 7y)$$

we interpret it as $+1(x + 4 - 7y)$. Hence,

$$+(x + 4 - 7y) = +1(x + 4 - 7y)$$

$$= (+1)x + (+1)(+4) + (+1)(-7y)$$

$$= x + 4 - 7y$$

Note that the signs of the terms within the grouping symbols remain unchanged.

$$(3x^3y)(-4xy^2) \qquad \textit{Reorder and regroup.}$$
$$= 3(-4)x^3 \cdot x \cdot y \cdot y^2 \qquad \textit{Multiply.}$$
$$= -12x^4y^3$$

The statement that "we can ignore the original order and grouping of variables and constants" is, in fact, a restatement of the commutative and associative properties of multiplication.

EXAMPLE 2

Multiply the following.

(a) $(-7a^2b^3c^2)(-2a^3b^4)(-3ac^5)$ (b) $-(3x)^4$ (c) $(-3x)^4$

Solution

(a) $(-7a^2b^3c^2)(-2a^3b^4)(-3ac^5) \qquad \textit{First we reorder and regroup.}$
$$= (-7)(-2)(-3)(a^2a^3a)(b^3b^4)(c^2c^5) \qquad \textit{Then multiply.}$$
$$= \boxed{-42a^6b^7c^7}$$

(b) $-(3x)^4 = -(3x)(3x)(3x)(3x) \qquad \textit{Rewrite without exponents, reorder, and regroup.}$
$$= -(3 \cdot 3 \cdot 3 \cdot 3 \cdot x \cdot x \cdot x \cdot x)$$
$$= \boxed{-81x^4}$$

(c) $(-3x)^4 = (-3x)(-3x)(-3x)(-3x) \qquad \textit{Rewrite without exponents, reorder,}$
$$= (-3)(-3)(-3)(-3)x \cdot x \cdot x \cdot x \qquad \textit{and regroup.}$$
$$= \boxed{+81x^4}$$

Note the differences between parts **(b)** *and* **(c)**. ∎

Combining Terms

We discussed the product of expressions; now we will discuss how we *combine* or add and subtract terms. You probably remember from elementary algebra that you can add "*like terms*," terms with identical literal parts, but you cannot add "*unlike terms*." What allows us to add like terms is the distributive property:

$$ba + ca = (b + c)a$$

For example,

$$5x + 7x = (5 + 7)x \qquad \textit{Distributive property}$$
$$= 12x$$

$$8ab - 17ab + 4ab = (8 - 17 + 4)ab \qquad \textit{Distributive property}$$
$$= -5ab$$

EXAMPLE 3

Combine the following.

(a) $2x^2 - 7x^2$ (b) $5x - 2y - 4x - 5y$ (c) $4xy^2 - 4y^2x + 3x^2y$

Solution

We will use the distributive property to demonstrate how it is used in combining terms. This step, however, should be done mentally.

(a) $2x^2 - 7x^2 = (2 - 7)x^2 \qquad \textit{This step is usually done mentally.}$
$$= \boxed{-5x^2}$$

(b) $5x - 2y - 4x - 5y = (5 - 4)x + (-2 - 5)y \qquad \textit{Note that we combine only}$
$$= 1x - 7y \qquad\qquad\qquad\qquad \textit{"like" terms.}$$
$$= \boxed{x - 7y} \qquad\qquad\qquad\qquad \textit{A coefficient of 1 is}$$
$$\qquad\qquad\qquad\qquad\qquad\qquad \textit{understood.}$$

EXAMPLE 4

Perform the following operations.

(a) $-5(2x - 3y + 5)$ (b) $-3x(-a + b)$

(c) $-3x - (a + b)$ (d) $3a - [5a - 3(2a - 1)]$

Solution

(a) $-5(2x - 3y + 5) = -5(2x) - 5(-3y) - 5(5)$ *Distributive property*

$$= \boxed{-10x + 15y - 25}$$

(b) $-3x(-a + b) = (-3x)(-a) - 3x(b)$ *Distributive property*

$$= \boxed{3ax - 3bx}$$ *(We prefer to write factors of terms in alphabetical order; hence, we write 3ax rather than 3xa.)*

Compare parts (b) and (c) of this example.

(c) $-3x - (a + b) = \boxed{-3x - a - b}$ *Since you are subtracting a + b, change the sign of each term.*

(d) $3a - [5a - 3(2a - 1)] = 3a - [5a - 6a + 3]$ *Simplify in brackets first (multiply 2a − 1 by −3). Then combine terms in brackets.*

$$= 3a - [-a + 3]$$ *Next, remove brackets.*

$$= 3a + a - 3$$ *Then combine terms.*

$$= \boxed{4a - 3}$$

EXAMPLE 5

Based on data from the U.S. Census Bureau, from 1985 to 1996, total enrollment in all public and private schools in the United States can be estimated by the equation

$$E = 0.8104(t - 1,985) + 56.65$$

where E is the total enrollment in all schools in millions during year t.

(a) Simplify the expression on the right of the equation.

(b) Compute the estimated enrollment for the year 1997 using the original equation and then with the simplified version completed in part **(a)**.

Solution

(a) We simplify the right side of the equation using a calculator as follows:

$E = 0.8104(t - 1,985) + 56.65$ *Distribute 0.8104.*

$\quad = 0.8104t - 1,608.644 + 56.65$ *Add −1,608.644 and 56.65 to get*

$E = 0.8104t - 1,551.994$

Hence the original equation can be written as $\boxed{E = 0.8104t - 1,551.994}$.

(b) We compute the enrollments by substituting 1,997 for t for each equation:

$E = 0.8104(t - 1,985) + 56.65$ $E = 0.8104t - 1,551.994$

$\quad = 0.8104(1,997 - 1,985) + 56.65$ $\quad = 0.8104(1,997) - 1,551.994$

$\quad = 0.8104(12) + 56.65 = 66.3748$ $\quad = 66.3748$

Note the differences in computing the answer using each form of the same equation. Which was easier?

We can see that we arrive at the same value for each equation as expected: 66.3748, which is $\boxed{66,374,800 \text{ students}}$.

EXAMPLE 6

In terms of x, find the area of the shaded region bounded by rectangles in Figure 1.4.

Figure 1.4

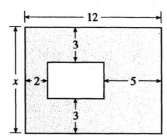

Solution

We first observe that the shaded area can be found by subtracting the area of the inner rectangle from the area of the outer rectangle:

$$\text{Area of shaded region} = \text{Area}_{\text{outer rectangle}} - \text{Area}_{\text{inner rectangle}}$$

The area of the outer rectangle is simple enough:

$$A_{\text{outer rectangle}} = \text{Length} \times \text{Width}$$
$$= 12x$$

The area of the inner rectangle can be found by observing that the length of the inner rectangle is $12 - 5 - 2 = 5$, and the width is $x - 3 - 3 = x - 6$. Hence

$$A_{\text{inner rectangle}} = \text{Length} \times \text{Width}$$
$$= 5(x - 6)$$

The area of the shaded region is therefore

$$A_{\text{shaded region}} = A_{\text{outer rectangle}} - A_{\text{inner rectangle}}$$
$$= 12x \qquad - 5(x - 6) \qquad \textit{First we multiply } x - 6 \textit{ by } -5.$$
$$= 12x - 5x + 30$$
$$= \boxed{7x + 30} \qquad \blacksquare$$

Study Skills 1.3

Reviewing Old Material

One of the most difficult aspects of learning algebra is that each skill and concept depends on those previously learned. If you have not acquired a certain skill or learned a particular concept well enough, this will more than likely affect your ability to learn the next skill or concept.

Thus, even though you have finished a topic that was particularly difficult for you, you should not breathe too big a sigh of relief. Eventually you will have to learn that topic well to be able to understand subsequent topics. It is important that you try to master all skills and understand all concepts.

Whether or not you have had difficulty with a topic, you should be constantly reviewing previous material as you continue to learn new subject matter. Reviewing helps to give you a perspective on the material you have covered. It helps you to tie the different topics together and makes them *all* more mean-

ingful. Some statement you read 3 weeks ago, and which may have seemed very abstract then, suddenly becomes simple and obvious in the light of all you now know.

Since many problems require you to draw on the skills you have developed previously, it is important for you to review so that you will not forget or confuse them. You will be surprised to find how much constant reviewing aids in learning new material.

When working the exercises, always try to work out some exercises from earlier chapters or sections. Try to include some review exercises at every study session, or at least at every other session. Take the time to reread the text material in previous chapters. When you review, think about how the material you are reviewing relates to the topic you are presently learning.

EXERCISES 1.3

In Exercises 1–68, simplify the expression as completely as possible.

1. $6x + 2x$

2. $5a + 4a$

3. $6x(2x)$

4. $5a(4a)$

5. $2x - 6x$

6. $5a - 4a$

7. $2x(-6x)$

8. $5a(-4a)$

9. $3m - 4m - 5m$

10. $-8y(-3y)(-2y)$

11. $3m(-4m)(-5m)$

12. $-8y - 3y - 2y$

13. $-2t^2 - 3t^2 - 4t^2$

14. $-5z^3 - 2z^3 - 4z^3$

15. $-2t^2(-3t^2)(-4t^2)$

16. $-5z^3(-2z^3)(-4z^3)$

17. $2x + 3y + 5z$

18. $3s + 5t + 6u$

19. $2x(3y)(5z)$

20. $3s(5t)(6u)$

21. $x^3 + x^2 + 2x$

22. $a^5 + 4a^3 + a^2$

23. $x^3(x^2)(2x)$

24. $a^5(4a^3)(a^2)$

25. $-5x(3xy) - 2x^2y$

26. $6r(-2r^2)(-4r^3t)$

27. $-5x(3xy)(-2x^2y)$

28. $6r(-2r^2t) - 4r^3t$

29. $2x^2 + 3x - 5 - x^2 - x - 1$

30. $-7t^3 - 4t^2 - 8 - t^3 - 5t^2 + 2$

31. $10x^2y - 6xy^2 + x^2y - xy^2$

32. $8a^2b^2 - 5a^2b^3 - a^2b^3 + a^2b^2$

33. $3(m + 3n) + 3(2m + n)$

34. $5(2u + 3w) + 4(u + 3w)$

35. $6(a - 2b) - 4(a + b)$

36. $7(3p - q) - 3(p + 2q)$

37. $8(2c - d) - (10c + 8d)$

38. $10(y - z) - (4y + 10z)$

39. $x(x - y) + y(y - x)$

40. $w(w^2 - 4) + w^2(w + 3)$

41. $a^2(a + 3b) - a(a^2 + 3ab)$

42. $t^3(t^2 - 3t) - t^2(t^3 - 3t)$

43. $5a^2bc(-2ab^2)(-4bc^2)$

44. $-2xyz(-4x^3y)(6yz^2)$

45. $(2x)^3(3x)^2$

46. $(5a)^2(2a)^4$

47. $2x^3(3x)^2$

48. $5a^2(2a)^4$

49. $(-2x)^5(x^6)$

50. $(-3a)^4a^8$

51. $(-2x)^4 - (2x)^4$

52. $(-5a)^2 - (5a)^2$

53. $(-2x)^3 - (2x)^3$

54. $(-5a)^3 - (5a)^3$

55. $4b - 5(b - 2)$

56. $8z - 9(z - 3)$

57. $8t - 3[t - 4(t + 1)]$

58. $7y - 5[y - 6(y - 1)]$

59. $a - 4[a - 4(a - 4)]$

60. $c - 6[c - 6(c - 6)]$

61. $x + x[x + 3(x - 3)]$

62. $y^2 + y[y + y(y - 4)]$

63. $x - \{y - 3[x - 2(y - x)]\}$

64. $y - 2\{x - [z - (x - y)]\}$

65. $3x + 2y[x + y(x - 3y) - y^2]$

66. $6r + 2t[r - t(r - 5t) - r^2]$

67. $6s^2 - [st - s(t + 5s) - s^2]$

68. $9z^3 - [wz - z(w - 4z^2) - z^3]$

In Exercises 69–72, (a) without simplifying, evaluate the expression for x = 2.82 and y = 7.25; (b) simplify and then evaluate the expression for x = 2.82 and y = 7.25.

69. $3x - 15y - 11x$

70. $-2x + 5y - 3x - 5y$

71. $2(3x - 4) - 5(3x + 8)$

72. $5(3x - 4y) - 2(5x - 10y)$

73. The number of physicians in the United States from 1980 to 1997 can be estimated by the equation

$$P = 16.75(t - 1,980) + 463.5$$

where P is the number of physicians in thousands during year t.

(a) Simplify the expression on the right of the equation.

(b) Compute the estimated number of physicians for 1998 using the original equation and then with the simplified version completed in part **(a).**

74. The number of dentists in the United States from 1980 to 1996 can be estimated by the equation

$$D = 3.58(t - 1,980) + 140$$

where D is the number of dentists in thousands during year t.

(a) Simplify the expression on the right side of the equation.

(b) Compute the estimated number of dentists for the year 1998 using the original equation and then with the simplified version completed in part **(a).**

In Exercises 75–78, find the area of the shaded region.

75.

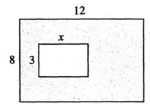

76.

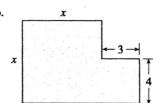

77.

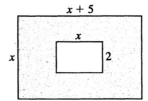

78.

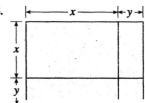

8. Solve and check a first-degree equation in one variable (Section 1.5).

   For example: Solve for x. $2x - 10 = \dfrac{x}{3}$

   Solution:

$2x - 10 = \dfrac{x}{3}$	*We "eliminate" the denominators by multiplying each side of the equation by 3.*
$3(2x - 10) = 3\left(\dfrac{x}{3}\right)$	*Multiply out the left side; simplify the right side.*
$6x - 30 = x$	*Subtract x from each side.*
$5x - 30 = 0$	*Add 30 to each side.*
$5x = 30$	*Divide both sides by 5.*
$x = 6$	

   Check $x = 6$: $2(6) - 10 \stackrel{?}{=} \dfrac{6}{3}$

   $12 - 10 \stackrel{\checkmark}{=} 2$

9. Solve a first-degree inequality and graph the solution set (Section 1.5).

   For example: Solve for x. $x - (3x + 5) \geq 2x$

   Solution:

$x - (3x + 5) \geq 2x$	*Simplify the left side of the inequality.*
$x - 3x - 5 \geq 2x$	
$-2x - 5 \geq 2x$	*Add $2x$ to each side of the inequality.*
$-5 \geq 4x$	*Divide each side by 4.*
$-\dfrac{5}{4} \geq x$	

   The sketch of the graph appears in Figure 1.8.

   Figure 1.8

10. Solve simple literal equations explicitly for a given variable (Section 1.5).

    For example: Given $8x - 3y = a + 2y$, solve explicitly for y.

    Solution: Since we are solving explicitly for y, we collect all the y terms on one side of the equation and all the non-y terms on the other side.

$8x - 3y = a + 2y$	*Add $3y$ to each side of the equation.*
$8x - 3y\ +\ 3y = a + 2y\ +\ 3y$	*Combine terms on each side where possible.*
$8x = a + 5y$	*Subtract a from each side.*
$8x\ -\ a = a + 5y\ -\ a$	*Simplify each side.*
$8x - a = 5y$	*Divide each side by 5.*
$\dfrac{8x - a}{5} = y$	

CHAPTER 1 REVIEW EXERCISES

In Exercises 1–6, you are given

$$A = \{x \mid x \leq 4, x \in N\} \qquad B = \{a \mid a > 5, a \in W\}$$
$$C = \{a, r, b, s, e\} \qquad D = \{b, c, f, g\}$$

List the elements in the following sets.

1. A

2. B

3. $C \cap D$

4. $C \cup D$

5. $A \cup B$

6. $A \cap B$

In Exercises 7–12, you are given

$$A = \{a \mid a \in W, \text{ and } a \text{ is a factor of } 12\}$$
$$B = \{b \mid b \in W, \text{ and } b \text{ is a multiple of } 12\}$$
$$C = \{c \mid c \in W, \text{ and } c \text{ is a multiple of } 6\}$$

List the elements in the following sets.

7. A

8. B

9. $A \cap B$

10. $A \cup B$

11. $B \cap C$

12. $A \cap C$

In Exercises 13–14, you are given

$$A = \{x \mid -2 < x \le 4, x \in Z\}$$
$$B = \{y \mid 3 \le y \le 12, y \in Z\}$$

Describe the sets using set notation.

13. $A \cap B$

14. $A \cup B$

In Exercises 15–20, graph the sets on the real number line.

15. $\{x \mid x \le 4\}$

16. $\{x \mid x > 4\}$

17. $\{b \mid -8 \le b \le 5\}$

18. $\{b \mid -8 < b < 5\}$

19. $\{a \mid -2 < a \le 4\}$

20. $\{b \mid -2 \le b < 4\}$

In Exercises 21–28, determine whether the statement is true or false.

21. $\frac{1}{2} \in Z$

22. $\sqrt{9} \in Z$

23. $0.476\overline{476} \in Q$

24. $\pi \in R$

25. $\pi \in Q$

26. $6\frac{2}{7} \in Q$

27. $I \subset R$

28. A rational number is an integer.

In Exercises 29–36, if the statement is true, state the property illustrated by the statement. If the statement is not true, write "false."

29. $(x - 4) + 3 = 3 + (x - 4)$

30. $(5 - x)7 = 7(5 - x)$

31. $(x - 4) \cdot 3 = x \cdot 3 - 4 \cdot 3$

32. $(x + 5)(y - 2) = x(y - 2) + 5(y - 2)$

33. $\left(\frac{1}{2x}\right)2x = 1 \quad (x \ne 0)$

34. $(5x + 2) + 0 = 5x + 2$

35. $(3x - 2) + (4x - 1) = 3x - (2 + 4x) - 1$

36. $3 \cdot 2(x - 1) = 6(2x - 2)$

In Exercises 37–54, perform the operations.

37. $(-2) + (-3) - (-4) + (-5)$

38. $(-6) - (-2) + (-3) - (+4)$

39. $6 - 2 + 5 - 8 - 9$

40. $-7 - 2 - 3 + 8 - 5$

41. $(-2)(-3)(-5)$

42. $(-7)(-3)(-5)(+2)$

43. $(-2)^6$

44. -2^6

45. $(-2) - (-3)^2$

46. $-5 - (-2)^3$

47. $(-6 - 3)(-2 - 5)$

48. $(-4 + 7)(-3 - 2)$

49. $5 - 3[2 - (4 - 8) + 7]$

50. $-6 + 2[5 - (3 - 9)]$

51. $5 - \{2 + 3[6 - 4(5 - 9)] - 2\}$

52. $-7 + \{3 - 6[12 - 5(9 - 11)]\}$

53. $\dfrac{4[5 - 3(8 - 12)]}{-6 - 2(5 - 6)}$

54. $\dfrac{6 - [2 - (3 - 5)]}{7 + [5 + 6(6 - 8)]}$

In Exercises 55–60, evaluate, given $x = -2$, $y = -1$, and $z = 0$.

55. $x^2 - 2xy + y^2$

56. $2x^2 + 3xy - 3y^2$

57. $|x - y| - (|x| - |y|)$

58. $|x + y| + |x| - |y|$

59. $\dfrac{2x^2y^3 + 3y^2}{zx^2y}$

60. $\dfrac{(5xy^3 + x^4)z}{x^2y}$

61. Given

$$t = \frac{\overline{X} - a}{\dfrac{s_x}{\sqrt{n}}}$$

compute t to two places, for $\overline{X} = 100$, $a = 95$, $s_x = 7.1$, and $n = 30$.

62. Given

$$\sigma_r = \sqrt{\frac{1 - \rho^2}{n - 1}}$$

compute σ_r to two places, for $\rho = 0.65$ and $n = 80$.

In Exercises 63–79, perform the operations and express your answer in simplest form.

63. $(2x + y)(-3x^2y)$

64. $(-6ab^2)(-3a^2b)(-2b)$

65. $(2xy^2)^2(-3x)^2$

66. $(-3r^2s^2)^3(-2r^2)$

67. $3x - 2y - 4x + 5y - 3x$

68. $-6a + 2b + 3a - 4b - 5a$

69. $-2r^2s + 5rs^2 - 3sr^2 - 4s^2r$

70. $-5x^2y^3 + 6xy^2 + 2x^2y^3 - 8y^2x$

71. $(y - 5) - (y - 4)$

72. $3a(a - b + c)$

73. $5rs(2r + 3s)$

74. $2x - 3(x - 4)$

75. $7y - 9(2x + 1)$

76. $3a - [5 - (a - 4)]$

77. $-2r + 3[s - 2(s - 6)]$

78. $5x - \{3x + 2[x - 3(5 - x)]\}$

79. $7 - 3\{y - 2[y - 4(y - 1)]\}$

80. The median cost of a home in the United States from 1991 to 1998 can be estimated by the equation

$$C = 4.695(t - 1{,}991) + 117.37$$

where C is the median cost in thousands of dollars at year t.

(a) Simplify the expression on the right-hand side of the equation.

(b) Compute the median cost of a home for 1993 using the original equation and then with the simplified version completed in part (a).

13

In Exercises 81–90, translate the statements algebraically.

81. Five less than the product of two numbers is 3 more than their sum.

82. Eight more than the sum of a number and itself is 3 less than the product of the number and itself.

83. The sum of the first two of three consecutive odd integers is 5 less than the third.

84. The product of the last two of three consecutive even integers is 8 more than 10 times the first.

85. The length of a rectangle is 5 less than 4 times its width. Express its area and perimeter in terms of one variable.

86. The length of a rectangle is 5 more than 3 times its width. Express its area and perimeter in terms of one variable.

87. The sum of the squares of two numbers is 8 more than the product of the two numbers.

88. The square of the sum of two numbers is 8 more than the product of the two numbers.

89. Xavier has 40 coins in nickels and dimes. Express the total value of his coins in terms of the number of dimes.

90. Cassandra makes $18 an hour as a garage mechanic and $10 an hour as a typist. If she works a total of 30 hours, and she works x of these hours as a mechanic, express the total amount she makes in terms of x.

In Exercises 91–107, solve the equation.

91. $5x - 2 = -2$

92. $3x - 4 = 8$

93. $3x - 5 = 2x + 6$

94. $3y - 5 = 8y - 9$

95. $11x + 2 = 6x - 3$

96. $7x + 8 = 3x$

97. $5(a - 3) = 2(a - 4)$

98. $7 - (2 - b) = 3b - 4(b - 1)$

99. $6(q - 4) + 2(q + 5) = 8q - 19$

100. $3(z - 7) + 2z - 4 = 5(z - 5)$

101. $3x - 5x = 7x - 4x$

102. $2a + 5a = 7a - 3a$

103. $x - \dfrac{2}{3} = 2x + 4$

104. $\dfrac{2x - 1}{3} = \dfrac{1}{2}$

105. $\dfrac{x - 3}{5} = x + 1$

106. $2y - \dfrac{1}{3} = y + \dfrac{1}{2}$

107. $3.2x + 0.14 = 1.4x - 21.46$

108. The number of physicians in the United States from 1980 to 1997 can be estimated by the equation

$$P = 16.75(t - 1,980) + 463.5$$

where P is the number of physicians in thousands during year t.

(a) Use this equation to estimate the number of physicians in the United States in 1995.

(b) In what year (between 1980 and 1997) were there 600,000 physicians in the United States?

In Exercises 109–112, solve each equation explicitly for the indicated variable.

109. $7x + 8y = 22$ for y

110. $3a - 5b = a + 2$ for a

111. $3x - 6y = 2 - 4x + 2y$ for y

112. $3a - 5b = \dfrac{a + 2}{2}$ for a

In Exercises 113–118, *solve each inequality and graph the solution on the number line.*

113. $3x + 12 < 2x - 9$

114. $5x - 8 \geq 3x - 6$

115. $5 - (2x - 7) > 3x - 15$

116. $3 - (8x + 12) \leq 9x + 24$

117. $3.2 - (5.3x - 1.2) \leq 3.4x - 1.8$

118. $8.2x - 8.3 + 1.4x > 5 - (3x - 2.4)$

CHAPTER 1 PRACTICE TEST

1. Given

$$A = \{x \mid x \text{ is a prime factor of } 210\}$$
$$B = \{y \mid y \text{ is a prime number less than } 25\}$$

(a) List the elements in $A \cap B$. (b) List the elements in $A \cup B$.

2. Indicate whether each of the following is true or false:

(a) $\sqrt{16} \in I$ (b) $2 \in Q$

(c) $-\dfrac{3}{4} \in Z$

3. Graph the following sets on the real number line.

(a) $\{a \mid a > 4\}$ (b) $\{x \mid -3 \leq x < 10\}$

4. If the statement is true for all real numbers, state the property that the given statement illustrates. If the statement is not true for all real numbers, write "false."

(a) $7(xy + z) = 7xy + z$ (b) $(x + y) + 3 = 3 + (x + y)$

5. Evaluate the following:

(a) $-3 - (-6) + (-4) - (-9)$ (b) $(-7)^2 - (-6)(-2)(-3)$

(c) $|3 - 8| - |5 - 9|$ (d) $6 - 5[-2 - (7 - 9)]$

6. Evaluate the following, given $x = -2$ and $y = -3$:

(a) $(x - y)^2$ (b) $\dfrac{x^2 - y^2}{x^2 - 2xy - y^2}$

7. Simplify the following:

(a) $(5x^3y^2)(-2x^2y)(-xy^2)$ (b) $3rs^2 - 5r^2s - 4rs^2 - 7rs$

(c) $2a - 3(a - 2) - (6 - a)$ (d) $7r - \{3 + 2[s - (r - 2s)]\}$

8. The length of a rectangle is 8 less than 3 times its width. Express its perimeter in terms of one variable.

9. Wallace has 34 coins in nickels and dimes. If x represents the number of dimes, express the number of nickels in terms of x. In terms of x, what is the total value of his coins?

10. Solve for x.

(a) $3x - 2 = 5x + 8$ (b) $2(x - 4) = 5x - 7$

(c) $\dfrac{2x + 1}{3} = \dfrac{1}{4}$ (d) $3x - (5x - 4) \leq 2x + 8$

(e) $2.1x - 5 > 5.3x - 4.9$

11. Solve explicitly for t. $3s - 5t = 2t - 4$

2.1 Equations as Mathematical Models

Let's suppose you are nearing the end of a course in which the final exam counts as 40% of your course grade. Your average grade for all but the final exam is 73, and you want to determine the minimum score needed on your final exam to get a grade of 80 for the course.

There are several ways we can approach this problem, but let's make sure we understand the relationship between the final exam grade and the course grade; that is, how does the final exam affect your already established grade of 73? In this example, the final exam is 40% of the course grade, and your average going into the final is 73; hence 60% of your grade is 73. If we let the final exam score be x, we would compute the course grade as follows:

$$\text{Course grade} = (0.60)(73) + 0.40x$$
$$= 43.8 + 0.40x$$

The course grade in this case is called a *weighted average* because it is computed by adding the products of grades with their percentage weights. Now that we have an equation or a *mathematical model* describing the relationship between the final exam score and the course grade, we can try to guess the value of x and check to see how close we come to our goal of a course grade of 80.

If you get a 95 on the final, then you would have

$$43.8 + 0.40(95) = 81.8$$

as a course grade. This is higher than 80.

Suppose you get 85 as a final exam score; then you would have

$$43.8 + 0.40(85) = 77.8$$

as a course grade. This is lower than we want.

Suppose you get 90 as a final exam score; then you would have

$$43.8 + 0.40(90) = 79.8$$

as a course grade. This is again too low (remember, we want the course grade to be 80). This guess-and-check method is quite uncertain and can take some time. How long would it take you to check other possible final course grades (and what you would need on the final to attain them) as well?

In the next section we will discuss algebraic solutions to these questions. For the remainder of this section we will continue to discuss model building.

If you haven't done so already, we suggest that you review Section 1.4 in preparation for this section.

In Section 1.4, we began to construct equations that describe the relationships between quantities discussed in word problems. A **mathematical model** is a mathematical description of a real-life situation. For example, the equation we discussed above, Course grade = 43.8 + 0.40x, is a mathematical model describing the relationship between course grade and final exam score x for a student with a 73 average before the final exam.

Building a mathematical model requires us to understand terminology from other fields or disciplines and to understand the mathematical relationships between quantities in these fields. For this reason, we often begin with relatively simple problems, borrowing from what we hope are our common everyday experiences. Granted that, in your daily experience, you may not be familiar with the approach we are about to describe; nevertheless a systematic model for approaching real-life problems is becoming more and more important for success in today's technological world. The approach we use throughout this book often begins with examining the relationships among the numbers involved, in an attempt to see the pattern and develop a general relationship.

Suppose that a salesperson is paid a base salary of $180 a week plus a 5% commission on her gross sales. Let's create a mathematical model describing the relationship between the salesperson's weekly pay and her gross sales. To develop this model, however, we need to understand the relationship between the quantities and/or variables under discussion. It is often helpful to substitute numbers for the variable expressions; as we examine the results, we should be able to spot a pattern to help us describe this relationship in general terms using symbolic notation. (Though this may seem too elementary a step for this problem, we encourage you to get in the habit of developing this general approach as a way to attack more difficult problems.)

To begin, let's note that if the salesperson sells $500 worth of merchandise one week, her commission is 5% of $500, found by multiplying $0.05 \times 500 = 25$ dollars. So her weekly pay would be $180 + $25 = $205. Let's try one or two more gross sales figures and compute her weekly pay:

Weekly pay $\quad\quad\quad$ = Base salary + Commission

Weekly pay with sales of $1,000 = $\quad$ $180 $\quad$ + $0.05 \times$ $1,000 = $230

Weekly pay with sales of $2,000 = $\quad$ $180 $\quad$ + $0.05 \times$ $2,000 = $280

Hence, if we let W = her weekly pay, then W is related to her gross sales, g, in the following way:

$$W = 180 + 0.05g$$

The equation $W = 180 + 0.05g$ is the (mathematical) model that describes this relationship.

Let's say that to pay her living expenses, the salesperson needs to earn at least $400 a week. How much does she have to sell to make enough for living expenses? The next example addresses this question.

EXAMPLE 1

A salesperson is paid a base salary of $180 a week plus a 5% commission on her gross sales. Use the model we developed above to make a table of values for the first $5,000 in gross sales. Use this table to *estimate* her weekly gross sales required to earn $400 a week.

Solution

We will return to this example in the next section.

The equation $W = 180 + 0.05g$ is the model we developed to describe the relationship between her weekly pay, W, and weekly gross sales, g. By substituting values for g, we can fill in the table as follows:

g	$180 + 0.05g$	$= W$
0	$180 + 0.05 \cdot 0$	$= 180$
1,000	$180 + 0.05 \cdot 1,000$	$= 230$
2,000	$180 + 0.05 \cdot 2,000$	$= 280$
3,000	$180 + 0.05 \cdot 3,000$	$= 330$
4,000	$180 + 0.05 \cdot 4,000$	$= 380$
5,000	$180 + 0.05 \cdot 5,000$	$= 430$

From the table above, we can estimate that for her to make $400, she will need to sell between $4,000 and $5,000 worth of merchandise. Actually, we can improve the estimate by noting that since $400 is closer to $380 than to $430, she will have to sell closer to $4,000; hence, we can narrow the estimated range to be between $4,000 and $4,500 worth of merchandise. ∎

In the next section we will get an exact answer to this question using algebraic methods. For now it is important that we learn how to create mathematical models. In the process of becoming familiar with certain models, we can also develop another important skill: estimating the reasonableness of our answers.

EXAMPLE 2

The length of a rectangle is 3 more than 4 times its width. Create a model expressing the perimeter in terms of its width, create a table for the model, and use the table to estimate the dimensions of the rectangle if the perimeter is to be 50 m.

Solution | A diagram is especially useful in a problem like this. Note that the length is described in terms of the width. Let

$$w = \text{Width}$$

Then

$$4w + 3 = \text{Length}$$ *The example tells us that the length of the rectangle is "3 more than 4 times its width."*

The rectangle is drawn in Figure 2.1.

Figure 2.1

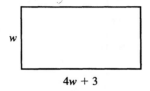

$$4w + 3$$

Recall that the formula for the perimeter of a rectangle is

$$P = 2w + 2L$$ *Where w = width and L = length*

With P as the perimeter and w as the width, we substitute $L = 4w + 3$ to get

$$P = 2w + 2(4w + 3)$$ *Which can be simplified to*
$$= 2w + 8w + 6$$
$$P = 10w + 6$$ *This is our model.*

If we are given the width, then from this model we can determine the length and the perimeter.

The table below shows the values of the length, L, and the perimeter, P, of the rectangle for some values of the width, w.

w	$L = 4w + 3$	$P = 10w + 6$
1	7	16
2	11	26
3	15	36
4	19	46
5	23	56

We can see from the table that for the perimeter to be 50 m, the width would be between 4 m and 5 m, and the length would be between 19 m and 23 m. We could get a more precise estimate by creating a table for values of w between 4 and 5, but this estimate is good enough for our purposes. ∎

EXAMPLE 3 | Jonas has $15,000 to invest. He decides to invest some of it in a long-term certificate that yields an annual interest rate of 7%, and the rest in a short-term certificate that yields an annual interest of 5%.

(a) Create a model that expresses the amount of interest earned in terms of the amount invested in the long-term certificate.

(b) Use this model to explain how the interest is affected by changes in the distribution of the $15,000 investment. Determine the maximum and minimum interest he could earn at the end of the year.

(c) Determine how much he should invest in each certificate if he wants to earn $1,100 in interest this year.

Solution

(a) As we discussed in Chapter 1, the amount of interest, I, earned in 1 year if P dollars is invested at a rate of $r\%$ (simple interest) per year is computed as

$$\text{Interest} = (\text{Principal})(\text{Rate})$$
$$I = P \cdot r \qquad \textit{Where r is written as a decimal}$$

For example, if \$2,000 is invested at 7% per year, then the interest earned in 1 year is

$$I = (2,000)(0.07) = \$140$$

Based on the information given in this example, let

$$x = \text{The amount invested at 7\%}$$

Then

$$15,000 - x = \text{The amount invested at 5\%}$$
Since the total amount invested is \$15,000 (total minus part equals remainder)

Let T be the total interest earned. We construct an equation that involves the yearly interest collected on each certificate:

$$\text{Total interest} = \text{Interest on the 7\% certificate} + \text{Interest on the 5\% certificate}$$
$$T = (0.07)(\text{Amount invested at 7\%}) + (0.05)(\text{Amount invested at 5\%})$$
$$T = \qquad 0.07x \qquad + \qquad 0.05(15,000 - x)$$

Hence our model is

$$T = 0.07x + 0.05(15,000 - x) \qquad \textit{Which is simplified to}$$
$$= 0.07x + 750 - 0.05x$$
$$\boxed{T = 0.02x + 750}$$

(b) What is the significance of the 0.02 and the 750 in the equation we found in part **(a)**? Let's examine this model by trying to understand how the relationship between the variables and constants explains what is occurring in this real-life situation. The model we have obtained is

$$T = 0.02x + 750$$

where T is the total amount of interest collected from both investments and x is *that portion of the \$15,000 invested in the 7% certificate.*

First note that if Jonas invests nothing in the 7% certificate, then he is setting $x = 0$ in the equation for T, obtaining $T = 0.02(0) + 750 = \$750$. This occurs because $x = 0$ means all the money goes into the 5% certificate and 5% of \$15,000 is \$750. This is the minimum interest Jonas would get from his investment.

Where does the 0.02 come from? Consider this: If Jonas puts all the money into the 5% certificate, then he would earn \$750 (i.e., $0.05 \times 15,000$) as his total annual interest. *For every dollar transferred from the 5% certificate to the 7% certificate, he gains 2% more interest on that dollar.* If x dollars are transferred, he gains 2% of x dollars, hence the interest equals $750 + 0.02x$. If all the money is put into the 7% certificate, Jonas gets $750 + 0.02(15,000) = 750 + 300 = \$1,050$ in interest. This is the maximum amount of interest he would get for his investment.

(c) How much should he put into the long-term certificate to get interest totaling \$1,100? Since the most he can get from the investment is \$1,050, he can never get \$1,100. ∎

EXAMPLE 4

A printer is determining the cost of producing a pamphlet. There will be a certain number of color pages that cost 13¢ each, and 28 more than that number of black and white pages that cost 5¢ each. In addition, there is a 25¢ per pamphlet cover charge. Create a model expressing the cost of the job in terms of the number of color pages. If the cost of the pamphlet is to be no more than $3.50, estimate how many pages can be put in the pamphlet.

Solution | Let

$$c = \text{Number of color pages}$$

Then

$c + 28 = $ Number of black and white pages   *There are 28 more black and white pages than color pages.*

Our model expresses the cost of printing each pamphlet. We let T be the total cost. (We will write our equation in cents to simplify the arithmetic.)

$$\begin{pmatrix} \text{Cost of printing} \\ \text{color pages} \end{pmatrix} + \begin{pmatrix} \text{Cost of printing} \\ \text{black and white pages} \end{pmatrix} + \begin{pmatrix} \text{Cover} \\ \text{charge} \end{pmatrix} = \begin{pmatrix} \text{Total} \\ \text{cost} \end{pmatrix}$$

$$\begin{pmatrix} \text{Number} \\ \text{of color} \\ \text{pages} \end{pmatrix} \cdot \begin{pmatrix} \text{Cost of} \\ \text{1 color} \\ \text{page} \end{pmatrix} + \begin{pmatrix} \text{Number of} \\ \text{black and} \\ \text{white pages} \end{pmatrix} \cdot \begin{pmatrix} \text{Cost of} \\ \text{1 b/w} \\ \text{page} \end{pmatrix} + \begin{pmatrix} \text{Cover} \\ \text{charge} \end{pmatrix} = \begin{pmatrix} \text{Total} \\ \text{cost} \end{pmatrix}$$

$$c \cdot 13 \quad + \quad (c + 28) \cdot 5 \quad + \quad 25 \quad = \quad T$$

Hence

$$T = 13c + 5(c + 28) + 25 \qquad \textit{Simplify.}$$
$$= 13c + 5c + 140 + 25$$
$$\boxed{T = 18c + 165}$$

*This equation represents how the total cost, T, is related to c, the number of **color** pages.*

If c is the number of color pages, then the number of black and white pages is $c + 28$, and the *total* number of pages, P, is found by

$$P = c + (c + 28) = 2c + 28$$

The table below shows how the total number of pages P and the total cost T are related to the number of color pages for a few values of c.

c	$P = 2c + 28$	$T = 18c + 165$
1	30	183
2	32	201
3	34	219

We are being asked to determine how many pages can be put into the pamphlet if the total cost is to be no more than $3.50. Rather than continuously computing the next several values to see where, on the table, the total cost is 350, we can see on the table above that starting at $T = 183$ (for $c = 1$), for every color page added, the total cost jumps 18¢. (We can see this in the equation $T = 18c + 165$ as well.) With some mental arithmetic, we can estimate the answer to fall somewhere in the neighborhood of $c = 10$. We create a table for values around $c = 10$.

c	$P = 2c + 28$	$T = 18c + 165$
9	46	327
10	48	345
11	50	363

By this table we can see that for the pamphlet to be no more than $3.50, c can be no more than 10. The total number of pages is then 48.   ∎

EXAMPLE 5

Jean can stuff 30 envelopes per hour, and Bob can stuff 45 envelopes per hour.

(a) Create a model that expresses the number of envelopes, E, they can stuff working together in terms of the number of hours, t, they work together.

(b) Create a model that expresses the number of envelopes, E, they can stuff working together if Bob starts 1 hour after Jean. Discuss how the two models differ.

Solution

(a) Let's carefully analyze how we construct this model.

THINKING OUT LOUD

What do we need to find?	An equation expressing the number of envelopes stuffed by Jean and Bob working together in terms of the number of hours t they work together
In general, how do we find the number of envelopes stuffed during a given time period?	Let's look at Jean alone. She can stuff 30 envelopes per hour. Therefore, in 1 hour, she can stuff 30 envelopes; in 2 hr, she can stuff $30 \times 2 = 60$ envelopes; in 3 hr, she can stuff $30 \times 3 = 90$ envelopes, etc. We can see by the pattern that in t hours, she can stuff $30t$ envelopes; hence $E_J = 30t$ is the model for the number *Jean* can stuff for t hours. In the same way, since Bob's rate is 45 envelopes per hour, the model for Bob is $E_B = 45t$.
How do we find the number of envelopes they can stuff working together?	The equation for Jean, $E_J = 30t$, gives the number of envelopes stuffed by Jean in t hours. Likewise, the equation for Bob, $E_B = 45t$, gives the number of envelopes stuffed by Bob in t hours. Together they stuff $E_J + E_B = 30t + 45t$ envelopes. Hence we have $$E = E_J + E_B = 30t + 45t = 75t$$ Thus the model is: $E = 75t$.

In general we see that the relationship between the amount of work done and the rate at which the work is being done is as follows:

$$\text{Amount of work done} = (\text{Work rate}) \cdot (\text{Time})$$

or

$$W = r \cdot t$$

The model we developed for Jean and Bob working together is $E = 75t$. We could have approached this more intuitively by saying that if Jean can stuff 30 envelopes an hour and Bob can stuff 45 envelopes per hour, then together they can stuff $30 + 45 = 75$ envelopes an hour. Hence our model will be

$$E = 75t$$

which is equivalent to the model we found before. Why bother with the first method at all? It will become apparent in part **(b)** of the example.

(b) How long would it take if Bob started an hour after Jean? Because we are starting with different rates at different hours, we cannot simply add the rates as we did above in the second method. Instead we will apply the logic of method 1: First we let

$$t = \text{Number of hours Jean spends stuffing envelopes}$$

Then

$$t - 1 = \text{Number of hours Bob spends stuffing envelopes}$$
Since Bob starts an hour later, he is working one hour less than Jean.

Thus we have

$$\begin{pmatrix} \text{Amount of work} \\ \text{done by Jean} \end{pmatrix} + \begin{pmatrix} \text{Amount of work} \\ \text{done by Bob} \end{pmatrix} = \begin{pmatrix} \text{Total amount of} \\ \text{work done} \end{pmatrix}$$

$$(\text{Jean's rate}) \cdot (\text{Jean's time}) + (\text{Bob's rate}) \cdot (\text{Bob's time}) = E$$

$$30 \cdot t + 45 \cdot (t - 1) = E$$

Hence the model is

$$E = 30t + 45(t - 1)$$

which simplifies to

$$E = 30t + 45t - 45$$

or

$$E = 75t - 45$$

Compare the two models. Note that the second model, $E = 75t - 45$, differs from the first model, $E = 75t$, by 45; that is, the second model will always produce 45 less envelopes than the first model for any value of t, the amount of time they work together. This is because in the second model, Bob worked one hour less; and since Bob stuffs 45 envelopes per hour, 45 less are being stuffed. ∎

Study Skills 2.1

Preparing for Exams: Is Doing Homework Enough?

At some point in time you will probably take an algebra exam. More than likely, your time will be limited and you will not be allowed to refer to any books or notes during the test.

Working problems at home may help you to develop your skills and to better understand the material, but there is still no guarantee that you can demonstrate the same high level of performace during a test as you may be showing on your homework. There are several reasons for this:

1. Unlike homework, exams must be completed during a limited time.

2. The fact that you are being assigned a grade may make you anxious and therefore more prone to careless errors.

3. Homework usually covers a limited amount of material, while exams usually cover much more material. This increases the chance of confusing or forgetting skills, concepts, and rules.

4. Your books and notes *are* available as a guide while working homework exercises.

Even if you do not deliberately go through your textbook or notes while working on homework exercises, the fact that you know what sections the exercises are from, and what your last lecture was about, cues you in on how the exercises are to be solved. You may not realize how much you depend on these cues and may be at a loss when an exam does not provide them for you.

If you believe that you understand the material and/or you do well on your homework, but your exam grades just do not seem to be as high as you think they should be, then the study skills discussed in this chapter should be helpful.

1. Tamara's math teacher counts the final exam as 25% of her course grade, and Tamara's average grade for all but the final exam is 82. Devise a mathematical model (an equation) that shows how Tamara's course grade is related to her final exam score.

   (a) Use this model to estimate the minimum score she would need on her final exam to get a course grade of 80.

   (b) Estimate the minimum score she would need on her final exam to get a course grade of 90.

2. Lisa's math teacher counts the final exam as 45% of her course grade, and Lisa's average grade for all but the final exam is 82. Devise a mathematical model that shows how Lisa's course grade is related to her final exam score.

   (a) Use this model to estimate the minimum score she would need on her final exam to get a course grade of 80.

   (b) Estimate the minimum score she would need on her final exam to get a grade of 90 for the course.

3. Carla's math teacher counts the final exam as 25% of her course grade, and Carla's average grade for all but the final exam is 78. Devise a mathematical model that shows how Carla's course grade is related to her final exam score. Use this model to estimate the minimum score she would need on her final exam to get a grade of 80 for the course.

4. Chuck's math teacher counts the final exam as 55% of his course grade, and Chuck's average grade for all but the final exam is 65. Devise a mathematical model that shows how Chuck's course grade is related to his final exam score. Use this model to estimate the minimum score he would need on his final exam to get a course grade of 80.

5. Suppose that a salesperson is paid a commission of 9% of his gross sales. Develop an equation relating his commission to his gross sales and use this equation to estimate the weekly gross sales he needs to earn a commission of $600 a week.

6. Suppose that a salesperson is paid a base salary of $100 plus a commission of 5% of her gross sales. Develop an equation relating her pay to her gross sales and use this equation to estimate the weekly gross sales she needs to earn $400 a week.

For Exercises 7–10, refer to the chart and table at the top of page 72.

7. On September 7, the euro (European dollar) was worth $0.8702 (U.S. dollars). Express the value of x euros in U.S. dollars. Use the model to estimate the value of 300 euros in U.S. dollars.

8. On September 7, the euro (European dollar) was worth $0.8702 (U.S. dollars). Express the value of x U.S. dollars in terms of euros. Use the model to estimate the value of $300 in euros.

9. On September 7, the British pound was worth $1.4388 (U.S. dollars). Express the value of x British pounds in terms of U.S. dollars. Use the model to estimate the value of 400 British pounds in U.S. dollars.

10. On September 7, the U.S. dollar was worth 105.94 Japanese yen. Express the value of x U.S. dollars in terms of the Japanese yen. Use the model to estimate the value of $200 in yen.

11. Suppose you are given the choice of two pay plans: strictly commission or a base salary plus commission. The strictly commission plan pays 9% of your gross sales, whereas the base salary plus commission plan pays you a base salary of $120 and a commission of 6% of your gross sales. Create a

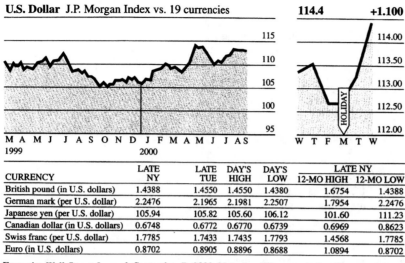

U.S. Dollar J.P. Morgan Index vs. 19 currencies   **114.4**   **+1.100**

CURRENCY	LATE NY	LATE TUE	DAY'S HIGH	DAY'S LOW	LATE NY 12-MO HIGH	LATE NY 12-MO LOW
British pound (in U.S. dollars)	1.4388	1.4550	1.4550	1.4380	1.6754	1.4388
German mark (per U.S. dollar)	2.2476	2.1965	2.1981	2.2507	1.7954	2.2476
Japanese yen (per U.S. dollar)	105.94	105.82	105.60	106.12	101.60	111.23
Canadian dollar (in U.S. dollars)	0.6748	0.6772	0.6770	0.6739	0.6969	0.8623
Swiss franc (per U.S. dollar)	1.7785	1.7433	1.7435	1.7793	1.4568	1.7785
Euro (in U.S. dollars)	0.8702	0.8905	0.8896	0.8688	1.0894	0.8702

From the *Wall Street Journal*, September 7, 2000. Note the differences in handling the conversions when currencies are given *in* U.S. dollars versus *per* U.S. dollar.

mathematical model that describes each plan and use these models to estimate *when* one plan is better than the other.

12. A cell phone company offers two basic plans for the poor executive: plan A and plan B. Plan A is a monthly service charge of $25, and a charge of 25¢ a minute for telephone airtime; plan B is a monthly service charge of $40, and a charge of 20¢ a minute for telephone airtime. Create a mathematical model that describes each plan and use these models to estimate *when* one plan is better than the other.

13. The length of a rectangle is 1 more than 3 times its width. Express the perimeter in terms of its width, and use this model to estimate the dimensions of the rectangle if the perimeter is to be 80 in.

14. The length of the first side of a triangle is twice the length of the second side, and the length of the third side is 5 more than the length of the second side. Express the perimeter of the triangle in terms of the length of its second side, and use this model to estimate the lengths of the three sides if the perimeter is to be 100 in.

15. Anna has decided to invest in a high-risk certificate that yields an annual interest rate of 8.3%. Express the amount of interest earned in terms of the amount she invests in this certificate and use this model to estimate how much she should invest if she wants to earn $1,000 in interest this year.

16. Maria has some money to invest and decides to invest in a low-risk certificate that yields an annual interest rate of 4.6%. Express the amount of interest earned in terms of the amount she invests in this certificate and use this model to estimate how much interest she would receive if she invested $12,500.

17. John has $12,500 to invest. He decides to invest some of it in a long-term certificate that yields an annual interest rate of 8%, and the rest in a short-term certificate that yields an annual interest rate of 5%. Express the amount of interest earned in terms of the amount invested in the long-term certificate and use this model to explain how the interest is affected by changes in the distribution of the $12,500 investment. Determine the maximum and minimum interest he could earn at the end of the year.

18. Estimate how much John of Exercise 17 should invest in each certificate if he wants to earn $865 in interest this year.

19. Alex has $24,000 to invest. He decides to invest some of it in a long-term certificate that yields an annual interest rate of 7.8%, and the rest in a short-term certificate that yields an annual interest rate of 4.2%. Express the amount of interest earned in terms of the amount invested in the short-term certificate and use this model to explain how the interest is affected by changes in the distribution of the $24,000 investment. Determine the maximum and minimum interest he could earn at the end of the year and estimate how much Alex should invest in each certificate if he wants to earn $1,200 in interest this year.

20. An LGP39 printer can print 9 copies per minute, whereas a GHJ27 printer can print only 4 copies per minute. Express the total number of copies made in terms of time for each machine and for both machines working together. Estimate how long it takes for 142 pages to be printed by each machine alone, and for both machines working together.

21. An LGP39 printer can print 9 copies per minute, whereas a GHJ27 printer can print only 4 copies per minute. Express the total number of copies made in terms of time (for the whole job) for both machines working together, if the slower model starts 5 minutes after the faster model starts. Use this model to estimate how long it takes for 142 pages to be printed by both machines.

22. A computer discount store held an end-of-summer sale on two types of computers; 58 computers were sold. If one type sold for $600 and the other type sold for $850, express the amount of money collected on the sale of the 58 computers in terms of the number of $600 computers sold. Use the model to estimate how many $600 computers were sold if $40,300 was collected on the sale of all the computers.

23. For the computer sale of Exercise 22, express the amount of money collected on the sale of the 58 computers in terms of the number of $850 computers sold. Use the model to estimate how many $850 computers were sold if $40,300 was collected on the sale of all computers.

24. On October 29, a stock loses 30% of its previous day's value. The next day, October 30, it gains 30% of its previous day's value. Express the value of the stock on October 30 in terms of its value on October 28. Use this model to estimate the value of the stock on October 28, if the stock is worth $2,500 on October 30.

25. Suppose you bought shares of stock at 61 ($61 per share) yesterday, and today the stock falls to 47. If the total value of all your shares yesterday was x, express the value of the stock today in terms of x. Use this model to estimate the value of the stock yesterday if the stock is worth $2,500 today.

26. Arthur can process 300 forms per hour, whereas Lewis can process 200 forms per hour. Express the total number of forms processed in terms of time (for the whole job) for both Arthur and Lewis working together. Use this model to estimate how long it takes to process 3,000 forms by both working together.

27. Arthur and Lewis of Exercise 26 worked together, but Arthur started a half-hour after Lewis. Express the total number of forms processed in terms of time (for the whole job). Use this model to estimate how long it takes for 3,000 forms to be processed if Arthur starts a half-hour after Lewis.

28. A truck carries a load of 50 boxes; some are 20-lb boxes, and the rest are 25-lb boxes. Devise a mathematical model that shows how the total weight of boxes in the truck is related to the number of 20-lb boxes. Use this model to estimate how many of each type of box there are if the total weight of boxes is 1,075 lb.

29. A merchant wishes to purchase a shipment of 24 clock radios. Simple AM models cost $35 each, whereas AM/FM models cost $50 each. In addition, there is a delivery charge of $70 for the shipment. Express the total cost of all radios together in terms of the number of AM radios. Use this model to estimate how many of each type of radio he purchased if the shipment cost $1,000.

30. A plumber charges $32 per hour for her time and $15 per hour for her assistant's time. On a certain job the assistant works alone for 2 hours doing preparatory work, then the plumber and her assistant complete the job together. Express the total cost of the job in terms of the amount of time the plumber worked. Use this model to estimate how many hours the plumber worked if the bill for the job was $312.

In this chapter we introduce the concepts of relations and functions, which play an important role in mathematics and its applications. We will pay particular attention to drawing, understanding, and interpreting the graphs of certain functions and the relationships they represent.

Suppose that a researcher collects data in the following table, which indicates the number of calories burned, c, during a brisk walk that lasts m minutes.

m	2	4	6	8	10
c	12	23	32	40	53

Based on these data, a researcher conjectures that the number of calories burned during a brisk walk and the number of minutes the walk lasts are related by the equation $c = 5m + 2$. In Section 3.2 we will examine this equation in more detail to analyze this relationship and determine how well this equation correlates with the data obtained. We will find that having a "picture" of this equation allows us to understand this relationship better. The ideas we develop in this chapter play an important role in performing this type of analysis and obtaining such a picture, called the graph of the equation.

3.1 The Rectangular Coordinate System and Graphing Straight Lines

Let's begin by considering a first-degree equation in two variables, such as

$$2x + y = 6$$

What does it mean to have a solution to this equation? A moment's thought reveals that a single solution to such an equation consists of a *pair* of numbers. We need an x value and a y value to produce *one* solution to this equation. For example, the pair of numbers $x = 1$ and $y = 4$ makes the equation true:

$$2x + y = 6 \qquad \textit{Substitute } x = 1, y = 4.$$
$$2(1) + 4 \overset{?}{=} 6$$
$$6 \overset{\checkmark}{=} 6$$

The pair $x = 2$ and $y = 2$ also satisfies the equation:

$$2x + y = 6 \qquad \textit{Substitute } x = 2, y = 2.$$
$$2(2) + 2 \overset{?}{=} 6$$
$$6 \overset{\checkmark}{=} 6$$

However, the pair $x = 3$ and $y = 1$ does *not* satisfy the equation:

$$2x + y = 6 \qquad \textit{Substitute } x = 3, y = 1.$$
$$2(3) + 1 \overset{?}{=} 6$$
$$7 \neq 6$$

Thus, we see that the equation $2x + y = 6$ is neither always true nor always false. Nevertheless, this equation has infinitely many solutions. In fact, we can produce as many solutions to this equation as we like by simply picking *any* value for one of the variables and solving for the other variable. (Remember that a single solution to this equation consists of two numbers.)

For instance, to obtain a solution to $2x + y = 6$ we can choose $x = 3$ and solve for y:

$$2x + y = 6 \qquad \textit{Substitute } x = 3.$$
$$2(3) + y = 6$$
$$6 + y = 6$$
$$y = 0 \qquad \textit{Thus, } x = 3 \textit{ and } y = 0 \textit{ is a solution.}$$

Or, we can choose $y = 6$ and solve for x:

$$2x + y = 6 \qquad \textit{Substitute } y = 6.$$
$$2x + 6 = 6$$
$$2x = 0$$
$$x = 0 \qquad \textit{Thus, } x = 0 \textit{ and } y = 6 \textit{ is a solution.}$$

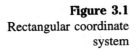

x	y
0	6
1	4
2	2
3	0

One way to keep track of the solutions to $2x + y = 6$ that we have found thus far is to make a table, as shown in the margin.

However, there is another way of listing the solutions that we will find more convenient and useful. We use *ordered pair* notation, which records the pair of numbers $x = 1$ and $y = 4$, for example, as $(1, 4)$. That is, an ordered pair of numbers is of the form (x, y), where the first number (sometimes called the first component or *abscissa*) is the x value and the second number or component (sometimes called the *ordinate*) is the y value. These are called *ordered pairs* for obvious reasons—the order of the numbers matters. As we saw earlier, the pair $(1, 4)$ satisfies the equation $2x + y = 6$, whereas the pair $(4, 1)$ does not.

As we have already pointed out, we can produce as many solutions as we want to a first-degree equation in two variables by simply choosing a value for one of the variables and solving for the other. How then can we exhibit all the solutions if there are infinitely many of them? Since we cannot list all of them, we need to develop an alternative method for displaying the solution set.

We introduce a two-dimensional coordinate system called a *rectangular* or *Cartesian coordinate system* (named after the French mathematician and philosopher René Descartes, 1596–1650). It is obtained by taking two number lines, one horizontal and one vertical, perpendicular to each other at their respective zero points.

As usual, the horizontal number line (commonly called the *x-axis*) is labeled positive to the right of 0 and negative to the left of 0. The vertical number line (usually called the *y-axis*) is, by convention, labeled positive above the 0 point and negative below the 0 point. The common 0 point of both axes is called the *origin*. Our coordinate system is illustrated in Figure 3.1. Usually, but not necessarily, the units of length are the same on both axes.

Figure 3.1
Rectangular coordinate system

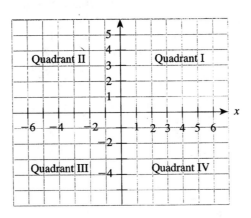

The x- and y-axes divide the plane into four parts, called *quadrants*. These are numbered in a conventional way, as indicated in the figure.

The *x*- and *y*-axes are referred to as the ***coordinate axes.*** The first and second members of the ordered pair are often called the *x*-coordinate and *y*-coordinate, respectively. *Note that points **on** the coordinate axes are not considered as being **in** any of the quadrants.*

This coordinate system allows us to associate a point in the plane with each ordered pair (x, y).

To plot (graph) the point associated with an ordered pair (x, y), we start at the origin and move $|x|$ units to the right if x is positive, to the left if x is negative, and then $|y|$ units up if y is positive, down if y is negative.

The point at which we arrive is the graph of the ordered pair (x, y):

$$(x, \quad y)$$
$$\uparrow \quad \uparrow$$

Tells you   *Tells you*
right/left   *up/down*

EXAMPLE 1

Plot (graph) the points with coordinates (3, 4), (–2, 1), (–3, –5), (2, –3), (5, 0), and (0, 4) on the rectangular coordinate system.

Solution

To graph the point (3, 4) we start at the origin and move 3 units to the right and then 4 units up. (Or, we could first move 4 units up and then 3 units to the right.) In a similar manner, we plot all the points as shown in Figure 3.2.

Figure 3.2
Solution for Example 1

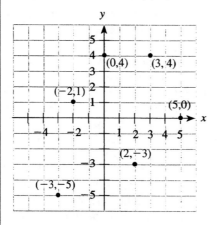

We call particular attention to the points (5, 0) and (0, 4). Notice that the point (5, 0) is on the *x*-axis because its *y-coordinate is* 0; the point (0, 4) is on the *y*-axis because its *x-coordinate is* 0. ∎

Just as every ordered pair is associated with a point, so too is every point associated with an ordered pair. If we want to see which ordered pair is associated with a specific point, *P,* we construct a perpendicular line from *P* to the *x*-axis. The point at which the perpendicular intersects the *x*-axis is the *x*-coordinate of the ordered pair associated with *P.* Similarly, we construct a perpendicular from *P* to the *y*-axis to find the *y*-coordinate of the ordered pair. Figure 3.3 illustrates this process.

Figure 3.3
Determining the coordinates of a point

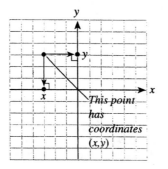

Thus, we have a one-to-one correspondence between the points in the plane and ordered pairs of real numbers; that is, every point on the plane is identified by a unique pair of real numbers, and every pair of real numbers corresponds to a unique point on the plane. For this reason we frequently say "the point (x, y)" rather than "the ordered pair (x, y)."

With this coordinate system in hand, we can now return to the question, "How can we exhibit the solution set of the equation $2x + y = 6$?" We have seen that the pairs of numbers in the accompanying table satisfy $2x + y = 6$. If we write them in ordered pair notation, we get the following ordered pairs (remember that x is the first coordinate and y the second):

x	y	(x, y)
0	6	(0, 6)
1	4	(1, 4)
2	2	(2, 2)
3	0	(3, 0)

Now we can plot these points, as shown in Figure 3.4. The figure strongly suggests that we "connect the dots" and draw a straight line. In doing so, we are making two statements: first, that every ordered pair that satisfies the equation is a point on the line, and second, that every point on the line has coordinates that satisfy the equation.

Figure 3.4

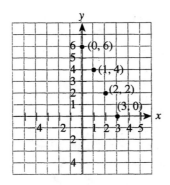

We will find the following definition useful.

DEFINITION	The *graph* of an equation is the set of all points whose coordinates satisfy the equation.

Thus, in drawing the straight line in Figure 3.5, we are saying that the graph of the equation $2x + y = 6$ is the straight line. This graph is now the "picture" of the solution set to the equation $2x + y = 6$.

Figure 3.5
The graph of the equation
$2x + y = 6$

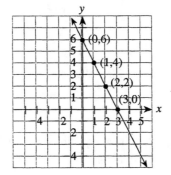

The following theorem, whose proof we will discuss further, generalizes this entire discussion.

THEOREM	The graph of an equation of the form $Ax + By = C$, where A and B are *not* both equal to 0, is a straight line.

It is for this reason that an equation of the form $Ax + By = C$ is often called a **linear equation.** This particular form, $Ax + By = C$, is called the **general form** of a linear equation. We postpone the proof of this theorem until Section 4.2; however, we can put this theorem to immediate use.

Basically, this theorem tells us that if we have a first-degree equation in two variables, we know that its graph is a straight line. For example, if we want to graph the equation $3x - 2y = 24$, the theorem tells us that the graph is going to be a straight line. Since two points determine a straight line, all we need find are two points that satisfy the equation.

As we mentioned earlier in this section, we can find as many points—that is, generate as many solutions to this equation—as we please, by simply picking a value for one of the variables and solving for the other variable. For example, for the equation $3x - 2y = 24$, let's pick two values for x and then find the y value associated with each x value.

Let $x = 4$: $3x - 2y = 24$ **Let** $x = 6$: $3x - 2y = 24$
$\qquad\qquad$ $3(4) - 2y = 24$ $\qquad\qquad\qquad$ $3(6) - 2y = 24$
$\qquad\qquad$ $12 - 2y = 24$ $\qquad\qquad\qquad$ $18 - 2y = 24$
$\qquad\qquad\qquad$ $-2y = 12$ $\qquad\qquad\qquad\qquad$ $-2y = 6$
$\qquad\qquad\qquad\qquad$ $y = -6$ $\qquad\qquad\qquad\qquad\qquad$ $y = -3$

Hence, two solutions are $(4, -6)$ and $(6, -3)$.

We would plot the two points and draw a line through them, as indicated in Figure 3.6. It is a good idea to check your graph by finding a third solution to the equation and checking to see that it lies on the line.

Figure 3.6
The graph of $3x - 2y = 24$

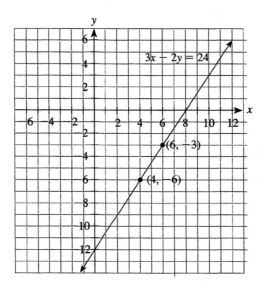

We see that we can graph a linear equation by arbitrarily finding two points. However, throughout our work in graphing there are certain points to which we want to pay particular attention.

DEFINITION	The *x-intercepts* of a graph are the x values of the points where the graph crosses the x-axis. The *y-intercepts* of a graph are the y values of the points where the graph crosses the y-axis.

If we look back at the graph of $3x - 2y = 24$ (Figure 3.6), we can see that the x-intercept is 8 and the y-intercept is –12.

Since the graph crosses the *x-axis* when $y = 0$ (why?),

the x-intercept of a graph occurs when $y = 0$.

Similarly, since the graph crosses the *y-axis* when $x = 0$ (why?),

the y-intercept of a graph occurs when $x = 0$.

Whenever possible (and practical), we label the x- and y-intercepts of a graph.

EXAMPLE 2

Sketch the graph of the following equation and label the intercepts.

$$-2x + 3y = 15$$

Solution

The graph of $-2x + 3y = 15$ will be a straight line. Thus, we need find only two points—the intercepts:

$-2x + 3y = 15$ *To find the x-intercept, set $y = 0$ and solve for x.*

$-2x + 3(0) = 15$

$-2x = 15$

$x = -\dfrac{15}{2}$ *The x-intercept is $-\dfrac{15}{2}$. Hence, the graph crosses the x-axis at $(-\frac{15}{2}, 0)$.*

$-2x + 3y = 15$ *To find the y-intercept, set $x = 0$ and solve for y.*

$-2(0) + 3y = 15$

$3y = 15$

$y = 5$ *The y-intercept is 5. Hence, the graph crosses the y-axis at $(0, 5)$.*

Now we can sketch the graph (see Figure 3.7).

Figure 3.7
The graph of
$-2x + 3y = 15$

It is easier to locate $-\dfrac{15}{2}$ if we rewrite it as -7.5.

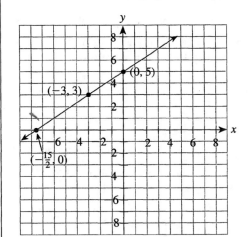

	x	y
x-intercept	$-\frac{15}{2}$	0
y-intercept	0	5
check	–3	3

We check with a third point. Letting $y = 3$, we find that $x = -3$. From the graph we can see that $(-3, 3)$ is on the line. ∎

The method we have outlined in Example 2 is called the ***intercept method*** for graphing a straight line.

DIFFERENT PERSPECTIVES: Intercepts

Consider the geometric and algebraic interpretations of the x- and y-intercepts of the graphs of $3x - 2y = 6$.

GEOMETRIC INTERPRETATION

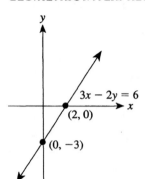

ALGEBRAIC INTERPRETATION

To find the x-intercept, set $y = 0$ and solve for x:

$$3x - 2y = 6$$
$$3x - 2(0) = 6$$
$$3x = 6$$
$$x = 2$$

To find the y-intercept, set $x = 0$ and solve for y:

$$3x - 2y = 6$$
$$3(0) - 2y = 6$$
$$-2y = 6$$
$$y = -3$$

The line crosses the x-axis at the point (2, 0). $\longleftrightarrow$ The x-intercept is 2.

The line crosses the y-axis at the point (0, −3). $\longleftrightarrow$ The y-intercept is −3.

While the intercept method is the preferred method to use, there are occasions when it does not quite do the job.

EXAMPLE 3

Sketch the graph of $y = -2x$.

Solution

Again, since this is a first-degree equation in two variables, we know that the graph is going to be a straight line. We will find the intercepts.

To find the x-intercept, we set $y = 0$ and solve for x:

$$y = -2x$$
$$0 = -2x$$
$$0 = x \qquad \textit{The x-intercept is 0.}$$

But (0, 0), as the origin, is on the y-axis as well, and so 0 is also the y-intercept. Since we get only one point from our search for the intercepts, we must find another point on the line.

Again, we simply choose a convenient value for x or y. We choose $x = 1$:

$$y = -2x$$
$$y = -2(1)$$
$$y = -2 \qquad \textit{Another point on the line is (1, −2).}$$

Now we can sketch the graph (see Figure 3.8). We use the point (−1, 2) as a check for this graph.

Figure 3.8
The graph of $y = -2x$

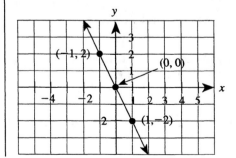

x	y
0	0
1	−2
−1	2

EXAMPLE 4

Sketch the graphs of:

(a) $x = -3$

(b) $y = 2$

Solution

First we must keep in mind that we are working in a two-dimensional coordinate system. Recall that we defined the standard form of a first-degree equation in two variables to be $Ax + By = C$, with A and B not both equal to 0.

(a) The equation $x = -3$ is of this form with $A = 1$, $B = 0$, and $C = -3$:

$$Ax + By = C$$
$$1 \cdot x + 0 \cdot y = -3$$

x	y
-3	-2
-3	1
-3	5

Try substituting various values for x and y in the equation $1 \cdot x + 0 \cdot y = -3$ and you will find that it does not matter what value we substitute for y, the x value must still be -3, as indicated in the accompanying table.

For an ordered pair to satisfy the equation $x = -3$, its x-coordinate must be -3. The equation $x = -3$ places no condition whatsoever on the y-coordinate—the y-coordinate can be any real number. Hence, the graph is a vertical line 3 units to the left of the y-axis, as illustrated in Figure 3.9.

Figure 3.9
The graph of $x = -3$

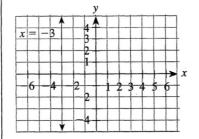

(b) Similarly, we can rewrite the equation $y = 2$ in general form with $A = 0$, $B = 1$, and $C = 2$:

$$Ax + By = C$$
$$0 \cdot x + 1 \cdot y = 2$$

We can substitute numbers for x and find that no matter what value is substituted for x, the y value will always be 2.

For an ordered pair to satisfy the equation $y = 2$, its y-coordinate must be 2, but the equation places no condition on the x-coordinate. Hence, the graph is a horizontal line 2 units above the x-axis (see Figure 3.10).

Figure 3.10
The graph of $y = 2$

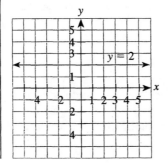

■

EXAMPLE 5

A salesperson earns $320 per week plus a commission of $0.50 per item sold. During a typical week, she sells a maximum of 900 items.

(a) Write an equation expressing the salesperson's weekly income, *I*, in terms of *n*, the number of items sold.

(b) Sketch a graph of this equation.

(c) Pick a point on the line, estimate its coordinates, and explain what it tells you about the salesperson's weekly income.

Solution

(a) If the salesperson were to sell 240 items during a particular week, the income for that week would be

$$I = 320 + 240(0.50)$$
$$= \$440$$

We multiply the number of items by 0.50 and add the $320.

In general, then, the weekly income *I* will be

$$\boxed{I = 320 + 0.50n \text{ dollars}}$$

(b) This equation is a first-degree equation in two variables and so its graph is a straight line. The equation is written in terms of *n* and *I* rather than *x* and *y*, so we will assign the variable *n* to the horizontal axis and the variable *I* to the vertical axis. Hence ordered pairs will be of the form (*n*, *I*) rather than (*x*, *y*). To sketch the graph properly, we should create appropriate scales for the axes. Given the fact that the salesperson can sell from 0 to 900 items, we label the horizontal *n*-axis from 0 to 900. For the vertical *I*-axis, we note that since the maximum she sells is 900 items, the salesperson's maximum weekly income will be *I* = 320 + 0.5(900) = 320 + 450 = $770. So the vertical axis should reach at least $770. For convenience of scaling, we will make it $800 (see Figure 3.11a).

Figure 3.11a

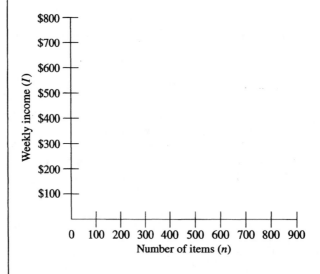

We must find two ordered pairs satisfying the equation. If *n* = 0, then *I* = 320 + 0.5(0) = 320. Hence we plot the ordered pair (0, 320). (This means that if she sold no items, she still makes $320.) As we saw above, if *n* = 900, then *I* = $770. So we may plot the ordered pair (900, 770), and graph the line (see Figure 3.11b).

Figure 3.11b

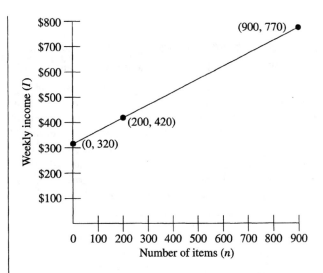

(c) This graph represents the relationship between the salesperson's weekly income and the number of items she sells. Every point on the graph gives a pair of numbers that are specific values of the weekly income for each number of items sold that week. For example, in Figure 3.11(b) we have chosen a point on the line and estimate its coordinates to be (200, 420): This tells us that for a week during which the salesperson sells 200 items, she makes an income of $420. ∎

DIFFERENT PERSPECTIVES: The Graph of an Equation

An equation and its graph offer two ways of looking at a relationship.

ALGEBRAIC DESCRIPTION

An equation such as $y = 3x - 5$ describes a relationship in which the y value is 5 less than 3 times the x value. Ordered pairs such as $(1, -2)$, $(0, -5)$, and $(3, 4)$ satisfy this relationship and hence are solutions to the equation.

GRAPHICAL DESCRIPTION

The graph of an equation gives a pictorial representation of the relationship. The following is the graph of the equation $y = 3x - 5$.

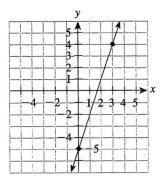

Every point (x, y) on the graph also gives a pair of numbers that satisfies the equation, and every pair of numbers that satisfies the equation corresponds to a point on the graph. We can see that the points $(1, -2)$, $(0, -5)$, and $(3, 4)$ are on the graph and by substituting we can check that they satisfy the equation $y = 3x - 5$.

37

Study Skills 3.1

Taking an Algebra Exam: Just Before the Exam

You will need to concentrate and think clearly during the exam. For this reason it is important that you get plenty of rest the night before the exam and that you have adequate nourishment.

It is *not* a good idea to study up until the last possible moment. You may find something that you missed and become anxious because there is not enough time to learn it. Then rather than simply miss- ing a problem or two on the exam, the anxiety may affect your performance on the entire exam. It is bet- ter to stop studying sometime before the exam and do something else. You could, however, review for- mulas you need to remember and warnings (common errors you want to avoid) just before the exam.

Also, be sure to give yourself plenty of time to get to the exam.

 EXERCISES 3.1

In Exercises 1–8, determine whether the given ordered pair satisfies the equation.

1. $3x - 5y = 17$; (4, 1)

2. $3x - 5y = 17$; (−6, −7)

3. $4y - 3x = 7$; (1, −1)

4. $4y - 3x = 20$; (2, −4)

5. $2x + 3y = 2$; $\left(\dfrac{3}{2}, -\dfrac{1}{3}\right)$

6. $5x - 4y = 0$; $\left(\dfrac{1}{10}, \dfrac{1}{8}\right)$

7. $\dfrac{2}{3}x - \dfrac{1}{4}y = 1$; (6, 12)

8. $\dfrac{3}{4}y - \dfrac{4}{5}x = 4$; (20, 16)

9. $y = 5$; (2, 5)

10. $x = 4$; (3, 7)

In Exercises 11–16, fill in the missing component of the given ordered pairs for the equations:

11. $x + y = 8$: (−1,), (0,), (1,), (, −2), (, 0), (, 4)

12. $x - 2y = 5$: (−3,), (−1,), (0,), (, −3), (, −1), (, 0)

13. $5x + 4y = 20$: (−2,), (0,), (4,), (, −5), (, 0), (, 4)

14. $3x + 7y = 15$: (−7,), (0,), (5,), (, −3), (, 0), (, 2)

15. $\dfrac{x}{3} + \dfrac{y}{4} = 1$: (−3,), (0,), (3,), (, −4), (, 0), (, 4)

16. $\dfrac{2x}{7} - \dfrac{y}{2} = 2$: (−7,), (0,), (7,), (, −2), (, 0), (, 2)

In Exercises 17–30, find the x- and y-intercepts of the graphs of the given equations.

17. $x + y = 6$

18. $y + x = 5$

19. $x - y = 6$

20. $y - x = 5$

21. $y - x = 6$

22. $x - y = 5$

23. $2x + 4y = 12$

24. $3x + 6y = 12$

25. $y = -\dfrac{4}{3}x + 4$

26. $y = -\dfrac{3}{2}x + 3$

27. $y = \dfrac{3}{5}x - 3$

28. $y = \dfrac{5}{3}x + 5$

29. $2y - 3x = 7$

30. $2x - 3y = 8$

In Exercises 31–58, sketch the graphs of the given equations. Label the x- and y-intercepts.

31. $4x + 3y = 0$

32. $5x - 2y = 0$

33. $y = x$

34. $y = -x$

35. $\dfrac{x}{2} - \dfrac{y}{3} = 1$

36. $\dfrac{y}{3} + \dfrac{x}{5} = 1$

37. $y = 3x - 1$

38. $y = -2x + 3$

39. $y = -\dfrac{2}{3}x + 4$

40. $y = \dfrac{3}{5}x - 6$

41. $5x - 4y = 20$

42. $3x + 6y = 18$

43. $5x - 7y = 30$

44. $3x + 8y = 15$

45. $5x + 7y = 30$

46. $3x - 8y = 16$

47. $x = 5$

48. $y = -3$

49. $-\dfrac{3}{4}x + y = 2$

50. $\dfrac{5}{3}x - y = 6$

51. $\dfrac{3}{4}x - y = 2$

52. $-\dfrac{5}{3}x + y = 6$

53. $y + 5 = 0$

54. $x - 7 = 0$

55. $5x - 4y = 0$

56. $3x + 6y = 0$

57. $5x - 4 = 0$

58. $3 + 6y = 0$

59. The number of physicians in the United States from 1980 to 1997 can be estimated by the equation

$$P = 16.75t - 32{,}702$$

where P is the number of physicians in thousands during year t. Sketch a graph of this equation using the vertical axis for P and the horizontal axis for t restricted to values between 1980 and 1997.

60. The number of dentists in the United States from 1980 to 1996 can be estimated by the equation

$$D = 3.58(t - 1{,}980) + 140$$

where D is the number of dentists in thousands during year t. Sketch a graph of this equation using the vertical axis for D and the horizontal axis for t restricted to values between 1980 and 1996.

61. A salesperson earns $220 per week plus a commission of 5% of the value of all the items she sells. She can sell a maximum of $10,000 worth of items during the week.

(a) Write an equation expressing the salesperson's weekly salary, S, in terms of v, the value of the items she sells weekly.

(b) Sketch a graph of this equation.

(c) Pick a point on the line, estimate its coordinates, and explain what it tells you about the salesperson's weekly income.

62. A cell phone company charges $30 a month and 21¢ a minute for each minute of airtime. Assume that the maximum amount of airtime you will use per month is 500 minutes.

(a) Write an equation expressing the cost, C, in terms of t, the time you spend on air per month.

(b) Sketch a graph of this equation.

(c) Pick a point on the line, estimate its coordinates, and explain what it tells you about the monthly costs under this plan.

63. At 11:00 A.M. John is 260 miles away from home. He continues to drive away from home at an average speed of 52 miles per hour for the next 6 hours.

 (a) Write an equation that expresses his distance, d, from home in terms of the number of hours, t, he has driven since 11:00 A.M.

 (b) Sketch a graph of this equation.

 (c) Pick a point on the line, estimate its coordinates, and explain what it tells you about John's distance from home.

64. A bank charges its checking account customers a monthly fee of $8.50 plus a charge of $0.30 per check.

 (a) Write an equation expressing the total monthly charge, C, in terms of the number of checks processed, n.

 (b) Sketch a graph of this equation.

 (c) Pick a point on the line, estimate its coordinates, and explain what it tells you about the total monthly checking charge.

65. A car rental company charges $29 per day plus a mileage charge of $0.14 per mile.

 (a) Write an equation expressing the total rental charge, C, for a 1-day rental in terms of the number of miles driven, n.

 (b) Sketch a graph of this equation.

 (c) Pick a point on the line, estimate its coordinates, and explain what it tells you about the total rental charge.

66. A telephone company charges a monthly fee of $17.50 plus a charge of $0.08 per local call.

 (a) Write an equation expressing the total monthly charge, C, in terms of the number of local calls made, n.

 (b) Sketch a graph of this equation.

 (c) Pick a point on the line, estimate its coordinates, and explain what it tells you about the total monthly telephone charge.

⍰ QUESTIONS FOR THOUGHT

67. Describe the x- and y-intercepts of a graph both geometrically and algebraically.

68. Sketch the graph of $2s + 3t = 6$ on a set of coordinate axes with t being the horizontal axis and s the vertical axis.

69. Repeat Exercise 68 with the axes reversed. Does reversing the labeling of the axes affect the graph? How?

70. Although we usually use the same scale on both the horizontal and vertical axes, sometimes it is necessary (or more convenient) to use different scales for each axis. Use appropriate scales on the x- and y-axes to sketch a graph of the following:

 (a) $y = 200x + 400$ **(b)** $y = 0.04x$

3.2   Graphs and Equations

In the previous section we discussed how to graph the line $Ax + By = C$, by using the equation to generate ordered pairs, plot the corresponding points, and draw the line. In this section we will do the opposite; that is, given a graph we will have to identify ordered pairs that lie on the graph. (In the next chapter we will do more—given a linear graph, we will construct its equation.) We do not need to confine our discussion to linear graphs.

A graph describes a relationship between variables. The graph in Figure 3.12 gives us values of y for various values of x, and values of x for various values of y. For example, we can see that the point $(-2, 3)$ is *on the graph*, hence we state that $y = 3$ when $x = -2$ (or $x = -2$ when $y = 3$).

Figure 3.12

When we want to focus on a particular point on the graph, we often exaggerate this point with a heavy dot, such as the dot on $(-2, 3)$. The arrowhead at either end of a graph indicates that the graph continues indefinitely in the direction the arrow is pointing.

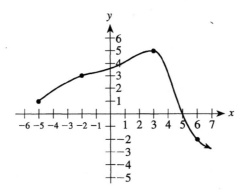

If we are asked to fill in the missing component of the "point" $(3, \quad)$ lying on the graph, we are being asked to find the y-coordinate on the graph whose x-coordinate is 3. To do this we locate $x = 3$ *on the graph*, and identify the y-coordinate of that point. If we can put a grid on the graph (Figure 3.13a), then we can easily see that on the graph, the y-coordinate is 5 when $x = 3$; or, the point $(3, 5)$ lies on the graph.

Figure 3.13a

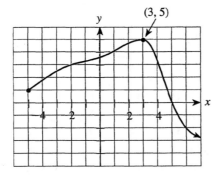

If we cannot put a grid on the graph then we have to locate the y value by locating the x value 3 on the x-axis (see Figure 3.13b) and move vertically toward the graph until we meet the graph. Then move horizontally toward the y-axis until we meet it. Read off the y value on the y-axis. This will give us the value $y = 5$.

Figure 3.13b

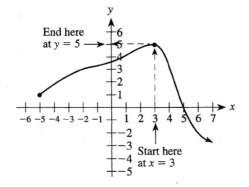

On the other hand, if we are asked to find the x value when $y = -2$, we would start on the y-axis (see Figure 3.13c) and move horizontally toward the graph until we meet the graph. Then move vertically toward the x-axis until we meet it. Read off the x value on the x-axis. This will give us the value $x = 6$. Hence when $y = -2$, $x = 6$, or the ordered pair $(6, -2)$ satisfies the equation of the graph.

Figure 3.13c

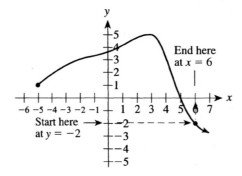

EXAMPLE 1

Using the graph in Figure 3.14, determine the following:

(a) Find y when $x = -3$, 2, and 4.

(b) Find x when $y = 2$.

(c) Fill in the missing component of the "point" $(6, \ )$ lying on the graph.

Figure 3.14

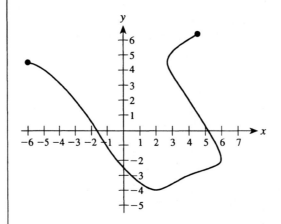

Solution

(a) To find y when $x = -3$, we start on the x-axis at $x = -3$, project vertically until we meet the graph, then move horizontally until we meet the y-axis, and read off the value on the y-axis: $y = 2$. See Figure 3.15a. Hence $y = 2$ when $x = -3$.

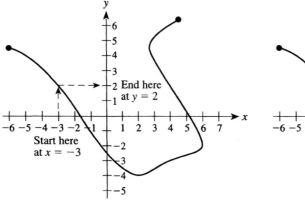

Figure 3.15a

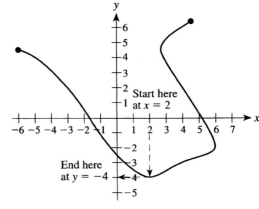

Figure 3.15b

To find y when $x = 2$, we start on the x-axis at $x = 2$, project vertically until we meet the graph, then move horizontally until we meet the y-axis, and read off the value on the y-axis: $y = -4$. See Figure 3.15b. Hence $y = -4$ when $x = 2$.

To find y when $x = 4$, we start on the x-axis at $x = 4$ and project vertically until we meet the graph. In this case, however, note that we meet the graph in three places. This means that there are three points on the graph where the x-coordinate has the value 4. For each point on the graph, we move horizontally until we meet the y-axis, and read off the values on the y-axis. We get three answers: $y = -3$, $y = 2$, and $y = 6$. See Figure 3.15c. Hence when $x = 4$, $y = -3, 2,$ and 6.

Figure 3.15c

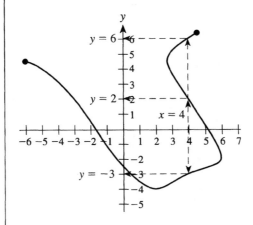

(b) To find x when $y = 2$, we start on the y-axis at $y = 2$ and project horizontally until we meet the graph. In this case, however, note that we meet the graph in two places. This means that there are two points on the graph where the y-coordinate has the value 2. For each point on the graph, we move vertically until we meet the x-axis, and read off the values on the x-axis. We get two answers: $x = -3$ and $x = 4$. See Figure 3.16a. Hence when $y = 2$, $x = -3$ and 4.

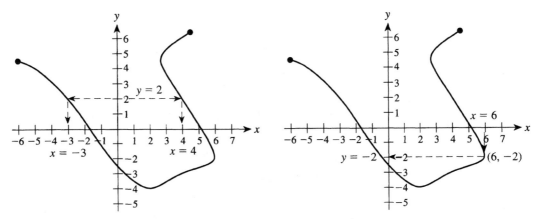

Figure 3.16a   **Figure 3.16b**

(c) Filling in the missing component of (6,) means we are looking for the value of y when $x = 6$. To find y when $x = 6$, we start on the x-axis at $x = 6$, project vertically until we meet the graph, then move horizontally until we meet the y-axis, and read off the value on the y-axis: $y = -2$. See Figure 3.16b. Hence (6, −2) lies on the graph. ∎

If the graph can also be expressed as an equation, then, as we have seen in Section 3.1, finding ordered pairs of points on the graph is equivalent to finding ordered pairs that satisfy the equation of the graph. Given a graph and its equation, the following are equivalent ways of expressing the same idea:

"$y = 5$ when $x = 3$," or

"The point $(3, 5)$ lies on the graph," or

"The ordered pair $(3, 5)$ satisfies the equation of the graph."

EXAMPLE 2

Figure 3.17 is the graph of the equation $x^2 + y^2 = 25$. Find y for $x = 3$ by using the graph, and verify the value(s) using the equation of the graph.

Figure 3.17
The graph of $x^2 + y^2 = 25$

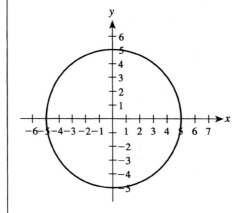

Solution

To find y when $x = 3$ by using the graph, we start on the x-axis at $x = 3$ and project vertically until we meet the graph. Note that we meet the graph in two places. This means that there are two points on the graph where the x-coordinate has the value 3. For each point on the graph, we move horizontally until we meet the y-axis, and read off the values on the y-axis. We get two answers: $y = -4$ and $y = 4$ (see Figure 3.18). Hence the points $(3, 4)$ and $(3, -4)$ lie on the graph.

Figure 3.18

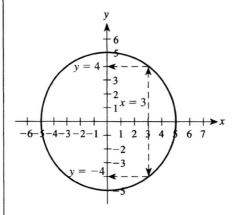

Since we are told that the equation $x^2 + y^2 = 25$ is the equation of the graph, we can verify that the point $(3, 4)$ lies on the graph by checking that the equation is satisfied by the ordered pair $(3, 4)$:

$$x^2 + y^2 = 25 \qquad \textit{Substitute } x = 3 \textit{ and } y = 4 \textit{ in the equation.}$$
$$3^2 + 4^2 \stackrel{?}{=} 25$$
$$9 + 16 \stackrel{\checkmark}{=} 25 \qquad \textit{Hence the point } (3, 4) \textit{ does lie on the graph.}$$

We can also verify that the point $(3, -4)$ lies on the graph by checking that the equation is satisfied by the ordered pair $(3, -4)$:

$$x^2 + y^2 = 25 \qquad \textit{Substitute } x = 3 \textit{ and } y = -4 \textit{ in the equation.}$$
$$3^2 + (-4)^2 \overset{?}{=} 25$$
$$9 + 16 \overset{\checkmark}{=} 25 \qquad \textit{Hence the point } (3, -4) \textit{ also lies on the graph.} \qquad \blacksquare$$

EXAMPLE 3

Figure 3.19 shows the graph of the equation $y = x^2 - 9$. Identify the x- and y-intercepts of the graph, and verify the intercepts using the equation.

Figure 3.19
The graph of $y = x^2 - 9$

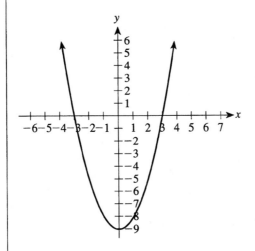

Solution

The y-intercept is the value of y where the graph crosses the y-axis. We can see that the graph crosses the y-axis when $y = -9$. Hence the y-intercept is -9.

The graph crosses the y-axis when $x = 0$; the point $(0, -9)$ lies on the graph. We verify that $(0, -9)$ is the y-intercept:

$$y = x^2 - 9 \qquad \textit{Substitute } x = 0 \textit{ and } y = -9 \textit{ in the equation.}$$
$$-9 \overset{?}{=} -0^2 - 9$$
$$-9 \overset{\checkmark}{=} -9 \qquad \textit{Hence the point } (0, -9) \textit{ lies on the graph.}$$

An x-intercept is a value of x where the graph crosses the x-axis. We can see that the graph crosses the x-axis twice: when $x = -3$ and when $x = 3$. Hence the x-intercepts are -3 and 3.

The graph crosses the x-axis when $y = 0$; the points $(-3, 0)$ and $(3, 0)$ lie on the graph. We verify that $(-3, 0)$ is an x-intercept:

$$y = x^2 - 9 \qquad \textit{Substitute } x = -3 \textit{ and } y = 0 \textit{ in the equation.}$$
$$0 \overset{?}{=} (-3)^2 - 9$$
$$0 \overset{\checkmark}{=} 9 - 9 \qquad \textit{Hence the point } (-3, 0) \textit{ lies on the graph.}$$

We leave it to the student to verify algebraically that $(3, 0)$ is also an x-intercept.

$\blacksquare$

EXAMPLE 4

Consider the graph in Figure 3.20.

(a) Determine the smallest and largest *x*-coordinate of any point on the graph.

(b) Determine the smallest and largest *y*-coordinate of any point on the graph.

Solution

To find the *smallest x*-coordinate on this graph, we are looking for the *x*-coordinate of the *leftmost* point on the graph. We can see that the value of *x* at the leftmost point occurs at the point (–2, 3), when *x* = –2. Hence the smallest *x*-coordinate is –2. The *largest x*-coordinate on this graph is the *x*-coordinate of the *rightmost* point on the graph. The arrowhead on the right end of the graph means that the graph goes on indefinitely in that direction. Therefore, there is no largest *x*-coordinate on this graph.

Figure 3.20

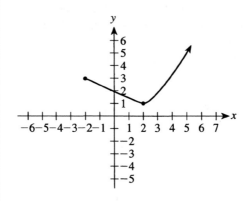

To find the *smallest y*-coordinate on this graph, we are looking for the *y*-coordinate of the *lowest* point on the graph. We can see that the value of *y* at the lowest point occurs at the point (2, 1), when *y* = 1. Hence the smallest *y*-coordinate on the graph is 1. The *largest y*-coordinate on this graph is the *y*-coordinate of the *highest* point on the graph. The arrowhead on the right end of the graph means that the graph goes on indefinitely in that direction. Therefore, there is no largest *y*-coordinate on this graph. ■

EXAMPLE 5

A bank charges its checking account customers a monthly fee of $7.50 plus a charge of $0.30 per check.

(a) Write an equation expressing the total monthly charge, *C*, in terms of the number of checks processed, *n*.

(b) Sketch a graph of this equation.

(c) Use the graph to estimate the total monthly charge if 40 checks are processed.

(d) Use the graph to determine how many checks were processed if the total monthly charge was $15.00.

Solution

(a) If you were to write 20 checks, the total monthly charge would be

$$C = 7.50 + 20(0.30) \qquad \textit{We multiply the number of checks by } 0.30$$
$$= \$13.50 \qquad\qquad\quad \textit{and add } \$7.50.$$

We can see that for *n* checks, the total monthly charge *C* would be

$$\boxed{C = 7.50 + 0.30n}$$

(b) The equation is written in terms of *n* and *C* rather than *x* and *y*, so we will assign the variable *n* to the horizontal axis and the variable *C* to the vertical axis. Hence ordered pairs will be of the form (*n*, *C*) rather than (*x*, *y*). We scale the horizontal axis *n* from 0 to 50, and the vertical *C*-axis from 0 to 25.

We find two ordered pairs satisfying the equation: If $n = 0$, then we have $C = 7.5 + 0.3(0) = 7.5$. Hence we plot the point $(0, 7.5)$. (This means that if no checks were processed, the charge is $7.50.) If the number of checks is $n = 50$, then $C = 7.50 + 0.30(50) = 22.50$. So we may plot the point $(50, 22.5)$ and draw the line (see Figure 3.21a).

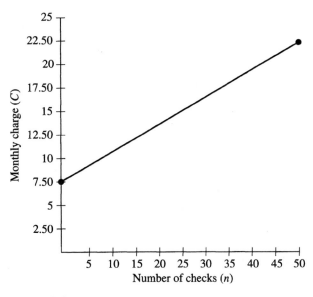

Figure 3.21a   **Figure 3.21b**

Find C when n = 40 using the equation C = 7.50 + 0.30n.

(c) Finding the monthly charge for 40 checks means we are looking for C when $n = 40$. We start on the horizontal axis at $n = 40$ and project vertically until we meet the graph. Then we move horizontally until we meet the vertical axis, and read off the value on the C-axis to get approximately $19.00. See Figure 3.21b. Hence the total monthly cost for processing 40 checks is about $19.00.

Find n when C = 15 using the same equation.

(d) Finding the number of checks processed given a monthly charge of $15.00 means we are looking for n when $C = 15.00$. We start on the vertical axis at $C = 15$ and project horizontally until we meet the graph. Then we move vertically until we meet the horizontal axis, and read off the value on the n-axis to get (approximately) 25. See Figure 3.21b. Hence the number of checks processed for a total monthly cost of $15.00 is about 25. ∎

Let's now return to the question posed at the beginning of this chapter.

EXAMPLE 6

Suppose that a researcher collects data in the following table, which indicates the number of calories burned, c, during a brisk walk that lasts m minutes.

m	2	4	6	8	10
c	12	23	32	40	53

Based on these data, a researcher conjectures that the number of calories c burned during a brisk walk and the number of minutes are related by the equation $c = 5m + 2$.

(a) Graph the data given in the chart using m as the horizontal axis and c as the vertical axis, and graph the equation on the same set of coordinate axes.

(b) Determine how well the proposed equation agrees with the observed data.

Solution

We recognize that $c = 5m + 2$ is a linear equation and therefore its graph is a straight line. To graph the equation $c = 5m + 2$, we see that if $m = 0$, then $c = 5(0) + 2 = 2$. Hence we plot the ordered pair $(0, 2)$. If $m = 10$, then $c = 5(10) + 2 = 52$. So we may plot the ordered pair $(10, 52)$ and graph the line (see Figure 3.22). The graph of the data appears in Figure 3.22 as well.

Figure 3.22

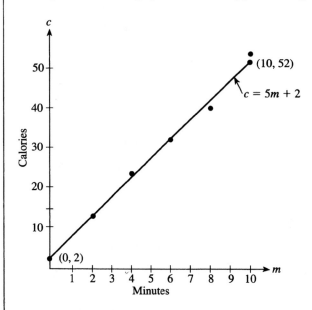

The data points do seem to "come close" to the line. We reproduced the table of data below and added a row of c values predicted by the equation $c = 5m + 2$. The following table illustrates numerically how close the equation predicts the recorded actual number of calories, c.

m	2	4	6	8	10
Actual c	12	23	32	40	53
$c = 5m + 2$	12	22	32	42	52

■

EXERCISES 3.2

1. Using the graph below, determine the following:

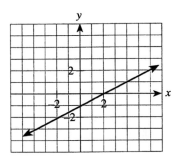

    (a) Find y when $x = -4$ and 4.

    (b) Find x when $y = 2$.

2. Using the graph below, determine the following:

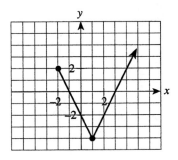

    (a) Find y when $x = 3$ and -2.

    (b) Find x when $y = -4$.

3. Using the graph below, determine the following:

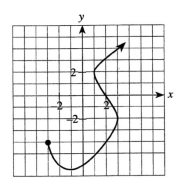

    (a) Find y when $x = -3$ and 2.

    (b) Find x when $y = 2$ and -6.

4. Using the graph below, determine the following:

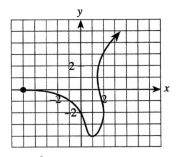

    (a) Find y when $x = -5$ and 2.

    (b) Find x when $y = -2$ and 4.

Exercises 5–8 refer to the figure given below.

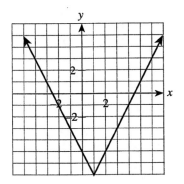

5. Find the value of y that satisfies the equation of the graph when $x = -2$.

6. Find the value of x that satisfies the equation of the graph when $y = 3$.

7. Find the value of x that satisfies the equation of the graph when $y = -3$.

8. Find the value of y that satisfies the equation of the graph when $x = 2$.

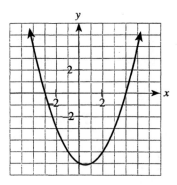

9. For the figure above, fill in the missing coordinates for the points that lie on the graph.

(a) (3,)   (b) (–4,)

(c) (, –3)   (d) (, 4)

10. For the figure above, fill in the missing coordinates for the ordered pairs that satisfy the equation of the graph.

(a) (, –5)   (b) (, 0)

(c) (0,)   (d) (1,)

11. The following is the graph of the equation $x^2 + y^2 = 13$.

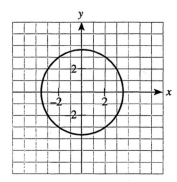

(a) Find y for $x = 2$ by using the graph, and verify the value(s) using the equation of the graph.

(b) Find x for $y = -3$ by using the graph, and verify the value(s) using the equation of the graph.

12. The following is the graph of the equation $16x^2 + 4y^2 = 16$.

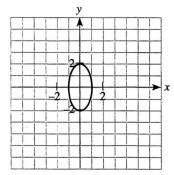

(a) Find y for $x = 0$ by using the graph, and verify the value(s) using the equation of the graph.

(b) Find x for $y = 0$ by using the graph, and verify the value(s) using the equation of the graph.

13. The following is the graph of the equation
$x + 2y = 8$.

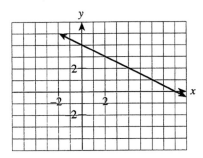

(a) Find the y-intercept using the graph, and verify your answers using the equation of the graph.

(b) Find the x-intercept using the graph, and verify your answer using the equation of the graph.

14. The following is the graph of the equation
$4y^2 - 4x = 16$.

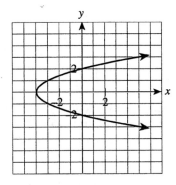

(a) Find the y-intercepts using the graph, and verify your answer using the equation of the graph.

(b) Find the x-intercept using the graph, and verify your answer using the equation of the graph.

15. The following is the graph of the equation
$y = \sqrt{x} + 4$.

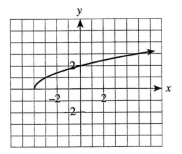

(a) Find the y-intercept using the graph, and verify your answer using the equation of the graph.

(b) Find the x-intercept using the graph, and verify your answer using the equation of the graph.

(c) Determine the smallest and largest x-coordinate of any point on the graph.

(d) Determine the smallest and largest y-coordinate of any point on the graph.

16. The following is the graph of the equation
$y = |x - 1|$.

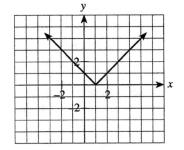

(a) Find the y-intercept using the graph, and verify your answer using the equation of the graph.

(b) Find the x-intercept using the graph, and verify your answer using the equation of the graph.

(c) Determine the smallest and largest x-coordinate of any point on the graph.

(d) Determine the smallest and largest y-coordinate of any point on the graph.

17. Given the accompanying graph.

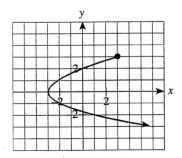

(a) Determine the smallest and largest x-coordinate of any point on the graph.

(b) Determine the smallest and largest y-coordinate of any point on the graph.

18. Given the accompanying graph.

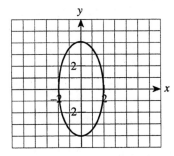

(a) Determine the smallest and largest x-coordinate of any point on the graph.

(b) Determine the smallest and largest y-coordinate of any point on the graph.

19. For each of the years indicated, the following table gives the percent of persons 25 years old and over who have completed 4 or more years of college in the United States.

Year	1992	1993	1994	1995	1996	1997	1998
Percent	21.4	21.9	22.2	23.0	23.6	23.9	24.4

Based on these data, a statistician suggests that the following formula can be used to approximate the percent P of those 25 and older who have completed 4 or more years of college for year t given in the table:

$$P = 0.5143t - 1,003.1$$

(a) Graph the data given in the chart using the horizontal axis for t and the vertical axis for P, and graph the given equation on the same set of coordinate axes.

(b) Determine how well the proposed equation agrees with the observed data.

20. The following table gives the value of all new construction (in billions of dollars) in place in the United States during the years 1992 to 1998. (The values include all residential as well as public buildings.)

Year	1992	1993	1994	1995	1996	1997	1998
Number	452	479	520	537	583	618	665

Based on these data, a statistician suggests that the following formula can be used to approximate the value of all construction (in billions of dollars), C, for year t given in the table:

$$C = 35t - 69,274$$

(a) Graph the data given in the chart using the horizontal axis for t and the vertical axis for C, and graph the given equation on the same set of coordinate axes.

(b) Determine how well the proposed equation agrees with the observed data.

21. A salesperson is paid a commission salary of 10% of her gross sales. Her weekly gross sales rarely exceed $10,000.

(a) Write an equation expressing her weekly commission, C, in terms of her gross sales, g.

(b) Sketch a graph of this equation.

(c) Use the graph to estimate her commission for the week in which her gross sales were $4,000.

(d) Use the graph to determine her gross sales for the week in which she makes $850 in commissions.

22. A salesperson is paid a base salary of $100 plus a commission of 8% of her gross sales.

(a) Write an equation expressing her weekly income, I, in terms of her gross sales, g.

(b) Sketch a graph of this equation.

(c) Use the graph to estimate her income for the week in which her gross sales were $4,000.

(d) Use the graph to determine her gross sales for the week in which her income is $850.

23. A bank charges its checking account customers a monthly fee of $10.00 plus a charge of $0.25 per check.

    (a) Write an equation expressing the total monthly charge, C, in terms of the number of checks processed, n.

    (b) Sketch a graph of this equation.

    (c) Use the graph to estimate the total monthly charge if 50 checks are processed.

    (d) Use the graph to determine how many checks were processed if the total monthly charge was $15.00.

24. Suppose you are given the choice of two salary plans: a strictly commission salary or a base salary plus commission. The strictly commission salary pays 5% of your gross sales, while the base salary plus commission pays you a weekly base salary of $120 and a commission of 3% of your gross sales.

    (a) Write an equation *for each plan* expressing the weekly income, I, in terms of weekly gross sales, g.

    (b) Sketch a graph of each equation on the same set of coordinate axes.

    (c) Use the graph to determine under what conditions one plan is better than the other.

3.3 Relations and Functions: Basic Concepts

The concept of a function is one of the most important in mathematics. We often hear or read statements such as "Insurance rates are a function of a person's age" or "Crop yields are a function of the weather." We understand these statements to mean that one of the quantities is dependent on the other.

We often find that two things are related to each other by some type of rule or correspondence. For example:

To each person there corresponds a Social Security number.

The distance d you travel at an average speed of 50 miles per hour is related to h, the number of hours you travel, according to the equation $d = 50h$.

To each positive number there correspond two square roots.

Not all correspondences can be expressed by some simple mathematical formula. Sometimes a graph can be a very efficient way to describe a relationship between two quantities. In the remainder of this chapter we develop two ideas: We make precise the idea of one quantity being dependent on another, and demonstrate the various ways we can express specific types of relationships.

A *relation* is a correspondence between two sets where to each element of the first set there is associated or assigned one or more elements of the second set. The first set is called the *domain* and the second set is called the *range*.

A relation is simply a rule by which we decide how to match up or associate elements from one set with elements from another. For example, students are usually assigned an identification number, as illustrated below:

Names of students (Domain)		Student numbers (Range)	
John Jones	$\longrightarrow$	#17345	*The arrow leads from the domain to the range.*
Sam Klass	$\longrightarrow$	#65734	
Carol Kane	$\longrightarrow$	#75664	

The relation shown above describes the assignment of numbers to names. The domain is the set of names, {John Jones, Sam Klass, Carol Kane}, and the range is the set of numbers assigned to the three names, {17345, 65734, 75664}. *The relation is the assignment.*

A relation can have many elements of the domain assigned to many elements of the range. For example, we can describe the following relation, by which we associate with each person his or her telephone number(s):

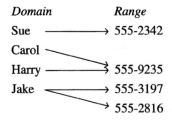

Note that Jake has two telephone numbers, while the number 555-9235 is associated with two people, Carol and Harry.

Let's consider another example. Let the domain be the set $A = \{a, b, c\}$ and the range be the set $B = \{1, 2, 3\}$. Four of the many possible relations between the two sets are shown below.

Relation R

Domain	Range
a ⟶	1
b ⟶	2
c ⟶	3

Relation S

Domain	Range
a ⟶	2
b ⟶	3
c ⟶	1

Relation T

Domain	Range
a ⟶	1
b	2
c	3

Relation U

Domain	Range
a	1
b	2
c	3

In relation *R, a* is assigned 1, *b* is assigned 2, and *c* is assigned 3.

In relation *S, a* is assigned 2, *b* is assigned 3, and *c* is assigned 1.

In relation *T, a* is assigned 1, *b* is assigned 1, *c* is assigned 2, and *c* is also assigned 3.

In relation *U, a* is assigned 1, *a* is also assigned 2, *b* is assigned 3, and *c* is assigned 3.

Thus, we can describe any type of correspondence we want as long as we assign to each element of the domain an element or elements of the range.

An alternative way to describe a relation is to use ordered pairs. For example, instead of writing the correspondence of relation *R*:

$$a \longrightarrow 1$$
$$b \longrightarrow 2$$
$$c \longrightarrow 3$$

we can write the correspondence without arrows as $(a, 1)$, $(b, 2)$, $(c, 3)$. Thus, the set $\{(a, 1), (b, 2), (c, 3)\}$ describes the relation *R* between the set *A* and the set *B*.

When using ordered pair notation, we will always assume that the first member of the ordered pair is an element of the domain and the second member is the associated element of the range. Thus, the first component, *x*, of the ordered pair (x, y) is an element of the domain. The second component, *y*, is an element of the range such that *y* is assigned to *x*.

We usually call the variable representing possible values of the domain the **independent variable** and the variable representing possible values of the range the **dependent variable.**

We can rewrite the other previous examples as follows:

Relation *S*: $\{(a, 2), (b, 3), (c, 1)\}$ *Note that this is all you need to*

Relation *T*: $\{(a, 1), (b, 1), (c, 2), (c, 3)\}$ *describe the relation.*

Relation *U*: $\{(a, 1), (a, 2), (b, 3), (c, 3)\}$

We define a relation using ordered pair notation as follows:

DEFINITION	A *relation* is a set of ordered pairs (x, y). The set of x values is called the *domain* and the set of y values is called the *range.*

If you haven't done so already, you may want to review set notation in Appendix A.

For example:

The set of ordered pairs $R = \{(8, 2), (6, -3), (5, 7), (5, -3)\}$ is the relation between the sets $\{5, 6, 8\}$ and $\{2, -3, 7\}$ where $\{5, 6, 8\}$ is the domain and $\{2, -3, 7\}$ is the range; 8 is assigned 2, 6 is assigned -3, 5 is assigned 7, and 5 is also assigned -3.

Another example:

$S = \{(a, b), (a, c), (b, c), (c, a)\}$ is a set of ordered pairs describing the relation between set $\{a, b, c\}$ and itself. Thus, $\{a, b, c\}$ is both the domain and the range: a is assigned b and c, b is assigned c, and c is assigned a.

If the domain and range are infinite, we cannot write out each element assignment, so instead we can use set-builder notation to describe the relation(ship) between the variables. For example,

$$S = \{(x, y) \mid y = x + 5, \ x \text{ and } y \text{ are real numbers}\}$$

is a relation between the set of real numbers and itself (both the domain and range are the set of real numbers). Each value of x is assigned a value, y, that is 5 more than x. Thus,

3 is assigned value 8 because $8 = 3 + 5$ *or* $(3, 8) \in S$.

9 is assigned value 14 because $14 = 9 + 5$ *or* $(9, 14) \in S$.

-10 is assigned value -5 because $-5 = -10 + 5$ *or* $(-10, -5) \in S$.

Another example:

$$R = \{(x, y) \mid x < y \text{ and } x \text{ and } y \text{ are real numbers}\}$$

In this relation, both the domain *and* range are the set of real numbers. If $x = 2$, then y must be greater than 2. Hence, $(2, 2\frac{1}{2})$, $(2, 3)$, $(2, 100)$, $(2, 50)$, and $(2, 2\frac{1}{10})$ satisfy the relation. Other ordered pairs that satisfy this relation are $(3, 8)$, $(7, 9)$, $(0, 4)$, $(-1, -\frac{1}{2})$, and $(-10, 16)$. (Why?)

We can drop the set notation and simply write $y = x + 5$ to represent the relation

$$\{(x, y) \mid y = x + 5, \ x \text{ and } y \text{ are real numbers}\}$$

When we write a relation as an equation in x and y, we assume that x represents the independent variable and y represents the dependent variable. *We also assume that the domain is the set of real numbers that will yield real-number values for y.* (The range is usually more difficult to identify.)

For example, suppose a relation is defined by

$$y = \frac{1}{x}$$

Then x can be any real number except 0 because 0 will produce an undefined y value. Therefore, the domain (allowable values of x) is the set of all real numbers except 0. We can also write the domain as $\{x \mid x \neq 0\}$.

EXAMPLE 1   Find the domains of the relations defined by each of the following:

(a) $y = \dfrac{3x}{2x + 1}$ (b) $y = -2x + 7$

Solution

(a) We are looking for the domain of the relation defined by the given equation, that is, the set of allowable values of x (values of x that will yield real-number values of y).

By our previous experiences with rational expressions, we know that a sum, difference, product, or quotient of real numbers is a real number *except* when the divisor of a quotient is 0 (in which case the quotient is undefined). Therefore, the denominator, $2x + 1$, cannot be 0, or x cannot be $-\frac{1}{2}$.

Thus, the domain is $\boxed{\left\{ x \,\middle|\, x \neq -\frac{1}{2} \right\}}$.

(b) Any real value substituted for x will produce a real value for y.

Therefore, the domain is $\boxed{\text{all real numbers.}}$ ∎

Functions

Let's consider a real-life relation described by the telephone keypad illustrated in Figure 3.23.

Figure 3.23
A typical telephone keypad

It is very common today to see a business advertise its phone number by saying something like

"To get an over-the-phone price quotation on a new car, dial BUY CARS."

Anyone wanting to call this number can easily decode BUY CARS as the number 289-2277. This is because the telephone keypad sets up a correspondence between the set of letters of the alphabet (except for Q and Z) and the set of numbers {2, 3, 4, 5, 6, 7, 8, 9}. The correspondence between the two sets is that indicated by the telephone keypad—that is, the letters A, B, and C correspond to the number 2; the letters D, E, and F correspond to the number 3; and so forth.

What is important to note is that although the telephone keypad sets up a correspondence between letters and numbers, as indicated in the figure, there is a qualitative difference between the letter → number correspondence and the reverse number → letter correspondence: Each letter corresponds to exactly one number, but each number corresponds to 3 letters. Consequently, a phone number such as 438-2253 cannot be *uniquely* encoded into words. The number 438-2253 can be interpreted as GET CAKE or IF U BAKE.

$$
\begin{array}{ccccccc}
4 & 3 & 8 & & 2 & 2 & 5 & 3 \\
\downarrow & \downarrow & \downarrow & & \downarrow & \downarrow & \downarrow & \downarrow \\
\text{G} & \text{E} & \text{T} & & \text{C} & \text{A} & \text{K} & \text{E}
\end{array}
\qquad \text{or} \qquad
\begin{array}{ccccccc}
4 & 3 & & 8 & & 2 & 2 & 5 & 3 \\
\downarrow & \downarrow & & \downarrow & & \downarrow & \downarrow & \downarrow & \downarrow \\
\text{I} & \text{F} & & \text{U} & & \text{B} & \text{A} & \text{K} & \text{E}
\end{array}
$$

Mathematically it is important for us to distinguish among relations that assign a *unique* range element to each domain element (such as the letter → number correspondence on the telephone) and those that do not.

DEFINITION	A *function* is a correspondence between two sets such that to each element of the first set (the domain) there is assigned *exactly* one element of the second set (the range).

Thus, for a relation to be a function, we cannot assign more than one element of the range to an element of the domain. However, in a function we can still assign an element of the range to more than one element of the domain.

For example, the relation

$$3 \longrightarrow 6$$
$$2 \longrightarrow 5$$
$$7 \longrightarrow 4$$

which is the set {(3, 6), (2, 5), (7, 4)}, *is* a function because each element in the domain {3, 2, 7} is assigned only one element in the range {6, 5, 4}.

Another example is the relation

$$3 \longrightarrow 6$$
$$2 \nearrow$$
$$7 \longrightarrow 4$$

which is the set {(3, 6), (2, 6), (7, 4)}. Even though the range element 6 corresponds to two elements of the domain, 3 and 2, this relation *is still* a function because *each element in the domain, {3, 2, 7}, is associated with one element of the range, {4, 6}:* 3 is assigned only one value, 6; 2 is assigned only one value, 6; and 7 is assigned only one value, 4.

On the other hand, the relation

$$3 \mathrel{\substack{\longrightarrow \\ \searrow}} 6$$
$$7 \longrightarrow 4$$

which is the set {(3, 6), (3, 4), (7, 4)}, is *not* a function, because the domain element 3 is assigned two elements of the range, 6 and 4.

Refer back to our example of telephone numbers given at the beginning of this section. The relation that assigns telephone number(s) to each person is often not a function since a person can have more than one number.

The following is a useful metaphor: We can describe a function as a machine into which you throw elements of the domain, and out of which come elements of the range (see Figure 3.24).

Figure 3.24
Function machine

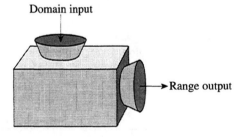

Consider the function {(3, 5), (2, 5), (7, 4)}. Note that if we put 3 into the machine, out comes 5; if we put 2 into the machine, out comes 5; and if we put 7 into the machine, out comes 4.

Of the relations R, S, T, and U given on p. 142, which are functions?

If we tried to use the function machine for the relation {(3, 5), (3, 4), (2, 6)}, what would happen when we throw in 3? If we throw in 3, we cannot be sure whether we will get 5 or 4. This ambiguity is precisely why this relation is *not* a function.

Remember	*All* functions are relations, but not all relations are functions. Functions are a special kind of relation such that every value in the *domain* is assigned *exactly one* value in the *range*.

EXAMPLE 2

Indicate the domain of the following relations and determine whether each relation is a function.

(a) {(3, 5), (4, 2), (3, 6), (5, 7)}   (b) {(7, −2), (6, −4), (5, 8), (−4, 8)}

Solution   (a) The domain is {3, 4, 5}.

The relation is $\boxed{\text{not a function}}$ since 3 is assigned more than one element of the range (3 is assigned both 5 and 6).

(b) The domain is {−4, 5, 6, 7}.

The relation $\boxed{\text{is a function}}$ since each element in the domain is assigned no more than one element of the range.   ∎

We can now give an alternate definition of a function.

DEFINITION	A *function* is a relation in which no two distinct ordered pairs have the same first coordinate.

A function can also be defined by an equation. Unless the contrary is stated, x will always represent values from the domain, and y will always represent values in the range.

EXAMPLE 3   Explain why the equation $y = 3x - 5$ defines y as a *function of x*.

Solution   As indicated previously, a function requires that exactly one range value corresponds to each domain value. In other words, there corresponds exactly one y value to each x value. The given equation $y = 3x - 5$ tells us that to obtain the range value y, we take the domain value x, multiply it by 3, and then subtract 5. For each x value the equation produces a unique y value, and so this equation does define y as a function of x.   ∎

EXAMPLE 4   Does the equation $y^2 = 3x - 5$ define y as a function of x?

Solution   If we choose $x = 7$, we get the equation

$$y^2 = 3x - 5 \qquad \textit{Substitute } x = 7.$$
$$y^2 = 3(7) - 5$$
$$y^2 = 16 \qquad \textit{We recognize that this equation has \textbf{two} solutions.}$$
$$y = \pm 4$$

The fact that there are two y values that correspond to $x = 7$ means that the relation $y^2 = 3x - 5$ is not a function. In fact, if we choose *any* number in its domain other than $x = \frac{5}{3}$, there will be two y values associated with it. However, to demonstrate that this equation does not define y as a function of x, all we need find is a single x value that has two y values associated with it.   ∎

EXAMPLE 5   Does the equation $y = 3x^2 - 5$ define y as a function of x?

Solution   Let's examine this function by making a table for various values of x:

x	y
−3	22
−2	7
−1	−2
0	−5
1	−2
2	7
3	22

From this table, we can see y values that are associated with two different x values. For example, we can see that both $x = -3$ and $x = 3$ give a y value of 22. The fact that two different x values (in the domain) give the same y value (in the range) is *not* a problem as far as the equation defining *y* as a function of *x* is concerned. A function merely requires that to each *x* value there corresponds one and only one *y* value. In this equation we take the *x* value, square it, multiply that result by 3, and then subtract 5. For each *x* value (input) there is only one *y* value (output), and so this equation *does* define *y* as a function of *x*. ∎

EXAMPLE 6

Find the domain of the function $y = \sqrt{2x - 6}$.

Solution

Let's analyze this question carefully, step by step, to develop a strategy for its solution.

THINKING OUT LOUD	
What do we need to find?	The domain of the function $y = \sqrt{2x - 6}$
What do we mean by the domain of a function?	According to our ground rules, the domain of a function is the set of real numbers *x* for which the corresponding *y* value is also a real number.
Are there any values of *x* that must be excluded?	Since the square root of a negative number is undefined in the real number system, we must *exclude* any value of *x* for which $2x - 6 < 0$. Equivalently, the domain *includes* all values of *x* for which $2x - 6 \geq 0$.
How can I restate the problem in simpler terms?	Solve the inequality $2x - 6 \geq 0$.

$$2x - 6 \geq 0$$
$$2x \geq 0$$
$$x \geq 3$$

If we allow x = 1 in the expression $\sqrt{2x - 6}$, we get $\sqrt{2(1) - 6} = \sqrt{-4}$, which is undefined in the real number system. There is no real number whose square is equal to −4.

Thus the domain is $\boxed{\{x \,|\, x \geq 3\}}$. Notice that any *x* value less than 3 will not give a real number for *y*. ∎

We began this section by describing the process of defining a relation or function as a set of ordered pairs. Since a graph is nothing more than the picture of a particular set of ordered pairs, we can actually define a relation or a function by means of a graph. Let's consider the graph in Figure 3.25.

Figure 3.25
The graph of a relation

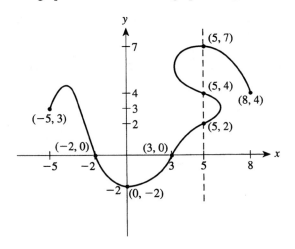

Each point on the graph corresponds to a pair of numbers (x, y). For example, we observe that the point $(-5, 3)$ is on the graph. This means that if we choose $x = -5$, the corresponding y value is 3. We can see that the graph crosses the x-axis at $x = -2$ and $x = 3$. This means that there are two domain values, -2 and 3, that give the range value $y = 0$.

However, we also observe that the points $(5, 2)$, $(5, 4)$, and $(5, 7)$ are on the graph. This means that if we choose $x = 5$, there are three possible y values: y can be 2, 4, or 7. This is exactly what a function is not allowed to do, and so this graph is not the graph of a function.

How can we look at a graph and determine whether it is the graph of a function? According to the definition of a function, if any x value in the domain has more than one y value associated with it, the relation is not a function. Using the graph in Figure 3.25 as an example, we see that the vertical line passing through $x = 5$ passes through three points on the graph. This means that there are three y values corresponding to $x = 5$, which in turn means that the graph cannot be the graph of a function. This condition is usually very easy to check and is called the *vertical line test*.

The Vertical Line Test	If any vertical line intersects a graph in more than one point, then the graph does not represent y as a function of x.

EXAMPLE 7

Determine which of the following relations are functions, by the vertical line test.

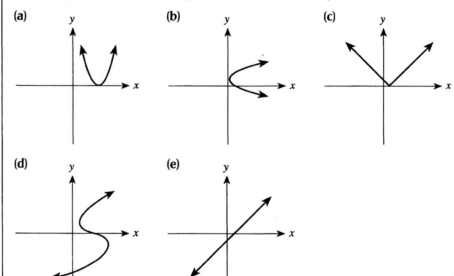

Solution

The relations in parts **(a)**, **(c)**, and **(e)** are functions, since any vertical line will intersect the graphs at only one point.

The relations in parts **(b)** and **(d)** are not functions, since some vertical lines will intersect the graphs at more than one point, as shown in the accompanying figures.

(b)

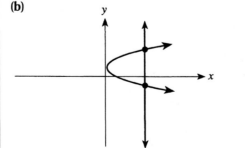

This vertical line intersects the graph at two points; therefore, this relation is not a function.

(d)

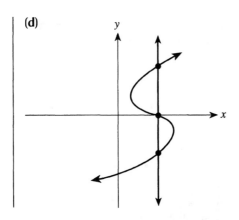

This vertical line intersects the graph at three points; therefore, this relation is not a function.

DIFFERENT PERSPECTIVES: The Vertical Line Test

Consider the geometric and algebraic descriptions of a function.

GRAPHICAL DESCRIPTION

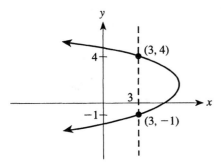

If any vertical line intersects a graph in more than one point, then the graph cannot be the graph of a function.

ALGEBRAIC DESCRIPTION

For an equation to define y as a function of x, each x value must correspond to exactly one y value. As the graph at the left illustrates, if a graph fails the vertical line test, then it follows that there is at least one x value to which there correspond at least two y values. In particular, since the points $(3, -1)$ and $(3, 4)$ are on the graph, there are two y values that correspond to $x = 3$. This means that if we had the equation of this graph, substituting $x = 3$ would give us *two* y values satisfying the equation, which violates the definition of a function.

One last comment about the graph in Figure 3.25: We can also use the graph to "read off" the domain and range of the relation from the graph. If we project vertically from the graph to the x-axis, we can see that every x value between $x = -5$ and $x = 8$ has at least one y value associated with it, and therefore the domain is $\{x \mid -5 \leq x \leq 8\}$; see Figure 3.26a.

Figure 3.26a
Finding the domain from a graph

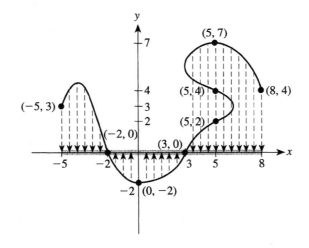

Similarly, if we project horizontally from the graph to the y-axis, we can see that every y value between $y = -2$ and $y = 7$ is associated with at least one x value, and so the range is $\{y \mid -2 \leq y \leq 7\}$; see Figure 3.26b.

Figure 3.26b
Finding the range
from a graph

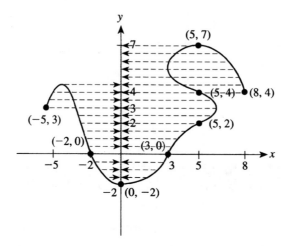

This is just a first illustration that much useful information about a relationship can be extracted from its graph.

In summary, we have seen that we can express a relation (or function) in four possible ways: We can use a table, or use a set of ordered pairs, or write an equation, or draw a graph. As we proceed through the text we will see how each of these modes of representing a function gives its own useful information about the function.

We have also used an arrow diagram to represent a function. Although a table and an arrow diagram are virtually the same, a table is more commonly used.

DIFFERENT PERSPECTIVES: Representing Functions

The following are four different ways of representing the same function.

ALGEBRAIC DESCRIPTION

We can represent a function by an equation:

$$y = 8 - x^2 \quad \text{for } x = -3, -1, 0, 2, 3$$

TABLE DESCRIPTION

We can represent a function by a table of values:

x	y
-3	-1
-1	7
0	8
2	4
3	-1

ORDERED PAIR DESCRIPTION

We can represent a function by a set of ordered pairs:

$$\{(-3, -1), (-1, 7), (0, 8), (2, 4), (3, -1)\}$$

GRAPHICAL DESCRIPTION

We can represent a function by a graph:

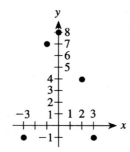

Functions are frequently used to describe real-life relationships, as illustrated in the next example.

EXAMPLE 8

Michelle wants to build a rectangular pen against her house with 50 ft of fencing. Only three sides of the pen are enclosed with fencing, and one of the sides adjacent to the house is x ft (see Figure 3.27).

(a) Express the *area* of the pen in terms of *x*.

(b) Determine the area of the pen when *x* = 5, 10, 20, and 24 ft.

Figure 3.27

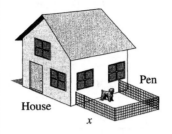

Solution

Let's analyze this question carefully, step by step, in order to develop a strategy for its solution.

THINKING OUT LOUD

What are we being asked to do?	To express the area of a rectangular pen in terms of *x*
How do we find the area of a rectangle?	Multiply its length by its width.
Are we given any dimensions of the rectangle?	We are given that one side adjacent to the house is *x* (and therefore the other adjacent side is *x*). We are not given the length of the other side.
To find the area of the rectangle, we need the length of the other side. Is there any given information that can help us determine the length of the missing side?	We are given that the total length of the fence is 50 ft. We can see that the entire length of the fence consists of the three sides: two are labeled *x*, and the third side, the side for which we are looking, is missing.

At this point we need to recognize that since the entire length of the fence is 50 ft, if we subtract the two *x*'s from 50, we will get the missing side:

$$\text{The missing side} = 50 - x - x = 50 - 2x$$

We now label the figure as shown in Figure 3.28.

Figure 3.28

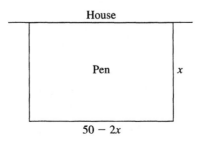

Hence the area is

$$A = x(50 - 2x)$$ or $$A = 50x - 2x^2$$

(b) To find the area for $x = 5, 10, 20$ and 24, we simply substitute the values for x into either formula to compute the corresponding values for A: We will use the formula $A = x(50 - 2x)$ and make a table for the four area values corresponding to the given values of x:

x	$A = x(50 - 2x)$
5	$5(50 - 2 \cdot 5)$ = 200 sq ft
10	$10(50 - 2 \cdot 10)$ = 300 sq ft
20	$20(50 - 2 \cdot 20)$ = 200 sq ft
24	$24(50 - 2 \cdot 24)$ = 48 sq ft

∎

Study Skills 3.3

Taking an Algebra Exam: What to Do First

Not all exams are arranged in ascending order of difficulty (from easiest to most difficult). Since time is usually an important factor, you do not want to spend too much time working on a few problems that you find difficult and then find that you do not have enough time to solve the problems that are easier for you. Therefore, it is strongly recommended that you first look over the exam and then follow the order given below:

1. Start with the problems that you know how to solve quickly.

2. Then go back and work on problems that you know how to solve but which take longer.

3. Then work on those problems that you find more difficult, but for which you have a general idea of how to proceed.

4. Finally, divide the remaining time between doing the problems you find most difficult and checking your solutions. Do not forget to check the warnings you wrote down at the beginning of the exam.

You probably should not be spending a lot of time on any single problem. To determine the average amount of time you should be spending on a problem, divide the amount of time given for the exam by the number of problems on the exam. For example, if the exam lasts for 50 minutes and there are 20 problems, you should spend an average of $\frac{50}{20} = 2\frac{1}{2}$ minutes per problem. Remember, this is just an estimate. You should spend less time on "quick" problems (or those worth fewer points), and more time on the more difficult problems (or those worth more points). As you work the problems be aware of the time; if half the time is gone, you should have completed about half of the exam.

 EXERCISES 3.3

In Exercises 1–4, write the relation depicted in the diagram using ordered pair notation.

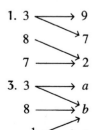

1. 3 ⟶ 9
   8 ⟶ 7
   7 ⟶ 2

2. 4 ⟶ 8
   2 ⟶ 7
   6

3. 3 ⟶ a
   8 ⟶ b
   −1 ⟶ c

4. 2 ⟶ 1
   3 ⟶ 2
   0 ⟶ 5

In Exercises 5–8, determine the domain and range.

5. $\{(3, 2), (4, 2), (5, 3)\}$

6. $\{(-1, 5), (-2, 6), (-3, 7)\}$

7. $\{(3, -2), (-2, 3), (3, -1), (4, 3)\}$

8. $\{(5, -1), (-1, 5)\}$

In Exercises 9–24, determine the domain.

9. $y = \dfrac{3}{x}$

10. $y = \dfrac{5}{x + 1}$

11. $y = 3x - 7$

12. $y = 2x - 3$

13. $y = \dfrac{4x}{2x + 3}$

14. $y = \dfrac{5x}{3x - 2}$

15. $y = x^2 - 3x + 4$

16. $y = 3x^2 - 5x + 2$

17. $y = \sqrt{x - 4}$

18. $y = \sqrt{x + 3}$

19. $y = \sqrt{5 - 4x}$

20. $y = \sqrt{6 - 5x}$

21. $y = 5 - \sqrt{4x}$

22. $y = 6 - \sqrt{5x}$

23. $y = \dfrac{x}{\sqrt{x - 3}}$

24. $y = \dfrac{2x}{\sqrt{3 - x}}$

In Exercises 25–44, determine which of the relations are functions.

25. $2 \longrightarrow 6$
    $3 \nearrow$
    $4 \longrightarrow 1$

26. $5 \longrightarrow 7$
    $4 \nearrow$
    $2 \longrightarrow 1$

27. $6 \searrow 3$
    $\quad 1$
    $5 \longrightarrow 4$

28. $3 \longrightarrow 9$
    $5 \searrow 4$
    $\quad\searrow 6$

29. $\{(6, 3), (5, 3)\}$

30. $\{(8, -2), (7, -2)\}$

31. $\{(3, 1), (3, 2)\}$

32. $\{(5, 1), (5, 7)\}$

33. $\{(6, 5), (5, 6)\}$

34. $\{(7, -2), (-2, 7)\}$

35. $\{(3, 1), (5, 2), (6, 2)\}$

36. $\{(6, 2), (5, 8), (6, 3)\}$

37. $\{(9, -1), (6, -2), (9, 3)\}$

38. $\{(7, 4), (5, -2), (3, -2)\}$

39. $y = x + 3$

40. $2y = x + 4$

41. $x^2 + y^2 = 81$

42. $x^2 + 3y^2 = 9$

43. $x = y^2 - 4$

44. $y = x^2 + 2$

In Exercises 45–52, determine which of the relations are functions.

45.

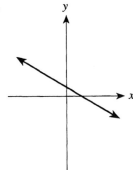

46.

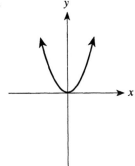

47.

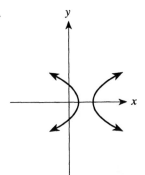

48.

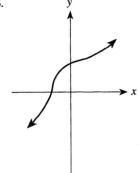

49.

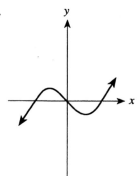

50.

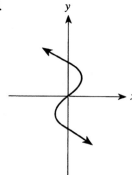

51.

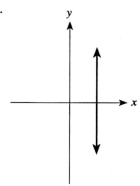

52.

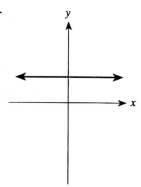

In Exercises 53–62, use the following graph to answer the question or complete the ordered pair.

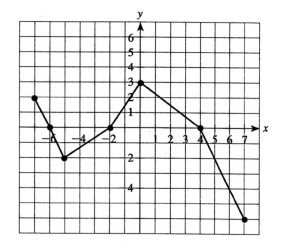

53. If $x = 4$, then $y = $ _____.

54. If $x = -5$, then $y = $ _____.

55. (, −6)

56. (−7,)

57. For how many values of x is $y = 0$? What are they?

58. For how many values of y is $x = 0$? What are they?

59. For how many values of y is $x = 3$?

60. For how many values of x is $y = 2$?

61. What is the domain of this function?

62. What is the range of this function?

In Exercises 63–72, use the following graph to answer the question or complete the ordered pair.

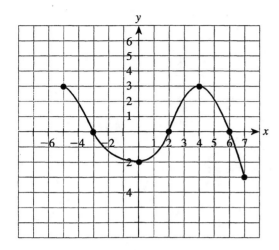

63. If $x = 4$, then $y =$ _____.

64. If $x = -5$, then $y =$ _____.

65. (, -3)

66. (-4,   )

67. For how many values of x is $y = 0$? What are they?

68. For how many values of y is $x = 0$? What are they?

69. For how many values of y is $x = 3$?

70. For how many values of x is $y = 2$?

71. What is the domain of this function?

72. What is the range of this function?

In Exercises 73–78, use the given graph to determine the domain and range of the relation or function.

73.

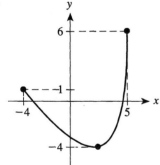

74.

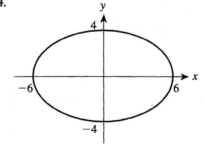

75.

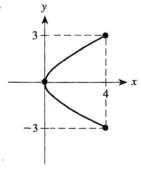

76.

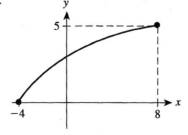

77.
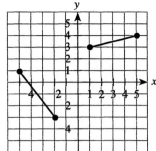

78.
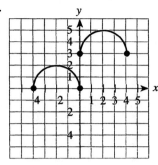

79. Express the area of a square as a function of the length, *s*, of its side.

80. The length of a rectangle is 5 cm less than twice its width, *w*. Express the area of the rectangle as a function of *w*.

81. Express the area of the shaded region of the accompanying figure as a function of *a*. Based on the dimensions given in the figure, what are the possible values for *a*?

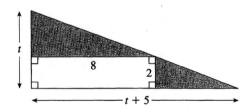

82. Express the area of the shaded region of the accompanying figure as a function of *t*.

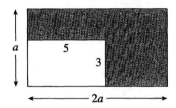

83. A car rental agency charges a flat fee of $29 per day plus a mileage charge of $0.12 per mile. Express the cost, *C*, of a 4-day rental as a function of *m*, the number of miles driven.

84. A person drives 3 hours at *r* mph, and then drives 15 mph faster for 5 additional hours. Express the total distance covered, *d*, as a function of *r*.

85. A retailer buys 10 shirts that cost *d* dollars each and 12 shirts that cost $5 more per shirt. Express the total cost of all the shirts as a function of *d*.

86. A farmer sets up a fence to enclose and subdivide a rectangular garden as indicated in the accompanying figure.

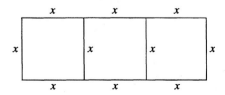

To provide greater security, heavy-duty fencing that costs $10 per foot is used for the outside boundary, whereas regular fencing that costs $8 per foot is used for the two dividers. Express the total cost to set up this enclosure, C, as a function of x.

87. A company knows that its production cost, C, in dollars is a function of n, the number of items produced, according to the formula $C = 0.02n^2 + 100n + 10,000$. Find the cost to produce 100, 200, 500, and 1,000 items.

88. Muriel's monthly income, I, is computed as $I = 0.03(x - 8,000) + 2,000$, where x is the number of items that she sells that month. Compute her monthly income if the monthly sales are 2,500; 10,000; 20,000; and 30,000 items.

89. A cellular phone company charges a flat monthly fee of $29.95 plus $0.33 per minute of airtime.

   (a) Express the monthly cellular phone charge, C, as a function of m, the number of minutes of airtime.

   (b) Find the monthly cellular phone charge with airtimes of 75 minutes, 180 minutes, and 300 minutes.

90. A building contractor charges a flat fee of $2,450 for planning and permits, plus a construction fee of $475 per square meter of construction.

   (a) Express the contractor's charge, C, as a function of x, the number of square meters of construction.

   (b) Compute the cost to construct an area of 90 square meters, 115 square meters, 140 square meters, and 175 square meters.

91. The relationship between the monthly profit (P) generated from all two-bedroom units and the rent (r) charged for each unit in an apartment complex is described in the accompanying graph.

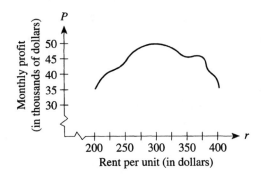

   (a) Is this the graph of a function?

   (b) What are its domain and range?

   (c) What rent per unit generates the maximum profit? What is the maximum profit?

② QUESTIONS FOR THOUGHT

92. State in words what makes a relation a function.

93. In Example 8 we found that the area of a rectangular pen built alongside a house is given by $A = x(50 - x)$. This describes the area A as a function of the length of one of the sides, x. Given that this function represents a real-life situation, what is the domain of this function?

3.4 Function Notation

In the previous section we discussed real-valued functions such as $y = x + 2$ and $y = 3x^2 - 2$. Because these equations are explicitly solved for y, we can say that y is a function of x, or that y is dependent on the values of x (hence, y is called the dependent variable). We now introduce a special notation for functions. The statement "y is a function of x" can be written symbolically as

$$y = f(x) \qquad f(x) \text{ is read "}f\text{ of }x\text{" and denotes the value of } f \text{ at } x.$$

We can bypass the y variable completely and describe an expression such as $3x^2 - 2$ as being a function of x by writing

$$f(x) = 3x^2 - 2 \qquad \text{The expression } 3x^2 - 2 \text{ is a function of } x.$$

The letters f, g, and h are used most frequently for functions. Other examples of functions are as follows:

$$f(x) = x^2 - 2x + 5$$
$$g(x) = 2 - 5x$$
$$h(a) = \frac{a}{a + 1}$$

Note that the parentheses in this notation are *not* used as grouping symbols—that is, $f(x)$ is *not* the product of f and x. The parentheses are being used to specify the independent variable.

The notation $f(x)$ is a useful shorthand for evaluating expressions or substituting variables. For example, if we want to know the value of the function $f(x)$ when $x = 3$, we write $f(3)$.

If $f(x) = 7x - 4$, and we want to find the function value when $x = 3$, then

$$f(3) = 7(3) - 4 = 21 - 4 = 17 \qquad \text{Thus, } f(3) = 17.$$

*Using the vocabulary introduced in the previous section, we can say that 3 is the **input** and f(3) is the **output**. In general, x is the input and f(x) is the output.*

In the same way, $f(-5)$ is the value of $f(x)$ when $x = -5$:

$$f(-5) = 7(-5) - 4 = -35 - 4 = -39 \qquad \text{Thus, } f(-5) = -39.$$

Thus,

> $f(a)$ is the value of $f(x)$ when a is substituted for x in $f(x)$.

For example, if we have $g(x) = 2x^2 - 4x + 5$, then $g(3)$ is the value of $g(x) = 2x^2 - 4x + 5$ when x is replaced by 3. Hence,

$$g(3) = 2(3)^2 - 4(3) + 5 \qquad g(3) \text{ is } g(x) \text{ evaluated when } x = 3.$$
$$= 2(9) - 4(3) + 5$$
$$= 11$$

We are not necessarily restricted to numbers as possible replacements for x. For example, if $f(x) = 7x - 4$, then

$$f(a) = 7a - 4 \qquad \text{Replace } x \text{ with } a \text{ in } f(x).$$
$$f(z) = 7z - 4 \qquad \text{Replace } x \text{ with } z \text{ in } f(x).$$

EXAMPLE 1 If $f(x) = 3x - 5$ and $g(x) = 2x^2 - 3x + 1$, find each of the following:

(a) $f(-2)$ **(b)** $g(4)$ **(c)** $g(-3)$ **(d)** $g(r)$

Solution **(a)** Evaluate $f(x)$ for $x = -2$:

$$f(-2) = 3(-2) - 5 = -11$$

> Thus, $f(-2) = -11$

Remember, $g(4) = 21$ tells us that the point $(4, 21)$ is on the graph of $y = g(x)$.

(b) Substitute 4 for x in $g(x)$:

$$g(4) = 2(4)^2 - 3(4) + 1 = 2 \cdot 16 - 3 \cdot 4 + 1 = 21$$

Thus, $g(4) = 21$

(c) Evaluate $g(x)$ for $x = -3$:

$$g(-3) = 2(-3)^2 - 3(-3) + 1 = 2 \cdot 9 + 9 + 1 = 28$$

Thus, $g(-3) = 28$

(d) Substitute r for x in $g(x)$:

$$g(r) = 2r^2 - 3r + 1$$

Thus, $g(r) = 2r^2 - 3r + 1$ ∎

EXAMPLE 2

Given $f(x) = 3x - 1$, find each of the following:

(a) $f(a + 1)$ **(b)** $f(2x - 1)$

Solution

(a) $f(a + 1)$ is the expression we get when we substitute $a + 1$ for x in $f(x)$. Since

$$f(x) = 3x - 1 \qquad \textit{Substituting } a + 1 \textit{ for } x, \textit{ we get}$$
$$f(a + 1) = 3(a + 1) - 1 \qquad \textit{Then simplify.}$$
$$= 3a + 3 - 1$$
$$= 3a + 2$$

Thus, $f(a + 1) = 3a + 2$

(b) $f(2x - 1)$ is the expression we get when we substitute $2x - 1$ for x in $f(x)$. Since

$$f(x) = 3x - 1 \qquad \textit{Substituting } 2x - 1 \textit{ for } x, \textit{ we get}$$
$$f(2x - 1) = 3(2x - 1) - 1$$
$$= 6x - 3 - 1 \qquad \textit{Then simplify.}$$
$$= 6x - 4$$

Thus, $f(2x - 1) = 6x - 4$ ∎

EXAMPLE 3

Given $f(x) = 4x - 1$, find each of the following:

(a) $f(x) + 2$ **(b)** $f(x + 2)$ **(c)** $f(x) + f(2)$ **(d)** $f(x + 2) - f(x)$

Solution

(a) $f(x) + 2$ *Means add 2 to $f(x)$; since $f(x) = 4x - 1$,*

$$= \underbrace{4x - 1}_{f(x)} + 2$$

$$= 4x + 1$$

Hence, $f(x) + 2 = 4x + 1$.

(b) $f(x + 2)$ means to substitute $x + 2$ for x in $f(x)$. Since $f(x) = 4x - 1$, we have

$$f(x) = 4x - 1$$
$$f(x + 2) = 4(x + 2) - 1$$
$$= 4x + 8 - 1$$
$$= 4x + 7$$

Hence, $f(x + 2) = 4x + 7$

(c) $f(x) + f(2)$ is the sum of two expressions: $f(x)$ and $f(2)$.

$$f(x) + f(2) = \underbrace{4x - 1}_{f(x)} + \underbrace{4(2) - 1}_{f(2)}$$

$$= 4x - 1 + 8 - 1$$

$$= 4x + 6$$

Hence, $f(x) + f(2) = 4x + 6$

Note the differences between part **(c)** and parts **(a)** and **(b)**. You cannot simply add $f(2)$ to $f(x)$ to get $f(x + 2)$. In general, $f(a + b) \neq f(a) + f(b)$.

(d) First find $f(x + 2)$; we found in part **(b)** that $f(x + 2) = 4x + 7$. Then

$$f(x + 2) - f(x) = \underbrace{4x + 7}_{f(x + 2)} - \underbrace{(4x - 1)}_{f(x)} \qquad \textit{Note the parentheses around } 4x - 1.$$

$$= 4x + 7 - 4x + 1$$

$$= 8$$

Hence, $f(x + 2) - f(x) = 8$ ∎

A function does not have to be defined algebraically; it can be defined by a graph and the functional values can be determined from this graph.

Interpreting f(x) from a graph

Let's carefully examine the graph in Figure 3.29a and review what it means for a point (x, y) to lie on a graph and how, given the graph of a relationship, we can determine y given x.

The x-coordinate is often called the "directed" distance from the y-axis, meaning that $|x|$ is the distance, and the sign of x gives the direction. Similarly, the y-coordinate is the directed distance from the x-axis.

We can see in Figure 3.29a that the point $(5, -6)$ is on the graph. This means that the graph passes through a point that is 5 horizontal units to the right of the y-axis and 6 vertical units below the x-axis. If we need to find the y value associated with a particular x value, we start at the x value on the x-axis, project vertically upward or downward to the graph, and then project horizontally to the y-axis and read this y value. Hence if $x = 3$, then we see that for this graph, $y = 1$. Notice that at $x = 3$, the "height" of the graph (the vertical distance from the x-axis) is 1; likewise, if $x = -4$, $y = 3$.

The x-coordinate gives the horizontal distance from the y-axis, and the y-coordinate gives the vertical distance from the x-axis.

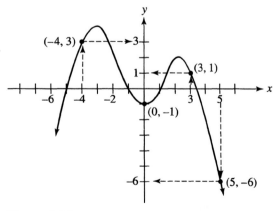

Figure 3.29a

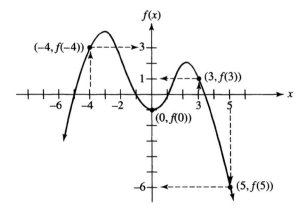

Figure 3.29b

Returning to the graph in Figure 3.29a, using function notation, we can label the graph $y = f(x)$. Then, instead of writing $y = 3$ when $x = -4$, we can write $f(-4) = 3$. Similarly, $y = -1$ when $x = 0$ can be written as $f(0) = -1$. Figure 3.29b repeats Figure 3.29a with the vertical axis labeled $f(x)$ instead of y.

Referring to Figure 3.29b, let's summarize the equivalence of these alternatives. See Table 3.1.

Table 3.1

(x,y) Notation	$y = f(x)$ Notation	$(x, f(x))$ Notation
$(-4, 3)$	$3 = f(-4)$	$(-4, f(-4))$
$(3, 1)$	$1 = f(3)$	$(3, f(3))$
$(0, -1)$	$-1 = f(0)$	$(0, f(0))$

Again, $f(x)$ is the y value at x, and gives the "height" of the graph (the vertical distance above or below the x-axis) at x. To be more precise, $f(x)$ is the directed distance of the graph from the x-axis at x. Hence, $f(a)$ is the directed distance of the graph from the x-axis at $x = a$; the directed distance of the graph from the x-axis at $x = b$ is $f(b)$. See Figure 3.30.

Figure 3.30

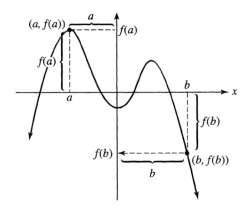

EXAMPLE 4

Consider the function defined by the graph in Figure 3.31 to find each of the following.

(a) $f(6)$ (b) $f(-3)$ (c) $f(0)$ (d) For what values of x is $f(x) = 0$?

(e) Which is larger, $f(-3)$ or $f(3)$?

Figure 3.31

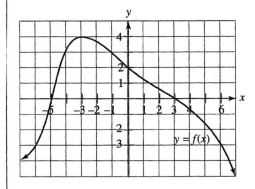

Solution

(a) To find $f(6)$, we must find the y value that corresponds to $x = 6$. Looking at the graph, we can see that when $x = 6$, the corresponding y value is $y = -3$. Therefore $f(6) = -3$.

(b) Similarly, from the graph we see that when $x = -3$, the corresponding y value is $y = 4$. Therefore $f(-3) = 4$.

(c) To find $f(0)$, we must determine where the graph crosses the y-axis (because when $x = 0$ the point must be on the y-axis). From the graph we can see that $y = 2$ when $x = 0$, hence $f(0) = 2$.

(d) We are looking for those x values for which $y = 0$ [remember that $f(x)$ is just another name for y]. But $y = 0$ means that the point must be on the x-axis. Therefore, from the graph we see that $f(-5) = 0$ and $f(3) = 0$, and so the x values that make $f(x) = 0$ are -5 and 3.

(e) While it is true that 3 is larger than -3, this question asks you to compare the y or f values, not the x values. We cannot answer this question until we determine what the function f actually does to x. We see on the graph that when $x = -3$, the corresponding y value is $y = 4$; hence $f(-3) = 4$. Similarly, the y value corresponding to $x = 3$ is $y = 0$; hence $f(3) = 0$. So $f(-3) = 4$ is larger than $f(3) = 0$. ∎

At the beginning of this section we learned that algebraically, $f(a + 3)$ and $f(a) + 3$ are not the same. Keeping in mind that $f(a)$ is the "height" of the graph at a, we can geometrically demonstrate the differences between the two quantities. See Figure 3.32.

Figure 3.32
Comparing $f(a) + 3$ and $f(a + 3)$

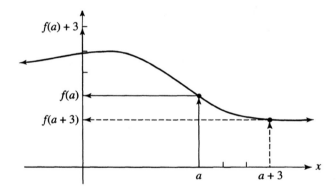

Notice that finding $f(a) + 3$ requires us first to find $f(a)$. To find $f(a)$, we first locate a on the x-axis, move vertically up until we intersect the graph, and then project horizontally onto the y-axis. To find $f(a) + 3$, we move vertically up three more units. In the language of Section 3.4, this is equivalent to using a as the input and then adding 3 to the output, $f(a)$.

On the other hand, finding $f(a + 3)$ requires us first to find $a + 3$, move vertically up until we intersect the graph, and then project horizontally onto the y-axis. This is the same as using $a + 3$ as the input and then finding the output, $f(a + 3)$. Notice the difference between the two expressions in their values as well as the procedures used to find each expression.

DIFFERENT PERSPECTIVES: Function Notation

Consider the geometric and algebraic interpretation of function notation. Let's consider the function $y = f(x) = x^2 - x - 6$, whose graph appears below.

GRAPHICAL DESCRIPTION

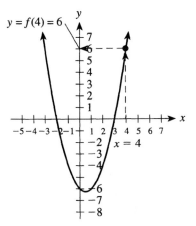

The graph of $y = f(x) = x^2 - x - 6$

To find $f(4)$ *using the graph,* we are looking for the y value that corresponds to $x = 4$. We can see by the graph that when $x = 4$, the corresponding y value is $y = 6$. Hence $f(4) = 6$.

ALGEBRAIC DESCRIPTION

To find $f(4)$ we substitute 4 for x in $f(x) = x^2 - x - 6$:

$$f(4) = 4^2 - 4 - 6 = 16 - 4 - 6 = 6$$

Hence $f(4) = 6$.

Study Skills 3.4

Taking an Algebra Exam: Dealing with Panic

In the first two chapters of this text we have given you advice on how to learn algebra and discussed how to prepare for an algebra exam. If you followed this advice and put the proper amount of time to good use, you should feel fairly confident and less anxious about the exam. But you may still find during the course of the exam that you are suddenly stuck or you draw a blank. This may lead you to panic and say irrational things like "I'm stuck. . . . I can't do this problem. . . . I can't do any of these problems. . . . I'm going to fail this test." Your heart may start to beat faster and your breath may quicken. You are entering a panic cycle.

These statements are irrational. Getting stuck on a few problems does not mean that you cannot do any algebra. These statements only serve to interfere with your concentration on the exam itself. How can you think about solving a problem while you are telling yourself that you cannot? The increased heart and breath rate are part of this cycle.

What we would like to do is break this cycle. What we recommend that you do is first put aside the exam and silently say to yourself **STOP!** Then try to relax, clear your mind, and encourage yourself by saying to yourself things such as "This is only one (or a few) problems, not the whole test" or "I've done problems like this before, so I'll get the solution soon." (Haven't you ever talked to yourself this way before?)

Now take some slow deep breaths and search for some problems that you know how to solve and start with those. Build your concentration and confidence slowly with more problems. When you are through with the problems you can complete, go back to the ones on which you were stuck. If you have the time, take a few minutes and rest your head on your desk, and then try again. But make sure you have checked the problems you have completed.

EXERCISES 3.4

In Exercises 1–12, given $f(x) = 2x - 3, g(x) = 3x^2 - x + 1,$ *and* $h(x) = \sqrt{x + 5}$, *find:*

1. $f(0)$ **2.** $g(0)$ **3.** $g(2)$ **4.** $f(2)$

5. $g(-2)$ **6.** $f(-2)$ **7.** $h(3)$ **8.** $h(4)$

9. $h(-3)$ **10.** $h(-4)$ **11.** $h(a)$ **12.** $g(a)$

In Exercises 13–24, given $f(x) = x^2 + 2$ *and* $g(x) = 2x - 3,$ *find (and simplify):*

13. $f(5) + f(2)$ **14.** $f(5 + 2)$ **15.** $f(6 - 4)$ **16.** $f(6) - f(4)$

17. $g(x + 2)$ **18.** $g(x) + g(2)$ **19.** $f(2x)$ **20.** $g(3x)$

21. $g(3x + 2)$ **22.** $3g(x) + 2$ **23.** $g(x + 2) - g(x)$ **24.** $g(x + 5) - g(x)$

In Exercises 25–34, given $f(x) = x^2 + 2x - 3,$ *find (and simplify):*

25. $f(-2) + f(3)$ **26.** $f(-2 + 3)$ **27.** $f(x) - 4$ **28.** $f(x) + 3$

29. $f(x) - f(4)$ **30.** $f(x) + f(3)$ **31.** $f(3x)$ **32.** $2f(x)$

33. $3f(x)$ **34.** $f(2x)$

In Exercises 35–40, given $g(x) = \dfrac{x}{x + 5},$ *find (and simplify):*

35. $g(-3)$ **36.** $g(10)$ **37.** $g\left(\dfrac{1}{4}\right)$

38. $g\left(-\dfrac{2}{3}\right)$ **39.** $g(x + 5)$ **40.** $g(x - 5)$

41. Use the following graph of $y = g(x)$ to find
     (a) $g(-5)$ **(b)** $g(-2)$ **(c)** $g(0)$
     (d) $g(1)$ **(e)** $g(3)$

42. Use the following graph of $y = h(x)$ to find
     (a) $h(-2)$ **(b)** $h(6)$ **(c)** $h(0)$
     (d) $h(4)$ **(e)** $h(-4)$

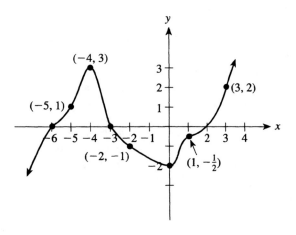
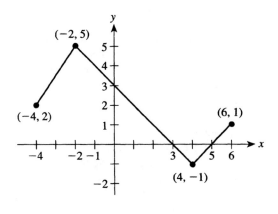

43. Use the following graph of $y = f(x)$ to find
    (a) $f(-1)$ (b) $f(0)$ (c) $f(4)$
    (d) For what value(s) of x is $f(x) = -2$?
    (e) For how many value(s) of x is $f(x) = 4$?

44. Use the following graph of $y = g(x)$ to find
    (a) $g(-1)$ (b) $g(0)$ (c) $g(4)$
    (d) For what value(s) of x is $g(x) = -2$?
    (e) For what value(s) of x is $g(x) = 4$?

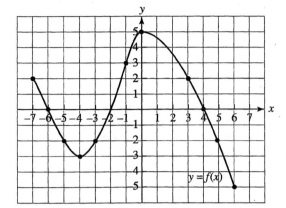
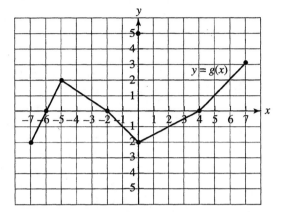

45. A car rental agency charges a flat fee of $29 per day plus a mileage charge of $0.14 per mile. Express the charge, C, for a 3-day rental as a function of m, the number of miles driven.

46. The length of a rectangle is 8 more than twice its width w. Express the perimeter, P, of the rectangle as a function of w.

47. The width of a rectangle is 12 less than three times its length, L. Express the area, A, of the rectangle as a function of L.

48. A cellular phone company charges a flat monthly fee of $33 per month plus an airtime fee of $0.54 per minute of phone usage. Express the monthly cellular phone bill, C, as a function of m, the number of minutes of phone usage.

49. A ticket club has 600 concert tickets to sell. It sells x tickets at a price of $30 per ticket, and all the remaining tickets at $24 per ticket. If all the tickets are sold, express the total amount collected, C, as a function of x.

50. A woman drives for a total of 10 hours. She drives for t hours at a rate of 45 mph, and the remaining time at a rate of 55 mph. Express the total distance covered, d, as a function of t.

51. Two copying machines are working on a project. Machine A can produce 20 copies per minute; machine B can produce 22 copies per minute. If machine A works for m minutes, and machine B works for 35 minutes longer than machine A, express the total number, N, of copies made as a function of m.

52. Two workers are packing items on an assembly line. One worker packages 30 items per hour for h hours and the second worker packages 35 items per hour for 3 hours longer than the first worker. Express the total number, N, of items packaged by the two workers as a function of h.

53. An electrician charges $45 per hour for her time and $25 per hour for her assistant's time. She works for h hours on a job and her assistant works 2 hours less than she does. Express the total amount, A, they earn as a function of h.

54. A plumber charges $42 per hour for his time and $27 per hour for his assistant's time. On a particular job that takes a total of 8 hours, the plumber works alone for h hours and the assistant then works alone for the remainder of the time. Express the total amount, A, earned by the plumber and his assistant as a function of h.

55. Lamont has part-time jobs as a tutor and also as a clerk. He earns $10 per hour as a tutor and $6.35 per hour as a clerk. During a particular week, he works a total of 15 hours tutoring and clerking. Express his weekly income, I, as a function of t, the number of hours he tutors.

56. Cheryl owns a gourmet food shop. During a certain week she sells p pounds of a $5.35-per-pound coffee blend and 12 fewer pounds of a $6.85 coffee blend. Express the total coffee revenue, R, for the week as a function of p.

3.5   Interpreting Graphs

In the first four sections of this chapter, we discussed the rectangular coordinate system and how we can get a picture of the solutions of an equation from its graph. In this section we will discuss how graphs themselves are legitimate mathematical tools that can help us understand or evaluate quantifiable relationships.

Most of us have had some experience with graphs outside a mathematics class: Graphs may accompany a newspaper or magazine article, or appear in a textbook. A graph is usually used to give us a convenient picture illustrating some relationship between two quantities that allows us to make, summarize, or clarify a point. The graph also gives more detail as to the nature of the relationship under discussion. In mathematics, the graph is a tool that helps us to visualize a trend or relationship between two quantities. While an equation is useful for finding exact values, a graph not only can be used to get reasonable estimates of these values but also has the added advantage of allowing us to "see" the nature of the relationship.

EXAMPLE 1

The graph in Figure 3.33 illustrates how the profit a company expects on the sale of a certain item depends on its selling price. The horizontal axis is labeled s and represents the selling price of the item (in dollars). The vertical axis is labeled P and represents the profit (in thousands of dollars) that the company earns. Use the information given in this graph to describe how the profit relates to the selling price.

Figure 3.33
The graph for Example 1

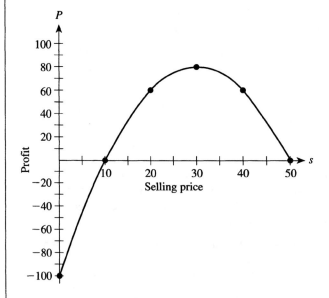

Solution

Examining the graph, we can draw the following conclusions:

1. The point $(0, -100)$ is on the graph. This means that when the selling price is $0 ($s = 0$), the profit is $-$100,000 ($P = -100$). We can interpret this negative profit to mean that if the item were given away free, the company would have a *loss* of $100,000. This loss may be due to fixed costs such as rent and taxes, which must be paid regardless of what the selling price is or how many items are sold.

2. As the selling price starts to increase, the profit increases as well. The point (10, 0) on the graph tells us that when the selling price is $10 ($s = 10$), the profit is $0 ($P = 0$). (This is often called the *break-even point.*)

3. As the selling price continues to increase, the profit continues to increase as well. The highest point on the graph is (30, 80). This highest point corresponds to the *maximum profit* the company can earn, which is $80,000.

4. As the selling price increases beyond $30 the profit decreases until, when the selling price is $50, the profit is again $0. This can be explained by the fact that once the selling price gets too large, fewer people will buy the item, thus decreasing the profit.

At a glance we can see that the trend is for the profit to increase as the selling price increases until it reaches the particular selling price where the profit is the highest value. Then, as the selling price continues to increase, the profit decreases until there is $0 profit. Thus, this graph gives a "snapshot" of the relationship between the selling price and the expected profit. ■

EXAMPLE 2

A psychologist developed a treatment for reducing certain compulsive behaviors. In order to collect preliminary evidence of the effectiveness of her treatment, she had 35 of her clients keep diaries, recording the number of times they exhibited their compulsive behavior daily. They did this for a total of 12 weeks (before, during, and after treatment), and then they reported the same information again a year later. Figure 3.34 shows the average daily number of compulsive behaviors exhibited by the group during the 12 weeks, and 1 year later (for 2 weeks). Assuming that the changes were a direct result of the therapy and nothing else, what can you conclude about the effectiveness of the treatment?

Figure 3.34

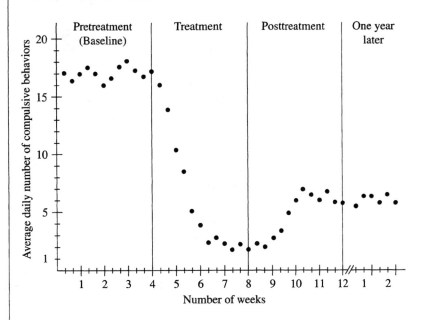

Solution

The graph is split into four sections: before the treatment (called the baseline), during the treatment, after the treatment, and a year later. During the first 4 weeks, we can see that the average daily number of compulsive behaviors exhibited by clients was between 16 and 18. During therapy, the next 4 weeks, the average number of compulsive behaviors reduced steadily until it fell in the range of about 2 to 3 at the end of the treatment. For the first week following the treatment, the number of compulsive behaviors remained about the same as during the last week of the treatment phase. Then the number of compulsive behaviors slowly increased during the next week until it reached a level between 6 and 7. A year later, the number remained at the same level as it had during the end of the posttreatment period.

One may conclude that although the treatment was not successful in eliminating the response entirely, it certainly reduced number of occurrences of the compulsive behavior by about 60–66%. ■

EXAMPLE 3

Jani is traveling on business in her car. Suppose that the graph in Figure 3.35 describes her day's travel. The horizontal axis is labeled *t* and represents the number of hours since Jani began her trip. The vertical axis is labeled *d* and represents the distance (in miles) that Jani is from her home. Use the information given in this graph to describe her day as best you can.

Figure 3.35
The graph for Example 3

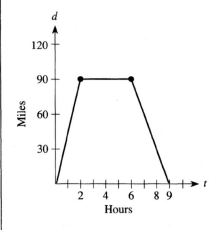

Solution

Examining the graph, we can draw the following conclusions:

1. The point (0, 0) is on the graph. This means that when $t = 0$, $d = 0$. Keeping in mind that *t* is the number of hours since Jani began her trip, $t = 0$ means that Jani has not yet begun her trip; since *d* is the number of miles that Jani is from her home, $d = 0$ means that she is 0 miles from her home. In other words, Jani is starting her trip from home.

2. The line is rising from (0, 0) to (2, 90), which means that during this 2-hour period Jani's distance from home is *increasing*.

3. The point (2, 90) is on the graph, which means that when $t = 2$, $d = 90$. In other words, after 2 hours, Jani is 90 miles from home.

4. The next portion of the graph is horizontal, which means that the distance is not changing. The distance from home remains 90 miles for the next 4 hours. Possibly Jani is at a business meeting that lasts for 4 hours.

5. The line is falling from (6, 90) to (9, 0), which means that during this 3-hour period Jani's distance from home is *decreasing*.

6. The point (9, 0) means that after 9 hours Jani's distance from home is again 0. After 9 hours Jani has returned to her home.

Actually, we can glean a bit more information from this graph. When Jani starts her trip, we can see that she covers a distance of 90 miles in 2 hours; hence, her average speed during her first 2 hours of travel is

$$\text{Averaged speed} = \frac{90 \text{ miles}}{2 \text{ hours}} = 45 \text{ mph}$$

On her return trip home (the 3-hour period from $t = 6$ to $t = 9$), Jani covers a distance of 90 miles in 3 hours, so her average speed during her return trip home is 30 mph.

The main point here is that the graph allows us to see at a glance some important aspects of Jani's trip. ■

EXAMPLE 4

Let's suppose that we want to determine how much of a medication is in the bloodstream at various times after the medication is taken. We might take a series of blood samples from a patient as follows: The first sample is taken before a particular medication is administered; subsequent blood samples are then taken at 20-minute intervals after the patient receives the medication, and the amount of medication in the blood at each time is determined.

By designating the horizontal axis, labeled *t,* as the time in minutes after the medication is taken, and the vertical axis, labeled *A,* as the amount of medication (in milligrams) present in the blood, we can represent the data collected as points on a graph (see Figure 3.36a). If we draw line segments connecting the points (see Figure 3.36b), then the resulting graph allows us to analyze the relationship between the elapsed time and the amount of medication in the bloodstream.

Use the graph to describe the connections between the time elapsed since the medication was taken and the amount of medication present in the bloodstream.

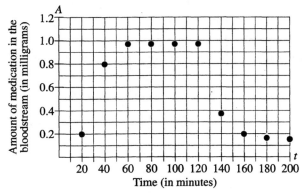

Figure 3.36a   **Figure 3.36b**

Solution

If we examine the graph in Figure 3.36a, we can see that over the first 20-minute interval, the amount of medication in the blood rises from 0 mg to 0.2 mg. In other words, the medication is entering the blood at an average rate of

$$\frac{0.2 \text{ mg}}{20 \text{ min}} = 0.01 \frac{\text{mg}}{\text{min}}$$

During the next 20-minute interval, the amount of medication in the blood rises from 0.2 mg to 0.8 mg; thus the amount of medication in the blood increases by 0.6 mg in 20 minutes. In other words, the medication is entering the blood at an average rate of

$$\frac{0.6 \text{ mg}}{20 \text{ min}} = 0.03 \frac{\text{mg}}{\text{min}}$$

Based on this analysis, we can say that during the second 20-minute interval, the medication is entering the bloodstream at 3 times the rate it did during the first 20 minutes.

Now that we have an idea of how to interpret the steepness of the line, we can identify the following trends:

1. The medication enters the blood relatively slowly during the first 20 minutes, then more quickly during the 20–40-minute time interval.

2. During the 40–60-minute time interval, the medication is still entering the blood, but the *rate* at which the medication is entering the bloodstream is slower than in the second interval. (The third line segment is less steep than the second line segment.)

3. During the next three 20-minute intervals (60–120 minutes), the line segment is horizontal, which indicates that no more medication is entering (or leaving) the bloodstream.

4. During the 120–140-minute time interval, the line is falling relatively steeply. This tells us that the amount of medication in the bloodstream is *decreasing* at a comparatively rapid rate.

5. During the next three 20-minute intervals, the line segments are also falling but are progressively less steep. This tells us that the amount of medication in the bloodstream is continuing to decrease but at a slower rate during each time period.

Figure 3.37 serves to summarize this analysis and interpretation of the graph.

Figure 3.37
Interpreting the rate of change from a graph

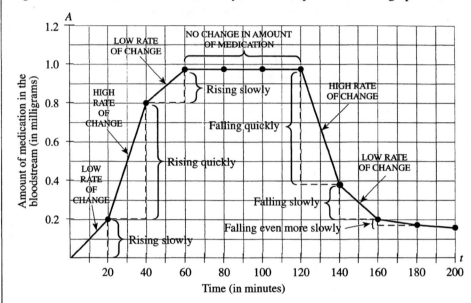

Keep in mind that our analysis and interpretation are dependent on the fact that we connected the data points with straight line segments. To actually justify such an assumption in the real world, we would need to collect more data. ■

EXAMPLE 5

The forestry service located a species of deer and monitored the size of the population for 15 years. The graph of the relationship between the size of the population and time is illustrated by Figure 3.38. Discuss the population growth illustrated by the graph.

Figure 3.38

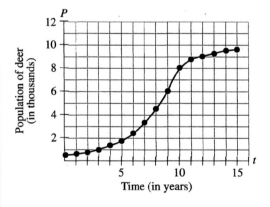

Solution

Look at the graph to get an overall picture of how the population increases. Divide the horizontal axis into 5-year intervals, and look at the population increases for each interval. Note that for the first 5-year interval, the graph rises a bit more than 1 unit (representing a population increase of over 1,000); and for the next 5-year interval, the graph rises a bit more than 6 units (representing a population increase of 6,000). For the last 5-year interval, the graph rises $1\frac{1}{2}$ units. We can restate these trends in general terms as follows: The population grows slowly during the first 5 years, then grows rapidly between the 5th and the 10th years. Between the 10th and the 15th years, the population growth tapers off or slows down (or the growth rate slows down during the last 5 years). ■

Study Skills 3.5

Taking an Algebra Exam: A Few Other Comments about Exams

Do not forget to check over all your work, as we have suggested on numerous occasions. Reread all directions and make sure that you have answered all the questions as directed.

If you are required to show your work (such as for partial credit), make sure that your work is neat. Do not forget to put your answers where directed or at least indicate your answers clearly by putting a box or circle around them. For multiple-choice tests be sure you have filled in the correct space.

One other bit of advice: Some students are unnerved when they see others finishing the exam early. They begin to believe that there may be something wrong with themselves because they are still working on the exam. They should not be concerned that some students can do the work quickly and that others leave the exam early, not because the exam was easy for them, but because they give up.

In any case, do not be in a hurry to leave the exam. If you are given 1 hour for the exam then take the entire hour. If you have followed the suggestions in this chapter such as checking your work, etc., and you still have time left over, relax for a few minutes and then go back and check your work again.

 EXERCISES 3.5

1. The telephone company monitored telephone usage in a small town by recording the number of calls made every two hours during a 24-hour period. The following graph illustrates the level of telephone usage during this period. The horizontal axis, labeled t, represents the hour of the day: 0 = midnight, 1 = 1 A.M., 14 = 2 P.M., etc. The vertical axis, labeled n, represents the number of phone calls (in thousands).

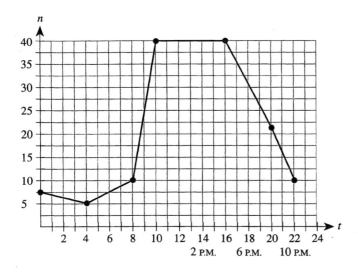

(a) How many calls are made at midnight?

(b) At what time is the number of phone calls a minimum?

(c) How many phone calls are made at 6:00 P.M.?

(d) During what period(s) of time is the number of phone calls decreasing?

(e) At what time is the number of phone calls a maximum?

(f) During what period of time does the number of phone calls remain constant?

2. The following graph illustrates the level of electrical power usage in a small town during a 1-year period. The horizontal axis, labeled *m*, represents the month of the year: 1–2 represents January; 2–3, February; . . . ; 12–13, December. The vertical axis, labeled *K*, represents the number of megawatts of electrical power being used.

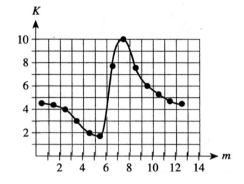

   (a) During which month does the power usage reach a maximum?

   (b) During which month does the power usage reach a minimum?

   (c) During which months does the power usage increase?

   (d) During which months does the power usage decrease?

3. The following graph, published by the Department of Labor Statistics, shows the amount of energy consumed, produced, and traded in the United States from 1980 to 1998, in quadrillion British thermal units (Btu). (A Btu is the amount of energy required to raise the temperature of 1 pound of water 1°F at or near 39.2°F.)

Energy Production, Trade, and Consumption: 1980 to 1998

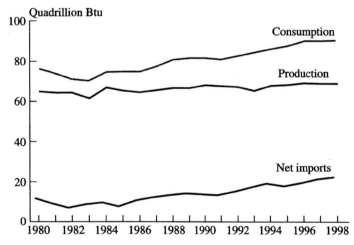

Source: Chart prepared by U.S. Census Bureau.

   (a) How many Btu's were consumed, produced, and imported in the United States in 1990?

   (b) Verbally describe the general trend shown by the graphs for each of production, consumption, and imports from 1980 to 1998.

4. A psychologist developed a treatment for reducing certain inappropriate social behaviors in children. In order to collect preliminary evidence of the effectiveness of her treatment, she observed 20 of her clients interacting socially, for 45 minutes a day, recording the number of times they exhibited inappropriate social behaviors. She did this for a total of 9 weeks (before, during, and after treatment). The accompanying graph shows the average daily number of inappropriate social behaviors exhibited by the group during the 9 weeks. Assuming that the changes were a direct result of the therapy and nothing else, what can you conclude about the effectiveness of the treatment?

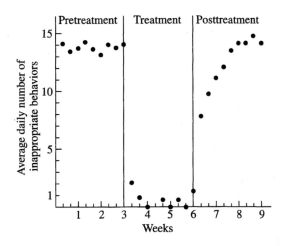

5. The following graph illustrates the relationship between air temperature and altitude. The horizontal axis, labeled *a*, represents the altitude (in kilometers). The vertical axis, labeled *T*, represents the temperature (in degree Celsius).

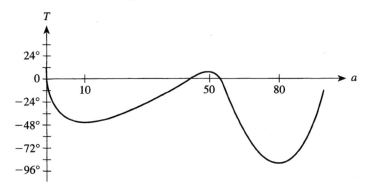

(a) It is commonly believed that the temperature drops steadily as the altitude increases. Does the graph confirm or deny this belief?

(b) If a temperature-measuring device is sent aloft, between what altitudes will the temperature be decreasing?

(c) As the device rises from an altitude of 45 km to an altitude of 55 km, how is the temperature changing?

6. The following graph illustrates the level of a certain substance in the blood after a medication containing this substance is taken. The horizontal axis, labeled *m*, represents the number of minutes after the medication is taken. The vertical axis, labeled *A*, represents the amount of the substance, measured in milligrams, present in the blood.

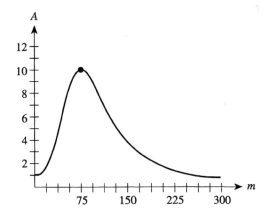

(a) How many milligrams of the substance are present in the blood before any medication is taken? This is the body's normal level of this substance. [*Hint:* Find A when $m = 0$.]

(b) How long does it take until the amount of this substance reaches its maximum level in the blood?

(c) After the medication is taken, how long does it take for the level of the substance to return to normal?

7. In a psychology experiment, a group of students was asked to memorize a list of nonsense syllables (meaningless three-letter words such as "ogu," "bir," or "gar"). After successfully demonstrating that they had memorized the entire list, all were retested at various time intervals afterward. The graph of the relationship between their (average) learning score and the retesting time is shown in the figure. The horizontal axis, labeled t, represents the time at which the students were retested; the vertical axis, labeled p, represents the group's average percent score. This is often called a *forgetting curve.*

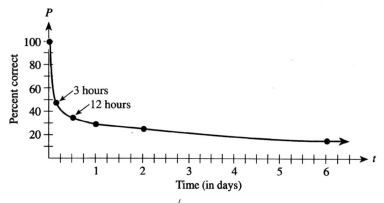

(a) Find the average score 1 day after the students learned the material.

(b) How long will it take for them to remember only 25% of what they had learned (or how long does it take them to forget 75% of what they learned)?

(c) Discuss the relationship between time and forgetting illustrated by the graph. Include in your discussion how quickly forgetting occurs as time passes.

8. Students were given a list of words to memorize. Each day they were given a new list to remember and were tested the following day only on the previous day's list. This continued for 15 days. The following is a graph of the approximate relationship between the percentage recalled on a list and number of different previous lists memorized.

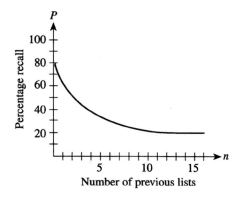

(a) Approximately what percentage of the words were recalled on the seventh list? (This means we want the percentage recall when the number of previous lists is 6.)

(b) *Interference* is the term used to describe the negative effects new learning can have on previous learning. Discuss the relationship between percentage recall and the number of previous lists memorized. What can you conclude about interference in this case?

9. The figure shows learning curves for massed and spaced practice. Students practiced keeping a pointer on a moving target. Each trial lasted 30 seconds. Some students had a 15-second rest period between trials (massed practice) and others a 45-second rest (spaced practice). (Keep in mind that these are actually two graphs: the graph of the massed practice group and the graph of the spaced practice group.)

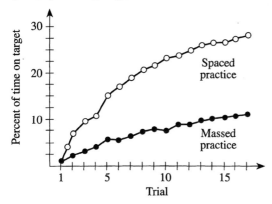

(a) For the massed practice group, approximately how many trials does it take before they can score 10%?

(b) For the spaced practice group, approximately how many trials does it take before they can score 10%?

(c) Based on the graphs or learning curves given, what conclusions can you draw about spaced versus massed practice for this type of skill?

10. Two groups of students memorized a list of nonsense syllables; we will designate them the awake group and the asleep group. Each group was divided into smaller subgroups where each subgroup was tested on the same words at differing time intervals; that is, one subgroup was tested 1 hour later, another was tested 2 hours later, etc. Students in the asleep group were asleep between the initial learning phase and the final testing phase; students in the awake group were awake between the learning and testing phases. The graph shows the results of the experiment.

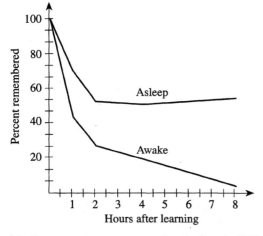

(a) Compare the two groups by the graph. Which group exhibited less forgetting? If the results of this graph were true for all learning, what conclusions could you draw about when to study?

(b) Look at the line segment covering only students tested at hour 1. How do these two (tested at 1 hour) groups compare?

(c) Look at the graph for the awake group only. Describe, in general, how quickly forgetting is occurring as time passes.

(d) Look at the graph for the awake group only. Use the graph to describe specifically the rates of forgetting (how quickly forgetting is occurring) for each segment.

11. Kyle is taking a business trip. Suppose that the following graph describes his day's travel. The horizontal axis is labeled t and represents the number of hours since Kyle began his trip. The vertical axis is labeled d and represents the distance (in miles) that Kyle is from his home. Use the information given in this graph to describe his day as best you can, and to determine his rate of speed and his direction.

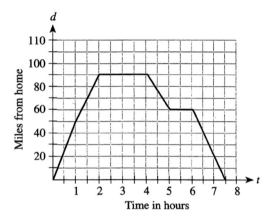

12. The graph below is called the *logistic growth curve*. It shows the growth of a population over time. The horizontal dashed line appearing on the graph is called the *carrying capacity* of the environment, which is defined to be the number of individuals in a population that the environment can support over an indefinite amount of time. The horizontal axis represents time and the vertical axis represents the number present in the population. Use the graph to discuss how population size changes over time. Discuss possible reasons why the graph looks this way.

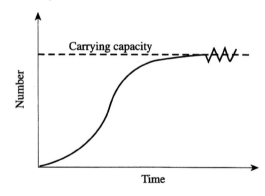

13. A psychologist wanted to test three different procedures or treatments to reduce aggressive behavior of 5-year-old children: treatment A, treatment B, and treatment C. An "aggressive child" was assigned to each treatment, which was administered twice a week for 4 weeks. Before starting treatment, the child was taken to a room where he or she was observed with a group of other children in a playroom for a half-hour. The psychologist's assistant recorded the number of times the child undergoing treatment exhibited aggressive behaviors. The child attended these play sessions after each treatment session, and continued attending the play sessions after the 4-week treatment was completed. The assistant continued recording the aggressive behaviors.

The accompanying graph shows the results both during and after each of the three different treatments. The horizontal axis is the time, labeled t, in days during and following treatment starting at $t = 0$, the first play session before treatment. The vertical axis is labeled b and represents the number of aggressive behaviors exhibited during each play session.

Discuss what the graph tells you about the effectiveness of the therapies relative to each other. Which therapy has the "best" results?

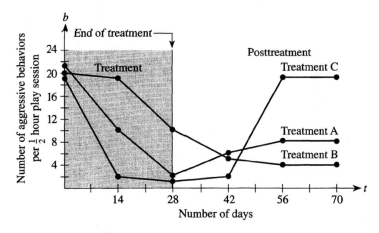

14. A biologist performed the following experiment with two paramecium species: *P. cyntia* and *P. soraria*.

(a) He first grew the two species under identical conditions in separate containers, as shown in the figure. How do the two compare? What conclusion can you make about one species versus the other?

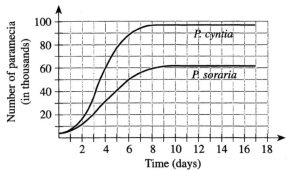

Two cultures grown in separate containers

(b) The biologist then grew the two together in the same container, with the results shown in the following figure. Grown together, how do the two now compare? What conclusions can you make?

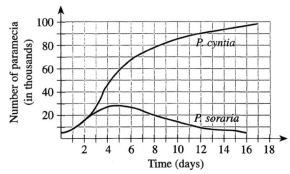

The same two cultures grown together
in the same container

After completing this chapter, you should be able to:

1. Sketch the graph of a first-degree equation in two variables (Section 3.1).

For example: Sketch the graph of $6y - 3x = 12$. Label the intercepts.

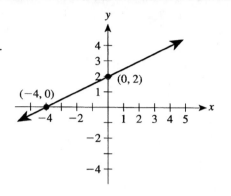

To find the x-intercept:
Set y = 0 and solve for x.

$$6y - 3x = 12$$
$$6(0) - 3x = 12$$
$$-3x = 12$$
$$x = -4$$

To find the y-intercept:
Set x = 0 and solve for y.

$$6y - 3x = 12$$
$$6y - 3(0) = 12$$
$$6y = 12$$
$$y = 2$$

The graph crosses the x-axis at $(-4, 0)$ and the y-axis at $(0, 2)$.

The graph of $6y - 3x = 12$ is shown at the right. Finding a check point is left to the student.

2. Be able to extract information about an equation from its graph (Section 3.2).

For example: Figure 3.39 shows the graph of an equation:

(a) Using the graph to find y when $x = 4$, we start on the x-axis at $x = 4$ and project vertically until we meet the graph. Move horizontally until we meet the y-axis, and read off the value on the y-axis to get $y = -7$ (see Figure 3.40). Hence $y = -7$ when $x = 4$, or, equivalently, we can say the "point" $(4, -7)$ lies on the graph, or the ordered pair $(4, -7)$ satisfies the equation of the graph.

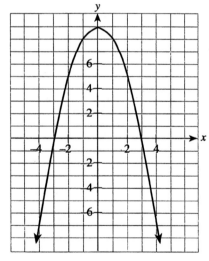

Figure 3.39

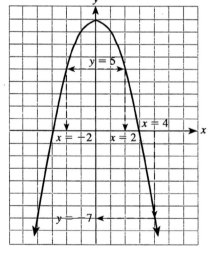

Figure 3.40

(b) To find x when $y = 5$ by using the graph, we start on the y-axis at $y = 5$ and project horizontally until we meet the graph. Note that we meet the graph in two places. This means that there are two points on the graph where the y-coordinate has the value 5. For each point on the graph, we move vertically until we meet the x-axis, and read off the values on the x-axis. We get two answers: $x = -2$, and $x = 2$ (see Figure 3.40). Hence the points $(-2, 5)$ and $(2, 5)$ lie on the graph.

(c) We can also see on the graph that the y-intercept is 9 (and therefore $(0, 9)$ lies on the graph), and the x-intercepts are -3 and 3 (and therefore $(-3, 0)$ and $(3, 0)$ lie on the graph).

(d) If we knew the equation of the graph given above is $y = 9 - x^2$, then we can verify that the points found in parts (a), (b), and (c) above lie on the graph by substituting the ordered pairs into the equation of the graph. For example, we verify that the point $(-2, 5)$ lies on the graph using the equation:

$y = 9 - x^2$ *Substitute $x = -2$ and $y = 5$ in the equation.*

$5 \overset{?}{=} 9 - (-2)^2$

$5 \overset{\checkmark}{=} 9 - 4$ *Hence the point $(-2, 5)$ lies on the graph.*

3. Understand the meaning of a relation and identify its domain and range (Section 3.3).

   For example:

   (a) The relation $\{(2, -3), (3, 4), (-2, -3)\}$ has domain $\{-2, 2, 3\}$ and range $\{-3, 4\}$. The relation assigns -3 to 2, 4 to 3, and -3 to -2.

   (b) The relation $4x^2 + y^2 = 4$ has the graph shown in Figure 3.41. By looking at the graph, we see that the domain is $\{x \mid -1 \le x \le 1\}$ and the range is $\{y \mid -2 \le y \le 2\}$.

   (c) The relation described by $y = \dfrac{2}{x - 1}$ has domain $\{x \mid x \ne 1\}$ because

   $x = 1$ is the only value of x that produces either an undefined or a nonreal value for y.

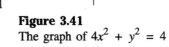

Figure 3.41
The graph of $4x^2 + y^2 = 4$

4. Understand the meaning of a function (Section 3.3).

   For example:

   (a) The relation $\{(2, -3), (2, 4)\}$ is not a function because the x value, 2, is assigned two y values, $y = -3$ and $y = 4$.

   (b) $\{(3, 5), (2, 5)\}$ is a function because no x value is assigned more than one y value.

   (c) Consider the relation described by the following graph:

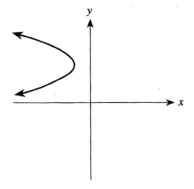

   In the next figure we apply the vertical line test:

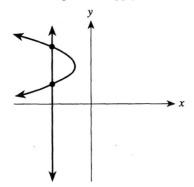

Since the graph of the relation intersects a vertical line at more than one point, this relation is not a function.

91

5. Use function notation (Section 3.4).

For example:

(a) If $f(x) = 3x^2 - 4$, then

$$f(2) = 3(2)^2 - 4 = 3 \cdot 4 - 4 = 8$$
$$f(-1) = 3(-1)^2 - 4 = 3 \cdot 1 - 4 = -1$$
$$f(s) = 3s^2 - 4$$

(b) If $f(x) = 2x - 1$ and $g(x) = x^2 + 3$, then

$f(x + 2) = 2(x + 2) - 1 = 2x + 4 - 1 = 2x + 3$

$f(x) + 2 = (2x - 1) + 2 = 2x + 1$

$f(x) + f(2) = (2x - 1) + (2 \cdot 2 - 1) = 2x - 1 + 4 - 1 = 2x + 2$

$g(2x) = (2x)^2 + 3 = 4x^2 + 3$

(c) Using the graph $y = f(x)$ given in Figure 3.42, we observe the following:

Figure 3.42

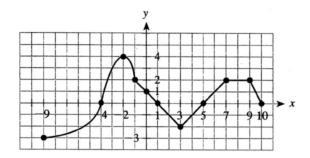

(i) $f(7) = 2$ (ii) $f(-9) = -3$ (iii) $f(-4) = 0$ (iv) $f(8) = 2$

(v) $f(-3)$ is greater than $f(3)$ [because $f(-3)$ is positive, whereas $f(3)$ is negative].

(vi) The graph of $y = f(x)$ has x-intercepts at $x = -4$, 1, 5, and 10.

6. Interpret data presented as a graph (Section 3.5).

For example: After a group of students memorized a list of random five-digit numbers, they were tested on their ability to recall the same list of numbers at regular hourly intervals for 5 hours. The graph in Figure 3.43 shows the average percent correct scores for the group at each testing.

Figure 3.43

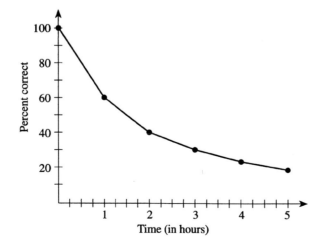

Some of the observations we can make are:

1. During the first hour, 40% of the numbers were forgotten. More numbers were forgotten during the first hour than during any other hour in the 5-hour period pictured in the graph.

2. During the third hour (that is, between time = 2 and time = 3), 10% of the numbers were forgotten.

3. At the end of this 5-hour period, 20% of the numbers were still remembered.

CHAPTER 3   REVIEW EXERCISES

In Exercises 1–26, sketch the graph of the equation. Label the intercepts.

1. $2x + y = 6$

2. $2x + y = -6$

3. $2x - 6y = -6$

4. $6y - 2x = 6$

5. $5x - 3y = 10$

6. $3x - 5y = 10$

7. $2x + 5y = 7$

8. $3x + 4y = 5$

9. $3x - 8y = 11$

10. $3x + 8y = 11$

11. $5x + 7y = 21$

12. $4x - 5y = 20$

13. $y = x$

14. $y = -x$

15. $y = -2x$

16. $x = 3y$

17. $y = \frac{2}{3}x + 2$

18. $y = -\frac{1}{2}x - 3$

19. $\frac{x}{3} + \frac{y}{2} = 12$

20. $\frac{x}{4} - \frac{y}{2} = 16$

21. $x - 2y = 8$

22. $x - 2y = 0$

23. $x - 2 = 0$

24. $y + 2 = 0$

25. $2y = 5$

26. $3x = 4$

27. Using the accompanying graph, determine the following:

(a) Find y when $x = -2$ and 2.

(b) Find x when $y = 3$.

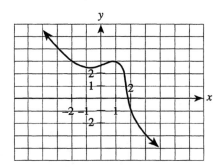

28. Using the graph below, determine the following:

(a) Find y when $x = -3$.

(b) Find x when $y = 2$ and -5.

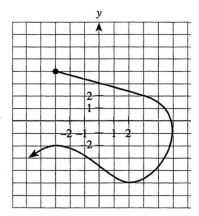

Exercises 29–32 refer to the figure given below.

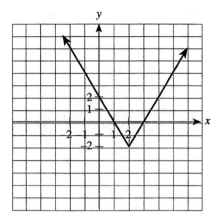

29. Find the value of y that satisfies the equation of the graph given above when $x = -2$.

30. Fill in the missing coordinate for the points that lie on the graph.

    (a) (5,)   **(b)** (, 4)

31. Find the x-intercepts.   **32.** Find the y-intercepts.

Exercises 33–34 refer to the graph of the equation $x^2 + y^2 = 20$ in the figure below.

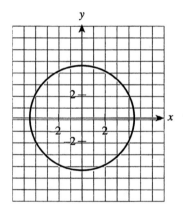

33. Find y for $x = 2$ by using the graph, and verify the value(s) using the equation of the graph.

34. Find x for $y = 4$ by using the graph, and verify the value(s) using the equation of the graph.

35. A salesperson is paid a base salary of $150 plus a commission of 5% of her gross sales.

    (a) Write an equation expressing her weekly income, I, in terms of her gross sales, g.

    (b) Sketch a graph of this equation.

    (c) Use the graph to estimate her income for the week in which her gross sales were $5,000.

    (d) Use the graph to determine her gross sales for the week in which her income was $750.

36. A car rental company charges $30.00 a day plus a mileage charge of 20¢ a mile.

    (a) Write an equation expressing the daily rental costs, C, of a car in terms of the number of miles driven, m.

    (b) Sketch a graph of this equation.

    (c) Use the graph to estimate the cost of driving 200 miles in a day.

    (d) Use the graph to determine how many miles can be driven if the costs are not to exceed $65.

In Exercises 37–42, identify the domain of the function.

37. $y = 2x + 1$ **38.** $2y = 3x$ **39.** $y = \sqrt{4 - x}$ **40.** $y = \sqrt{x + 3}$

41. $y = \dfrac{3x}{x + 2}$ **42.** $y = \dfrac{x}{2x + 1}$

In Exercises 43–50, determine whether the given relation is a function.

43. $\{(2, -5), (3, 8), (4, -5)\}$ **44.** $\{(6, 2), (5, 1), (6, 8)\}$

45. $\{(3, -1), (4, 2), (4, 7)\}$ **46.** $\{(-3, 1), (1, -3)\}$

47. $y = 2x + 3$ **48.** $2y = 3x - 1$

49. $y = x^2 - 4$ **50.** $x = y^2 - 4$

In Exercises 51–54, determine which of the graphs of relations represent functions.

51.

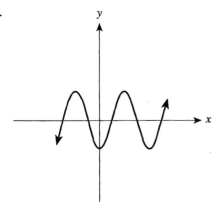

52.

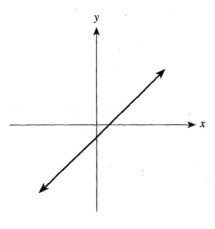

53.

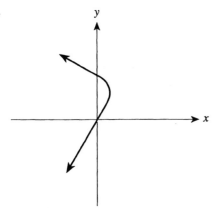

54.

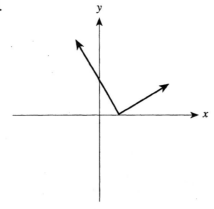

In Exercises 55–62, find the domain and range of the given relation or function; also indicate whether the relation is a function.

55. $\{(-2, 3), (0, 5), (3, 7), (5, 4)\}$ **56.** $\{(-3, -8), (0, 0), (-3, 7), (2, 10)\}$

57. $\{(4, 9), (6, 9), (1, 9), (8, 9)\}$ **58.** $\{(6, -5), (6, 2), (6, 0), (6, -3)\}$

59.

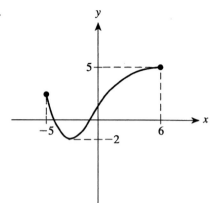

60.

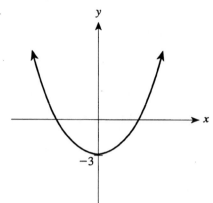

61.

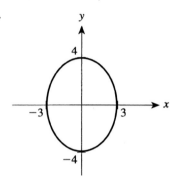

62.

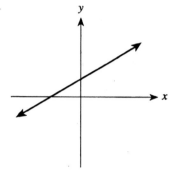

In Exercises 63–72, evaluate the functions at the given values. If a value is not in the domain of the function, state so.

63. $f(x) = 3x + 5$; $f(-1), f(0), f(1), f(2)$

64. $g(x) = 5 - 4x$; $g(-1), g(0), g(1), g(2)$

65. $f(x) = 2x^2 - 3x + 2$; $f(-1), f(0), f(1), f(2)$

66. $g(x) = 3x^3 + 2x - 3$; $g(-1), g(0), g(1), g(2)$

67. $h(x) = \sqrt{x - 5}$; $h(6), h(5), h(4)$

68. $g(x) = \sqrt{5 - 3x}$; $g(1), g(2), g(-1)$

69. $h(x) = \dfrac{x - 1}{x + 3}$; $h(1), h(3), h(-3)$

70. $h(x) = \dfrac{x + 1}{x}$; $h(-1), h(0), h(4)$

71. $f(x) = 2x^2 + 4x - 1$; $f(a), f(z)$

72. $f(a) = 2a^2 - 4a + 2$; $f(x), f(z)$

In Exercises 73–84, $f(x) = 5x + 2$ and $g(x) = 6 - x$. Find:

73. $f(x + 2)$ **74.** $f(x + 3)$ **75.** $f(x) + 2$ **76.** $f(x) + 3$

77. $f(x) + f(2)$ **78.** $f(x) + f(3)$ **79.** $g(x + 2)$ **80.** $g(x + 3)$

81. $g(2x)$ **82.** $g(3x)$ **83.** $2g(x)$ **84.** $3g(x)$

85. Use the graph of $y = f(x)$ given in Figure 3.44 to answer the following questions.

Figure 3.44
The graph of $y = f(x)$

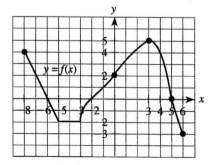

(a) Find $f(-6)$.   **(b)** Find $f(0)$.   **(c)** Find $f(-4)$.   **(d)** Find $f(6)$.

(e) Which is smaller, $f(4)$ or $f(5)$?   **(f)** Identify the x-intercepts of the graph.

86. Use the graph of $y = h(x)$ in Figure 3.45 to answer the following questions:

(a) $h(-2)$ (b) $h(6)$

(c) $h(0)$ (d) $h(4)$

(e) $h(-4)$

(f) For what value(s) of x is $h(x) = 0$?

Figure 3.45
The graph of $y = h(x)$

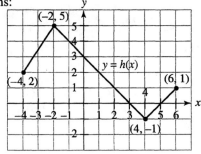

87. Rasheed is taking a business trip. Suppose that the graph at the right describes his day's travel.

The horizontal axis is labeled t and represents the number of hours since Rasheed began his trip. The vertical axis is labeled d and represents the distance (in miles) that Rasheed is from his home.

Use the information given in this graph to describe his day as best you can.

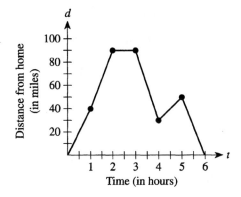

88. At time $t = 0$, an object is dropped from the top of a building, and we record the distance, d, the object is from the top of the building after each half-second elapses. We plot the graph of the relationship as shown at the right. The horizontal axis is the time, t, in seconds, and the vertical axis is the distance, d, in feet.

Discuss the relationship between the distance the object falls and the amount of time it is in the air. What happens to the speed of the object as it drops?

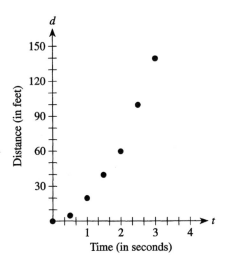

89. An office equipment leasing company rents out computer equipment. It charges a delivery fee of $30 plus a fee of $42 each day the computer is rented. Express the total charges, C, for a rental as a function of n, the number of days the computer is rented.

90. An airline is offering a special promotion to join its frequent flyer program. If you join the program, you get a joining bonus of 5,000 miles plus 2,500 miles for each shuttle flight you take. Express the mileage, M, you earn for joining the program and taking s shuttle flights as a function of s.

1. Graph the following using the intercept method:

   (a) $3x - 5y = 30$ (b) $x - 7 = 0$

2. The graph of the equation $y = \sqrt{x + 4}$ appears in the figure below. Use the graph to find y for $x = 5$, and verify the value(s) using the equation of the graph.

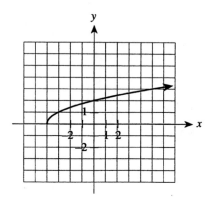

3. Identify the domain and range of each of the following relations:

   (a) $\{(2, -3), (2, 5), (3, 5), (4, 6)\}$ (b)

   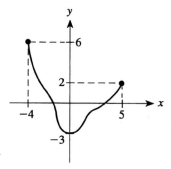

4. Identify the domain of each of the following functions:

   (a) $y = \sqrt{x - 4}$ (b) $y = \dfrac{x}{3x - 4}$

5. Identify which of the following relations are functions:

   (a) $\{(2, 5)\}, (2, 4)\}$ (b) $\{(3, 2), (4, 3), (5, 2)\}$

   (c) $x = 3y^2$ (d)

   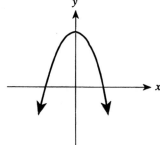

6. Given $f(x) = 3x^2 - 4$, $g(x) = \sqrt{2x + 1}$, and $h(x) = 5x - 3$, find:

   (a) $g(2)$ (b) $f(-3)$ (c) $h(x - 2)$ (d) $f(x^2)$ (e) $f(x) - f(5)$

7. Use the graph of $y = f(x)$ given in Figure 3.46 to answer the following questions.

Figure 3.46

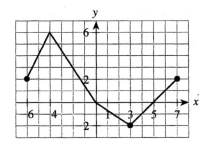

(a) Find $f(-6)$.   (b) Find $f(3)$.   (c) Find $f(0)$.   (d) Find $f(7)$.

(e) Which is the largest, $f(-4)$, $f(3)$, or $f(5)$?

(f) Find all x such that $f(x) = 0$.

8. The graph in Figure 3.47 illustrates the blood level, L, in milligrams of a certain substance m minutes after a medication is taken.

Figure 3.47

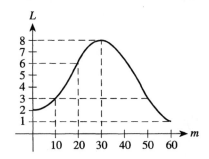

(a) How long does it take for the substance to reach its maximum level in the bloodstream?

(b) What is the maximum level of the substance in the bloodstream?

(c) During which of the 10-minute intervals indicated along the m-axis does the substance level increase the most? By how much does it increase?

4.1 Straight Lines and Slope

Recall that the graph of a first-degree equation in two variables is a straight line. We can state this algebraically: The graph of an equation of the form $Ax + By = C$ (where A and B are not both 0) is a straight line. For this reason, such an equation is called a ***linear equation.*** We also saw that (provided $B \neq 0$) we can solve such an equation explicitly for y, and such an equation defines y as a function of x. This type of function is called a ***linear function.***

EXAMPLE 1

The Celsius (C) and Fahrenheit (F) temperature scales are related according to the equation $F = 1.8C + 32$. Sketch the graph of this relationship.

Solution

The equation $F = 1.8C + 32$ is a first-degree equation in two variables. We must first decide which variables should be represented along the horizontal axis and the vertical axis. We choose to let the horizontal axis represent the Celsius temperature, C, and the vertical axis to represent the Fahrenheit temperature, F. Recognizing this as a first-degree equation in two variables, we know that the graph will be a straight line. Using the intercept method discussed in Section 3.1, we find that the graph crosses the C-axis at approximately $(-17.8, 0)$ and crosses the F-axis at $(0, 32)$. Using these two points, we obtain the graph in Figure 4.1.

We have also found a third check point, $(-10, 14)$.

Figure 4.1
The graph of
$F = 1.8C + 32$

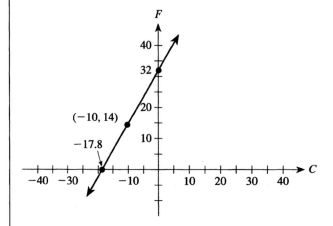

This graph certainly satisfies the vertical line test, which reinforces the fact that such a linear equation defines F as a function of C. ∎

In graphing the equation $F = 1.8C + 32$ of Example 1, we are looking for all ordered pairs that satisfy the particular condition that "the F-coordinate is 32 more than 1.8 times the C-coordinate." The straight line we obtained in Example 1 is the graph of all the ordered pairs that satisfy this particular condition.

In general, a first-degree equation in two variables can be viewed as a condition on the two variables. If we let the variables x and y represent the first and second coordinates of points in a rectangular coordinate system, then certain points satisfy the condition and others do not. The set of all points that do satisfy this condition—that is, the graph of a first-degree equation in two variables—is a straight line.

What if we now reverse this situation? Suppose we have a straight-line graph. How do we find its equation? The importance of this question is illustrated by the following example.

EXAMPLE 2   The following table contains employee data for a certain manufacturing company.

Years of Operation	x	1	2	3	4	5	6	7	8	9	10
Number of Employees	y	26	29	34	38	44	48	53	59	62	67

In this table, x represents the number of years the company has been operating, and y represents the number of employees working at the firm. Sketch a graph of these data and use the graph to guess how many employees will be working at this firm in year 11.

Solution   In Figure 4.2(a), we have plotted the points corresponding to the ordered pairs given in the table. We observe that the data points appear to fall "approximately" along a straight line, as indicated in Figure 4.2(b). If the trend indicated by these data continues, then from the graph we can "guess" that in year 11 (that is, when $x = 11$), the company would have 72 employees ($y = 72$).

Figure 4.2

The points corresponding to the data given in Example 2

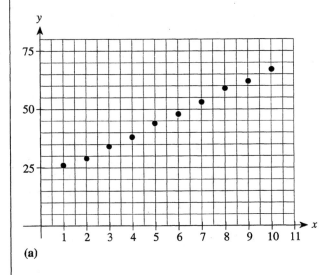

(a)

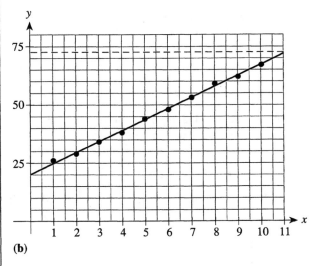

(b)

If we knew that the equation of this approximation line were $y = 4.7x + 20$, then we could simply substitute $x = 11$ to obtain $y = 4.7(11) + 20 = 71.7$. This tells us that after 11 years the company will have approximately 71.7 employees, which we would round to 72 employees.   ∎

As Example 2 indicates, having an equation of a straight line gives us easy access to x and y values that correspond to points that lie on the line. This section and the next are devoted to the question, How do we determine an equation of a line whose graph is given? Suppose we are given the graph of a straight line and we want to produce an equation for this straight line. Keeping in mind that an equation of a line is the condition that the points on the line must satisfy, we must naturally ask what condition must the points on the given line satisfy.

Look at Figure 4.3. From basic geometry we find that triangles ABC and DEF are similar triangles. ($\angle BAC \cong \angle EDF$ because $\overline{AC}$ and $\overline{DF}$ are parallel, and $\angle ABC \cong \angle DEF$ since $\overline{BC}$ and $\overline{EF}$ are parallel. So corresponding angles are equal.) Therefore, their corresponding sides are in proportion. That is,

$$\frac{|BC|}{|AC|} = \frac{|EF|}{|DF|} \qquad \textit{Note:} \quad |BC| \textit{ means the length of line segment BC.}$$

Figure 4.3

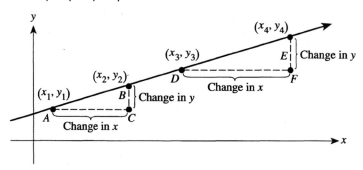

In other words, as we move from any point on a nonvertical line to any other point on the line, the ratio of the change in the y-coordinates of the points to the change in the x-coordinates of the points is constant. This fact is what we are looking for—a condition that all points on a line must satisfy.

The remainder of this section is devoted to further development of this idea. In the next section we will return to answer the question raised earlier about how to obtain an equation for a line when we have its graph.

We define the following:

DEFINITION	Let $P_1(x_1, y_1)$ and $P_2(x_2, y_2)$ be any two points on a nonvertical line L. The *slope* of the line L, denoted by m, is given by $$m = \frac{y_2 - y_1}{x_2 - x_1} \qquad (x_1 \neq x_2)$$

Note that this definition uses what we saw in Figure 4.3, that the ratio of the change in y to the change in x is *independent* of the points chosen; that is, for any two points on a particular line, the ratio will remain the same.

For example, let's see how we would find the slope of the line passing through the points $(2, -3)$ and $(8, 1)$. Although it is not always necessary, it is usually helpful to draw a diagram illustrating the given information (see Figure 4.4).

Figure 4.4

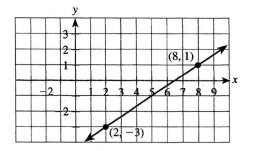

The formula for the slope of a line is

$$m = \frac{y_2 - y_1}{x_2 - x_1}$$

but which of our points is (x_1, y_1) and which is (x_2, y_2)? The fact of the matter is that it does not make any difference which we call the "first" point and which we call the "second" point, as long as we are consistent for both the x- and y-coordinates.

We can let $P_1(x_1, y_1) = (2, -3)$ and $P_2(x_2, y_2) = (8, 1)$ and we get

$$m = \frac{y_2 - y_1}{x_2 - x_1} = \frac{1 - (-3)}{8 - 2} = \frac{4}{6} = \frac{2}{3}$$

or we can let $P_1(x_1, y_1) = (8, 1)$ and $P_2(x_2, y_2) = (2, -3)$ and we get

$$m = \frac{y_2 - y_1}{x_2 - x_1} = \frac{-3 - 1}{2 - 8} = \frac{-4}{-6} = \frac{2}{3}$$

Thus, the slope is $m = \frac{2}{3}$.

EXAMPLE 3

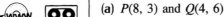

Compute the slope of the line, and sketch the line passing through each pair of points.

(a) $P(8, 3)$ and $Q(4, 6)$ (b) $R(2, -5)$ and $S(5, -2)$

Solution

(a) Let $(x_1, y_1) = (8, 3)$ and $(x_2, y_2) = (4, 6)$. Then the slope formula gives

$$m = \frac{y_2 - y_1}{x_2 - x_1} = \frac{6 - 3}{4 - 8} = \frac{3}{-4}$$

Therefore, the slope is $-\frac{3}{4} = -0.75$.

(b) Let $(x_1, y_1) = (2, -5)$ and $(x_2, y_2) = (5, -2)$. The slope formula gives

$$m = \frac{y_2 - y_1}{x_2 - x_1} = \frac{-2 - (-5)}{5 - 2} = \frac{3}{3} = 1$$

Therefore, the slope is 1.

Figure 4.5 illustrates the lines passing through each pair of points.

Figure 4.5

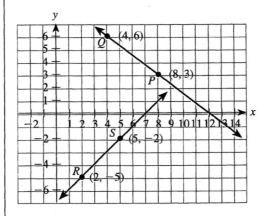

Note that if we start at any point on the line through P and Q and we move 4 units to the right, then we must also move 3 units down to get back on the line. Alternatively, we can think of the slope as $\frac{-0.75}{1}$, and thus if we move 1 unit to the right from a point on the line, then we must also move down 0.75 unit to get back on the line.

Similarly, we note that if we start at any point on the line through R and S and we move 1 unit to the right, then we must also move 1 unit up to get back on the line. We have more to say about this idea a bit later in this section. ∎

EXAMPLE 4

Find the slope of the line whose equation is $y = \frac{3}{2}x - 4$.

Solution

In the next section we will find a quick way to arrive at the answer to this question. But for now, to find the slope of a line, we need two points on the line. Since the slope is independent of the points chosen, we can arbitrarily choose any two points that satisfy the equation and therefore lie on the line.

If $x = 0$ then $y = \frac{3}{2}(0) - 4 = -4$; thus $(0, -4)$ is one point on the line.

If $x = 4$ then $y = \frac{3}{2}(4) - 4 = 6 - 4 = 2$; thus $(4, 2)$ is another point on the line.

Using the slope formula, we have

$$m = \frac{2 - (-4)}{4 - 0} = \frac{6}{4} = \frac{3}{2} = 1.5$$

Hence, the slope of the line whose equation is $y = \frac{3}{2}x - 4$ is $\boxed{\dfrac{3}{2}}$.

If we choose two other points that satisfy the equation, for example $(2, -1)$ and $(10, 11)$ (check for yourself that these points satisfy the equation), we will get the same result because the slope of a line is independent of the points chosen on the line:

$$m = \frac{-1 - 11}{2 - 10} = \frac{-12}{-8} = \frac{3}{2} = 1.5$$

The graph of the equation $y = \frac{3}{2}x - 4$ appears in Figure 4.6. ■

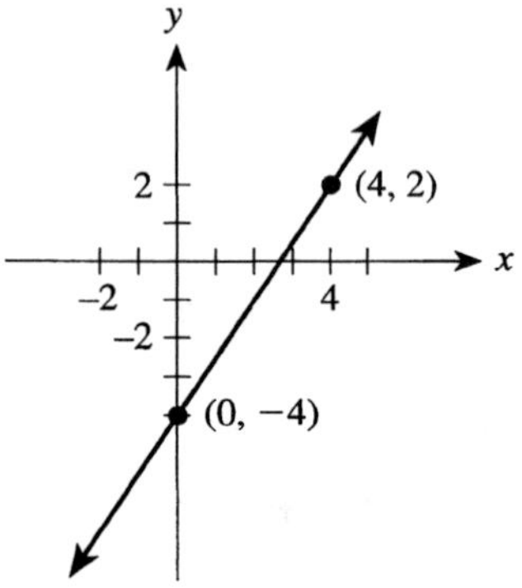

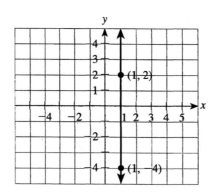

Figure 4.6
The graph of $y = \frac{3}{2}x - 4$

It is important to note that in the definition of the slope of a line, we have specified that the line be nonvertical. The reason for this is that for a vertical line, all x-coordinates are the same; we would be forced to divide by 0 in the computation of the slope.

For example, if we *try* to compute the slope of the vertical line passing through the points $(1, -4)$ and $(1, 2)$ (see Figure 4.7), we get

$$m = \frac{2 - (-4)}{1 - 1} = \frac{6}{0}$$

which is undefined. (This is why, in the definition of the slope, we specified $x_1 \neq x_2$.)

Figure 4.7
The vertical line through $(1, -4)$ and $(1, 2)$

Thus, we find that the following is true:

> The slope of a vertical line is undefined.

Let us now examine what this number, the slope, tells us about a line. Recall that *whenever we describe a graph, we describe it for increasing values of x (that is, moving from left to right).*

The line in Figure 4.8(a) is rising (as we move from left to right), while the line in Figure 4.8(b) is falling (as we move from left to right).

Figure 4.8

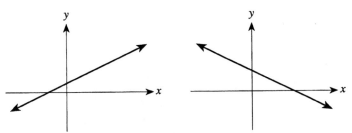

The y-values are increasing as we move from left to right.
(a) This line is rising.

The y-values are decreasing as we move from left to right.
(b) This line is falling.

The slope of a line is a number that tells us the *rate* at which its y values are increasing or decreasing. In other words, it is a measure of the steepness of a line. For example, if the slope of a line is $\frac{2}{5}$, this tells us that

$$m = \frac{2}{5} = \frac{\text{Change in } y}{\text{Change in } x}$$

This means that a 5-unit change in x gives a 2-unit change in y. Therefore, the line has the *steepness* shown in Figure 4.9.

Figure 4.9
A line whose slope is $\frac{2}{5}$

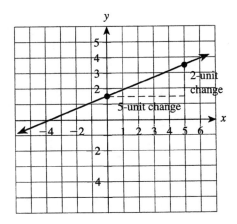

A line whose slope is $\frac{5}{2}$ has the steepness indicated in Figure 4.10.

Figure 4.10
A line with slope $\frac{5}{2}$

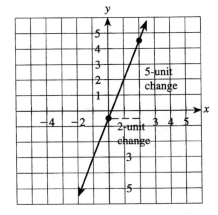

Figure 4.11 shows what happens when we vary the slope of a rising line passing through the point (2, 3). Notice that the greater the slope, the steeper the line. We can see that, as we move from *left to right,*

> A line with positive slope rises.

Figure 4.11

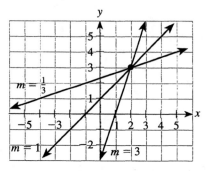

What about lines with negative slope? Let's look at a line with a slope of $-\frac{3}{4}$. We can view $m = -\frac{3}{4}$ as $\frac{-3}{4}$ or $\frac{3}{-4}$. A slope of $\frac{-3}{4}$ means that a 4-unit change in x gives a -3-unit change in y. A slope of $\frac{3}{-4}$ means that a -4-unit change in x gives a 3-unit change in y. Thus we can draw the line as shown in Figures 4.12(a) and 4.12(b). In both cases we get the same figure.

Figure 4.12
Line passing through the point (3, 1) with slope $-\frac{3}{4}$

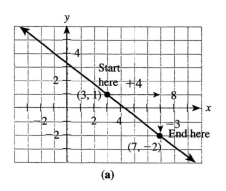

(a)

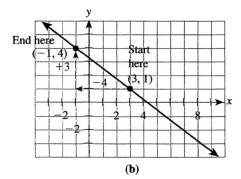

(b)

We can see that, as we move from *left to right,*

> A line with negative slope falls.

Figure 4.13 illustrates that the greater the *absolute value* of the slope, the steeper the line.

Figure 4.13

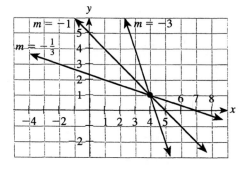

EXAMPLE 5

What is the slope of the line through the points (1, 4) and (3, 4)?

Solution

$$m = \frac{4 - 4}{3 - 1} = \frac{0}{2} = 0$$

This line is horizontal, as shown in Figure 4.14.

Figure 4.14

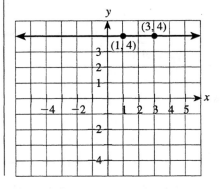

Any horizontal line, for which the y-coordinates will all be equal, will have slope equal to 0. It is perfectly reasonable that a horizontal line should have a slope equal to 0, since it has *no steepness.*

A horizontal line has zero slope.

Do not confuse a slope of 0 with undefined slope.

A line with slope 0 has no steepness (it is horizontal).

A line with undefined slope has "infinite" steepness (it is vertical).

It is fairly intuitive that lines that have the same slope and therefore the same steepness are parallel. Conversely, lines that are parallel have the same steepness and hence the same slope. This fact is the subject of the following theorem.

THEOREM

Two distinct lines L_1 and L_2 with slopes m_1 and m_2, respectively, are parallel if and only if $m_1 = m_2$.

EXAMPLE 6

Show that the points $P(2, 4)$, $Q(8, 0)$, $R(3, -3)$, and $S(-3, 1)$ form the vertices of a parallelogram.

Solution

We first plot the given points as shown in Figure 4.15.

Figure 4.15

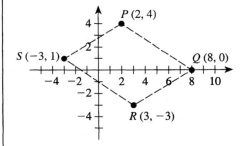

A parallelogram is a quadrilateral (a four-sided polygon) whose opposite sides are parallel. Thus, we must show that $\overline{PQ}$ is parallel to $\overline{SR}$ and that $\overline{SP}$ is parallel to

$\overline{RQ}$. By the previous theorem, we can find out whether those sides are parallel by examining their slopes. Thus, we compute the slopes of each side:

$$m_{\overline{PQ}} = \frac{4 - 0}{2 - 8} = \frac{4}{-6} = -\frac{2}{3} \qquad m_{\overline{SR}} = \frac{1 - (-3)}{-3 - 3} = \frac{4}{-6} = -\frac{2}{3}$$

$$m_{\overline{SP}} = \frac{1 - 4}{-3 - 2} = \frac{-3}{-5} = \frac{3}{5} \qquad m_{\overline{RQ}} = \frac{-3 - 0}{3 - 8} = \frac{-3}{-5} = \frac{3}{5}$$

Since the slopes of the opposite sides are the same, the opposite sides are parallel and therefore $\boxed{\text{the figure is a parallelogram}}$. ∎

If two lines pass through a single point and have the same slope, then they must be the same line. We can restate this as follows:

> A point and a slope determine a line.

Thus, just as we can draw a line by knowing two points, we should also be able to draw a line given one point and the slope of the line.

EXAMPLE 7

(a) Graph the line passing through the point (3, 1) with slope = $\frac{2}{5}$.

(b) Graph the line passing through the point (−2, 1) with slope = −4.

Solution

(a) First we plot the point (3, 1). Since the line must have slope $m = \frac{2}{5}$, this means that

$$m = \frac{\text{Change in } y}{\text{Change in } x} = \frac{2}{5}$$

or that for every 5 units we move off the line to the right (change in x equal to +5), we must move 2 units up to return to the line (change in y equal to +2) and return to the line. Hence, we start at (3, 1), count 5 units right and then 2 units up, and the point where we arrive is another point on the line. We draw a line through the two points, as illustrated in Figure 4.16.

Figure 4.16

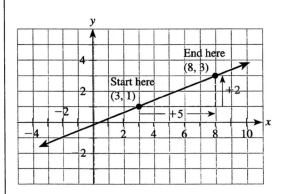

Notice that if we decided to move 10 units right (change in x equal to +10), then we would have to move 4 units up to return to the line (change in y equal to +4) and make the ratio $m = \frac{4}{10} = \frac{2}{5}$. On the other hand, if we moved 5 units *left* (change in x equal to −5), then we would have to move 2 units *down* (change in x equal to −2) to keep $m = \frac{-2}{-5} = \frac{2}{5}$.

(b) To graph the line passing through (−2, 1) with slope = −4, we start by plotting the point (−2, 1). To find the next point, we note that since the slope, m, is −4, we can rewrite −4 as

$$\frac{-4}{1} = \frac{\text{Change in } y}{\text{Change in } x}$$

Therefore, for every 1 unit we move off the line to the right (change in x equal to +1), we must travel *down* 4 units (change in y equal to −4) before we find another point on the line. Thus, we start at (−2, 1), move 1 unit right and 4 units down to find another point, and then draw a line through the two points (see Figure 4.17).

Figure 4.17

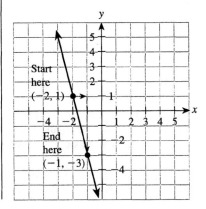

Example 7 demonstrates that given a point and a slope, we can geometrically determine the graph of the line. In the next section we will find that given the same information, we can (algebraically) determine the equation of the line.

We have already discussed parallel lines. What about the slopes of perpendicular lines?

EXAMPLE 8

Sketch the lines with slopes $\frac{6}{7}$ and $-\frac{7}{6}$ that pass through the point (10, 4).

Solution

$m = \frac{6}{7}$ means a 7-unit change (increase) in x produces a 6-unit change (increase) in y.

$m = -\frac{7}{6}$ means a −6-unit change (decrease) in x produces a 7-unit change (increase) in y.

Let's sketch two lines with slopes $\frac{6}{7}$ and $-\frac{7}{6}$ (see Figure 4.18).

Figure 4.18

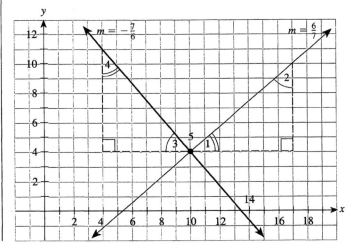

On the figure we have drawn in two triangles to help us visualize the following:

We know that $\angle 1 + \angle 2 = 90°$.

Since these two triangles are congruent (compare the lengths of their sides), we also know that $\angle 2 = \angle 3$ (they are both opposite the side of the triangle whose length is 7).

Therefore, $\angle 1 + \angle 3 = 90°$.

But then $\angle 5$ must also be 90° (because $\angle 1 + \angle 3 + \angle 5 = 180°$) and so the two lines are perpendicular.

Note that $\left(\frac{6}{7}\right)\left(-\frac{7}{6}\right) = -1$.

Example 8 is a particular case of the following theorem.

THEOREM	Two nonvertical lines L_1 and L_2 with slopes m_1 and m_2, respectively, are perpendicular if and only if $m_1 \cdot m_2 = -1$.

If $m_1 \cdot m_2 = -1$, we can write $m_2 = -\dfrac{1}{m_1}$ or $m_1 = -\dfrac{1}{m_2}$.

For this reason we often say that the slopes of nonvertical perpendicular lines are "negative reciprocals" of each other.

We should note that throughout the previous discussion we have insisted on nonvertical lines. While it is true that a horizontal line and a vertical line are perpendicular, the slope of a vertical line is undefined and so is not covered by the last theorem.

EXAMPLE 9

Given two points on each of the lines L_1, L_2, L_3, and L_4, compute the slope of each line and determine whether any two of the lines are parallel or perpendicular.

L_1: (1, 3) and (4, 5) L_2: (−2, 5) and (0, 2)

L_3: (−3, 0) and (0, 2) L_4: (2, 1) and (−1, 3)

Solution

$$m_1 = \frac{5 - 3}{4 - 1} = \frac{2}{3}$$

$$m_2 = \frac{2 - 5}{0 - (-2)} = \frac{-3}{2} = -\frac{3}{2}$$

$$m_3 = \frac{2 - 0}{0 - (-3)} = \frac{2}{3}$$

$$m_4 = \frac{3 - 1}{-1 - 2} = \frac{2}{-3} = -\frac{2}{3}$$

Note that L_4 is neither parallel nor perpendicular to L_1, L_2, or L_3.

Since $m_1 = m_3$, $\boxed{L_1 \text{ and } L_3 \text{ are parallel}}$.

Since $m_2 = -\dfrac{1}{m_1}$ and $m_2 = -\dfrac{1}{m_3}$, $\boxed{L_2 \text{ is perpendicular to } L_1 \text{ and } L_3}$. ■

EXAMPLE 10

Find a value for c so that the line passing through the points (3, 4) and (−1, c) has slope $\frac{1}{2}$.

Solution

Using the formula for the slope of a line, we determine that the slope is

$$\frac{c - 4}{-1 - 3} = \frac{c - 4}{-4}$$

and we want this to be equal to $\frac{1}{2}$. The equation is

$$\frac{c - 4}{-4} = \frac{1}{2} \qquad \textit{Multiply both sides by } -4.$$

$$\frac{-4}{1} \cdot \frac{c - 4}{-4} = \frac{1}{2} \cdot \frac{-4}{1}$$

$$c - 4 = -2$$

$$\boxed{c = 2}$$ ■

EXAMPLE 11

An engineer has specified that sewage pipe for a certain building must have a 3% drop in grade.

(a) How much vertical clearance must a builder allow for a sewage pipe that is to carry waste from a point in a building to a point in the street that is 300 feet away in a horizontal direction?

(b) How long does this pipe have to be (to the nearest tenth of a foot)?

Solution

Figure 4.19

(a) Figure 4.19 illustrates the given situation.

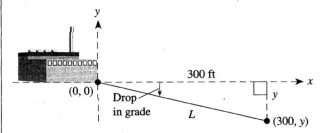

To simplify the computation, we have set up the situation as if the pipe were situated at the origin. As the diagram illustrates, we need the horizontal distance (the *x*-coordinate) to be 300 ft and we want to find the vertical clearance (the *y*-coordinate) that will give a 3% drop in grade. A 3% drop in grade (or downgrade) means that the ratio of the vertical distance to the horizontal distance is −0.03. In effect, we require that the slope of the line segment *L* be −0.03. We therefore have

$$\frac{y - 0}{300 - 0} = -0.03 \qquad \textit{Now we solve for y.}$$

$$y = -0.03(300) = -9$$

Therefore, the builder must set the pipe so that the street end of the pipe is 9 feet lower than the building end.

Recall that the Pythagorean theorem states that in a right triangle, $c^2 = a^2 + b^2$, where c is the length of the hypotenuse, and a and b are the lengths of the legs.

(b) In Figure 4.19 we have labeled the length of the pipe *L*. Since we have a right triangle, we can use the Pythagorean theorem to find the length *L*.

$$L^2 = 9^2 + 300^2$$
$$L^2 = 90{,}081 \qquad \textit{Find the square root of 90,081 on a calculator.}$$
$$L = \boxed{300.1 \text{ ft}} \qquad \textit{Rounded to the nearest tenth} \qquad \blacksquare$$

Interpreting the Slope of the Graph of a Line

EXAMPLE 12

In Example 1 we indicated that the Celsius and Fahrenheit temperature scales are related by the equation $F = 1.8C + 32$. Use the graph found in Example 1 to describe this relationship.

Solution

The graph of this equation is repeated in Figure 4.20.

Figure 4.20
The graph of
$F = 1.8C + 32$

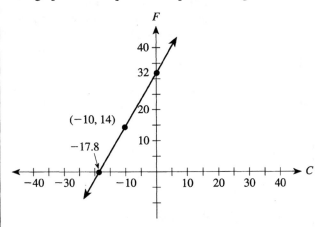

We see some points on the graph with which we may already be familiar—for example, the temperature at which water freezes is 0°C or 32°F. In other words, 0°C is equivalent to 32°F and so the point (0, 32) is on the graph. We can see that the line is rising, which means that as the Celsius temperature increases, so does the Fahrenheit temperature, but at what rate?

Recall that the slope of a line tells us the ratio of the vertical change to the horizontal change as we move along the line. Hence, the slope is a *rate* that tells us how much one quantity changes with respect to another. For example, by its definition, a slope of 3 means that

$$\frac{\text{Change in } y}{\text{Change in } x} = 3 \qquad \textit{This means that}$$

$$\text{Change in } y = 3 \cdot (\text{Change in } x)$$

Hence, as we move along the line, vertical change in position will be 3 times any horizontal change in position. We have pointed out that a slope is a characteristic of a line that does not change regardless of where we are on the line. Hence, we can state that a straight line always increases (or decreases) *at the same rate.*

Using the two points (0, 32) and (−10, 14), we compute the slope of the line to be $\frac{9}{5}$ or, equivalently, 1.8. This slope means that as C increases by 5 degrees, F increases by 9 degrees. Alternatively, we can rewrite $\frac{9}{5}$ as $\frac{9/5}{1}$ and say that every 1-unit increase in the horizontal (C) direction is accompanied by a 1.8-unit increase in the vertical (F) direction. We interpret this to mean that a 1-degree change in the Celsius temperature is equivalent to a 1.8-degree change in the Fahrenheit temperature. Since the slope of a line is constant, this statement is true for *all* values of C and F. ■

EXAMPLE 13

The average normal body temperature of a human being is approximately 98.6°F or 37°C. If Samantha has a temperature of 39°C, is this cause for concern? (Something like this actually did happen to one of the authors. His daughter looked feverish, and he wanted to take her temperature, but the only thermometer available was in °C. While he was familiar with how to interpret °F, he was not accustomed to interpreting a thermometer reading in °C.)

Solution

Samantha's temperature is 2° above normal on the Celsius scale. On the Fahrenheit scale, 2 degrees above normal is 100.6°F, which in most cases is usually interpreted as a slight fever, and no cause for alarm. However, a 2-degree change on the Celsius scale means something different.

We could substitute 39°C into the formula above, converting Celsius to Fahrenheit, and determine whether there is cause for concern based on the °F temperature. However, we pointed out in Example 12 that the slope of the line $F = 1.8C + 32$ tells us that a 1-degree increase in °C is approximately equivalent to a 2-degree increase in °F. Therefore, a 2-degree increase in °C is equivalent to an increase of approximately 4 degrees Fahrenheit. This means that Samantha has a temperature of approximately 102.6°F [the exact value is 98.6 + 2(1.8) = 102.2°F]. This is a cause for some concern. ■

In Example 12 the slope tells us how much the Fahrenheit temperature changes in relation to Celsius temperature. (Fahrenheit temperature increases 1.8° for each 1° increase in Celsius.) In general, the slope gives us the *rate* at which the vertical units change in comparison to the change in horizontal units. As with interpreting trends, how the slope is interpreted depends on what quantities the axes represent.

EXAMPLE 14

Use the graph of Jani's trip described in Example 3 of Section 3.5, which we repeat here as Figure 4.21, to interpret the slope of each line segment.

Figure 4.21

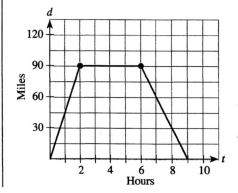

112

Solution

Looking at the graph in Figure 4.21, we note that the horizontal axis is time (in hours) and the vertical axis is distance (in miles). Hence, the slope—being the change in vertical units compared to horizontal units—is interpreted in this example as the change in distance compared to the change in time:

$$m = \frac{\text{Change in distance}}{\text{Change in time}}$$

But we define speed as $\frac{\text{Distance}}{\text{Time}}$. Hence, we can use the slope of each line segment to find Jani's speed for each line segment, or time interval. The slope for the first line segment covering the first two hours is $m_1 = \frac{90}{2} = 45$. Hence, her speed in the first leg of her journey is 45 miles per hour. For the second line segment, between hour 2 and hour 6, $m_2 = 0$. Hence, her speed during that time period is 0 miles per hour. For the last line segment, between hour 6 and hour 9, $m_3 = -\frac{90}{3} = -30$. At this point, you may see that since the last line segment is decreasing it makes sense to have a negative slope, but you may question how the number −30 is related to Jani's speed on the last leg of her trip.

Speed has no sign: It simply tells us how much distance is traveled in a particular time span. On the other hand, the slopes for this graph give more information. The slopes not only tell us how much the distance from home is changing in relation to time, they also tell us "directon" or whether distance is increasing (positive slope) or decreasing (negative slope) as time increases. For the first line segment, the distance from Jani's home was increasing and so the slope was positive. For the last line segment, however, her average speed was still 30 mph, as she did travel a distance of 90 miles over 3 hours, but the negative sign indicates that her distance from her home *decreased* during that time span. Hence, the slope for this graph gives us both the speed and the direction Jani is traveling to and from her home. We can say that for this graph the absolute value of the slope is the *speed,* and the sign of the slope tells us whether the distance from her home is increasing or decreasing. ∎

Let's return to Example 4 of Section 3.5. Figure 4.22 is the graph of the amount of medication (in milligrams), m, entering the bloodstream of a patient at time t (at 20-minute intervals) after the medication is administered.

Figure 4.22

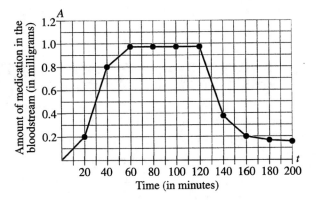

The graph is made up of several line segments, each of which has a slope. What do the slopes of the line segments tell us? Let's look at the time interval between 40 and 60 minutes. We note that this segment joins the points (40, 0.8) and (60, 0.97) (we estimated 0.97 on the graph). The slope of that line segment is

$$\frac{0.97 - 0.8 \text{ mg}}{60 - 40 \text{ min}} = \frac{0.17 \text{ mg}}{20 \text{ min}} = 0.0085 \text{ mg/min}$$

Hence, we can see that the slope tells us the *rate* at which the medication enters (or leaves) the bloodstream. Line segments with different slopes indicate different rates. Figure 4.23 on page 210 shows the slopes, or rates, for each time interval or line segment. Compare this graph with Figure 3.37 on page 170.

Figure 4.23

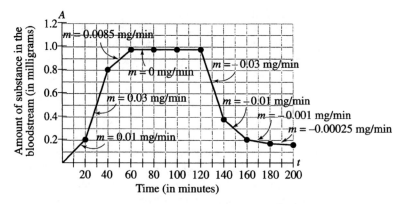

For the first 20 minutes, the rate at which the medication enters the bloodstream is 0.01 mg/min. Notice that the slope is positive (this line segment is rising), indicating that more medication is in the bloodstream at the end of the 20-minute interval than at the beginning. For the next 20 minutes, the rate is 0.03 mg/min. Notice that m is larger for the second 20 minutes—that is, medication is entering the bloodstream at a faster rate, and therefore the line is steeper. For the 40–60-minute time interval, the line is less steep as the *rate* at which medication is entering the bloodstream is slowing down ($m = 0.0085$ mg/min). From 60 to 120 minutes the slope of the line segments is 0, which means that no additional medication is entering (or leaving) the bloodstream.

From 120 to 140 minutes, the slope is –0.03 mg/min. The slope is negative (the line segment is falling); this means that there is less medication in the bloodstream at the end of the 20-minute interval than at the beginning. Hence medication is *leaving* the bloodstream—leaving at a rate of 0.03 mg/min. From 140 to 160 minutes, the slope of the line segment is –0.01 mg/min. Since the slope is negative, the medication is still leaving the bloodstream, but since $0.01 < 0.03$, it is leaving at a slower rate than during the previous 20 minutes. Note that the 140–160-minute interval segment is less steep than the 120–140-minute interval segment.

Study Skills 4.1

Reviewing Your Exam: Diagnosing Your Strengths and Weaknesses

Your exam will be a useful tool in helping you to determine what topics, skills, or concepts you need to work on in preparation for the next topic, or in preparation for future exams. After you get your exam back, you should review it carefully: Examine what you did correctly and the problems you missed.

Don't quickly gloss over your errors and assume that any errors were minor or careless. Students often mistakenly label many of their errors as "careless," when in fact they are a result of not clearly understanding a certain concept or procedure. Be honest with yourself. Don't delude yourself into thinking that all errors are careless. Ask yourself the following questions about your errors:

Did I understand the directions or perhaps misunderstand them?

Did I understand the topic to which the question relates?

Did I misuse a rule or property?

Did I make an arithmetic error?

Look over the entire exam. Did you consistently make the same type of error throughout the exam? Did you consistently miss problems covering a particular topic or concept? You should try to follow your work and see what you were doing on the exam. If you think you have a problem understanding a concept, topic, or approach to a problem, you should immediately seek help from your teacher or tutor, and reread relevant portions of your text.

EXERCISES 4.1

In Exercises 1–6, sketch the line through the given pair of points and compute its slope.

1. $(1, -2)$ and $(-3, 1)$

2. $(2, -3)$ and $(-1, 4)$

3. $(0, 2)$ and $(2, 0)$

4. $(5, 0)$ and $(0, 5)$

5. $(-3, -4)$ and $(-2, -5)$

6. $(-4, -3)$ and $(-2, -1)$

In Exercises 7–18, compute the slope of the line passing through the given pair of points.

7. $(2, 4)$ and $(-3, 4)$

8. $(1, -5)$ and $(1, 3)$

9. $(4, 2)$ and $(4, -3)$

10. $(-5, 1)$ and $(3, 1)$

11. (a, a) and (b, b) $(a \neq b)$

12. (a, b) and (b, a) $(a \neq b)$

13. (a, a^2) and (b, b^2) $(a \neq b)$

14. (a, b^2) and (b, a^2) $(a \neq b)$

15. $(0.7, -0.2)$ and $(0.06, 0.14)$

16. $(1250, 22)$ and $(700, 12)$

17. $(-0.2, 7)$ and $(0.14, 0.06)$

18. $(22, 1250)$ and $(12, 700)$

In Exercises 19–22, estimate the slope of the line.

19.

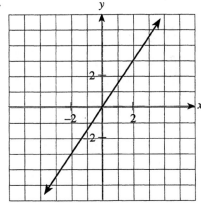

20.

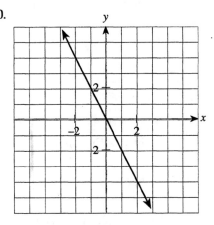

21.

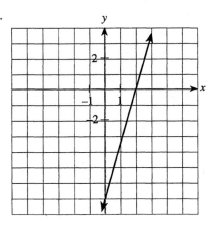

22.

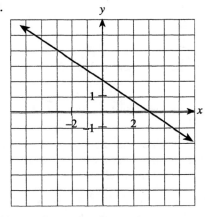

23. Find the slope of the line that crosses the x-axis at $x = 5$ and the y-axis at $y = -3$.

24. Find the slope of the line that crosses the y-axis at $y = 7$ and the x-axis at $x = -4$.

In Exercises 25–36, sketch the graph of the line L that contains the given point and has the given slope m.

25. $(1, 3)$, $m = 2$

26. $(2, 5)$, $m = 1$

27. $(1, 3)$, $m = -2$

28. $(2, 5)$, $m = -1$

29. $(0, 3)$, $m = -\dfrac{1}{4}$

30. $(0, 3)$, $m = -4$

31. $(4, 0)$, $m = \dfrac{2}{5}$

32. $(-4, 0)$, $m = -\dfrac{2}{5}$

33. $(2, 5)$, $m = 0$

34. $(-1, 3)$, undefined slope

35. $(2, 5)$, undefined slope

36. $(-1, 3)$, $m = 0$

In Exercises 37–42, find the slope of the line by picking two points on the line.

37. $y = 2x - 7$

38. $y = -\dfrac{1}{3}x + 4$

39. $y = -0.4x + 5$

40. $y = 5x - 3$

41. $2y - 3x = 8$

42. $3x + 4y = 7$

In Exercises 43–48, determine whether the line passing through the points P_1 and P_2 is parallel to or perpendicular to (or neither parallel nor perpendicular to) the line passing through the points P_3 and P_4.

43. $P_1(1, 2)$, $P_2(3, 4)$, $P_3(-1, -2)$, $P_4(-3, -4)$

44. $P_1(5, 6)$, $P_2(7, 8)$, $P_3(-5, -6)$, $P_4(-7, -8)$

45. $P_1(0, 4)$, $P_2(-1, 2)$, $P_3(-3, 5)$, $P_4(1, 7)$

46. $P_1(2, 3)$, $P_2(3, 0)$, $P_3(-2, -5)$, $P_4(1, -6)$

47. $P_1(3, 5)$, $P_2(-2, 5)$, $P_3(1, 4)$, $P_4(1, -2)$

48. $P_1(a, b)$, $P_2(b, a)$, $P_3(c, d)$, $P_4(-d, -c)$ $(a \neq b, c \neq d)$

49. Find a number h so that the line passing through the points $(4, -2)$ and $(1, h)$ has slope -5.

50. Find a number k so that the line passing through the points $(k, 2)$ and $(-3, -1)$ has slope 4.

51. Using slopes, show that the points $(0, 0)$, $(2, 1)$, $(-2, 5)$, and $(0, 6)$ are the vertices of a parallelogram.

52. Using slopes, show that the points $(-3, 1)$, $(-7, 4)$, $(0, 5)$, and $(-4, 8)$ are the vertices of a rectangle.

53. Using slopes, show that the points $(-3, 2)$, $(-1, 6)$, and $(3, 4)$ are the vertices of a right triangle.

54. Using slopes, show that the points $(1, 1)$, $(3, 5)$, $(-1, 6)$, and $(-5, -2)$ are the vertices of a trapezoid.

55. A highway engineer specifies that a certain section of roadway covering a horizontal distance of 2 km should have an upgrade of 8%. Compute the change in elevation of this section of the road.

56. An escalator with an upgrade of 5% carries people through a vertical distance of 80 ft. Through what horizontal distance does this escalator carry passengers?

57. A cable car is carrying passengers down a hill at a downgrade of 12%. If the passengers descend 1,250 ft, through what horizontal distance have they traveled?

58. A wire is attached from a window to a pole standing 60 ft away from a building. If the slope of the wire is −0.6, how far below window level is the wire attached to the pole?

59. Suppose that in a rectangular coordinate system the horizontal axis represents the amount of time that has passed (in seconds), and the vertical axis represents the distance that a sprinter covers (in meters). How would you interpret the slope of the line segment joining the points (2, 15) and (8, 80)?

60. Suppose that in a rectangular coordinate system the horizontal axis represents the number of items a company produces, and the vertical axis represents the profit (in dollars) the company earns on the production of that many items. How would you interpret the slope of the line segment joining the points (0, 0) and (100, 875)?

61. Suppose that in a rectangular coordinate system the horizontal axis, labeled t, represents the hour of a particular afternoon, and the vertical axis, labeled F, represents the temperature in °F. How would you interpret the slope of the line segment joining the points (1, 56) and (5, 42)?

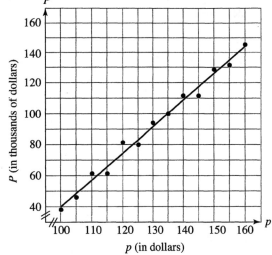

62. Suppose that in a rectangular coordinate system the horizontal axis, labeled n, represents the year, and the vertical axis, labeled P, represents the population of a small town. How would you interpret the slope of the line segment joining the points (1980, 8972) and (1990, 7456)?

63. A company manufactures monitors. The accompanying figure shows a graph of the relationship between the wholesale price of a monitor, p, in dollars, and the company's daily profit, P, in thousands of dollars. The horizontal axis represents the wholesale price of a monitor and the vertical axis represents the daily profit. For the price range given in the figure, the actual data points are plotted. These data points can be approximated by the given line. Estimate the slope of the line. What does the slope of the line tell you about this relationship?

64. The figure below shows a graph of the relationship between the daily cost, C, of electricity to keep a particular home at a constant 72°, and the average daily outdoor temperature, T, in July. The horizontal axis represents the average daily temperature and the vertical axis represents the daily cost of electricity. For the temperature range given in the figure, the actual data points are plotted. These data points can be approximated by the given line. Estimate the slope of the line. What does the slope of the line tell you about this relationship?

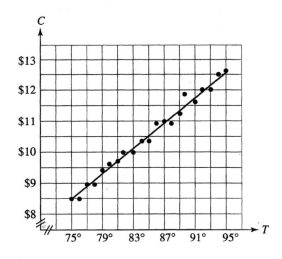

Q QUESTIONS FOR THOUGHT

65. How could you use the idea of slope to determine whether the three points $(-2, -1)$, $(0, 4)$, and $(2, 9)$ all lie on the same line (are collinear)?

66. How would you describe a line with positive slope? Negative slope? Zero slope? Undefined slope?

67. Suppose we do not insist on the units along the x- and y-axes being the same. Sketch the graph of the line with slope 3 passing through the point $(1, 2)$ if the units on the x-axis are twice as large as the units on the y-axis.

68. Repeat Exercise 67 if the units on the y-axis are twice as large as the units on the x-axis.

69. Sketch the graphs of $y = 2x$, $y = 2x + 3$, $y = 2x + 5$, $y = 2x - 3$, and $y = 2x - 5$ on the same set of coordinate axes. Determine the slope of each line from its graph. Can you draw any conclusions about determining the slope of a line from its equation?

 **MINI-REVIEW**

70. *Simplify.* $(3x^4)^2(6x^3)$

71. *Simplify.* $2xy(3x - 5y) - 6y(2x^2 + xy)$

72. *Evaluate for $x = 3$ and $y = -2$.* $|5y + x| - y^2$

73. *Solve for t.* $\dfrac{t}{3} - 2 = 5$

4.2 Equations of a Line and Linear Functions as Mathematical Models

In our previous discussions we have stressed the idea that a first-degree equation in two variables is a *condition* that an ordered pair must satisfy. We have seen that the set of all points that satisfy such an equation is a straight line.

We are now prepared to reverse the question. Suppose we "specify a line." How can we find its equation? In other words, what condition must all the points on the line satisfy?

To answer this question we must first understand what is meant by the phrase "specify a line." We know that a line is determined by two points, but we also saw in the last section that, for a nonvertical line, if we know one point on the line and its slope, we can find as many additional points on the line as we choose. Therefore, equivalently we can say that to specify a nonvertical line we specify a point on the line and its slope.

Let us suppose we have a line passing through a given point (x_1, y_1) with slope m (see Figure 4.24). To determine whether another point (x, y) is on this line, we must check whether the points (x_1, y_1) and (x, y) give us the required slope of m.

If $\dfrac{y - y_1}{x - x_1} = m$, then (x, y) is on the line.

If $\dfrac{y - y_1}{x - x_1} \neq m$, then (x, y) is not on the line.

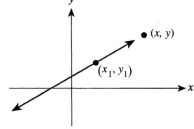

Figure 4.24

Thus, the equation

$$\frac{y - y_1}{x - x_1} = m$$

is the condition that a point (x, y) must satisfy for it to be on this line.

If we multiply both sides of the equation by $x - x_1$, we get the relationship given in the box.

Point–Slope Form of the Equation of a Straight Line	An equation of the line with slope m passing through (x_1, y_1) is $$y - y_1 = m(x - x_1)$$

EXAMPLE 1   Write an equation of the line with slope $\frac{2}{3}$ that passes through $(-3, 4)$.

Solution   The given point $(-3, 4)$ corresponds to (x_1, y_1) and $m = \frac{2}{3}$.

$$y - y_1 = m(x - x_1)$$
$$\uparrow \quad \uparrow \quad \uparrow$$
$$y - 4 = \frac{2}{3}[x - (-3)]$$

$$\boxed{y - 4 = \frac{2}{3}(x + 3)}$$

This is the equation of the line shown in Figure 4.25.

Figure 4.25
Line with slope $\frac{2}{3}$ passing through $(-3, 4)$

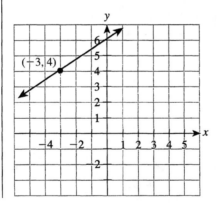

The point–slope form allows us to write an equation of a nonvertical line if we know *any* point on the line and its slope. What if the given point happens to be where the graph of the line crosses the y-axis? That is, suppose the line has slope m and y-intercept equal to b. Then the graph passes through the point $(0, b)$. Using the point–slope form, we can write its equation as

$$y - y_1 = m(x - x_1)$$
$$y - b = m(x - 0)$$
$$y - b = mx$$
$$y = mx + b$$

This last form is called the ***slope–intercept form*** of the equation of a straight line.

Slope–Intercept Form of the Equation of a Straight Line	An equation of the line with slope m and y-intercept b is $$y = mx + b$$

EXAMPLE 2

Write an equation of the line with slope 4 and y-intercept -3, and graph the equation.

Solution

Since we are given the slope and y-intercept, it is appropriate to use the slope–intercept form.

$$y = mx + b \qquad \textit{We are given } m = 4 \textit{ and } b = -3.$$
$$y = 4x + (-3)$$
$$\boxed{y = 4x - 3}$$

We could also use the point–slope form with $m = 4$ and $(x_1, y_1) = (0, -3)$.

$$y - y_1 = m(x - x_1)$$
$$y - (-3) = 4(x - 0)$$
$$y + 3 = 4x$$
$$\boxed{y = 4x - 3}$$

We graph the equation as we graphed equations in the previous section, given the slope and a point. Since the point is the y-intercept, we start at the y-axis at -3. Since the slope $= 4 = \frac{4}{1}$, we move right 1 unit and up 4 units to find another point on the line and then draw the line (see Figure 4.26).

Figure 4.26

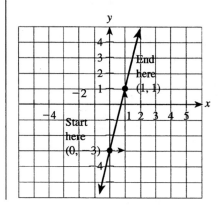

EXAMPLE 3

Find the slopes of the lines with the following equations:
(a) $y = -3x + 5$ (b) $3y + 5x = 8$

Solution

(a) Perhaps the most useful feature of the slope–intercept form is the fact that when the equation of a straight line is written in this form, it is easy to "read off" the slope (as well as the y-intercept):

$$y = -3x + 5$$
$$\uparrow \qquad \uparrow$$
$$y = mx + b$$

Therefore, $\boxed{\text{the slope is } -3}$.

(b) To "read off" the slope of a line from its equation, the equation must be *exactly* in slope–intercept form. That is, the equation must be in the form $y = mx + b$.

$$3y + 5x = 8 \qquad \textit{We solve for } y.$$
$$3y = -5x + 8$$
$$y = \frac{-5}{3}x + \frac{8}{3}$$

Therefore, $\boxed{\text{the slope is } -\frac{5}{3}}$.

In Section 3.1, we stated that the graph of a first-degree equation in two variables is a straight line. In fact, the following statement is also true.

> Any nonvertical line can be represented by an equation of the form $y = mx + b$.

EXAMPLE 4

Write an equation of the line passing through the points $(1, -2)$ and $(-3, -5)$.

Solution

The graph of the line appears in Figure 4.27.

Figure 4.27

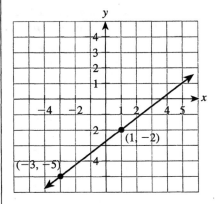

Whether we decide to write an equation for this line using the point–slope form or the slope–intercept form, we must know the slope of the line:

$$m = \frac{-2 - (-5)}{1 - (-3)} = \frac{3}{4}$$

We can now write an equation using the point–slope form *or* the slope–intercept form.

Using point–slope form: If we choose to use the point–slope form, we have another choice to make. We can choose to use either $(1, -2)$ or $(-3, -5)$ as our given point (x_1, y_1).

Using $(1, -2)$: $\quad y - (-2) = \frac{3}{4}(x - 1)$ or $\boxed{y + 2 = \frac{3}{4}(x - 1)}$

Using $(-3, -5)$: $\quad y - (-5) = \frac{3}{4}[x - (-3)]$ or $\boxed{y + 5 = \frac{3}{4}(x + 3)}$

As we shall see in a moment, these two equations are in fact equivalent, although they may look different.

Using slope–intercept form: The slope–intercept form is $y = mx + b$. Since we know $m = \frac{3}{4}$, we can write

$$y = \frac{3}{4}x + b$$

We do not yet know the value of b since we do not know the y-intercept. However, we do know that the points $(1, -2)$ and $(-3, -5)$ are on the line and so must satisfy the equation. Therefore, if we substitute one of these points, say $(1, -2)$, into the equation $y = \frac{3}{4}x + b$, we can solve for b.

121

$$y = \frac{3}{4}x + b \qquad \textit{Substitute } (1, -2).$$

$$-2 = \frac{3}{4}(1) + b$$

$$-2 = \frac{3}{4} + b$$

$$-2 - \frac{3}{4} = b$$

$$-\frac{11}{4} = b$$

Thus, the equation is

$$\boxed{y = \frac{3}{4}x - \frac{11}{4}}$$

While the three answers we have obtained look different, they are in fact equivalent. If we take our first two answers and solve for y we get:

First answer

$$y + 2 = \frac{3}{4}(x - 1)$$

$$y + 2 = \frac{3}{4}x - \frac{3}{4}$$

$$y = \frac{3}{4}x - \frac{3}{4} - 2$$

$$y = \frac{3}{4}x - \frac{11}{4}$$

Second answer

$$y + 5 = \frac{3}{4}(x + 3)$$

$$y + 5 = \frac{3}{4}x + \frac{9}{4}$$

$$y = \frac{3}{4}x + \frac{9}{4} - 5$$

$$y = \frac{3}{4}x - \frac{11}{4}$$

and so all three answers are equivalent. ■

Using the slope–intercept form in the example required the most work, but it had the advantage of giving us a uniform answer.

Unless there are instructions to the contrary, you may use whichever form *you* find most convenient. As the last example illustrates, anytime you are asked to write an equation of a nonvertical line, you may use either the point–slope or slope–intercept form. The given information in each problem will determine which form is more efficient to use.

EXAMPLE 5

Write an equation of the line passing through the point (2, 3) and parallel to the line whose equation is $3x - 6y = 12$.

Solution

The example becomes much clearer if we draw a diagram illustrating exactly what is being asked. Figure 4.28 illustrates that we are being asked to find the equation of the red line.

Figure 4.28

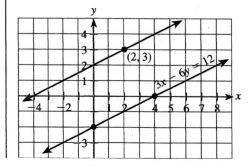

Let's analyze this question carefully, step by step, to develop a strategy for its solution.

THINKING OUT LOUD

What do we need to find?	The equation of a line satisfying certain conditions
What information is needed to write an equation of a line?	A point on the line and the slope of the line
What information is given in the problem?	The point is given, along with the equation of a line parallel to the line whose equation we want to find.
How do we find the slope of a line given the equation of a line parallel to it?	The slopes of parallel lines are equal. If we find the slope of the parallel line, then we have the slope of the line whose equation we want to find.
How do we find the slope of a line whose equation is given?	As we saw in Example 3, the easiest way is to put the given equation in slope–intercept form

Based on this analysis, we take the equation of the parallel line, put it in slope–intercept form, and then "read off" the slope:

$$3x - 6y = 12 \qquad \textit{We solve explicitly for y.}$$
$$-6y = -3x + 12$$
$$y = \frac{-3}{-6}x + \frac{12}{-6}$$
$$y = \frac{1}{2}x - 2$$

Therefore the slope of the parallel line is $\frac{1}{2}$.

Now we can use the point–slope form to write the equation:

$$y - y_1 = m(x - x_1) \qquad \textit{The given point is (2, 3); } m = \frac{1}{2}.$$

$$\boxed{y - 3 = \frac{1}{2}(x - 2)} \quad \text{or} \quad \boxed{y = \frac{1}{2}x + 2}$$

Notice that in this solution we used both the slope–intercept and point–slope forms. We used the slope–intercept form because it was the most efficient way to find the slope of the parallel line, and then we used the point–slope form because it was the most efficient method to write the equation. ■

EXAMPLE 6 Write an equation of the line passing through each pair of points:
(a) (2, 5) and (−3, 5)   **(b)** (1, 3) and (1, −4)

Solution (a) The slope of the line is

$$m = \frac{5 - 5}{2 - (-3)} = \frac{0}{5} = 0$$

123

Using the point–slope form with the point (2, 5), we get

$$y - 5 = 0(x - 2)$$
$$y - 5 = 0$$
$$\boxed{y = 5}$$

Alternatively, we may recognize at the outset that the line passing through the points (2, 5) and (–3, 5) is a horizontal line 5 units above the *x*-axis (see Figure 4.29). As we saw in Section 3.1, the equation of this line is $y = 5$.

Figure 4.29

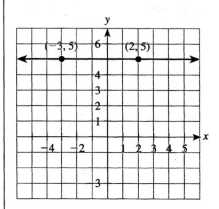

(b) If we attempt to compute the slope of this line, we get

$$m = \frac{3 - (-4)}{1 - 1} = \frac{7}{0} \quad \text{which is undefined!}$$

Therefore, we cannot use the point–slope or slope–intercept form to write an equation. (Both these forms require the line to have a slope. That is why in the discussion leading up to obtaining those forms we always specified a "nonvertical line.")

However, once we recognize that this is a vertical line 1 unit to the right of the *y*-axis (see Figure 4.30), we can write its equation as

$$\boxed{x = 1}$$

Figure 4.30

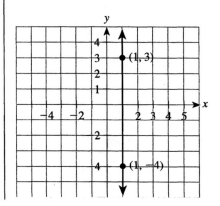

EXAMPLE 7 A manufacturer determines that the relationship between the profit earned, *P*, and the number of items produced, *x*, is linear. Suppose the profit is $1,500 on 45 items and $2,500 on 65 items.

(a) Write an equation relating *P* and *x*.

(b) What would the expected profit be if 100 items were produced?

Solution

Keep in mind that labeling the points (x, P) means that the horizontal axis is the x-axis and the vertical axis is the P-axis.

(a) The fact that the relationship is linear means we can write a first-degree equation in two variables, x and P. It is natural to assume that the profit, P, depends on the number of items produced, x. Thus x is the independent variable and P is the dependent variable, and we will label the points (x, P). We can write the information we are given as two points: $(45, 1500)$ and $(65, 2500)$. Thus, the slope of the line is

$$m = \frac{2{,}500 - 1{,}500}{65 - 45} = \frac{1{,}000}{20} = 50$$

We can now write the equation using the point–slope form with the point $(45, 1500)$ and $m = 50$ (keep in mind that we are using P instead of y):

$$P - 1{,}500 = 50(x - 45)$$

Or, if we put this in slope–intercept form, we have

$$\boxed{P = 50x - 750}$$

It is worthwhile to note that in real-life applications, the slope of a line often has a practical significance. In this example, there are actual units attached to the numbers when we compute the slope:

$$m = \frac{\$2{,}500 - \$1{,}500}{65 \text{ items} - 45 \text{ items}} = \frac{\$1{,}000}{20 \text{ items}} = \frac{\$50}{\text{item}} = \$50 \text{ per item}$$

Thus the significance of the slope is that it tells us the amount of profit earned *per item*. Looking at the equation $P = 50x - 750$, we now recognize that it says the *total* profit is \$50 per item minus \$750. In fact, we recognize that profit depends on the number of items: Using the language of functions we can state "P is a function of x," or write this symbolically as $P = P(x)$.

(b) We want the expected profit if 100 items are produced. In other words, we want to find P when $x = 100$, or, in the language of functions, we want to find $P(100)$:

$$P = P(x) = 50x - 750 \qquad \text{\textit{To find }} P(100), \textit{ substitute } x = 100 \textit{ in } P(x) \textit{ to get}$$
$$= 50(100) - 750$$
$$= 5{,}000 - 750$$
$$= \$4{,}250$$

Thus the expected profit if 100 items are produced is $\boxed{\$4{,}250}$.

It is often helpful to graph the equation to visualize the relationship between the variables (see Figure 4.31).

Figure 4.31

Having a graph allows us to approximate an answer or check its reasonableness and accuracy.

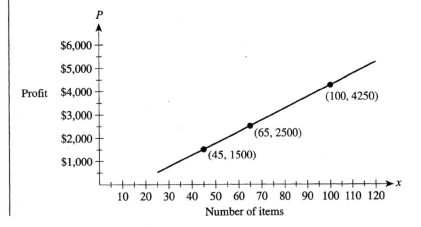

125

EXAMPLE 8

An automobile dealership recognizes that there is an approximately linear relationship between the number of cars and trucks sold each week. During a certain week, 42 cars and 18 trucks were sold, whereas during another week 35 cars and 16 trucks were sold. Find and graph a function relating the number c of cars and the number t of trucks sold each week.

Solution

It is unlikely that the number of cars sold *depends* on the number of trucks sold, or vice versa. Therefore, we may choose to make c the independent variable and t the dependent variable [in which case we will record the ordered pairs as (c, t), and the horizontal axis will be labeled c and the vertical axis will be labeled t], or we may do the reverse. We illustrate both approaches.

Approach 1 We record the ordered pairs as (c, t). The horizontal axis is c and the vertical axis is t.

Since we are told that the relationship is approximately linear, we will use the point–slope form for the equation of a line with the points $(42, 18)$ and $(35, 16)$. The slope of the line is

$$m = \frac{t_2 - t_1}{c_2 - c_1} = \frac{18 - 16}{42 - 35} = \frac{2}{7}$$

We can now write the equation of the line as

$$t - 18 = \frac{2}{7}(c - 42) \quad \text{or equivalently} \quad t = \frac{2}{7}c + 6$$

Approach 2 We record the ordered pairs as (t, c).

We use the point–slope form for the equation of a line with the points $(18, 42)$ and $(16, 35)$. The slope of the line is

$$m = \frac{c_2 - c_1}{t_2 - t_1} = \frac{42 - 35}{18 - 16} = \frac{7}{2}$$

We can now write the equation of the line as

$$c - 42 = \frac{7}{2}(t - 18) \quad \text{or equivalently} \quad c = \frac{7}{2}t - 21$$

Note that both approaches produce functions that describe the relationship between c and t. Figure 4.32 shows the graphs of these functions.

Figure 4.32

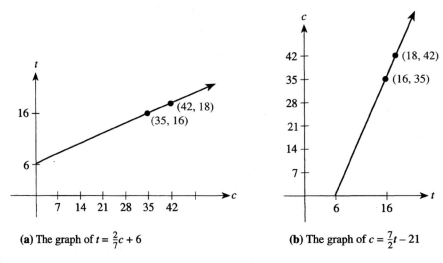

(a) The graph of $t = \frac{2}{7}c + 6$

(b) The graph of $c = \frac{7}{2}t - 21$

Note that we have drawn the graphs in the first quadrant only, since it makes no sense for either c or t to be negative. Both graphs give us information about the relationship between c and t; they differ simply in terms of the perspective from which we view the relationship. ∎

EXAMPLE 9

A company manufactures optical scanners. Figure 4.33 shows a graph of the relationship between the selling price, d, of a certain model scanner, in dollars, and the company's daily profit, P, on that model, in thousands of dollars. The horizontal axis represents the selling price of the scanner, and the vertical axis represents the daily profit on that model. For the price range given in the figure, the actual data points are plotted. These data points can be approximated by the given line. Find an equation of the line.

Figure 4.33

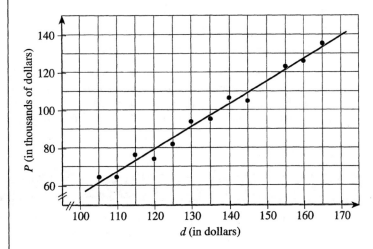

Solution

Here is a case where we are given the graph of a line and we need to find its equation. We could proceed by estimating the slope of the line (as we have done in the previous section), and identifying a point through which the line passes. Another approach would be to identify two points on the line, and find the equation as we have done in the previous examples. We will take the latter approach.

Which points do we use to construct an equation of the line? First, we note that the points we choose must be *on* the line: We cannot pick data points if they do not lie on the line. Second, the best choices of points are those that require the least estimation—those that lie on the grid if possible. See Figure 4.34.

For this example, we choose the points (120, 80) and (145, 110).

Figure 4.34

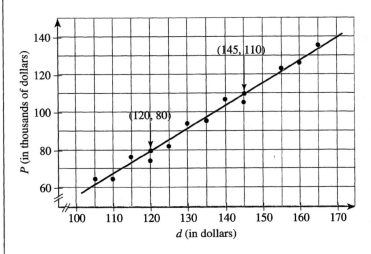

The slope is

$$\frac{110 - 80}{145 - 120} = \frac{30}{25} = 1.2$$

Hence, using the point (120, 80), the equation is

$$P - 80 = 1.2(d - 120)$$

which simplifies to

$$P = 1.2p - 64 \qquad \textit{Remember that P is in thousands of dollars.}$$

We should check with a point (keeping in mind that our equation is only as good as the accuracy of the points we chose). If we let the price p be 150, then the equation yields a daily profit of

$$P = 1.2(150) - 64 = 116 \qquad \textit{which means a profit of } \$116,000$$

Hence, the point (150, 116) should lie on (or very close to) the line if the equation is accurate. We can see by the figure that the point does lie on or close the line. ∎

One final comment: In this section we have shown that the equation of a straight line is a first-degree equation in x and y. However, we have still not proven the theorem stated in Section 2.1 that the graph of a first-degree equation in two variables is a straight line. A proof of this fact is outlined in Exercise 73.

Study Skills 4.2

Reviewing Your Exam: Checking Your Understanding

If you carefully looked over your exam and you believe that you understand the material and what you did wrong, then do the following:

Copy the problems over on a clean sheet of paper and rework the problems without your text, notes, or exam. When you are finished, check to see whether your answers are correct. If your answers are correct, try to find problems in the text similar to those problems and work the new problems on a clean sheet of paper (again without notes, text, or exam). If some of your new answers are incorrect then you may have

learned how to solve your test problems, but you probably have not thoroughly learned the topic being tested. You may need to repeat these steps several times until you are confident you understand your errors.

If any case, you should keep your exams (with the correct answers) because they are a good source of information for future studying. You may want to record errors that you consistently made on the exam on your warning cards: Types of exam problems can be used when you make up your quiz cards (see Study Skills 1.6).

 EXERCISES 4.2

In Exercises 1–28, write an equation of the line L satisfying the given conditions.
Where possible, express your answer in slope–intercept form.

1. L has slope 5 and passes through the point $(1, -3)$.
2. L has slope -4 and passes through the point $(-2, 4)$.
3. L has slope -3 and passes through the point $(-5, 2)$.
4. L has slope 2 and passes through the point $(-1, 6)$.
5. L passes through $(6, 1)$ and has slope $\frac{2}{3}$.
6. L passes through $(10, 3)$ and has slope $\frac{3}{5}$.
7. L passes through $(4, 0)$ and has slope $-\frac{1}{2}$.
8. L passes through $(0, 4)$ and has slope $-\frac{1}{2}$.
9. L has slope $\frac{3}{4}$ and passes through $(0, 5)$.
10. L has slope $\frac{4}{3}$ and passes through $(5, 0)$.
11. L has slope 0 and passes through $(-3, -4)$.
12. L has undefined slope and passes through $(-3, -4)$.
13. L has undefined slope and passes through $(-4, 7)$.
14. L has slope 0 and passes through $(-4, 7)$.
15. L passes through the points $(2, 3)$ and $(5, 7)$.
16. L passes through the points $(1, 4)$ and $(3, 8)$.
17. L passes through the points $(-2, -1)$ and $(-3, -5)$.
18. L passes through the points $(-3, -2)$ and $(-1, -4)$.
19. L passes through the points $(2, 3)$ and $(0, 5)$.
20. L passes through the points $(0, -1)$ and $(3, 1)$.
21. L has slope 4 and crosses the y-axis at $y = 6$.
22. L has slope 4 and crosses the x-axis at $x = 6$.
23. L has slope -2 and crosses the x-axis at $x = -3$.
24. L has slope $-\frac{1}{5}$ and crosses the y-axis at $y = -2$.

25. L passes through the points $(2, 3)$ and $(6, 3)$.

26. L passes through the points $(3, 2)$ and $(3, 6)$.

27. L is vertical and passes through $(-2, -4)$.

28. L is horizontal and passes through $(-5, -3)$.

In Exercises 29–44, write an equation of the line L satisfying the given conditions.

29. L crosses the x-axis at $x = -3$ and the y-axis at $y = 2$.

30. L crosses the y-axis at $y = -5$ and the x-axis at $x = -2$.

31. L passes through $(2, 2)$ and is parallel to $y = 3x + 7$.

32. L passes through $(2, 2)$ and is perpendicular to $y = 3x + 7$.

33. L passes through $(-3, 2)$ and is perpendicular to $y = -\frac{2}{3}x - 1$.

34. L passes through $(-3, 2)$ and is parallel to $y = -\frac{2}{3}x - 1$.

35. L passes through $(0, 0)$ and is perpendicular to $y = x$.

36. L passes through $(0, 0)$ and is parallel to $x + y = 6$.

37. L passes through $(-1, -2)$ and is parallel to $2y - 3x = 12$.

38. L passes through $(-1, -2)$ and is perpendicular to $2y - 3x = 12$.

39. L passes through $(1, -3)$ and is perpendicular to $4x - 3y = 9$.

40. L passes through $(1, -3)$ and is parallel to $4x - 3y = 9$.

41. L is perpendicular to $8x - 5y = 20$ and has the same y-intercept.

42. L is perpendicular to $8x - 5y = 20$ and has the same x-intercept.

43. L passes through the point $(0, 4)$ and is parallel to the line passing through the points $(3, -6)$ and $(-1, 2)$.

44. L passes through the point $(4, 0)$ and is perpendicular to the line passing through the points $(-3, 1)$ and $(2, 6)$.

In Exercises 45–48, identify the line L as horizontal or vertical and write its equation.

45. L passes through $(4, 3)$ and is parallel to the x-axis.

46. L passes through $(4, 3)$ and is parallel to the y-axis.

47. L passes through $(-1, -2)$ and is perpendicular to the x-axis.

48. L passes through $(-1, -2)$ and is perpendicular to the y-axis.

In Exercises 49–52, find the equation of the line.

49.

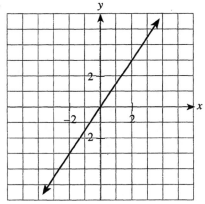

50.

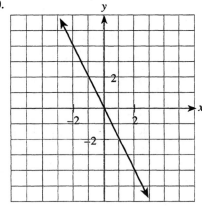

51.

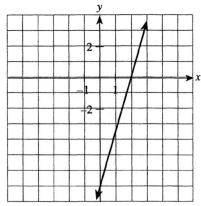

52.

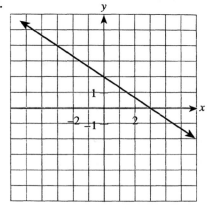

53. The figure shows the graph of the total national health expenditures, *H,* in the United States in billions of dollars, for each year *t,* from 1990 to 1997. The vertical axis represents *H* and the horizontal axis represents *t.* For the time range given in the figure, the actual data points are plotted. These data points can be approximated by the given line.

   (a) Find an equation of the line.

   (b) Use the equation found in part **(a)** to predict *H* for 1999.

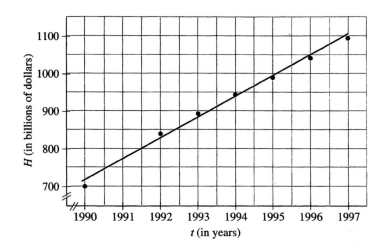

54. The figure shows the graph of the total enrollments in public schools, *E,* in the United States, in millions, for each year *t,* from 1990 to 1996. The vertical axis represents *E* and the horizontal axis represents *t.* For the time range given in the figure, the actual data points are plotted. These data points can be approximated by the given line.

   (a) Find an equation of the line.

   (b) Use the equation found in part **(a)** to predict *E* for 1999.

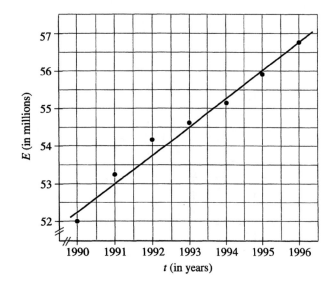

In Exercises 55–62, determine whether the given pairs of lines are perpendicular, parallel, or neither.

55. $3x - 2y = 5$ and $3x - 2y = 6$

56. $5x - 7y = 4$ and $5x + 7y = 4$

57. $2x = 3y - 4$ and $2x + 3y = 4$

58. $6x - 2y = 7$ and $3x - y = 8$

59. $5x + y = 2$ and $5y = x + 3$

60. $2x - y = 8$ and $4x = 2y + 9$

61. $3x - 7y = 1$ and $6x = 14y + 5$

62. $3x + 5y = 2$ and $4 + 10x = 6y$

63. A car rental company charges a flat fee of $29 per day plus a mileage fee of $0.12 per mile. Express C, the cost of a 1-day rental, as a linear function of n, the number of miles driven. What is the slope of the line whose equation you just found?

64. Each month a local utility company charges a flat fee of $12 plus a fee of $0.13 per kilowatt-hour. Express the monthly utility cost, U, as a linear function of k, the number of kilowatt-hours used. What is the slope of the line whose equation you just found?

65. Each month a local phone company charges a flat fee of $23 plus a fee of $0.825 per local call. Express the amount of the monthly phone bill, B, as a linear function of n, the number of local phone calls made. What is the slope of the line whose equation you just found?

66. A typesetter charges a flat fee of $85 as a setup charge, plus a fee of $0.825 per page. Express the cost, C, of a typesetting job as a linear function of p, the number of pages. What is the slope of the line whose equation you just found?

67. A manufacturer determines that the relationship between the profit earned, P, and the number of items produced, x, is linear. If the profit is $200 on 18 items and $2,660 on 100 items, write an equation relating P to x and determine what the expected profit would be if 200 items were produced.

68. Joe found that the relationship between the profit, P, he made on his wood carvings and the number of wood carvings he produced, x, is linear. If he made a profit of $10 on 5 carvings and $90 on 15 carvings, write an equation relating P to x and determine his expected profit if he produced 35 carvings.

69. A psychologist found that the relationship between the scores on two types of personality tests, test A and test B, was perfectly linear. An individual who scored a 35 on test A would score a 75 on test B, and an individual who scored a 15 on test A would score a 35 on test B. What test B score would an individual get if she scored a 40 on test A?

70. A factory foreman found a perfectly linear relationship between the number of defective widgets produced weekly, D, and the total number of overtime hours per week, h, put in by the widget inspectors. When the inspectors put in 100 hours total overtime, 85 defective widgets were found that week; when the inspectors put in 40 hours total overtime, 30 defective widgets were found. How many defective widgets should be found during the week the inspectors put in 120 hours total overtime?

71. A math teacher found that the performance, E, of her students on their first math exam was related linearly to their performance, V, on a video game located in the recreation room. A student who scored a 70 on his math exam scored 35,000 points on the video game. On the other hand, a student who scored an 85 on her exam scored a 20,000 on the video game. Write an equation relating E and V, and predict what exam score a student would have received if he scored 15,000 points on the video game.

72. A physiologist found that the relationship between the length of the right-hand thumb, T, and the length of the left little toe, t, was perfectly linear for a group of hospital residents. For one of the residents, the right-hand thumb was 5 cm and the left little toe was 2.5 cm; for another resident, the right-hand thumb was 7 cm and the left little toe was 2 cm. Write an equation relating T to t and predict the size of a resident's toe if his thumb is 8 cm.

? QUESTIONS FOR THOUGHT

73. We have already proven that if a graph is a straight line, then its equation can be put in the form $y = mx + b$ (or $x = k$ if the line is vertical). In either case, its equation is first degree. To prove the converse we need to show that any first-degree equation in two variables has as its graph a straight line.

Suppose we have the equation $Ax + By = C$, where $B \neq 0$. Show that *any* two ordered pairs (x_1, y_1) and (x_2, y_2) that satisfy the equation will yield the same slope. [*Hint:* If (x_1, y_1) satisfies the equation $Ax + By = C$, then

$$Ax_1 + By_1 = C$$

Now solve for y_1 and we have

$$y_1 = \frac{C - Ax_1}{B}$$

Therefore, we can write our ordered pair as $\left(x_1, \dfrac{C - Ax_1}{B}\right)$.

Similarly, for (x_2, y_2), we get $\left(x_2, \dfrac{C - Ax_2}{B}\right)$.

Now show that the slope you get from these two points is independent of x_1 and x_2.]

74. Put the equation of the line $Ax + By = C$ in slope–intercept form. What is the slope of the line (in terms of A, B, and C)?

◇ MINI-REVIEW

75. *Evaluate.* $\dfrac{-4(-2)(-6)}{-4 - 2(-6)}$

76. *Solve.* $8 - 5(x - 3) \leq 28$

77. Find the domain of $f(x) = \dfrac{x}{4x - 5}$

78. *Solve for y.* $8x - 3y = 12$

4.3 Linear Systems in Two Variables

It is frequently the case that we are considering a problem that requires us to satisfy two or more different conditions simultaneously. For example, given its particular circumstances, a business may want to choose a method of advertising that minimizes cost but also maximizes exposure.

Each condition can sometimes be represented by an equation in two or more variables. We then seek the numbers (if any) that satisfy all the equations (conditions) simultaneously.

In this section we will examine systems of two linear equations in two variables, and discuss methods that involve manipulation of these equations. In Chapter 10 we will generalize these methods to other systems, as well as discuss other methods for solving linear systems.

Let's begin by considering the following situation.

EXAMPLE 1   As an employee in a sales department, your employer offers you the option of receiving your weekly income in two possible ways: You can either be paid a straight commission of 8% of your gross sales, or you can receive a base pay of $180 per week plus a commission of 6% of your gross sales. Which plan should you choose?

Solution   The answer to this question depends on how much you expect to sell each week. For example, if you expect to sell $3,000 worth of merchandise in a week, you would receive a weekly income of 0.08 · $3,000 = $240 taking the straight commission plan, but 0.06 · $3,000 + $180 = $360 taking the base pay plus commission plan. On the other hand, if you expect to sell $10,000 worth of merchandise in a week, you would receive a weekly income of 0.08 · $10,000 = $800 taking the straight commission plan, but 0.06 · $10,000 + $180 = $780 taking the base pay plus commission plan.

Notice that if you expect to sell "a lot" of merchandise, the straight commission plan is more desirable than the base pay plus commission plan. On the other hand, if you do not expect to sell "a lot," the base pay plus commission plan is better. We can write an equation for each plan expressing the weekly income, I, in terms of the gross sales, g, as follows:

$$I = 0.08g \qquad \text{for straight 8% commission}$$
$$I = 180 + 0.06g \quad \text{for base pay plus 6% commission}$$

Each of these equations is a first-degree or linear equation in two variables, and hence has a straight line as its graph. We represent g along the horizontal axis, and I along the vertical axis, and graph each line on the same set of axes in Figure 4.35.

Figure 4.35
Graphs of
$I = 180 + 0.06g$
and $I = 0.08g$

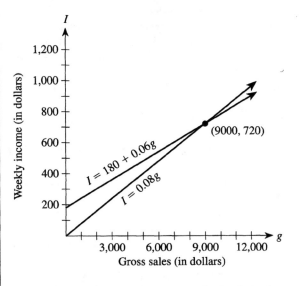

In the previous section we emphasized the importance of drawing the graph of an equation in order to better understand the relationship between the variables. Notice that the graph of each line tells us the weekly income, I, of each plan based on gross sales, g.

The point of intersection of the two lines, (9000, 720), can be determined algebraically. We will do this later on in this section.

By determining the point of intersection of the lines, we find what the gross sales should be for the incomes yielded by each plan to be the same. For this example, gross sales of $9000 will yield the same weekly income, $720, for both plans. The point of intersection of the two lines, (9000, 720) is important for our purposes because it tells us when one plan is more advantageous than the other. You can see from the graph in Figure 4.35 that if you sell less than $9,000 worth of merchandise per week, the base pay plus commission plan yields a higher income; if you sell more than \$9,000 worth of merchandise per week, the straight commission plan yields a higher income.

Your decision as to what plan to take reduces to whether you think you can average above or below \$9,000 in gross sales per week. ∎

The process of solving a system of equations by graphing both equations and observing the point(s) of intersection is called the *graphical method* of solution.

As we saw in the preceding example, finding the point of intersection of two lines was a crucial step in making the decision about which plan to choose. Determining a point of intersection by the graphical method often gives an approximate solution. We would like to develop algebraic methods for finding the *exact* solution to such a problem. We will also see that algebraic solutions can sometimes be very efficient and time-saving. Let's begin by introducing some basic terminology.

DEFINITION	Two or more equations considered together are called a ***system of equations***. In particular, if the equations are of the first degree, it is called a ***linear system***.

Thus,

$$\begin{cases} 2x - 3y = 6 \\ x - y = 1 \end{cases}$$

is an example of a linear system in two variables. This is called a **2 × 2** (read "2 by 2") *system*, since there are two equations and two variables. The "{" indicates that the two equations are to be considered together.

Solving such a *system of equations* means finding all the ordered pairs that satisfy *all* the equations in the system. Keep in mind that *one* solution to the system consists of *two* numbers—an x value and a y value.

We know that a single linear equation has an infinite number of solutions. How many solutions can a 2 × 2 linear system have? Or how many ordered pairs can satisfy two linear equations in two unknowns? Each of the equations in a 2 × 2 linear system is a straight line. Thus, we have the following three possibilities:

Case 1 The lines intersect in exactly one point. The coordinates of the point are the solution to the system.

Such a system is called ***consistent*** and ***independent*** (see Figure 4.36(a)).

Case 2 The lines are parallel and therefore never intersect. There are no solutions to the system.

Such a system is called ***inconsistent*** (see Figure 4.36(b)).

Case 3 The lines coincide. All the points that satisfy one of the equations also satisfy the other. Thus, there are infinitely many solutions.

Such a system is called ***dependent*** (see Figure 4.36(c)).

Figure 4.36

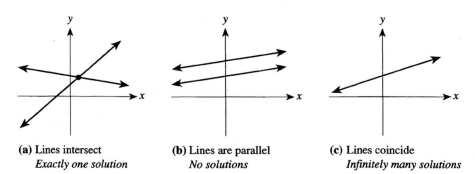

(a) Lines intersect
Exactly one solution

(b) Lines are parallel
No solutions

(c) Lines coincide
Infinitely many solutions

The algebraic methods we are about to discuss will allow us to determine which situation we have and, in case 1, to find the unique solution.

The Elimination Method

The *elimination* (or *addition*) *method* is based on the following idea. We already know how to solve a variety of equations involving *one* variable. If we can manipulate our system of equations so that one of the variables is eliminated, we can then solve the resulting equation in one variable.

We illustrate the elimination method with several examples.

EXAMPLE 2

Solve the following system of equations:

$$\begin{cases} x + y = -5 \\ x - y = 9 \end{cases}$$

Solution

In solving an equation, we are used to adding the same number or quantity to both sides. However, the addition property of equality allows us to add equal *quantities* to both sides of an equation. According to the second equation, $x - y$ and 9 are equal quantities; thus, we can just "add" that quantity to both sides of the equation $x + y = -5$, but we add $x - y$ to the left side of $x + y = -5$ and 9 to the right side. Thus, we "add" the two equations together.

$$\begin{array}{r} x + y = -5 \\ x - y = 9 \quad \text{Add.} \\ \hline 2x = 4 \end{array}$$

Notice that we have *eliminated* one of the variables and now we have an equation in one variable. We solve for that variable:

$$x = 2$$

To find the other variable, y, we substitute $x = 2$ in either one of the equations and solve for y:

$$\begin{aligned} x - y &= 9 \qquad \text{\textit{Substitute } } x = 2 \text{ \textit{in the second equation and solve for } } y. \\ 2 - y &= 9 \\ y &= -7 \end{aligned}$$

The solution is $\boxed{(2, -7)}$.

Check: We substitute $x = 2$ and $y = -7$ into both equations:

$$\begin{array}{ll} x + y = -5 & x - y = 9 \\ 2 + (-7) \overset{\checkmark}{=} -5 & 2 - (-7) \overset{\checkmark}{=} 9 \end{array}$$ ∎

EXAMPLE 3

Solve the following system of equations:

$$\begin{cases} 2x - 3y = 6 \\ x - y = 1 \end{cases}$$

Solution

We would like to "add" the two equations in such a way that one of the variables is eliminated. To do this we must change the coefficients of either the x or y variable so that they are exact opposites. Thus, when we add the two equations, the variables with opposite coefficients will be eliminated.

For example, to eliminate the y variable, we multiply the second equation by -3. This produces a y coefficient of $+3$ in the second equation, which is the opposite of -3, the y coefficient in the first equation.

We proceed as follows:

$$2x - 3y = 6 \qquad \textit{As is} \rightarrow \qquad 2x - 3y = 6 \qquad \textit{Add the resulting}$$
$$x - y = 1 \qquad \textit{Multiply by } -3 \rightarrow \qquad \underline{-3x + 3y = -3} \qquad \textit{equations.}$$
$$-x \quad = 3 \qquad \textit{Solve for x.}$$
$$x \quad = -3$$

Now we can substitute $x = -3$ into one of the original equations (we will use the first one) and solve for y:

$$2x - 3y = 6$$
$$2(-3) - 3y = 6$$
$$-6 - 3y = 6$$
$$-3y = 12$$
$$y = -4$$

Thus, the solution is $\boxed{(-3, -4)}$.

Check: We substitute $x = -3$ and $y = -4$ into both equations:

$$2x - 3y = 6 \qquad\qquad x - y = 1$$
$$2(-3) - 3(-4) \overset{?}{=} 6 \qquad\qquad -3 - (-4) \overset{?}{=} 1$$
$$-6 + 12 \overset{\checkmark}{=} 6 \qquad\qquad -3 + 4 \overset{\checkmark}{=} 1 \qquad\qquad\blacksquare$$

Note that we could have chosen to eliminate x in Example 3 by multiplying the second equation by -2 and then adding the two equations. The elimination method is also called the *addition method*.

EXAMPLE 4

Solve the following system of equations:

$$\begin{cases} 3x = 4y + 6 \\ 5y = 2x - 4 \end{cases}$$

Solution

To make the elimination process easier to perform, we should first line up "like" variables to make it easier to see how to eliminate one of them.

$$3x = 4y + 6 \qquad \rightarrow \qquad 3x - 4y = 6$$
$$5y = 2x - 4 \qquad \rightarrow \qquad -2x + 5y = -4$$

A system in this form with the variables lined up is said to be in **standard form.**

We choose to eliminate x. To keep the arithmetic as simple as possible, we convert the coefficients of x to $+6$ and -6. Note that 6 is the least common multiple (LCM) of 3 and 2.

$$3x - 4y = 6 \qquad \textit{Multiply by } 2 \rightarrow \qquad 6x - 8y = 12 \qquad \textit{Add the resulting}$$
$$-2x + 5y = -4 \qquad \textit{Multiply by } 3 \rightarrow \qquad \underline{-6x + 15y = -12} \qquad \textit{equations.}$$
$$7y = 0 \qquad \textit{Solve for y.}$$
$$y = 0$$

Substitute $y = 0$ into one of the original equations and solve for x:

$$3x = 4y + 6 \qquad \textit{We substitute } y = 0 \textit{ into the first equation.}$$
$$3x = 4(0) + 6$$
$$3x = 6$$
$$x = 2$$

Thus, our solution is $\boxed{(2, 0)}$.

You should check to see that $(2, 0)$ does indeed satisfy both equations. $\qquad\blacksquare$

We can summarize the elimination method as follows.

The Elimination (Addition) Method	1. Put the system of equations in standard form—that is, make sure the variables and constants line up vertically.
	2. Decide which variable you want to eliminate.
	3. Multiply one or both equations by appropriate constants so that the variable you have chosen to eliminate appears with opposite coefficients.
	4. Add the resulting equations.
	5. Solve the resulting equation in *one* variable.
	6. Substitute the value of the variable obtained into one of the original equations, and solve for the other variable.
	7. Check your solution in both of the original equations.

EXAMPLE 5

Solve the following system of equations:

$$\begin{cases} 3a - \dfrac{b}{2} = 7 \\[2mm] \dfrac{a}{5} - \dfrac{2b}{3} = 3 \end{cases}$$

Solution

We begin by clearing the system of fractions.

$$3a - \frac{b}{2} = 7 \qquad \textit{Multiply by 2} \rightarrow \qquad 6a - b = 14$$

$$\frac{a}{5} - \frac{2b}{3} = 3 \qquad \textit{Multiply by 15} \rightarrow \qquad 3a - 10b = 45$$

We choose to eliminate *a:*

$$6a - b = 14 \qquad \textit{As is} \rightarrow \qquad 6a - b = 14 \qquad \textit{Add.}$$
$$3a - 10b = 45 \qquad \textit{Multiply by} -2 \rightarrow \qquad \underline{-6a + 20b = -90}$$
$$19b = -76 \qquad \textit{Solve for b.}$$
$$b = -4$$

To obtain the value for *a*, we may substitute $b = -4$ into any of the equations containing *a* and *b*. We substitute $b = -4$ into the equation $6a - b = 14$ (the first of our equations without fractional coefficients):

$$6a - b = 14$$
$$6a - (-4) = 14$$
$$6a + 4 = 14$$
$$6a = 10$$
$$a = \frac{10}{6} = \frac{5}{3}$$

Thus, the solution is $\boxed{a = \dfrac{5}{3}, \, b = -4}$.

Check: (in the original equations)

$$3a - \frac{b}{2} = 7 \qquad\qquad \frac{a}{5} - \frac{2b}{3} = 3$$

$$3\left(\frac{5}{3}\right) - \frac{(-4)}{2} \overset{?}{=} 7 \qquad\qquad \frac{\frac{5}{3}}{5} - \frac{2(-4)}{3} \overset{?}{=} 3$$

$$5 + 2 \overset{\checkmark}{=} 7 \qquad\qquad \frac{5}{3} \cdot \frac{1}{5} - \left(\frac{-8}{3}\right) \overset{?}{=} 3$$

$$\frac{1}{3} + \frac{8}{3} \overset{\checkmark}{=} 3 \qquad\qquad\blacksquare$$

The Substitution Method

There is another method we can use to solve a system of equations. While our goal remains the same—to obtain an equation in one variable—our approach will be slightly different. We illustrate the substitution method with several examples.

EXAMPLE 6   Solve the following system of equations:

$$\begin{cases} 5x - 3y = 7 \\ x = 6y - 4 \end{cases}$$

Solution   We notice that the second equation is solved explicitly for x. Since $x = 6y - 4$, we can substitute $6y - 4$ into the first equation in place of x:

$5x - 3y = 7$ *Replace each occurrence of x by 6y − 4.*

$5(6y - 4) - 3y = 7$ *Now we have an equation in one variable. Solve for y.*

$30y - 20 - 3y = 7$

$27y - 20 = 7$

$27y = 27$

$y = 1$

Now we substitute $y = 1$ into the second of our original equations (since it is already solved explicitly for x):

$$x = 6y - 4$$
$$x = 6(1) - 4$$
$$x = 2$$

Thus, the solution is $\boxed{(2,\ 1)}$.

Check:

$$5x - 3y = 7 \qquad x = 6y - 4$$
$$5(2) - 3(1) \overset{?}{=} 7 \qquad 2 \overset{?}{=} 6(1) - 4$$
$$10 - 3 \overset{\checkmark}{=} 7 \qquad 2 \overset{\checkmark}{=} 6 - 4 \qquad\blacksquare$$

We can summarize the substitution method as follows.

The Substitution Method	1. Solve one of the equations explicitly for one of the variables.
	2. Substitute the expression obtained in step 1 into the other equation.
	3. Solve the resulting equation in one variable.
	4. Substitute the obtained value into one of the original equations (usually the one solved explicitly in step 1) and solve for the other variable.
	5. Check the solution.

EXAMPLE 7

Solve the following system of equations:

$$\begin{cases} \dfrac{5}{2}x + y = 4 \\ 2y + 5x = 10 \end{cases}$$

Solution

We solve the first equation explicitly for *y*:

$$\frac{5}{2}x + y = 4 \quad \rightarrow \quad y = -\frac{5}{2}x + 4$$

Substitute for *y* in the second equation:

$$2y + 5x = 10 \qquad \textit{Substitute } -\frac{5}{2}x + 4 \textit{ for y.}$$

$$2\left(-\frac{5}{2}x + 4\right) + 5x = 10$$

$$-5x + 8 + 5x = 10$$

$$8 = 10 \qquad \textit{This is a contradiction.}$$

Thus, there are no solutions common to both equations.

If we solve the *second* equation in our system for *y*, we get

$$y = -\frac{5}{2}x + 5 \qquad \textit{This equation is in the form } y = mx + b.$$

We can see that the two lines never meet (they both have the same slope of $-\frac{5}{2}$ but have different *y*-intercepts).

This system of equations has no solutions and is therefore $\boxed{\text{inconsistent}}$. ∎

EXAMPLE 8

Solve the following system of equations:

$$\begin{cases} 6x - 4y = 10 \\ 2y + 5 = 3x \end{cases}$$

Solution

If we choose to use the substitution method, then we must solve one of the equations explicitly for one of the variables. Whichever equation and whichever variable we choose, we are forced to work with fractional expressions. (Try it!) In this case the elimination method seems to be easier.

We begin by getting the system in standard form, and then eliminate *y*:

$$\begin{array}{llll} 6x - 4y = 10 & \rightarrow & 6x - 4y = 10 \quad \textit{As is} \rightarrow & 6x - 4y = 10 \\ 2y + 5 = 3x & \rightarrow & -3x + 2y = -5 \quad \textit{Multiply by 2} \rightarrow & \underline{-6x + 4y = -10} \\ & & & 0 = 0 \end{array}$$

$$\textit{This is an identity.}$$

If we solve both equations for *y*, we obtain

$$y = \frac{3}{2}x - \frac{5}{2}$$

and we see that the lines are identical (they have the same slope *and* the same *y*-intercept). Thus, every ordered pair that satisfies one of the equations also satisfies the other. There are infinitely many solutions. The equations are $\boxed{\text{dependent}}$.

The solution set is the set of all the points on the line, that is,

$$\boxed{\{(x, y) \mid 6x - 4y = 10\}}$$ ∎

EXAMPLE 9

In Example 1 of this section we constructed two equations to describe two possible income plans:

$$\begin{cases} I = 0.08g \\ I = 180 + 0.06g \end{cases}$$

We graphed the two equations, assigning g as the independent variable (represented by the horizontal axis) and I as the dependent variable (represented by the vertical axis). Find the intersection of the graphs of these two equations.

Solution

An ordered pair that satisfies two linear equations is a solution to the system. The point representing the solution lies on both lines. Therefore the solution represents the point of intersection. Hence we are being asked to solve the system of equations.

Since both equations are solved explicitly for I, we can substitute for I in either equation:

$I = 180 + 0.06g$ *Use the first equation to substitute 0.08g for I in the second equation.*

$0.08g = 180 + 0.06g$ *Subtract 0.06g from both sides to get*

$0.02g = 180$ *Divide each side by 0.02.*

$g = \dfrac{180}{0.02} = 9{,}000$

Substitute $g = 9{,}000$ for I into the first equation to get

$$I = 0.08g$$
$$I = 0.08(9{,}000) = 720$$

Since g is the independent variable, the ordered pairs are of the form (g, I): The point of intersection is (9000, 720). The graphs of these equations appear in Figure 4.35 on page 229. ∎

Having the ability to solve a system of equations gives us a great deal of flexibility in how we set up our solutions to verbal problems. In many cases we may be able to solve a verbal problem either by using a one-variable approach as we did in Chapters 2 and 3, or by writing a system of equations.

EXAMPLE 10

A stationery store ordered 50 cases of envelopes costing a total of $551.50. Among the 50 cases were some that contained legal-size envelopes and cost $11.95 each, whereas the remaining cases contained letter-size envelopes and cost $9.95 each. How many of each type were ordered?

Solution

If we want to use more than one variable, then we must have as many independent equations as we have variables.

Let x = Number of cases of legal-size envelopes

Let y = Number of cases of letter-size envelopes

We must create two equations—the first will relate the *number* of cases, the second will relate the *cost* of the cases.

Our equations are

$$\begin{cases} x + y = 50 & \text{\textit{There are 50 cases altogether.}} \\ 11.95x + 9.95y = 551.50 & \text{\textit{The total cost is \$551.50.}} \end{cases}$$

$x + y = 50$ *Multiply by −995* → $-995x - 995y = -49{,}750$

$11.95x + 9.95y = 551.50$ *Multiply by 100* → $\underline{1{,}195x + 995y = 55{,}150}$

         $200x = 5{,}400$

         $x = 27$

Substitute $x = 27$ into the first equation:

$$x + y = 50$$
$$27 + y = 50$$
$$y = 23$$

Hence, there are 27 cases of legal-size envelopes and 23 cases of letter-size envelopes.

The check is left to the student. ∎

EXAMPLE 11

The length of a rectangle is 5 inches more than 4 times the width, and the perimeter is 182 inches. Find the dimensions of the rectangle.

Solution

The applications discussed earlier in the text were solved using a one-variable approach. In fact many applications can be solved using either a one-variable or a two-variable approach. We illustrate both approaches in this example.

One-Variable Approach: We draw a rectangle and label the width as w.

$$\text{Let } w = \text{Width}$$

Then

$$4w + 5 = \text{Length} \qquad \textit{Since the length is 5 more than 4 times the width}$$

We label the length of the rectangle $4w + 5$ (see Figure 4.37).

Figure 4.37

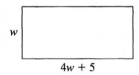

$4w + 5$

The formula for the perimeter of a rectangle is $P = 2L + 2W$, where P is the perimeter, L is the length, and W is the width. Hence

$P = 2L + 2W$	*Since $P = 182$ and the width is w and the length is $4w + 5$, we have*
$182 = 2(4w + 5) + 2w$	*Which can be simplified to*
$182 = 8w + 10 + 2w$	
$182 = 10w + 10$	*This is a first-degree equation. We proceed to solve it: Subtract 10 from each side.*
$172 = 10w$	*Divide each side by 10 to get*
$\dfrac{172}{10} = \dfrac{10w}{10}$	
$17.2 = w$	*The width is 17.2 in.*

Hence the width $w = 17.2$ in. and the length $l = 4w + 5 = 4(17.2) + 5 = 73.8$ in.

The dimensions of the rectangle are $\boxed{17.2 \text{ in. by } 73.8 \text{ in.}}$

Check:

Is 73.8 (the length) 5 more than 4 times 17.2 (the width)? $73.8 \overset{\checkmark}{=} 4(17.2) + 5.$

Is the perimeter 182 inches? $182 \overset{\checkmark}{=} 2(73.8) + 2(17.2)$

Two-Variable Approach: We draw a picture of a rectangle and label the sides using *two* variables, *l* and *w*, as shown in Figure 4.38.

Figure 4.38

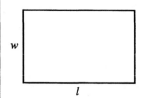

We create two equations—one relating the sides, and the other relating the perimeter to the sides:

$l = 4w + 5$ *The length is 5 inches more than 4 times the width.*
$182 = 2l + 2w$ *The perimeter is 182 inches.*

Using the first equation, we substitute into the second equation and get

$$182 = 2(4w + 5) + 2w$$

This is exactly the same equation we obtained using the one-variable approach. The rest of the solution is as it appears above. ■

In Examples 10 and 11, neither the one-variable nor the two-variable approach offers any particular advantages. Sometimes, however, as the following example illustrates, the way a problem is stated makes the two-variable approach significantly easier.

EXAMPLE 12

George and Ruth both go into a store to buy blank audio cassettes. George buys eight 60-minute cassettes and five 90-minute cassettes for a total of $39.45, while Ruth buys six 60-minute cassettes and ten 90-minute cassettes for a total of $51.40. What are the prices of a single 60-minute and a single 90-minute cassette?

Solution

If we try the one-variable approach here we will find that it is difficult to represent both prices in terms of one variable. (Try it!) However, the statement of the problem allows us to use the two-variable approach quite naturally.

Let s = price of a single 60-minute cassette

Let n = price of a single 90-minute cassette

From the statement of the problem, we obtain the following system:

$8s + 5n = 39.45$ *This equation represents George's purchase.*
$6s + 10n = 51.40$ *This equation represents Ruth's purchase.*

We choose to eliminate n.

$8s + 5n = 39.45$ *Multiply by –2* $\rightarrow$ $-16s - 10n = -78.90$
$6s + 10n = 51.40$ *As is* $\rightarrow$ $\underline{6s + 10n = 51.40}$
$$-10s = -27.50$$
$$s = 2.75$$

Substitute $s = 2.75$ into the first equation:

$$8s + 5n = 39.45$$
$$8(2.75) + 5n = 39.45$$
$$22 + 5n = 39.45$$
$$5n = 17.45$$
$$n = 3.49$$

> A 60-minute cassette costs $2.75 and a 90-minute cassette costs $3.49.

The check is left to the student. ■

Study Skills 4.3

Preparing for a Comprehensive Final Exam

Many algebra courses require students to take a comprehensive final exam—an exam covering the entire course. Because of the amount of material covered in this type of exam, your preparation should necessarily differ from your preparation for other exams.

To succeed in a comprehensive final, even those students who have been doing well on exams all along will need to take the time to review the ideas and procedures covered earlier in the course. As more material is learned, it becomes easier to forget and/or confuse concepts learned previously.

For example, we often find that, on finals, students manage to correctly solve complex problems from the later chapters, but have difficulty with some of the simpler problems covered in the earlier chapters. This is because the more complex material was most recently learned, whereas some of the "simple" topics, covered much earlier in the course, were forgotten or became obscured by the newer material. Even if you knew the material well earlier in the course, there is no substitute for timely review of the *entire* course syllabus.

Your studying should begin at least two weeks before the exam. Starting two weeks early means that you will probably be learning new material as you are studying for the final exam. You should consider studying for the final as separate from learning the new material. This means that your total math study time should be increased and divided between learn-

ing the new material and reviewing previous material (even the "simple" topics).

Your studying should include the following:

1. Review your class notes. Pay particular attention to those topics you may have found a bit difficult the first time you learned them.

2. If you have been writing out Study Cards, be sure to review them. Pay particular attention to the Warning Cards.

3. Review a selection of homework exercises. Be sure to choose a wide variety of exercises to cover all the topics in your syllabus, and the various types of exercises within each topic.

4. Review all your class exams and quizzes. Be sure you understand how every single problem is solved, and where you made your errors.

5. Find out whether copies of previous final exams are available for you to examine. Be sure you know the format of the final exam: Will the exam be multiple choice, fill-in, or a combination? Will there be partial credit?

6. A few days before the final exam, make up a practice final exam and follow the directions given in Study Skills 2.6: Using Quiz Cards.

Remember, going over all this material takes time, so be sure to start your studying well in advance of the final exam date.

 EXERCISES 4.3

In Exercises 1–38, solve the system of equations. State whether the system is independent, inconsistent, or dependent. Use whichever method you prefer.

1. $\begin{cases} 2x + y = 12 \\ 3x - y = 13 \end{cases}$

2. $\begin{cases} x + 4y = 6 \\ -x + 3y = 8 \end{cases}$

3. $\begin{cases} -x + 5y = 11 \\ x - 2y = -2 \end{cases}$

4. $\begin{cases} 4x + y = 16 \\ 3x - y = 5 \end{cases}$

5. $\begin{cases} 3x - y = 0 \\ 2x + 3y = 11 \end{cases}$

6. $\begin{cases} 5x - y = 13 \\ 3x - 2y = 5 \end{cases}$

7. $\begin{cases} x + 7y = 20 \\ 5x + 2y = 34 \end{cases}$

8. $\begin{cases} -x + 5y = 12 \\ -3x + 4y = 3 \end{cases}$

9. $\begin{cases} 4x + 5y = 0 \\ 2x + 3y = -2 \end{cases}$

10. $\begin{cases} 5x - 3y = 18 \\ 4x - 6y = 0 \end{cases}$

11. $\begin{cases} 2x + 3y = 7 \\ 4x + 6y = 14 \end{cases}$

12. $\begin{cases} 3x - 5y = 4 \\ 6x - 10y = 9 \end{cases}$

13. $\begin{cases} 5x - 6y = 3 \\ 10x - 12y = 5 \end{cases}$

14. $\begin{cases} -2x + 14y = 8 \\ x - 7y = -4 \end{cases}$

15. $\begin{cases} 2x - 3y = 10 \\ 3x - 2y = 15 \end{cases}$

16. $\begin{cases} 2x + 3y = 18 \\ 3x + 2y = 12 \end{cases}$

17. $\begin{cases} y = 2x + 3 \\ 2x + y = -1 \end{cases}$

18. $\begin{cases} x = 3y - 4 \\ 3x + 2y = 10 \end{cases}$

19. $\begin{cases} 6a - 3b = 1 \\ 8a + 5b = 7 \end{cases}$

20. $\begin{cases} 2a - 6b = -4 \\ 5a - 7b = -4 \end{cases}$

21. $\begin{cases} s = 3t - 5 \\ t = 3s - 5 \end{cases}$

22. $\begin{cases} s = 5t - 8 \\ t = 5s - 8 \end{cases}$

23. $\begin{cases} 3m - 2n = 8 \\ 3n = m - 8 \end{cases}$

24. $\begin{cases} 5m - 3n = 2 \\ m - 4 = 2n \end{cases}$

25. $\begin{cases} 3p - 4q = 5 \\ 3q - 4p = -9 \end{cases}$

26. $\begin{cases} 5p + 6q = 1 \\ 5q + 6p = -1 \end{cases}$

27. $\begin{cases} \dfrac{u}{3} - v = 1 \\ u - \dfrac{v}{2} = 5 \end{cases}$

28. $\begin{cases} u - \dfrac{v}{4} = 4 \\ \dfrac{u}{5} - v = -3 \end{cases}$

29. $\begin{cases} \dfrac{w}{4} + \dfrac{z}{6} = 4 \\ \dfrac{w}{2} - \dfrac{z}{3} = 4 \end{cases}$

30. $\begin{cases} \dfrac{w}{6} - \dfrac{z}{5} = 2 \\ \dfrac{w}{2} - \dfrac{z}{10} = 1 \end{cases}$

31. $\begin{cases} \dfrac{x}{6} + \dfrac{y}{8} = \dfrac{3}{4} \\ \dfrac{x}{4} + \dfrac{y}{3} = \dfrac{17}{12} \end{cases}$

32. $\begin{cases} \dfrac{x}{5} + \dfrac{y}{3} = \dfrac{2}{3} \\ \dfrac{x}{10} - \dfrac{y}{4} = \dfrac{3}{4} \end{cases}$

33. $\begin{cases} \dfrac{x+3}{2} + \dfrac{y-4}{3} = \dfrac{19}{6} \\ \dfrac{x-2}{3} + \dfrac{y-2}{2} = 2 \end{cases}$

34. $\begin{cases} \dfrac{a-2}{4} - \dfrac{b+1}{2} = \dfrac{3}{2} \\ \dfrac{a-3}{3} + \dfrac{b+1}{4} = \dfrac{25}{4} \end{cases}$

35. $\begin{cases} 0.1x + 0.01y = 0.37 \\ 0.02x + 0.05y = 0.41 \end{cases}$

36. $\begin{cases} 0.3x - 0.7y = 2.93 \\ 0.06x - 0.2y = 0.58 \end{cases}$

37. $\begin{cases} \dfrac{x}{2} + 0.05y = 0.35 \\ 0.3x + \dfrac{y}{4} = 0.65 \end{cases}$

38. $\begin{cases} 0.02x + \dfrac{y}{2} = 0.3 \\ \dfrac{x}{2} - 0.4y = 2.34 \end{cases}$

Solve the following problems algebraically by writing an equation or a system of equations. Clearly label what each variable represents.

39. Susan wants to invest a total of $14,000 so that her yearly interest is $835. If she chooses to invest part in a certificate of deposit paying 5% and the remainder in a corporate bond paying 8%, how much should she invest at each rate?

40. Harry makes two investments. He invests $6,000 more at 8.5% than he invests at 7.5%. If the total yearly interest from both investments is $1,022, how much is invested at each rate?

41. To the nearest cent, how can $10,000 be split into two investments, one paying 10% interest and the other paying 8% interest, so that the yearly interest from the two investments is equal?

42. A person invests money at 6% and at 4%, earning a total yearly interest of $540. Had the amounts invested been reversed, the yearly interest would have been $510. How much was invested altogether?

43. The perimeter of a rectangle is 36 cm. If the length is 2 cm more than the width, find the dimensions of the rectangle.

44. The side of a square is 2 less than 3 times the side of an equilateral triangle. If the perimeter of the square is 12 more than twice the perimeter of the triangle, find the lengths of the sides of both figures.

45. Albert and Audrey both go into a camera store to buy film. Albert spends $35.60 on 5 rolls of 35-mm film and 3 rolls of movie film. Audrey spends $43.60 on 3 rolls of 35-mm film and 5 rolls of movie film. What are the costs of a single roll of each type of film?

46. Jim has a part-time job selling newspaper and magazine subscriptions. One week he earns $62.20 by selling 10 newspaper and 6 magazine subscriptions. The following week he earns $79 by selling 12 newspaper and 8 magazine subscriptions. How much does he earn for each newspaper and each magazine subscription he sells?

47. A donut shop sells a box containing 7 cream-filled and 5 jelly donuts for $3.16, and a box containing 4 cream-filled and 8 jelly donuts for $3.04. Find the costs of a single cream-filled and a single jelly donut.

48. A candy shop sells a mixture containing 1 pound of hard candy and 2 pounds of chocolates for $15.39, and a mixture containing 2 pounds of hard candy and 1 pound of chocolates for $12.93. What are the costs for 1 pound of hard candy and 1 pound of chocolates?

49. An electronics manufacturer produces two types of transmitters. The more expensive model requires 6 hours to manufacture and 3 hours to assemble. The less expensive model requires 5 hours to manufacture and 2 hours to assemble. If the company can allocate 730 hours for manufacturing and 340 hours for assembly, how many of each type can be produced?

50. The mathematics department hires tutors and graders. For the month of October, the department budgets $830 for 80 hours of tutoring and 45 hours of grading. In November, the department budgets $600 for 60 hours of tutoring and 30 hours of grading. How much does the department pay for each hour of tutoring and for each hour of grading?

51. A couple has a choice of two health insurance plans: one through the husband's employer and one through the wife's employer. The husband's plan will cost $140 per month and will pay for 90% of all medical expenses. The wife's plan will cost $100 per month and will pay for 75% of all medical expenses. At what level of annual medical expenses are the two plans equivalent?

52. A family has a choice of two health insurance plans: one through the father's company and one through the mother's employer. The father's plan will cost $150 per month and will pay for 100% of all medical expenses. The mother's plan will cost $125 per month and will pay for 80% of all medical expenses. At what level of annual medical expenses should the family choose the mother's plan?

53. The Cheapo Car Rental Company charges $29 per day plus $0.12 per mile, whereas the Cut-Rate Car Rental Company charges $22 per day plus $0.15 per mile. On a 1-day rental, how many miles must be driven to make the cost of the two companies the same?

54. An office equipment rental company offers two different leases on a copying machine. One lease agreement costs $75 per month plus $0.024 per copy. A second lease agreement costs $85 per month plus $0.019 per copy. How many copies per month must a customer make for the second lease agreement to be cheaper than the first?

55. The costs, C, that a manufacturer incurs in producing a product are usually divided into two parts: *fixed costs* and *unit costs*. The unit costs are computed by multiplying the number of units manufactured, x, by the cost of manufacturing each unit. The *break-even* point for a company is the number of units the company must sell so that its costs and revenue are equal. Suppose that a company's costs are given by the equation $C = 1.6x + 7,200$ and its revenue is given by the equation $R = 2.1x$. Find the break-even point.

56. Suppose that a company's costs are given by the equation $C = 3.5x + 18,750$ and its revenue is given by the equation $R = 4.2x$. Find the break-even point. (See Exercise 55.)

57. The telephone company offers two billing plans for local service. Under the first plan, the customer pays a fee of $18 per month plus a per-call fee of $0.11. The second plan charges the customer a fee of $24 per month, which includes 50 free calls plus a per-call fee of $0.09 for each call above 50 per month. How many local calls per month make the two plans equivalent?

58. A cellular phone company offers two billing plans for its monthly service. Under the first plan, the customer pays a fee of $33 per month, which includes 30 minutes of free airtime, plus a fee of $0.57 for each minute of airtime above 30. The second plan charges the customer a monthly fee of $40 per month plus a fee of $0.34 per minute of airtime. How many minutes of phone usage per month make the two plans equivalent?

59. A bank teller receives a deposit of 43 bills totaling $340. If the bills are all $5 and $10 bills, how many of each are there?

60. Dorothy purchases a total of 80 stamps for $25.76. If she bought 34-cent and 25-cent stamps, how many of each did she buy?

61. A car rental agency charges a flat fee plus a mileage rate for a 1-day rental. If the charge for a 1-day rental with 85 miles is $44.30 and the charge for a 1-day rental with 125 miles is $51.50, find the flat fee and the charge per mile.

62. A discount airline has a fixed charge for processing tickets plus a mileage fee. A ticket for a 200-mile trip costs $48, while a ticket for a 300-mile trip costs $61. Find the fixed charge and the charge per mile.

63. A plane can cover a distance of 2,310 km in 6 hours with a tailwind (with the wind) and a distance of 1,530 km in the same time with a headwind (against the wind). Find the speed of the plane and the speed of the wind.

64. An express train travels 35 kph faster than a freight train. After 3 hours they have traveled a total of 465 km. Find the rate of each train.

65. Find the point (x, y) so that the line passing through the points (x, y) and $(2, 3)$ with a slope of -1 intersects the line passing through (x, y) and $(1, -2)$ with a slope of 2.

66. Find the values of A and B so that the line whose equation is $Ax + By = 8$ passes through the points $(1, -8)$ and $\left(5, \frac{8}{3}\right)$.

67. Between 1990 and 1997, the number of physicians who specialize in dermatology in the United States can be estimated by the equation $P = 201(t - 1{,}990) + 5{,}974$, where P is the number of dermatologists during the given year t. Between 1990 and 1997, the number of physicians who specialize in gastroenterology in the United States can be estimated by the equation $P = 395(t - 1{,}990) + 5{,}190$, where P is the number of gastroenterologists during the given year t. In what year (between 1990 and 1997) was the number of dermatologists equal to the number of gastroenterologists?

 QUESTIONS FOR THOUGHT

68. When asked to solve a system of equations, describe what you look for in deciding whether to use the elimination or substitution method.

69. Solve the following system by the elimination method:

$$\begin{cases} 4x - 9y = 3 \\ 10x - 6y = 7 \end{cases}$$

In using the elimination method, we eliminated a variable and then used *substitution* to find the value of the variable eliminated. A variation of the elimination method is to use the elimination process twice—once for each variable—to solve for each variable. Would this be easier for the system you just solved? Why?

70. Solve the following systems for u and v by first substituting x for $\dfrac{1}{u}$ and y for $\dfrac{1}{v}$:

(a) $\begin{cases} \dfrac{1}{u} + \dfrac{1}{v} = 5 \\ \dfrac{1}{u} - \dfrac{1}{v} = 1 \end{cases}$

(b) $\begin{cases} \dfrac{2}{u} + \dfrac{1}{v} = 3 \\ \dfrac{6}{u} + \dfrac{1}{v} = 5 \end{cases}$

 MINI-REVIEW

71. *Solve.* $4(x - 3) - 6(x - 8) = 10 - (x - 18)$

72. $\dfrac{x}{3} - \dfrac{x}{5} = \dfrac{16}{5}$

73. If $f(x) = 3x^2 - 2x + 1$, find $f(-4)$ and $f(a)$.

4.4 Graphing Linear Inequalities in Two Variables

Let's begin by reexamining the *number line* graph of a first-degree inequality in *one variable.* As illustrated in Figure 4.39, on the number line, the graph of a first-degree conditional inequality in one variable, $x \le a$, forms a half-line. This half-line has, as its endpoint, the point that is the solution of the *equation* $x = a$. In other words, on the number line, the graph of the inequality $x \le a$ is bounded by the graph of the equation $x = a$.

Figure 4.39
The graph of $x \le a$ on the number line

In graphing linear inequalities in *two variables* on the *rectangular coordinate system,* we find an analogous situation. The graph of $Ax + By \le C$ will be a *half-plane* bounded by the graph of the *equation* $Ax + By = C$ (see Figure 4.40).

Figure 4.40
A possible graph of
$Ax + By \le C$

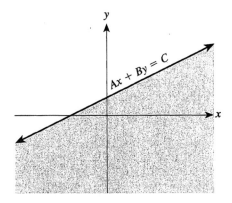

Using what we have learned thus far, we can graph linear inequalities in two variables.

EXAMPLE 1 Sketch the solution set to the inequality $x + y \le 4$.

Solution We begin by graphing the equation $x + y = 4$. We sketch the graph by the intercept method as outlined in Section 4.1 (see Figure 4.41 on page 244).

65. How long will it take for Bobby running 6 mph to overtake Linda running 5 mph if Linda had an hour head start?

66. The new DVX model machine can process 40 items per minute, whereas the old DVX model can process 32 items per minute. How long will it take to complete a job of processing 3,960 items if both machines are operating together?

CHAPTER 4 SUMMARY

After completing this chapter you should be able to:

1. Use the definition of slope to compute the slope of a line when two points on the line are known (Section 4.1).

   For example: Compute the slope of the line passing through the points $(-1, 3)$ and $(2, -5)$.

$$m = \frac{y_2 - y_1}{x_2 - x_1} = \frac{3 - (-5)}{-1 - 2} = \frac{8}{-3} = -\frac{8}{3}$$

2. Recognize that lines with equal slopes are parallel and that lines whose slopes are negative reciprocals of each other are perpendicular (Section 4.1).

   For example:

   If line L_1 has slope $\frac{2}{5}$, then any line parallel to L_1 must have slope $\frac{2}{5}$.

   If line L_2 has slope $\frac{3}{7}$, then any line perpendicular to L_2 must have slope $-\frac{7}{3}$.

3. Write an equation of a line using either

   the point–slope form $y - y_1 = m(x - x_1)$

   or

   the slope–intercept form $y = mx + b$

   (Section 4.2).

   For example: Write an equation of the line passing through the points $(-2, 1)$ and $(1, 2)$.

   We first find the slope:

$$m = \frac{y_2 - y_1}{x_2 - x_1} = \frac{1 - 2}{-2 - 1} = \frac{-1}{-3} = \frac{1}{3}$$

   The point–slope form is $y - y_1 = m(x - x_1)$. We can use either $(-2, 1)$ or $(1, 2)$ as our given point (x_1, y_1). Using $(1, 2)$ as the given point, we get

$$y - 2 = \frac{1}{3}(x - 1)$$

4. Find the slope of a line by putting its equation in slope–intercept form (Section 4.2).

   For example: Find the slope of the line whose equation is $5x + 4y = 7$.

   We can find the slope by putting the equation in slope–intercept form—that is, in the form $y = mx + b$:

$$5x + 4y = 7$$
$$4y = -5x + 7$$
$$y = \frac{-5}{4}x + \frac{7}{4}$$

   Therefore, we can "read off" the slope, which is $-\frac{5}{4}$.

5. Write an equation of a line satisfying certain conditions (Section 4.2).

   For example: Write an equation of the line that passes through the point $(3, -2)$ and is perpendicular to $2x - 7y = 11$.

   We first find the slope of $2x - 7y = 11$ by putting it in slope–intercept form:

   $$2x - 7y = 11$$
   $$-7y = -2x + 11$$
   $$y = \frac{2}{7}x - \frac{11}{7} \qquad \textit{The slope of this line is } \tfrac{2}{7}.$$

   Since the required line is perpendicular to $2x - 7y = 11$, it will have slope $-\frac{7}{2}$. We can now write the equation using point–slope form:

   $$y - y_1 = m(x - x_1)$$
   $$y - (-2) = -\frac{7}{2}(x - 3)$$
   $$y + 2 = -\frac{7}{2}(x - 3)$$

6. Solve a 2 × 2 system of linear equations by using either the elimination or the substitution method (Section 4.3).

   For example: Solve for x and y:

   $$\begin{cases} 3x - 4y = 10 \\ 4x - 5y = 13 \end{cases}$$

   Solution: We use the elimination method. We choose to eliminate y.

   $$\begin{cases} 3x - 4y = 10 & \textit{Multiply by } -5 \rightarrow & -15x + 20y = -50 \\ 4x - 5y = 13 & \textit{Multiply by } 4 \rightarrow & \underline{16x - 20y = 52} \\ & & x = 2 \end{cases}$$

   Substitute $x = 2$ into the first equation:

   $$3x - 4y = 10$$
   $$3(2) - 4y = 10$$
   $$6 - 4y = 10$$
   $$-4y = 4$$
   $$y = -1$$

   The solution is $(2, -1)$. Check in both equations.

7. Solve a variety of verbal problems that give rise to a linear system of equations (Section 4.3).

   For example: A candy shop sells a mixture containing 1 lb of regular jelly beans and $\frac{1}{2}$ lb of gourmet jelly beans for \$2.75, and a mixture containing $\frac{1}{2}$ lb of regular jelly beans and 1 lb of gourmet jelly beans for \$3.25. What is the cost per pound of each type of jelly bean?

   Solution:

   $$\text{Let } r = \text{the cost per pound of regular jelly beans}$$
   $$\text{Let } g = \text{the cost per pound of gourmet jelly beans}$$

   Then the given information translates into the following system of equations:

   $$\begin{cases} 1r + \dfrac{1}{2}g = 2.75 & \textit{Represents the cost of the first mixture} \\[2mm] \dfrac{1}{2}r + 1g = 3.25 & \textit{Represents the cost of the second mixture} \end{cases}$$

Multiplying both sides of each equation by 2 yields the following system:

$$\begin{cases} 2r + g = 5.5 \\ r + 2g = 6.5 \end{cases}$$

As is → $2r + g = 5.5$

Multiply by −2 → $\underline{-2r - 4g = -13}$ *Add.*

$$-3g = -7.5$$
$$g = 2.5$$

To find *r*, substitute 2.5 for *g* in $2r + g = 5.5$:

$$2r + g = 5.5$$
$$2r + 2.5 = 5.5$$
$$2r = 3$$
$$r = 1.5$$

The cost of regular jelly beans (*r*) is $1.50 per pound and the cost of gourmet jelly beans (*g*) is $2.50 per pound.

8. Sketch the graph of an inequality in two variables (Section 4.4).

   For example: Sketch the graph of $x - 3y \leq 6$.

   We first sketch the graph of $x - 3y = 6$, whose intercepts are (6, 0) and (0, −2), using a solid line. Now we use (0, 0) as a test point:

$$x - 3y \leq 6$$
$$0 - 3(0) \overset{?}{\leq} 6$$
$$0 - 0 \overset{?}{\leq} 6$$
$$0 \overset{\checkmark}{\leq} 6$$

Since (0, 0) satisfies the inequality, we shade the region containing (0, 0), as indicated in the figure.

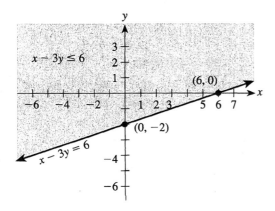

9. Use two-variable linear inequalities and their graphs to represent and visualize real-life situations (Section 4.4).

   For example: A furniture manufacturer has a warehouse with 8,400 sq ft of storage space, which will be used to store recliners and couches. Each recliner requires 15 sq ft of space and each couch requires 32 sq ft. Write an inequality describing the number of recliners and couches that can be stored in this area and sketch the graph of this inequality.

   Solution: If we let *r* be the number of recliners, then since each recliner requires 15 sq ft of space, all the recliners will require 15*r* sq ft of space. Similarly, if we let *c* be the number of couches, then the number of square feet required for all the couches is 32*c*. Since the total storage space available is 8,400 sq ft, we have the inequality

$$15r + 32c \leq 8,400$$

Using the outline for graphing a linear inequality, we obtain the graph in Figure 4.49. Since it makes no sense for either r or c to be negative, we have shaded only the region in the first quadrant.

Figure 4.49
The graph of
$15r + 32c \leq 8,400$

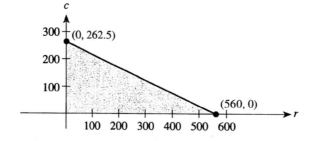

The points (300, 100) and (100, 200) are in the shaded region, which means that, for example, 300 recliners and 100 couches, or 100 recliners and 200 couches could be stored. These are examples of feasible points. It is also important to note that although a point such as (50.3, 71.5) is in this region, it is not a feasible point for this problem, because it is impossible to have a fraction of a couch or recliner.

CHAPTER 4   REVIEW EXERCISES

In Exercises 1–18, find the slope of the line satisfying the given condition(s).

1. Passing through the points $(-1, 0)$ and $(3, -2)$

2. Passing through the points $(6, -3)$ and $(-4, 3)$

3. Its equation is $y = 3x - 5$.

4. Its equation is $3y = 2x + 1$.

5. Its equation is $4y - 3x = 1$.

6. Its equation is $x = 3y - 5$.

7. Parallel to the line passing through the points $(3, 5)$ and $(1, 4)$

8. Parallel to the line passing through the points $(2, 4)$ and $(5, 0)$

9. Perpendicular to the line passing through the points $(4, 7)$ and $(4, 9)$

10. Perpendicular to the line passing through the points $(3, 5)$ and $(1, 4)$

11. Passing through the points $(-7, 6)$ and $(2, 6)$

12. Passing through the points $(3, 5)$ and $(3, -2)$

13. Parallel to the line whose equation is $y = 3x - 7$

14. Perpendicular to the line whose equation is $y = 5x + 1$

15. Perpendicular to the line whose equation is $3y - 5x + 6 = 0$

16. Parallel to the line whose equation is $6x - 4y - 9 = 0$

17. Parallel to the line whose equation is $x = 3$

18. Perpendicular to the line whose equation is $x = 4$

*In Exercises 19–22, find the value(s) of **a** that satisfy the given conditions.*

19. The line through the points $(4, a)$ and $(1, 2)$ has slope 4.

20. The line through the points $(a, 3)$ and $(2, 5)$ has slope 1.

21. The line through the points $(-3, a)$ and $(0, 3)$ is parallel to the line through the points $(7, a)$ and $(0, 0)$.

22. The line through the points $(2, a)$ and $(0, 5)$ is perpendicular to the line through the points $(0, -1)$ and $(a, 4)$.

In Exercises 23–44, write an equation of the line satisfying the given conditions.

23. The line passes through the points $(-2, 3)$ and $(1, -4)$.

24. The line passes through the points $(-1, -4)$ and $(0, -2)$.

25. The line passes through the points $(3, 5)$ and $(-3, -5)$.

26. The line passes through the points $(2, -6)$ and $(-2, 6)$.

27. The line passes through the point $(2, 5)$ and has slope $\frac{2}{5}$.

28. The line passes through the point $(0, 4)$ and has slope -4.

29. The line passes through the point $(4, 7)$ and has slope 5.

30. The line passes through the point $(3, 8)$ and has slope $-\frac{3}{4}$.

31. The line has slope 5 and y-intercept 3.

32. The line has slope -3 and y-intercept -4.

33. The horizontal line passes through the point $(2, 3)$.

34. The horizontal line passes through the point $(-3, -4)$.

35. The line passes through the point $(0, 0)$ and is parallel to the line $y = \frac{3}{2}x - 1$.

36. The line passes through the point $(-3, 0)$ and is perpendicular to the line $y = -5x + \frac{3}{7}$.

37. The line is perpendicular to $2y - 5x = 1$ and passes through the point $(0, 6)$.

38. The line is parallel to $6x - 7y + 3 = 0$ and passes through the point $(5, 5)$.

39. The line is perpendicular to $3x = -5y$ and passes through the point $(0, 0)$.

40. The line is parallel to $3x = -5y$ and passes through the point $(0, 0)$.

41. The line crosses the x-axis at $x = 3$ and the y-axis at $y = -5$.

42. The line has x-intercept 5 and y-intercept 8.

43. The line is parallel to $3x - 2y = 5$ and has the same y-intercept as $5y = x + 3$.

44. The line is parallel to $2x + 5y = 4$ and has the same y-intercept as $2y = x - 4$.

45. A manufacturer found that the relationship between his profit, P, and the number of gadgets produced, x, is linear. If he makes \$12,000 by producing 250 gadgets and \$20,000 by producing 300 gadgets, write an equation relating P to x and predict how much he would make if he produced 400 gadgets.

46. A psychologist found that the relationship between scores on two tests, test A and test B, was perfectly linear. Joe scored 32 on test A and 70 on test B; Sue scored 45 on test A and 96 on test B. If Jake scored 40 on test A, what would he score on test B? If Charles scored 80 on test B, what would he score on test A?

47. The figure below shows the graph of the number of physicians in the United States from 1980 to 1997, P, in thousands, for each year t. The horizontal axis represents t and the vertical axis represents P. For the time range given in the figure, the actual data points are plotted. These data points can be approximated by the given line.

    (a) Find an equation of the line.

    (b) Use the equation found in part (a) to predict P in 1999.

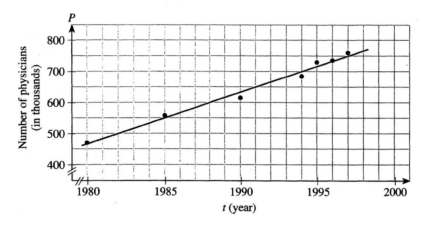

48. The figure below shows the graph of the number of dentists in the United States from 1980 to 1996, D, in thousands, for each year t. The horizontal axis represents t and the vertical axis represents D. For the time range given in the figure, the actual data points are plotted. These data points can be approximated by the given line.

    (a) Find an equation of the line.

    (b) Use the equation found in part (a) above to predict D in 1999.

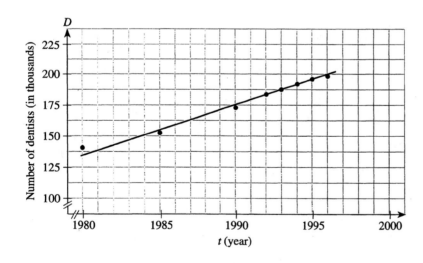

In Exercises 49–56, solve the systems of equations.

49. $\begin{cases} x - y = 4 \\ 2x - 3y = 7 \end{cases}$

50. $\begin{cases} 4x + 5y = 2 \\ 7x + 6y = 9 \end{cases}$

51. $\begin{cases} \dfrac{x}{6} - \dfrac{y}{4} = \dfrac{4}{3} \\ \dfrac{x}{5} - \dfrac{y}{2} = \dfrac{8}{5} \end{cases}$

52. $\begin{cases} \dfrac{2x}{3} + \dfrac{3y}{4} = \dfrac{7}{12} \\ \dfrac{6x}{5} - \dfrac{3y}{2} = \dfrac{1}{10} \end{cases}$

53. $\begin{cases} 3x - \dfrac{y}{4} = 2 \\ 6x - \dfrac{y}{2} = 4 \end{cases}$

54. $\begin{cases} \dfrac{x}{6} + y = 1 \\ \dfrac{x}{3} + 2y = 4 \end{cases}$

55. $\begin{cases} x = 2y - 3 \\ y = 3x + 2 \end{cases}$

56. $\begin{cases} 2s - 5t = 6 \\ 4t + 3s = 8 \end{cases}$

57. A total of $8,500 is split into two investments. Part is invested in a certificate of deposit paying 4.75% per year and the rest is invested in a bond paying 6.65% per year. If the annual interest from the two investments is $512.05, how much is invested at each rate?

58. Tom goes into a bakery and orders 3 pounds of bread and 5 pounds of cookies for a total of $22.02. Sarah buys 2 pounds of bread and 3 pounds of cookies in the same bakery for a total of $13.43. What are the prices per pound for bread and for cookies?

In Exercises 59–68, graph the inequality on a rectangular coordinate system.

59. $y - 2x < 4$ 60. $y + 2x < 4$

61. $2y - 3x > 6$ 62. $2y + 3x < 12$

63. $5y - 8x \leq 20$ 64. $2y - 7x \geq 14$

65. $\frac{x}{2} + \frac{y}{3} \geq 6$ 66. $\frac{x}{5} - \frac{y}{3} < 15$

67. $y < 5$ 68. $x \leq -1$

69. The perimeter of a rectangle of length x and width y must exceed 100 feet. Write an inequality that represents this situation and sketch the graph of the solution set. List three feasible points in the solution set.

70. You are shopping at a discount clothes outlet where all ties are priced at $9 and all belts are priced at $6. Suppose you buy t ties and b belts. Write an inequality that represents the number of ties and belts you can purchase on a maximum budget of $72. Sketch the graph of this inequality and list three feasible points in the solution set.

CHAPTER 4   PRACTICE TEST

1. Sketch the graph of each of the following equations in a rectangular coordinate system. Be sure to label the intercepts.
   (a) $4x + 3y - 24 = 0$ (b) $2x = 8$
   (c) $y = \frac{1}{2}x - 6$

2. Find the slope of the line satisfying the given conditions:
   (a) Passing through $(3, 9)$ and $(-2, 4)$ (b) Equation is $3x - 2y = 8$

3. Find the value of a if a line with slope 2 passes through the points $(a, 2)$ and $(2, 5)$.

4. Write the equation of the line satisfying the given conditions.
   (a) The line passes through points $(2, -3)$ and $(3, 5)$.
   (b) The line passes through $(1, 0)$ with slope -4.
   (c) The line passes through $(2, 5)$ with y-intercept 3.
   (d) The line passes through $(2, -3)$ and is parallel to $x + 3y = 8$.
   (e) The line passes through $(2, -3)$ and is perpendicular to $x + 3y = 8$.
   (f) The horizontal line passes through $(3, -1)$.

5. A psychologist finds that the relationship between scores on two tests, test A and test B, is perfectly linear. A person scoring 60 on test A scores 90 on test B; someone scoring 80 on test A scores 150 on test B. What should a person receive on test B if he or she scores 85 on test A?

6. Find an equation of the line given in the figure below.

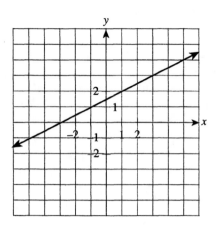

7. Solve the following systems of simultaneous equations:

(a) $\begin{cases} 2x + 3y = 1 \\ 3x + 4y = 4 \end{cases}$

(b) $\begin{cases} \dfrac{a}{3} + \dfrac{b}{2} = 2 \\ \\ a = \dfrac{b}{3} - 5 \end{cases}$

8. Jerry invested $3,500 in two savings certificates. One yields $8\frac{1}{2}\%$ annual interest and the other yields 9% annual interest. How much was invested in each certificate if Jerry receives $309 in annual interest?

9. Graph the inequality $3x - 8y > 12$.

10. A personnel department is going to hire clerks and salespeople. Clerks receive a salary of $315 per week, whereas salespeople receive a salary of $425 per week. The department will hire c clerks and s salespeople but must not exceed a total weekly salary of $7,200. Write an inequality representing this situation and list three feasible points in the solution set.

In Chapter 1, we discussed the real number system and demonstrated how the properties of the real numbers can be used to simplify various algebraic expressions. Most of the algebraic expressions we dealt with were of a particular type: They were polynomial expressions.

In this chapter we will take a closer look at polynomial functions and operations on polynomial expressions.

5.1 Polynomial Functions as Mathematical Models

Let's begin by introducing some basic terminology.

DEFINITION	A *monomial* is an algebraic expression that is either a constant or a product of constants and one or more variables with whole-number exponents.

The following are examples of monomials:

$$3x^2y \quad \text{(or } 3xxy\text{)} \qquad 5xy^4 \quad \text{(or } 5xyyyy\text{)} \qquad \frac{x}{4} \quad \left(\text{or } \frac{1}{4}x\right) \qquad 7$$

Note that each is a product of constants and/or variables. On the other hand,

$$3x + 2y \qquad 5x^{1/2} \qquad \frac{3}{x} \qquad x - 4$$

cannot be represented as products of constants and/or variables with whole-number exponents, and are therefore *not* monomials.

DEFINITION	A *polynomial* is a finite sum of monomials.

We may name polynomials by the number of monomials or terms making up the polynomial: A *binomial* is a polynomial consisting of two terms and a *trinomial* is a polynomial consisting of three terms.

Besides the number of terms, we can also classify a polynomial by its *degree*. Before defining the degree of a polynomial, however, we first define the degree of a monomial.

DEFINITION	The *degree of a monomial* is the sum of the exponents of its variables. The degree of a nonzero constant is zero. The degree of the *number* 0 is undefined.

For example:

$3x^4$ has degree 4 since the exponent of its variable is 4.

$5x^3y^6$ has degree 9 since the sum of the exponents of the variables is 9.

$-3x^2y^3z$ has degree 6 since $2 + 3 + 1 = 6$ (remember $z = z^1$).

4 has degree 0 (as we will see in Chapter 7, we can write 4 as $4x^0$).

Now we can define the degree of a polynomial:

DEFINITION	The *degree of a polynomial* is the highest degree of any monomial in it.

EXAMPLE 1

Identify the degree of each of the following:

(a) $3x^5 + 2x^3 + 6$ (b) $7x^2y^4 - 3x^7y^5z^2$ (c) $2^5x^3y^4$ (d) -7

Solution

(a) $\underbrace{3x^5}_{\text{Degree 5}}$ $+$ $\underbrace{2x^3}_{\text{Degree 3}}$ $+$ $\underbrace{6}_{\text{Degree 0}}$

$3x^5 + 2x^3 + 6$ has $\boxed{\text{degree 5}}$ since the highest monomial degree is 5.

(b) $\underbrace{7x^2y^4}_{\text{Degree 6}}$ $-$ $\underbrace{3x^7y^5z^2}_{\text{Degree 14}}$

$7x^2y^4 - 3x^7y^5z^2$ has $\boxed{\text{degree 14}}$ since the highest degree of any monomial in it is 14.

(c) According to the definition of degree, we add the exponents of the *variables*; thus, we ignore the exponent of the constant 2. Hence $2^5x^3y^4$ has $\boxed{\text{degree 7}}$.

(d) -7 is a constant. We can rewrite it as $-7x^0$. Therefore, it has $\boxed{\text{degree 0}}$. ∎

When the number 0 is considered as a polynomial, we call it the **zero polynomial.** Since we can write 0 as $0x^4$ or as $0x^{10}$, you can see that we would have difficulty assigning a degree to the zero polynomial. Hence, *the zero polynomial has no degree.* Thus, whereas constants other than 0 have zero degree, 0 has no degree.

A third way to classify polynomials is by the number of variables. For example, $3x^2y^2 - 2xz$ is a fourth-degree binomial in three variables: x, y, and z; similarly, $5x^3 - 2x^2 + 3x$ is a third-degree trinomial in one variable.

We usually write polynomials in descending powers; that is, the highest-degree term is written first, followed by the next-highest-degree term, and so on.

Symbolically, we often see polynomials in one variable defined as follows:

DEFINITION

A *polynomial in one variable* is an expression of the form

$$a_nx^n + a_{n-1}x^{n-1} + a_{n-2}x^{n-2} + \cdots + a_2x^2 + a_1x + a_0, \quad a_n \neq 0$$

where the a_i's are real numbers, x is a variable, and n is a nonnegative integer called the *degree* of the polynomial.

Let's examine this definition, especially the notation, more closely. To begin with, $a_0, a_1, a_2, a_3, \ldots.$ are simply real-number coefficients: a_2 is the coefficient of x^2, a_4 is the coefficient of x^4, a_n is the coefficient of x^n. The subscript numbers are used to conveniently distinguish the constants from one another. We could have used letters of the alphabet instead, but then we would have to stop at 26 since there are only 26 letters in our alphabet.

When a polynomial is written with *descending powers,* it is said to be in *standard form.* The polynomial $5 + 3x - 4x^2$ in standard form is $-4x^2 + 3x + 5$. In this form, by the definition above, n would be 2, $a_2 = -4$, $a_1 = 3$, and $a_0 = 5$. Note how the subscripts of a conveniently match the exponents of x.

When a polynomial is written with descending powers, we can assume that missing powers of the variable have coefficients of 0. For example:

$$3x^5 - 2x + 3 \quad \text{can be rewritten as} \quad 3x^5 + 0x^4 + 0x^3 + 0x^2 - 2x + 3$$

Then, $n = 5$, $a_5 = 3$, $a_4 = 0$, $a_3 = 0$, $a_2 = 0$, $a_1 = -2$, and $a_0 = 3$.

Notice how the meaning of *degree* is worked into the preceding definition of a polynomial in one variable: The highest power of x is n and therefore the degree of the polynomial is n.

A *polynomial function* is a function of the form "$f(x)$ = a polynomial." Numerous real-life situations can be described using polynomial functions, as the next few examples illustrate.

EXAMPLE 2

Suppose that a particular company knows that if the price of an item is x dollars, then it can sell $80{,}000 - 1{,}000x^2$ items.

(a) Express the revenue, R, as a function of x.

(b) Use the function R to compute the revenue when the price of an item is \$4, \$5, and \$6.

Solution

(a) *Revenue* refers to the amount of money a business takes in. In a manufacturing business, the revenue earned is computed by multiplying the price charged per item by the number of items sold. For example, if an item sells for \$6.35, and 1,200 items were sold, the revenue R will be $R = (6.35)(1{,}200) = \$7{,}620$. Using the given information we have

$$\text{Revenue} = (\text{Price per item}) \cdot (\text{Number of items sold})$$
$$R = x \cdot (80{,}000 - 1{,}000x^2)$$
$$= 80{,}000x - 1{,}000x^3$$

Hence $\boxed{R = R(x) = 80{,}000x - 1{,}000x^3}$. Notice that this function is a third-degree polynomial.

(b) We compute the revenue, $R(x)$ (or R), for various prices of the item x by substituting the values $x = 4$, 5, and 6 in the function $R(x) = 80{,}000x - 1{,}000x^3$. Recall that when we use the functional notation, $R(x)$, rather than stating "find $R(x)$ when $x = 4$," we say "find $R(4)$." Hence, $R(4)$ is the revenue when $x = 4$. Similarly, $R(5)$ and $R(6)$ are the revenues when $x = 5$ and $x = 6$, respectively.

$R(x) = 80{,}000x - 1{,}000x^3$ *We find $R(4)$ by substituting 4 for x in $R(x)$.*

$R(4) = 80{,}000(4) - (1{,}000)4^3 = 256{,}000$ *Next we find $R(5)$.*

$R(5) = 80{,}000(5) - (1{,}000)5^3 = 275{,}000$ *Finally, we find $R(6)$.*

$R(6) = 80{,}000(6) - (1{,}000)6^3 = 264{,}000$

Thus, when the price of an item is \$4, the revenue is \$256,000; when the price is \$5, the revenue is \$275,000; when the price is \$6, the revenue is \$264,000. ∎

EXAMPLE 3

The base of a rectangular box has a length that is 5 cm more than its width, which is w cm; its height is twice its width. Express the volume of the box as a function of w, and use this function to compute the volume when the width of the box is 15 cm, 25 cm, and 48 cm.

Solution

Figure 5.1 depicts the box with width, length, and height as described in the statement of the example.

Figure 5.1
The box described in Example 3

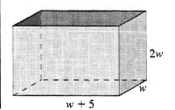

$2w$

w

$w + 5$

If we let V = the volume of the box, then V is found by multiplying its width, length, and height. Thus

$$V = V(w) = w(2w)(w + 5) = 2w^2(w + 5) = 2w^3 + 10w^2$$

which expresses the volume as a third-degree polynomial function of the width, w.

To compute the volume $V = V(w)$ for $w = 15, 25,$ and 48 cm, we substitute these values of w into the function and evaluate V. In the language of functions, we are finding $V(15)$, $V(25)$, and $V(48)$:

$V(w) = 2w^3 + 10w^2$ *We find V(15) by substituting 15 for w in V(w). We can use a calculator to get*

$V(15) = 2(15)^3 + 10(15)^2 = 9{,}000$ *Next we find V(25).*

$V(25) = 2(25)^3 + 10(25)^2 = 37{,}500$ *Finally we find V(48).*

$V(48) = 2(48)^3 + 10(48)^2 = 244{,}224$

We can see that when the width is 15 cm, the volume is 9,000 cm³; when the width is 25 cm, the volume is 37,500 cm³; when the width is 48 cm, the volume is 244,224 cm³. ∎

EXAMPLE 4

If an object is thrown straight up from a height of 10 meters with an initial velocity of 50 meters per second, then its height, h (in meters), above the ground t seconds after the object is thrown is given by the function

$$h = h(t) = 10 + 50t - 4.9t^2$$

(a) Use this function to find the height of the object at 2-second intervals, and describe the motion of the object.

(b) Use the information in part (a) to estimate *when* the object reaches its maximum height, and estimate the maximum height of the object.

(c) Estimate when the object will hit the ground.

Solution

(a) To determine the height of the object at 2-second intervals, we create a table of values:

These repetitive computations should be done with a calculator.

t	$h(t) = 10 + 50t - 4.9t^2$	*Height at t Seconds*
0	$h(0) = 10 + 50(0) - 4.9(0)^2$	$= 10$
2	$h(2) = 10 + 50(2) - 4.9(2)^2$	$= 90.4$
4	$h(4) = 10 + 50(4) - 4.9(4)^2$	$= 131.6$
6	$h(6) = 10 + 50(6) - 4.9(6)^2$	$= 133.6$
8	$h(8) = 10 + 50(8) - 4.9(8)^2$	$= 96.4$
10	$h(10) = 10 + 50(10) - 4.9(10)^2$	$= 20$
12	$h(12) = 10 + 50(12) - 4.9(12)^2$	$= -95.6$

Examining the table, we can see that when $t = 2$ (meaning that 2 seconds have elapsed since the object was thrown), $h(t) = 90.4$ (meaning that the object is 90.4 meters above the ground). We can see by the table of values that at the initial time ($t = 0$), the height of the object is 10 meters. The height continues to grow until "around" the 6th second ($t = 6$), where the highest value of $h(t)$ *in the table* is 133.6 (the object is 133.6 meters above the ground), and then $h(t)$ gets smaller.

If we were to add additional data points within the 2-second intervals, we would find that the height of the object seems to increase until it reaches a maximum, and then decreases. If we graph the data using t as the independent variable, we can clearly see this trend (see Figure 5.2).

Figure 5.2
The graph of
$h(t) = 10 + 50t - 4.9t^2$

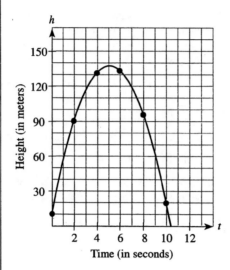

The shape of this graph is called a *parabola*. The graph of a second-degree polynomial function such as $h(t)$ will have the shape of a parabola. We will discuss this in more detail in Chapter 8.

Try to estimate the answers to parts **(b)** *and* **(c)** *using the graph. Do your answers agree?*

(b) Based on the analysis in part **(a)**, we know that the maximum height, or the highest value of $h(t)$, occurs somewhere near $t = 6$ seconds. But does this occur between 4 and 6 seconds or between 6 and 8 seconds? We check the value of $h(t)$ for $t = 5$ to get

$$h(5) = 10 + 50(5) - 4.9(5)^2 = 137.5$$

which is the largest value yet. Hence, the maximum value must lie near $t = 5$. We could improve the estimate by checking the values $h(4.5)$ and $h(5.5)$, but $t = 5$ is a good enough estimate for our purposes. Hence, the maximum height occurs at approximately $t = 5$ seconds. The maximum height at that time is approximately 138 meters.

Recall that $h(10) = 20$ means when $t = 10$, $h(t) = 20$.

(c) We note from the table that $h(10) = 20$, and $h(12) = -95.6$. This tells us that after 10 seconds ($t = 10$), the object was 20 meters *above* the ground [$h(t) = 20$], whereas after 12 seconds ($t = 12$), the object would be 95.6 meters *below* the ground [$h(t) = -95.6$]. Now since the object cannot travel below ground, this must be interpreted to mean that sometime between 10 and 12 seconds, the object hits the ground.

We are trying to find the value of t when $h(t) = 0$.

We check the value of $h(t)$ for $t = 11$ to get

$$h(11) = 10 + 50(11) - 4.9(11)^2 = -32.9$$

We can now narrow down the time of impact to be between 10 and 11 seconds. If we want to improve our estimate, we can compute $h(10.5)$, the height from the ground when $t = 10.5$:

$$h(10.5) = 10 + 50(10.5) - 4.9(10.5)^2 = -5.225$$

We can continue to examine values between 10 and 10.5 to improve the estimate even more, but for now we see that it takes between 10 and 10.5 seconds for the object to hit the ground. ∎

The remainder of this chapter focuses on the various algebraic operations that can be performed with polynomial expressions and functions.

EXERCISES 5.1

In Exercises 1–12, determine whether the expression is polynomial or not. If it is a polynomial, determine

(a) *The number of terms (monomial, binomial, trinomial, etc.)*

(b) *The degree of the polynomial*

(c) *The number of variables*

(d) *The coefficient of each term*

1. $5x^2 + 4$

2. $7x^3 - 6xy^4 + 10$

3. 59

4. $-5x$

5. $-25x^{1/3} + 9x^4$

6. $-x^4 + 2x^3 - 6x + 1$

7. $-4xy^3z^7$

8. $3x^5y^7 - 6xyz^3 + x^2 - 4t$

9. $\dfrac{3}{x^2}$

10. $\dfrac{-8b^2}{2b^3 - 5b + 1}$

11. $4 - x - 2x^3 + x^2$

12. 0

13. The following table gives the per capita poultry consumption (in pounds per year) in the United States from 1970 to 1995.

Year	1970	1975	1980	1985	1990	1995
Number	33.8	32.9	40.8	45.5	56.3	62.9

Based on these data, a statistician suggests that the following formula can be used to approximate the value of the per capita poultry consumption (in pounds per year) P, for year t given in the table, where $t = 0$ represents 1970, $t = 1$ represents 1971, $t = 2$ represents 1972, etc.:

$$P = P(t) = 0.035t^2 + 0.38t + 32.6$$

Use this function to compute the per capita poultry values for each year given in the table. How well does the proposed equation agree with the observed data?

14. The median income of all families (in 1997 dollars) in the United States from 1990 to 1997 can be estimated by the equation

$$M = 0.163t^2 + 0.17t + 35.43$$

where M is the median income (in thousands of dollars) during year t, where $t = 0$ represents 1990, $t = 1$ represents 1991, $t = 2$ represents 1992, etc.

(a) Use this equation to estimate the median income for 1990, 1992, 1994, and 1996.

(b) Use the information obtained in part (a) to estimate during what year the median income reached $40,000.

15. A candy manufacturer finds that when he charges d dollars per pound, he can sell $4{,}300 - 10d^2$ pounds of candy per week.

(a) Express the revenue, R, as a function of d.

(b) Use the function R to compute the revenue when he charges $8, $10, $12, and $14 per pound.

16. An electronics distributor finds that when she charges x dollars per unit, she can sell $1{,}080 - 10x^2$ units.

    (a) Express the revenue, R, as a function of x.

    (b) Use the function R to compute the revenue when she charges \$4, \$5, and \$7 per unit.

17. A hardware manufacturer can sell n items at a price of $2 + 0.45n - 0.001n^2$ dollars per item.

    (a) Express the revenue, R, as a function of n.

    (b) Use the function R to compute the revenue *and price* when 100, 200, and 300 items are sold.

18. A cellular phone company can lease n phones per month at a price (in dollars) of $24 + 0.58n - 0.003n^2$ per phone per month.

    (a) Express the revenue, R, as a function of n.

    (b) Use the function R to compute the revenue *and price* when 50, 100, and 150 phones are leased per month.

19. The base of a closed rectangular box has length equal to 3 times its width, which is w inches; its height is 6 inches less than its width. Express the surface area, S, of the box as a function of w, and use this function to compute the surface area when the width of the box is 20 in., 26 in., and 42 in.

20. The base of a rectangular box has length equal to twice its width, which is w cm; its height is 3 cm less than its width. Express the volume, V, of the box as a function of w, and use this function to compute the volume when the width of the box is 12 cm, 18 cm, and 36 cm.

21. A pharmaceutical company finds that the amount A (in milligrams) of a new medication present in the bloodstream m minutes after the medication is taken can be approximated by the function

$$A = A(m) = 0.28m + 0.39m^2 - 0.02m^3$$

    (a) Use this function to approximate the number of milligrams of the medication present in the bloodstream at 5-minute intervals for the first 30 minutes after it is taken.

    (b) Use the information obtained in part (a) to estimate when the amount of medication in the bloodstream is at a maximum.

22. If an object is thrown straight up from ground level with an initial velocity of 45 feet per second, then its height h (in feet) above the ground t seconds after the object is thrown is given by the function

$$h = h(t) = 45t - 16t^2$$

    (a) Use this function to find the height of the object at half-second intervals.

    (b) Use the information obtained in part (a) to estimate (to the nearest half-second) when the object will hit the ground.

◇ MINI-REVIEW

23. Evaluate. $-3 - (-4) + (-5) - (-8)$

24. Evaluate. $-3 - (-2)^2 - (4 - 5)$

25. The length of the first side of a triangle is twice the length of the second side; the third side is 24 inches. If the perimeter of the triangle is 75 inches, find the length of the first and second sides.

26. A carpenter charges $30 per hour for his time and $18 per hour for his assistant's time. On a certain job the assistant works alone for 3 hours, and is then joined by the carpenter so that they complete the job together. If the total bill was $270, how many hours did the carpenter work?

5.2   Polynomials: Sums, Differences, and Products

Adding and Subtracting Polynomials

Addition and subtraction of polynomials is simply a matter of grouping with parentheses (if not supplied in the problem), removing grouping symbols, and combining like terms.

EXAMPLE 1   (a) Add the polynomials $3x^2 - 2x + 5$, $5x^3 - 4$, and $3x + 2$.

(b) Subtract $3x^3 + 5x^2 - 2x - 3$ from $7x - 4$.

Solution   (a) We fill in the grouping symbols to distinguish the given polynomials:

$(3x^2 - 2x + 5) + (5x^3 - 4) + (3x + 2)$ *Remove the grouping symbols.*

$= 3x^2 - 2x + 5 + 5x^3 - 4 + 3x + 2$ *Then combine like terms.*

$= \boxed{5x^3 + 3x^2 + x + 3}$

(b) Subtraction can be tricky. Make sure you understand what is being subtracted:

$(7x - 4) - (3x^3 + 5x^2 - 2x - 3)$ *Note how the polynomials are placed. Remove grouping symbols by distributing -1 (observe the sign of each term).*

$= 7x - 4 - 3x^3 - 5x^2 + 2x + 3$ *Combine like terms.*

$= \boxed{-3x^3 - 5x^2 + 9x - 1}$ ∎

EXAMPLE 2   Perform the given operations and simplify.

(a) $(3x^2 + 2x - 4) + (5x^2 - 3x + 2) - (3x^2 - 2x + 1)$

(b) Subtract the sum of $2x^3 - 3x$ and $5x^2 - x + 4$ from $3x^2 - 2x + 5$.

Solution   (a) $(3x^2 + 2x - 4) + (5x^2 - 3x + 2) - (3x^2 - 2x + 1)$ *Removing grouping symbols.*

$= 3x^2 + 2x - 4 + 5x^2 - 3x + 2 - 3x^2 + 2x - 1$ *Then combine like terms.*

$= \boxed{5x^2 + x - 3}$

(b) We translate the problem as follows:

$(3x^2 - 2x + 5) - [(2x^3 - 3x) + (5x^2 - x + 4)]$ *Remove parentheses in brackets.*

$= (3x^2 - 2x + 5) - [2x^3 - 3x + 5x^2 - x + 4]$ *Then combine terms in brackets.*

$= (3x^2 - 2x + 5) - [2x^3 + 5x^2 - 4x + 4]$ *Remove remaining grouping symbols.*

$= 3x^2 - 2x + 5 - 2x^3 - 5x^2 + 4x - 4$ *We write the answer in standard form.*

$= \boxed{-2x^3 - 2x^2 + 2x + 1}$ ∎

Products of Polynomials

The distributive property gives us a procedure for multiplying polynomials. Recall that the property states that multiplication distributes over addition, that is:

$$a(b + c) = a \cdot b + a \cdot c$$

or

$$(b + c)a = b \cdot a + c \cdot a$$

As we discussed in Chapter 1, the real number properties, along with the first rule of exponents, give us a procedure for multiplying monomials by polynomials.

EXAMPLE 3   Perform the operations for each of the following:

(a) $5a^2b(4ab + 3ab^2)$ (b) $3x^3y^2(2x^2 - 7y^3)$

Solution   (a) $5a^2b(4ab + 3ab^2)$ *Apply the distributive property.*

$= (5a^2b)(4ab) + (5a^2b)(3ab^2)$ *Then use the first rule of exponents.*

$= \boxed{20a^3b^2 + 15a^3b^3}$

(b) $3x^3y^2(2x^2 - 7y^3) = 3x^3y^2(2x^2) - 3x^3y^2(7y^3)$

$= \boxed{6x^5y^2 - 21x^3y^5}$ ■

Our next step is to demonstrate how to multiply two polynomials of more than one term. We can distribute any polynomial in the same way that we distribute a monomial. For example, in multiplying $(2x + 1)(x + 3)$, we distribute $(x + 3)$ as

$$(2x + 1)(x + 3) = 2x(x + 3) + 1(x + 3)$$
$$(B + C) \cdot A \quad = B \cdot A \quad + C \cdot A$$

It is important for you to understand that variables may stand not only for numbers, but also for other variables, expressions, or polynomials as well. Hence, we can let A stand for the binomial $x + 3$ and apply the distributive property above. The problem is still unfinished, for we must now apply the distributive property again and then combine terms:

$(2x + 1)(x + 3)$ *Distribute $x + 3$.*

$= (2x)(x + 3) + 1(x + 3)$ *Apply the distributive property again.*

$= (2x)x + (2x)3 + (1)x + (1)3$

$= 2x^2 + 6x + x + 3$ *Combine like terms.*

$= 2x^2 + 7x + 3$

You may have learned to multiply binomials by some memorized procedure such as *FOIL*, or to multiply polynomials by the vertical method. However, our factoring problems will require that you thoroughly understand the logic underlying polynomial multiplication. For this reason, it is important that you realize that polynomial multiplication is derived from the *distributive property*.

EXAMPLE 4   Multiply the following:

(a) $(3a - 2)(2a + 5)$

(b) $(2y^2 + 3y + 1)(y - 5)$

(c) $(3x - 5)^2$

Solution   (a) $(3a - 2)(2a + 5) = (3a)(2a + 5) - 2(2a + 5)$

$= 6a^2 + 15a - 4a - 10$

$= \boxed{6a^2 + 11a - 10}$

(b) $(2y^2 + 3y + 1)(y - 5) = (2y^2)(y - 5) + 3y(y - 5) + 1(y - 5)$

$$= 2y^3 - 10y^2 + 3y^2 - 15y + y - 5$$

$$= \boxed{2y^3 - 7y^2 - 14y - 5}$$

(c) $(3x - 5)^2 = (3x - 5)(3x - 5)$ *First distribute $3x - 5$.*

$$= 3x(3x - 5) - 5(3x - 5)$$

$$= 9x^2 - 15x - 15x + 25$$

$$= \boxed{9x^2 - 30x + 25}$$ *Note that the answer is **not** $9x^2 - 25$.* ∎

We can find the product of two polynomials by the ***vertical method*** as well; for example, $(x^2 - 3x + 4)(2x^2 - 3)$ can be multiplied as follows:

$$
\begin{array}{r}
x^2 - 3x + 4 \\
2x^2 \qquad - 3 \\
\hline
-3x^2 + 9x - 12 \\
2x^4 - 6x^3 + 8x^2 \qquad\qquad \\
\hline
2x^4 - 6x^3 + 5x^2 + 9x - 12
\end{array}
$$

$\leftarrow (-3)(x^2 - 3x + 4)$

$\leftarrow (2x^2)(x^2 - 3x + 4)$

Like terms lined up in columns

The previous examples illustrate the following general rule for multiplying polynomials.

Rule for Multiplying Polynomials	To multiply two polynomials, multiply each term in the first polynomial by each term in the second polynomial.

As the next example illustrates, polynomial operations can be applied to polynomial functions as well.

EXAMPLE 5

Suppose $f(x) = x - 3$ and $g(x) = x^2 + 3x + 9$. Find:

(a) $g(x) - f(x)$

(b) $f(x) \cdot g(x)$

Solution

(a) $g(x) - f(x) = \underbrace{(x^2 + 3x + 9)}_{g(x)} - \underbrace{(x - 3)}_{f(x)}$ *Note that the parentheses around $g(x)$ are optional, whereas the parentheses around $f(x)$ are essential to ensure that we subtract each term of $f(x)$. We remove the parentheses.*

$$= x^2 + 3x + 9 - x + 3$$ *Now combine like terms.*

$$= \boxed{x^2 + 2x + 12}$$

(b) To multiply the two functions, we follow the rule for multiplication of polynomials given in the box.

$f(x) \cdot g(x) = (x - 3)(x^2 + 3x + 9)$ *Each term in the first set of parentheses multiplies each term in the second.*

$$= x^3 + 3x^2 + 9x - 3x^2 - 9x - 27$$ *Combine like terms.*

$$= x^3 - 27$$ ∎

167

We will have more to say about operations on functions in Chapter 9.

EXAMPLE 6

A circular garden has a radius of 10 ft.

(a) If a brick walkway with a uniform width of x ft is to be built surrounding the garden, express the area of the walkway in terms of x.

(b) Find the area of the walkway if the width of the walkway is 2.5 ft. Round your answer to the nearest tenth.

Solution

(a) We draw a diagram of the circular garden and surrounding brick walkway, labeling the radius of the garden, 10 ft, and the width of the walkway, x ft, as shown in Figure 5.3.

Figure 5.3

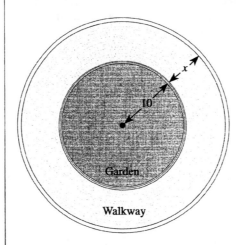

To find the area of the brick walkway, we have to find the area of the inner and outer circles, and then subtract the area of the inner circle from the area of the outer circle. Since the area of a circle is πr^2, where r is the radius of the circle, we need to find the radius of each circle.

The radius of the inner circle is given as 10 ft and, as we can see by the figure, the radius of the outer circle must be $(10 + x)$ ft. Thus,

$$\text{Area}_{\text{walkway}} = \text{Area}_{\text{outer circle}} - \text{Area}_{\text{inner circle}}$$

Where R is the radius of the outer circle and r is the radius of the inner circle

$$= \pi R^2 \qquad\qquad - \pi r^2$$

$$= \pi(10 + x)^2 - \pi(10)^2$$

Now we perform the operations.

$$= \pi(10 + x)(10 + x) - \pi(10)^2$$
$$= \pi(100 + 20x + x^2) - 100\pi$$
$$= 100\pi + 20\pi x + \pi x^2 - 100\pi \qquad \textit{Simplify.}$$
$$= (\pi x^2 + 20\pi x) \text{ sq ft}$$

(b) In part **(a)** of this example, we found that the area, A, of the walkway is given by $A = \pi x^2 + 20\pi x$ sq ft, where x is the width of the walkway. We are given that $x = 2.5$ ft. Thus

$$A = \pi x^2 + 20\pi x \qquad \textit{Substitute } x = 2.5.$$

$$= \pi(2.5)^2 + 20\pi(2.5) \qquad \textit{We use the } \pi \textit{ key on a calculator to get}$$

$$\approx 176.7 \text{ sq ft}$$

Note that if you approximate π using 3.14, you will get the answer 176.6 sq ft.

EXERCISES 5.2

In Exercises 1–54, perform the indicated operations.

1. $(3x^2 - 2x + 5) + (2x^2 - 7x + 4)$

2. $(7xy^2 - 3x^2y) - (4xy^2 - 3x)$

3. $(15x^2 - 3xy - 4y^2) - (16x^2 - 3x + 2)$

4. $(2x^2 - 3x) - (-4x + 5) - (3x^2 - 2x + 1)$

5. $(3a^2 - 2ab + 4b^2) + [(3a^2 - b^2) - (3ab)]$

6. $[(5s^2 - 3) - (2st - 4t^2)] - 7s^2 - 3st + 2t^2$

7. $(3a^2 - 2ab + 4b^2) - [(3a^2 - b^2) - (3ab)]$

8. $7s^2 - 3st + 2t^2 - [(5s^2 - 3) - (2st - 4t^2)]$

9. $[(3a^2 - b^2) - (3ab)] - (3a^2 - 2ab + 4b^2)$

10. Subtract $5y^2 - 3y + 2$ from $y - 1$.

11. Add $3xy + 2y^2$ to $-7y^2 - 3y + 4$.

12. Subtract $y - 1$ from $5y^2 - 3y + 2$.

13. Subtract $3x^2 - 2xy + 7y^2$ from $-8x^2 - 5xy + 9y^2$.

14. Find the sum of $3a^2 - 6ab + 16b^2$, $3ab - 6b^2$, and $-5a^2 - 3ab$.

15. Subtract the sum of $2a^2 - 3ab + 4b^2$ and $6a^2 + 2ab - 2b^2$ from $3a^2 - 2b^2$.

16. Subtract the sum of $3x + 2y$ and $3y - 2x$ from the sum of $x - y$ and $x + y$.

17. $x^2y(3x^2 - 2xy + 2y^2)$

18. $-3a^2b^2(4a^2b - 3ab + 2a)$

19. $(3x^2 - 2xy + 2y^2)(x^2y)$

20. $-13a^3b^2(5a^2b - 3a^2 + 2)$

21. $(x + 3)(x + 4)$

22. $(y - 4)(y - 8)$

23. $(3x - 1)(2x + 1)$

24. $(2x - 3)(3x + 5)$

25. $(3x + 1)(2x - 1)$

26. $(2x + 3)(3x - 5)$

27. $(3a - b)(a + b)$

28. $(2a - 5b)(a + 2b)$

29. $(2r - s)^2$

30. $(3b - 2)^2$

31. $(2r + s)(2r - s)$

32. $(3b - 2)(3b + 2)$

33. $(3x - 2y)(3x + 2y)$

34. $(2x^2 + y)(2x^2 - y)$

35. $(3x - 2y)^2$

36. $(2x^2 - y)^2$

37. $(x - y)(a - b)$

38. $(a + b)(x + y)$

39. $(2r + 3s)(2a + 3b)$

40. $(4x^2 - 5y)(5x - 3y^2)$

41. $(2y^2 - 3)(y^2 + 1)$

42. $(3a^2 - x^3)(3a^2 + x^3)$

43. $(5x^2 - 3x + 4)(x + 3)$

44. $(5x^2 - 3x + 4)(x - 3)$

45. $(9a^2 + 3a - 5)(3a + 1)$

46. $(7x^2 + 4x - 7)(5x - 2)$

47. $(a^2 - ab + b^2)(a + b)$

48. $(a^2 + ab + b^2)(a - b)$

49. $(x - y - z)^2$

50. $(x + y + z)^2$

51. $(x^2 - 2x + 4)(x + 2)$

52. $(x^2 + 2x + 4)(x - 2)$

53. $(a + b + c + d)(a + b)$

54. $(x^3 + x^2 + x + 1)(x - 1)$

55. The length of a rectangle is 5 more than 3 times its width. If the width of the rectangle is w, express the area and perimeter of the rectangle in terms of w.

56. The length of a rectangle is 1 less than twice its width. If the width of the rectangle is w, express the area and perimeter of the rectangle in terms of w.

57. A circular garden has a radius of 8 ft. If a walkway with a uniform width of x ft is to be built surrounding the garden, express the area of the walkway in terms of x.

58. A circular swimming pool has a radius of 50 ft. If a concrete walkway with a uniform width of x ft surrounds the pool, express the area of the walkway in terms of x.

59. A 20 ft by 60 ft rectangular swimming pool is surrounded by a path of uniform width. If the width of the walkway is x ft, express the area of the walkway in terms of x.

60. A 30 ft by 30 ft square swimming pool is surrounded by a concrete walkway of uniform width. If the width of the walkway is x ft, express the total area of the pool and walkway in terms of x.

In Exercises 61–74, given $f(x) = 2x - 3$, $g(x) = 3x^2 - 5x + 2$, and $h(x) = x^3 - x$, find and simplify.

61. $f(x) - g(x)$

62. $g(x) - f(x)$

63. $h(x) - [f(x) - g(x)]$

64. $f(x) - [g(x) - h(x)]$

65. $f(x) \cdot g(x)$

66. $g(x) \cdot h(x)$

67. $h(x)[f(x) + g(x)]$

68. $f(x)[h(x) - g(x)]$

69. $g(x) + g(2)$

70. $g(x) + 2$

71. $g(x + 2)$

72. $h(x - 1)$

73. $h(x) - 1$

74. $h(x) - h(1)$

 QUESTIONS FOR THOUGHT

75. The rule for multiplying polynomials that was stated in this section is based on the fundamental properties of the real numbers. Supply the real-number property that justifies each of the following steps.

$$
\begin{aligned}
(x + y)(3x - 2y) &= (x + y)(3x) + (x + y)(-2y) \\
&= x(3x) + y(3x) + x(-2y) + y(-2y) \\
&= (3x)x + (3x)y + (-2y)x + (-2y)y \\
&= 3(xx) + 3(xy) - 2(yx) - 2(yy) \\
&= 3x^2 + 3xy - 2yx - 2y^2 \\
&= 3x^2 + 3xy - 2xy - 2y^2 \\
&= 3x^2 + (3 - 2)xy - 2y^2 \\
&= 3x^2 + xy - 2y^2
\end{aligned}
$$

76. Discuss what is ***wrong*** (if anything) with the following:

(a) $(3x^2)(2x^3) \overset{?}{=} 6x^6$

(b) $2x - \{3x - 2[4 - x]\} \overset{?}{=} 2x - \{3x - 8 + 2x\}$
$\overset{?}{=} 2x - \{5x - 8\}$
$\overset{?}{=} -10x^2 + 16x$

 MINI-REVIEW

77. *Evaluate.* $\dfrac{-4 - [4 - 5(2 - 8)]}{4 - 5 \cdot 2 - 8}$

78. A truck carries a load of 60 packages. Some are 25-lb packages and the rest are 30-lb packages. If the total weight of all the packages is 1,680 lb, how many packages of each kind are in the truck?

79. *Solve for x.* $|3 - 2x| \leq 5$

80. *Solve for a.* $3a - 8 = 5a - (4 + 2a)$

5.3 General Forms and Special Products

We can now develop some procedures for multiplying polynomials quickly as long as we keep in mind *why* the process works. Our emphasis will be on quick procedures for *binomial* multiplication since such products occur frequently in algebra. Later on in this section, we will generalize the procedures to more complex cases.

General Forms

If we multiplied $(x + a)(x + b)$, we would get the following:

$$(x + a)(x + b) \qquad \text{\textit{Distribute } x + b.}$$
$$= x(x + b) + a(x + b) \qquad \text{\textit{Distribute } x \text{ and } a.}$$
$$= x^2 + bx + ax + ab \qquad \text{\textit{Factor } x \text{ from the middle terms.}}$$
$$= x^2 + (a + b)x + ab$$

Thus, we have:

General Form 1	$(x + a)(x + b) = x^2 + (a + b)x + ab$

Verbally stated, when two binomials of the form (Variable + Constant) are multiplied, the product will be a trinomial, where the coefficient of the first-degree term will be the *sum* of the binomial constants and the numerical term will be the *product* of the binomial constants. Knowing this form allows us to quickly multiply binomials of this type mentally.

EXAMPLE 1   (a) $(x + 3)(x + 5)$ (b) $(y - 7)(y + 4)$ (c) $(a - 6)(a - 5)$

Solution $(x + a)(x + b) = x^2 + (a + b)x + ab$

(a) $(x + 3)(x + 5) = x^2 + (3 + 5)x + 3 \cdot 5$
$$= \boxed{x^2 + 8x + 15}$$

(b) $(y - 7)(y + 4) = y^2 + (-7 + 4)y + (-7)(4)$
$$= \boxed{y^2 - 3y - 28}$$

(c) $(a - 6)(a - 5) = a^2 + (-6 - 5)a + (-6)(-5)$
$$= \boxed{a^2 - 11a + 30}$$ ∎

If we multiplied out $(ax + b)(cx + d)$, we would get:

$$(ax + b)(cx + d) \qquad \text{\textit{Distribute } cx + d.}$$
$$= ax(cx + d) + b(cx + d) \qquad \text{\textit{Distribute } ax \text{ and } b.}$$
$$= acx^2 + adx + bcx + bd \qquad \text{\textit{Factor } x \text{ from the middle terms.}}$$
$$= acx^2 + (ad + bc)x + bd$$

Thus, we have:

General Form 2	$(ax + b)(cx + d) = acx^2 + (ad + bc)x + bd$

171

This form is certainly more complicated than the previous general form. Therefore, rather than trying to memorize this form to perform quick multiplication of binomials, we will present another view of the same procedure for multiplying binomials, called the **FOIL method.**

FOIL stands for

*F*irst, *O*uter, *I*nner, *L*ast

It is a systematic way to keep track of the terms to be multiplied, demonstrated as follows:

$$
(3x + 4)(2x + 5) = (3x)(2x) + (3x)(5) + (4)(2x) + (4)(5)
$$
$$
= 6x^2 + 15x + 8x + 20
$$
$$
= 6x^2 + 23x + 20
$$

Keep in mind that FOIL is only a name to help us to be systematic in carrying out *binomial* multiplication; *each term of one binomial is still being multiplied by each term of the other.*

EXAMPLE 2

Perform the indicated operations.

(a) $(5x - 4)(2x + 1)$

(b) $(3a + 4)(3a - 4)$

(c) $(3x + 1)^2$

Solution

(a) $(5x - 4)(2x + 1) = (5x)(2x) + (5x)(1) - 4(2x) + (-4)(1)$
$$
= 10x^2 + 5x - 8x - 4
$$
$$
= \boxed{10x^2 - 3x - 4}
$$

(b) $(3a + 4)(3a - 4) = (3a)(3a) - (3a)4 + 4(3a) - 4(4)$
$$
= 9a^2 - 12a + 12a - 16
$$
$$
= \boxed{9a^2 - 16}
$$

(c) $(3x + 1)^2 = (3x + 1)(3x + 1)$
$$
= (3x)(3x) + (3x)(1) + 1(3x) + 1(1)
$$
$$
= 9x^2 + 3x + 3x + 1
$$
$$
= \boxed{9x^2 + 6x + 1}
$$
■

You should practice your multiplication skills in the Exercise sets until you can do the multiplications flawlessly in your head.

Special Products

Special products are specific products of binomials that can be derived from the general forms given previously (which, in turn, are derived from the distributive properties).

Special Products	
1. $(a + b)(a - b) = a^2 - b^2$	*Difference of two squares*
2. $(a + b)^2 = a^2 + 2ab + b^2$	*Perfect square of sum*
3. $(a - b)^2 = a^2 - 2ab + b^2$	*Perfect square of difference*

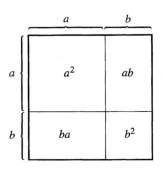

The area of the square with side a + b illustrates the perfect square of a sum:
$(a + b)^2 = a^2 + 2ab + b^2$

Proof:

1. $(a + b)(a - b) = a(a - b) + b(a - b)$
$$= a^2 - ab + ba - b^2$$
$$= a^2 - b^2$$

2. $(a + b)^2 = (a + b)(a + b)$
$$= a(a + b) + b(a + b)$$
$$= a^2 + ab + ba + b^2$$
$$= a^2 + 2ab + b^2$$

Proof of special product 3 is left as an exercise.

Special product 1 is known as the **difference of two squares,** whereas special products 2 and 3 are known as **perfect squares.** Note the differences between the special products, especially between special products 1 and 3, which are often confused with each other.

The expressions $a + b$ and $a - b$ are called **conjugates of each other.** A *conjugate* of a binomial is formed by changing the sign of one of its terms. Special product 1 tells us that the product of conjugates yields the differences of two squares.

Conjugates will be important to us in subsequent chapters, but for now you should understand that $-a - b$ is *not* the conjugate of $a + b$, but rather it is the *negative* of $a + b$, since

$$-(a + b) = -a - b$$

A *conjugate* of $x - 4$ is $x + 4$, but the *negative* of the expression $x - 4$ is $-(x - 4) = -x + 4$, usually written as $4 - x$.

Notice that in the negative of a binomial, the signs of *both* terms are changed, whereas in a conjugate only one sign is changed.

Special products are important in factoring; in many cases, the quickest way to factor an expression is to recognize it as a special product. In addition, recognizing and using special products can reduce the time needed for multiplication.

EXAMPLE 3

Perform the indicated operations.

(a) $(3x + 5)^2$

(b) $(2a - 7b)(2a + 7b)$

(c) $(2a - 7b)^2$

Solution

All these problems can be worked by using the general forms, or more slowly by using the distributive property. The quickest way, however, is to use the special products.

Remember that
$(A + B)^2 \neq A^2 + B^2.$

(a) $(3x + 5)^2$ *This is a perfect square of a sum.*
$$= (3x)^2 + 2(3x)(5) + (5)^2$$
$$= \boxed{9x^2 + 30x + 25}$$

(b) $(2a - 7b)(2a + 7b)$ *This is the difference of two squares.*
$$= (2a)^2 - (7b)^2$$
$$= \boxed{4a^2 - 49b^2}$$

(c) $(2a - 7b)^2$ *This is a perfect square of a difference.*
$$= (2a)^2 - 2(2a)(7b) + (7b)^2$$
$$= \boxed{4a^2 - 28ab + 49b^2} \qquad\qquad ∎$$

Study the differences between parts **(b)** and **(c)** of Example 3; note their similarities. Keep in mind that when you square a binomial, you will get a middle term in the product. Again, practice these so that you can quickly do them mentally.

Multiple Operations

Let's put together what we have learned so far and examine how to simplify expressions requiring multiple operations with polynomials. We follow the same order of operations discussed in Chapter 1 (that is, parentheses, exponents, multiplication and division, addition and subtraction).

EXAMPLE 4

Perform the indicated operations.

(a) $2x - 3x(x - 5)$ (b) $(x - y)^3$

(c) $2x(x - 3)(3x + 1)$ (d) $5x^3 - 2x(x - 4)(2x + 3)$

(e) $(a - b)^2 - (a - b)(a + b)$

Solution

(a) $2x - 3x(x - 5)$ *Multiplication before subtraction: First distribute $-3x$.*

    $= 2x - 3x^2 + 15x$ *Then combine terms.*

    $= \boxed{-3x^2 + 17x}$

(b) $(x - y)^3$ *Rewrite $(x - y)^3$ as a product.*

    $= (x - y)(x - y)(x - y)$ *Then multiply two binomials together.*

    $= (x - y)(x^2 - 2xy + y^2)$ *Multiply the result by the third binomial.*

    $= x^3 - 2x^2y + xy^2 - x^2y + 2xy^2 - y^3$ *Combine like terms.*

    $= \boxed{x^3 - 3x^2y + 3xy^2 - y^3}$

(c) $2x(x - 3)(3x + 1)$ *There is less chance of your making an error if you multiply the binomials first.*

    $= 2x(3x^2 - 8x - 3)$

    $= \boxed{6x^3 - 16x^2 - 6x}$

(d) $5x^3 - 2x(x - 4)(2x + 3)$ *Multiply binomials first.*

    $= 5x^3 - 2x(2x^2 - 5x - 12)$ *Distribute $-2x$.*

    $= 5x^3 - 4x^3 + 10x^2 + 24x$ *Combine like terms.*

    $= \boxed{x^3 + 10x^2 + 24x}$

(e) $(a - b)^2 - (a - b)(a + b)$ *$(a - b)^2$ is a perfect square.*

    $= a^2 - 2ab + b^2 - (a - b)(a + b)$ *$(a + b)(a - b)$ is the difference of two squares.*

    $= a^2 - 2ab + b^2 - (a^2 - b^2)$ *The parentheses around $a^2 - b^2$ are necessary. Next remove parentheses.*

    $= a^2 - 2ab + b^2 - a^2 + b^2$

    $= \boxed{-2ab + 2b^2}$

Note that in part (e), we multiplied $(a + b)(a - b)$ before we subtracted. It is necessary to retain parentheses around $a^2 - b^2$ since we are subtracting the entire expression $(a^2 - b^2)$. ∎

EXAMPLE 5

Given $g(x) = x^2 - 3x + 1$, find each of the following:

(a) $g(a + 2)$ (b) $g(2x)$

Solution

(a) $g(a + 2)$ is the expression we get when we substitute $a + 2$ for x in $g(x)$:

$$g(x) = x^2 - 3x + 1$$
$$g(a + 2) = (a + 2)^2 - 3(a + 2) + 1 \qquad \textit{Then simplify.}$$
$$= a^2 + 4a + 4 - 3a - 6 + 1$$
$$= a^2 + a - 1$$

Thus,

$$\boxed{g(a + 2) = a^2 + a - 1}$$

(b) $g(2x)$ is the expression we get when we substitute $2x$ for x in $g(x)$:

$$g(x) = x^2 - 3x + 1$$
$$g(2x) = (2x)^2 - 3(2x) + 1 \qquad \textit{Simplify.}$$
$$= 4x^2 - 6x + 1$$

Thus,

$$\boxed{g(2x) = 4x^2 - 6x + 1} \qquad\qquad\qquad \blacksquare$$

Applying Special Products

Of course, we can apply the special products to binomials containing more complex monomials, as shown in the next example.

EXAMPLE 6

Perform the operations using special products or general forms.

(a) $(2x^2 - 3y)(2x^2 + 3y)$ 　　　(b) $(3r^3 - 5x^2)^2$

Solution

(a) $(2x^2 - 3y)(2x^2 + 3y) = (2x^2)^2 - (3y)^2 \qquad \textit{Difference of two squares}$

$$= \boxed{4x^4 - 9y^2}$$

(b) $(3r^3 - 5x^2)^2 = (3r^3)^2 - 2(3r^3)(5x^2) + (5x^2)^2 \qquad \textit{Perfect square}$

$$= \boxed{9r^6 - 30r^3x^2 + 25x^4} \qquad\qquad \blacksquare$$

General forms and special products allow us to multiply quickly without going through intermediate steps. They can also be applied to more complex expressions. For example, to multiply

$$[x - (r + s)][x + (r + s)]$$

you could simplify the expressions within the brackets and multiply out using the horizontal or vertical method. On the other hand, if you recognize this problem as a form of special product 1 (the difference of two squares), and apply what you already know about special products, you could reduce your labor for this problem. Again, keep in mind that in equivalent expressions such as special products, the variables can represent polynomials as well as other letters and numbers.

$$(a - \quad b) \quad \cdot (a + \quad b) \quad = a^2 - \quad b^2$$
$$[x - (r + s)] \cdot [x + (r + s)] = x^2 - (r + s)^2$$

We finish the problem by applying special product 2 to $(r + s)^2$:

$$x^2 - (r + s)^2 = x^2 - (r^2 + 2rs + s^2)$$
$$= \boxed{x^2 - r^2 - 2rs - s^2}$$

EXAMPLE 7 Perform the operations using special products. $[x + y + z]^2$

Solution We can view this expression as the square of the sum of two terms, $(x + y)$ and z, and use the special product for the square of a sum:

We are viewing $[x + y + z]^2$ as $[(x + y) + z]^2$. Try regrouping the given expression as $[x + (y + z)]^2$ and verify that you get the same result.

$$(a \quad + b)^2 = \quad a^2 \quad + 2 \cdot a \cdot b + b^2$$
$$[(x + y) + z]^2 = (x + y)^2 + 2(x + y)z + z^2 \qquad \text{\textit{Apply special}}$$
$$= x^2 + 2xy + y^2 + 2z(x + y) + z^2 \qquad \text{\textit{product 2 to}}$$
$$= \boxed{x^2 + 2xy + y^2 + 2xz + 2yz + z^2} \qquad (x + y)^2.$$

The key is to recognize complex expressions as being in special product form.

■

Multiplication in the manner illustrated in Example 7 is much faster than using the horizontal or vertical method. Again, you should practice these problems because we will return to these forms again in the next sections.

EXAMPLE 8 An open cardboard box is to be made from a 20-inch by 30-inch rectangular sheet of cardboard by cutting out identical squares of side x from each of the corners of the sheet and folding up the sides to form a box, as shown in Figure 5.4. Express the volume of the box in terms of x.

Figure 5.4

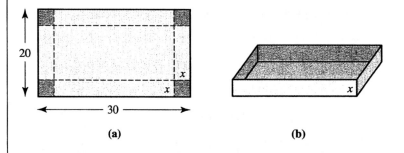

20

← 30 →

(a)   (b)

Solution

THINKING OUT LOUD	
What do we need to find?	An expression for the volume of the box in terms of x
How do we find the volume of the box in the figure?	The formula for the volume of a rectangular box is $V = Length \times Width \times Height$. Hence we need to identify the length, width, and height.
How do we identify the length, width, and height of the box?	First note that the box is constructed by cutting out squares with sides of length x, from the *sheet*, and folding up the sides at the dashed lines. We can therefore see that both the length and width of the *box* are found by subtracting x twice (once from each end) from each dimension. By looking at Figure 5.4(b), we can see that the height of the box is x. See Figure 5.5.

Figure 5.5

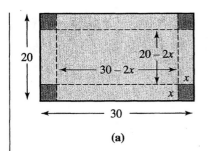

(a)

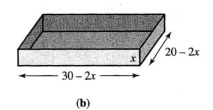

(b)

From Figure 5.5, we see that the length is $30 - 2x$, the width is $20 - 2x$, and the height is x. The volume of the box is therefore

$$V = Length \times Width \times Height$$

$$= (30 - 2x)(20 - 2x)x \qquad \text{We multiply out the right-hand side:}$$
$$\qquad \qquad \qquad \qquad \qquad \text{First multiply out the binomial.}$$

$$= (600 - 100x + 4x^2)x$$

$$V = 600x - 100x^2 + 4x^3$$

Hence the volume (written in standard form) is $V = 4x^3 - 100x^2 + 600x$. ∎

EXERCISES 5.3

Perform the operations and simplify. Use special products wherever possible.

1. $(x + 4)(x + 5)$ **2.** $(a - 2)(a + 4)$ **3.** $(x + 3)(x - 7)$ **4.** $(y - 3)(y - 9)$

5. $(x - 8)(x - 11)$ **6.** $(x - 21)(x + 20)$ **7.** $(x + 5)(x - 6)$ **8.** $(x + 5) + (x - 6)$

9. $x + 5(x - 6)$ **10.** $(x - 7)(x - 4)$ **11.** $(x - 7) - (x - 4)$ **12.** $x - 7(x - 4)$

13. $(2x + 1)(x - 4)$ **14.** $(3a + 2b)(a - b)$ **15.** $(5a - 4)(5a + 4)$ **16.** $(6s - 4)(6s + 4)$

17. $(3z + 5)^2$ **18.** $(7r - 3t)(7r + 3t)$ **19.** $(3z - 5)^2$ **20.** $(7r - 3t)^2$

21. $(3z - 5)(3z + 5)$ **22.** $(7r + 3t)^2$ **23.** $(5r^2 + 3s)(3r + 5s)$ **24.** $(4x^2 - 5)(5x - 4)$

25. $(3s - 2y)^2$ **26.** $(7x - y)(7x - y)$ **27.** $(3y + 10z)^2$ **28.** $(y - 2x)(y + 2x)$

29. $(3y + 10z)(3y - 10z)$ **30.** $(y - 2x)^2$ **31.** $(3a + 2b)(3a + 4b)$ **32.** $(4x - y)(4x + y)$

33. $(8a - 1)^2$ **34.** $(8a - 1)(8a + 1)$ **35.** $(5r - 2s)(5r - 2s)$ **36.** $(2r - 3x)(2r + 7x)$

37. $(7x - 8)(8x - 7)$ **38.** $(5x + 9y)(9x - 5y)$ **39.** $(5t - 3s^2)(5t + 3s)$ **40.** $(2x^2 - 3)(2x + 3)$

41. $(3y^3 - 4x)^2$ **42.** $(2x^2 - 3)^2$ **43.** $(3y^3 - 4x)(3y^3 + 4x)$ **44.** $(7r^2s^2 - 5g)(7r^2s^2 + 5g)$

45. $(2rst - 7xyz)^2$ **46.** $(7r^2 - t^3)^2$ **47.** $(x - 4) - (3x + 1)^2$ **48.** $5x^2 - (2x + 1)(3x + 2)$

49. $(a - b)^2 - (b + a)^2$ **50.** $(3x - 1)(2x + 3) - (x - 4)(x + 1)$

51. $(3a + 2)(-5a)(2a - 1)$ **52.** $(3x - 1)(2x + 3) - x - 4x - 1$

53. $(3a + 2) - 5a(2a - 1)$ **54.** $b^2 - 2b(3b + 2)(2b - 3)$

55. $3r^3 - 3r(r - s)(r + s)$ **56.** $(5r - 2)3r - (5r - 2)(r - 1)$

57. $(3y + 1)(y + 2) - (2y - 3)^2$ **58.** $(x - 2y)^2 - (x - 2y)^2$

59. $(5a - 3b)^3$ **60.** $(x - 3y)^3$

61. $3x(x + 1) - 2x(x + 1)^2$ **62.** $[x - (a + b)][x + (a + b)]$

63. $[(a + b) + 1][(a + b) - 1]$ **64.** $[(x + 2y) - 3z]^2$

65. $[(a - 2b) + 5z]^2$

66. $[(x + 2y) - 3z][(x + 2y) + 3z]$

67. $[a - 2b + 5z][a - 2b - 5z]$

68. $[2(a + b) + 1][3(a + b) - 5]$

69. $[(a + b) + (2x + 1)][(a + b) - (2x + 1)]$

70. $(a - b - 3)(a + b + 3)$

71. $(a^n - 3)(a^n + 3)$

72. $(x^n - y^n)(x^n + y^n)$

In Exercises 73–82, given $f(x) = 3x^2 - 2x + 1$ *and* $g(x) = x^2 - 4$, *find*

73. $f(x + 2)$

74. $g(x - 3)$

75. $f(x) + f(2)$

76. $g(x) - g(3)$

77. $f(2x)$

78. $g(3x)$

79. $2f(x)$

80. $3g(x)$

81. $3f(x) - 2g(x)$

82. $2g(x) + 3f(x)$

83. An open cardboard box is to be made from a 1-foot-square sheet of cardboard by cutting out identical squares of side x from each of the corners of the sheet and folding up the sides to form a box, as shown in Figure 5.4 on page 276. Express the volume of the box in terms of x and simplify.

84. An open cardboard box is to be made from a 12-inch by 8-inch rectangular sheet of cardboard by cutting out identical squares of side x from each of the corners of the sheet and folding up the sides to form a box, as shown in Figure 5.4 on page 276. Express the volume of the box in terms of x and simplify.

In Exercises 85–88, express the shaded area in terms of x.

85.

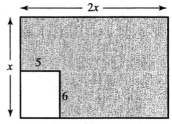

86.

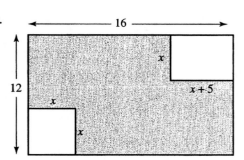

87.

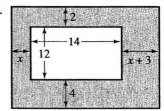

88.

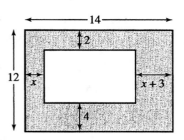

? QUESTIONS FOR THOUGHT

89. *Verbally* describe how to find the product $(x + a)(x + b)$.

90. Discuss what is **wrong** (if anything) with each of the following.

(a) $(x + y)^2 - (x + y)(x - y) \overset{?}{=} x^2 + 2xy + y^2 - x^2 - y^2$

$$\overset{?}{=} 2xy$$

(b) $3x(x - 5)(x + 5) \overset{?}{=} (3x^2 - 15x)(3x^2 + 15x)$

$$\overset{?}{=} 9x^4 - 225x^2$$

91. Discuss the differences between the expression $(x + y)^2$ and the expression $x^2 + y^2$.

92. Describe the relationships among the following expressions:

$$a + b, \quad a - b, \quad b - a, \quad -a + b, \quad -a - b$$

 **MINI-REVIEW**

93. *Solve for x.* $|3x - 2| > 5$.

94. Two cars leave at the same time from the same location and travel in opposite directions. If one car is traveling at 45 mph and the other is traveling at 55 mph, how long will it be until they are 325 miles apart?

95. The length of a rectangle is 4 more than 5 times its width. If the perimeter of the rectangle is 41.6 inches, find the dimensions of the rectangle.

96. Sketch the graphs of the following equations in a rectangular coordinate system.
   (a) $4x - 5y + 20 = 0$ **(b)** $y - 3 = 0$

5.4   Factoring Out the Greatest Common Factor

We can view polynomial multiplication as changing products to sums. In the same way, we can view factoring as changing sums to products. The distributive property gives us the method for multiplying polynomials and it also gives us a method for factoring polynomials:

$$Multiplying \longrightarrow$$
$$(a + b)c = a \cdot c + b \cdot c$$
$$\longleftarrow Factoring$$

Before we begin to factor polynomials, we should mention that in factoring whole numbers, we were interested in a representation as a product of *whole numbers*. Thus, 12 could be factored as $4 \cdot 3$, $6 \cdot 2$, $3 \cdot 2 \cdot 2$, or $12 \cdot 1$. Even though 12 could be represented as a product of $\frac{1}{3}$ and 36, we did not consider factors that are not whole numbers.

In the same way, we will not consider factors of polynomials with fractional or irrational coefficients; *all polynomial factors should have integer coefficients.* Hence, although $x - 1$ can be represented as the product $\frac{1}{4}(4x - 4)$, we will not consider $\frac{1}{4}$ as a factor of $x - 1$ because it is not an integer.

The first type of factoring we will consider is called ***common monomial factoring.*** Essentially, we are interested in factoring out the greatest monomial common to each term in a polynomial.

For example, the greatest common monomial factor of $6x^2 + 8x$ is $2x$ because $2x$ is the greatest common factor of *both* terms $6x^2$ and $8x$. Therefore, we can rewrite $6x^2 + 8x$ as $2x \cdot 3x + 2x \cdot 4$ and then factor out $2x$ by the distributive property to get $2x(3x + 4)$. Thus,

$$6x^2 + 8x = 2x \cdot 3x + 2x \cdot 4 = 2x(3x + 4)$$

Keep in mind that this is a two-step process: First you find the greatest common factor; then you determine what remains within the parentheses.

EXAMPLE 1 | Factor the following as completely as possible.
   (a) $3x^2 + 2x^3 - 4x^5$ **(b)** $24x^2y^3 - 16xy^3 - 8y^4$
   (c) $3x^3y^3 - 9xy^4 + 3$ **(d)** $2a^2b - 8ab^2c + 5c^2$

Solution | In general, it is probably easiest to begin by first determining the greatest common numerical factor, then the greatest common x factor, then the greatest common y factor, and so forth.

(a) $3x^2 + 2x^3 - 4x^5$ *We factor out x^2 from each term since it is the*

$= \boxed{x^2(3 + 2x - 4x^3)}$ *greatest common factor of $3x^2$, $2x^3$, and $4x^5$.*

Always check your answer by multiplying (you can check each term mentally).

Check: $x^2(3 + 2x - 4x^3) = 3x^2 + 2x^3 - 4x^5$

(b) $24x^2y^3 - 16xy^3 - 8y^4$ *The greatest common factor of $24x^2y^3$, $16xy^3$, and $8y^4$ is $8y^3$.*

$= \boxed{8y^3(3x^2 - 2x - y)}$ *Check this answer.*

(c) $3x^3y^3 - 9xy^4 + 3$ *The greatest common factor is 3.*

$= \boxed{3(x^3y^3 - 3xy^4 + 1)}$ *Do not forget to include +1 to hold a place for the 3.*

Check: $3(x^3y^3 - 3xy^4 + 1) = 3x^3y^3 - 9xy^4 + 3$

(d) $2a^2b - 8ab^2c + 5c^2$ *Since there is no common factor of $2a^2b$, $8ab^2c$, and $5c^2$ other than 1, we write:*

$\boxed{\text{not factorable}}$

If we had factored part **(b)** as $4y(6x^2y^2 - 4xy^2 - 2y^3)$, it would check when we multiplied it out. But it is not factored *completely;* we have not factored out the *greatest* common factor. We could still factor $2y^2$ from the trinomial. Thus,

$4y(6x^2y^2 - 4xy^2 - 2y^3)$ *Factor $2y^2$ from $6x^2y^2 - 4xy^2 - 2y^3$.*

$= 4y[2y^2(3x^2 - 2x - y)]$

$= 8y^3(3x^2 - 2x - y)$

Always check that there are no more common factors in the parentheses.   ■

We can generalize common factoring to factoring *polynomials* of more than one term from expressions as follows:

Factor the following: $3x(y - 4) + 2(y - 4)$

Note that $y - 4$ is common to both expressions, $3x(y - 4)$ and $2(y - 4)$, and therefore can be factored out, just as we would factor A from $3xA + 2A$.

$$3x \cdot A + 2 \cdot A = A \cdot (3x + 2)$$
$$3x(y - 4) + 2(y - 4) = (y - 4)(3x + 2)$$

If we read the equation from right to left, we see multiplication by the distributive property.

EXAMPLE 2 | Factor the following completely:

(a) $5a(x - 2y) - 3b(x - 2y)$ (b) $3x(x - 3) + 5(x - 3)$

(c) $(x + 2)^2 + (x + 2)$

Solution | (a) $5a(x - 2y) - 3b(x - 2y)$ *Since $x - 2y$ is common to both terms, $5a(x - 2y)$ and $-3b(x - 2y)$, we can factor $x - 2y$ out, and are left with $5a$ and $-3b$.*

$= \boxed{(x - 2y)(5a - 3b)}$

(b) $3x(x - 3) + 5(x - 3)$ *Factor out $x - 3$ and we are left with $3x$ and $+ 5$.*

$$= \boxed{(x - 3)(3x + 5)}$$

(c) $(x + 2)^2 + (x + 2)$ *$x + 2$ is the factor common to both $(x + 2)^2$ and $x + 2$. This is like factoring $A^2 + A$ to get $A(A + 1)$.*

$$A^2 \quad + \quad A \quad = \quad A \cdot (\quad A \quad + 1)$$
$$(x + 2)^2 + (x + 2) = (x + 2)[(x + 2) + 1] \quad \textit{Simplify inside brackets.}$$
$$= (x + 2)[x + 2 + 1]$$
$$= \boxed{(x + 2)(x + 3)} \quad\blacksquare$$

Not all polynomials are conveniently grouped as in Example 2. We often have to take a step or two to put the polynomial in factorable form. For example, in factoring

$$ax + ay + bx + by$$

you can see that there is no common *monomial* we can factor from *all four terms*. However, if we group the terms by pairs and factor the pairs, we can then factor the *binomial* from each group as follows:

$ax + ay + bx + by$ *Group the pairs together.*

$= ax + ay \quad + \quad bx + by$ *Then factor a from the first pair and b from the second pair.*

$= a(x + y) + b(x + y)$ *Factor $x + y$ from each group.*

$= (x + y)(a + b)$

Grouping and factoring *parts* of a polynomial to factor the polynomial itself is called ***factoring by grouping.***

EXAMPLE 3

Factor the following completely.

(a) $7xy + 2y + 7xa + 2a$

(b) $3xb - 2b + 15x - 10$

Solution

(a) $7xy + 2y + 7xa + 2a$ *Since there is no common factor of all terms, we group in pairs.*

$= 7xy + 2y \quad + \quad 7xa + 2a$ *Factor each pair.*

$= y(7x + 2) + a(7x + 2)$ *Factor $7x + 2$ from each group.*

$= \boxed{(7x + 2)(y + a)}$

(b) $3xb - 2b + 15x - 10$ *There is no common factor, so group each pair.*

$= 3xb - 2b \quad + \quad 15x - 10$ *Factor each pair.*

$= b(3x - 2) + 5(3x - 2)$ *Factor $3x - 2$ from each group.*

$= \boxed{(3x - 2)(b + 5)} \quad\blacksquare$

A word of caution: Factoring parts of a polynomial, as in

$$3xb - 2b + 15x - 10 = b(3x - 2) + 5(3x - 2)$$

is an intermediate step to guide us in factoring by grouping. It is *not* the factored form of the polynomial. (You would not say 13 is factored as $3 \cdot 3 + 2 \cdot 2$, would you?) Thus, keep in mind that when you are asked to factor a polynomial, the whole polynomial must be represented as a *product* of polynomials.

When a negative sign appears between the pairs of binomials we intend to group, we occasionally have to factor out a negative factor first, to see whether each group contains the same binomial factor. In factoring $5ac + 20c - 3a - 12$, for example, we would have to factor out -3 in $-3a - 12$:

$$5ac + 20c - 3a - 12 \qquad \textit{First separate the pairs.}$$
$$= 5ac + 20c \quad - \quad 3a - 12 \qquad \textit{Factor out 5c and } -3.$$

Be careful. Check signs with multiplication.

$$\downarrow \qquad \downarrow$$
$$= 5c(a + 4) - 3(a + 4) \qquad \textit{Factor out } a + 4.$$
$$= \boxed{(a + 4)(5c - 3)}$$

EXAMPLE 4

Factor the following completely.

(a) $10xy - 2y + 5x - 1$ (b) $6x^2 + 2x - 9x - 3$

(c) $x^3 + x^2 + x + 1$ (d) $x^3 + x^2 - x + 1$

Solution

(a) $10xy - 2y + 5x - 1 \qquad \textit{Group each pair.}$

$\quad = 10xy - 2y \ + \ 5x - 1 \qquad \textit{Then factor each pair.}$

$\quad = 2y(5x - 1) + 1(5x - 1)$

$\qquad\qquad\qquad\qquad \uparrow$

Note: It is helpful to hold this place with the understood factor of 1.

$\quad = \boxed{(5x - 1)(2y + 1)}$

Normally we would first combine like terms for this problem, but here we want to illustrate a point.

(b) $6x^2 + 2x - 9x - 3 = 6x^2 + 2x \ - \ 9x - 3 \qquad$ *Factor out 2x from the first pair, -3 from the second pair.*

$\quad = 2x(3x + 1) - 3(3x + 1)$

$\quad = \boxed{(3x + 1)(2x - 3)}$

(c) $x^3 + x^2 + x + 1 = x^3 + x^2 \ + \ x + 1$

$\qquad\qquad\qquad\quad = x^2(x + 1) + 1(x + 1)$

$\qquad\qquad\qquad\quad = \boxed{(x + 1)(x^2 + 1)}$

(d) $x^3 + x^2 - x + 1 = x^2(x + 1) - 1(x - 1) \qquad$ *Note that the binomials $x - 1$ and $x + 1$ are not identical and therefore this expression cannot be factored by grouping.*

Answer: $\boxed{\text{Not factorable}}$

Note the differences between parts **(c)** and **(d).** Even if we tried grouping in part **(d)** without factoring out -1, we would get $x^2(x + 1) + 1(-x + 1)$, which is still not factorable by grouping since $x + 1$ and $-x + 1$ are not identical.

 EXERCISES 5.4

Factor the following completely.

1. $4x^2 + 2x$ 2. $5ab + ab^2$ 3. $x^2 + x$ 4. $3x^3 + 9$

5. $3xy^2 - 6x^2y^3$ 6. $7x^2 - 3xy + 2x$ 7. $6x^4 + 9x^3 - 21x^2$ 8. $12x^2y^3 - 18x^2$

9. $35x^4y^4z - 15x^3y^5z + 10x^2y^3z^2$ 10. $15a^2b - 10ab^2 - 10$

11. $24r^3s^4 - 18r^3s^5 - 6r^2s^3$ 12. $15a^2b - 10ab^2$

13. $35a^2b^3 - 21a^3b^2 + 7ab$

14. $15rs^4t - 15r^2s^3 + 10rs^2$

15. $3x(x + 2) + 5(x + 2)$

16. $7r(2s + 1) + 3(2s + 1)$

17. $3x(x + 2) - 5(x + 2)$

18. $7r(2s + 1) - 3(2s + 1)$

19. $2x(x + 3y) + 5y(x + 3y)$

20. $2s(a - b) + 3(a - b)$

21. $3x(x + 4y) - 5y(x + 4y)$

22. $2x(x - 5) + (x - 5)$

23. $(2r + 1)(a - 2) + 5(a - 2)$

24. $(3a + 4)(x - 1) + 2x(x - 1)$

25. $2x(a - 3)^2 + 2(a - 3)^2$

26. $5y(a - b)^2 - 5(a - b)^2$

27. $16a^2(b - 4)^2 - 4a(b - 4)$

28. $3y(y - 2)^2 + (y - 2)$

29. $2x^2 - 8x + 3x - 12$

30. $5a^2 + 10a + 7a + 14$

31. $3x^2 - 12xy + 5xy - 20y^2$

32. $2a^2 + 2ab + 3ab + 3b^2$

33. $7ax - 7bx + 3ay - 3by$

34. $5ra - 5rb + 3sa - 3sb$

35. $7ax + 7bx - 3ay - 3by$

36. $5ra + 5rb - 3sa - 3sb$

37. $7ax - 7bx - 3ay + 3by$

38. $5ra - 5rb - 3sa - 3sb$

39. $7ax - 7bx - 3ay - 3by$

40. $5ra - 5rb - 3sa + 3sb$

41. $2r^2 + 2rs - sr - s^2$

42. $3x^2 + 6x - 4x - 8$

43. $2r^2 + 2rs - sr + s^2$

44. $3x^2 - 4x + 6x - 8$

45. $5a^2 - 5ab - 2ab + 2b^2$

46. $2x^2 + 10x - x - 5$

47. $3a^2 - 6a - a + 2$

48. $5x^2 + 20x + x + 4$

49. $3a^2 - 6a + a - 2$

50. $5x^2 - 20x + x - 4$

51. $3a^2 + 6a - a - 2$

52. $5x^2 + 20x - x + 4$

53. $a^3 + 2a^2 + 4a + 8$

54. $a^3 - 3a^2 + a - 3$

QUESTIONS FOR THOUGHT

55. Verbally describe what is **wrong** (if anything) with the following:

    (a) $9x^2 + 15x + 3 \overset{?}{=} 3(3x^2 + 5x)$ (b) $(x - 2)^2 + (x - 2) \overset{?}{=} (x - 2)^3$

56. Factoring by grouping illustrates what property?

57. Complete the following expressions so that they can be factored by grouping:

    (a) $5x + 10y + 3x + ?$ (b) $4a - 12y - 5a^2 + ?$

MINI-REVIEW

58. *Solve for a.* $5 - [3 - (a - 2)] = 5a - 2$

59. *Solve for a.* $|9 - 3a| \le 6$

60. *Solve for a.* $|9 - 3a| \ge 6$

61. Sketch the graph of the line with slope $-\frac{2}{3}$ that passes through the point (4, −1).

5.5   Factoring Trinomials

Factoring $x^2 + qx + p$

When we multiplied $x + a$ by $x + b$ in Section 5.3, we found that

$$(x + a)(x + b) = x^2 + (a + b)x + ab$$

Note the relationship between the constants a and b in the binomials to be multiplied, and the coefficients of the trinomial product: The x term coefficient is the *sum* of a and b; the numerical term is the product of a and b. Therefore, if the trinomial $x^2 + qx + p$ could be factored into two binomials, $(x + a)$ and $(x + b)$, then q is the *sum* of a and b whereas p is the *product* of a and b. Thus, all we need to find are two factors of p that sum to q. For example,

To factor $x^2 + 8x + 12$, we need to find two factors of $+12$ that sum to $+8$.

We first determine the signs of the two factors, arriving at the answer by logical deduction as follows:

The two factors must have the same signs since their product, $+12$, is positive.

Both signs must be positive since the sum $+8$ is positive.

If we systematically check the factors of 12 ($1 \cdot 12$; $2 \cdot 6$; $3 \cdot 4$), we arrive at $+6$ and $+2$ as the factors of $+12$ that sum to $+8$. Thus,

$$x^2 + 8x + 12 = (x + 6)(x + 2)$$

EXAMPLE 1   Factor each of the following.

(a) $x^2 - 4x - 12$ (b) $x^2 - 21x + 54$

(c) $a^2 - 10a + 25$ (d) $a^2 - 25$

(e) $3y^3 - 6y^2 - 105y$ (f) $x^2 + 2x + 3$

Solution   (a) $x^2 - 4x - 12$ Find factors of -12 that sum to -4. First consider the signs of the two factors: The signs must be opposite since the product is negative.

Since we know the signs are *opposite,* we ignore the signs and look for two factors of 12 whose *difference* is 4.

Possible candidates are 12 and 1, 6 and 2, and 3 and 4. The pair 6 and 2 yields a difference of 4 and therefore the two factors are 6 and 2. Now, looking at the signs, we must have -6 and $+2$ to sum to -4 as required. Hence,

$$\boxed{x^2 - 4x - 12 = (x - 6)(x + 2)}$$

Always take the time to check your answer by multiplying the factors. Be careful with the signs.

(b) $x^2 - 21x + 54$ Find the two factors of $+54$ that sum to -21. The signs of the two factors must be the same (since $+54$ is positive): Both factors must be negative since their sum, -21, is negative.

Since we know the signs are the same, we ignore the signs and look for two factors of 54 whose *sum* is 21.

Possible candidates are 1 and 54, 2 and 27, 3 and 18, and 6 and 9. The answer is 3 and 18; considering the signs, we must have -3 and -18. Hence,

$$\boxed{x^2 - 21x + 54 = (x - 18)(x - 3)}$$

Check the answer.

(c) $a^2 - 10a + 25$ Find two factors of $+25$ that sum to $+10$. Since $+25$ is positive, the signs must be the same. Both factors must be negative since their sum is -10.

The factors must be –5 and –5. Hence,

$$\boxed{a^2 - 10a + 25 = (a - 5)(a - 5)}$$

(d) $a^2 - 25$ We can rewrite this as $a^2 + 0a - 25$ to determine that we are seeking two factors of –25 that sum to 0. The signs of the two factors must be opposite (since –25 is negative).

Ignoring the signs for the moment, we are searching for two factors of 25 whose *difference* is 0.

The factors must be –5 and 5. It obviously does not matter which factor has the negative sign:

$$\boxed{a^2 - 25 = (a - 5)(a + 5)}$$ *Note this is a difference of two squares.*

Compare this problem with the one in part **(c)**.

(e) Remember always to look for the greatest common factor first:

$$3y^3 - 6y^2 - 105y = 3y(y^2 - 2y - 35)$$

Now try to factor $y^2 - 2y - 35$: The signs of two factors of –35 are opposite. Therefore, ignoring the signs, what two factors of 35 yield a *difference* of 2? Answer: 7 and 5. Including signs: –7 and +5, since they must sum to –2.

Thus,

$$y^2 - 2y - 35 = (y - 7)(y + 5)$$

and

$$3y^3 - 6y^2 - 105y = 3y(y^2 - 2y - 35)$$
$$= \boxed{3y(y - 7)(y + 5)}$$

(f) $x^2 + 2x + 3$ Find two factors of +3 that sum to +2.

Since +3 is positive, the signs of the two factors must be the same, and both factors must be positive since their sum is +2. But the only factors of +3 are 1 and 3, and +1 and +3 do not add up to +2. Since no factors satisfy these conditions, $x^2 + 2x + 3$ is

$$\boxed{\text{not factorable}}$$ ■

Factoring $Ax^2 + Bx + C$

We saw in Section 5.3 that

$$(ax + b)(cx + d) = acx^2 + (ad + bc)x + bd$$

which is obviously more complex than the previous case; it is complicated by the coefficients of the x terms in the binomials.

Note the relationships between the constants a, b, c, and d, and the coefficients of the trinomial product. Therefore, if $Ax^2 + Bx + C$ were to factor into two binomials, A would be the product of the x coefficients in the binomials ($a \cdot c$); C would be the product of the numerical term coefficients in the binomials ($b \cdot d$); and B would be the interaction (inner + outer) of the four coefficients a, b, c, and d. We will demonstrate the trial-and-error process by example.

EXAMPLE 2 Factor $2x^2 + 5x + 3$.

Solution Note first that there are no common factors.

The only possible factorization of 2 is $2 \cdot 1$. These must be the binomial x term coefficients.

The only possible factorization of 3 is $3 \cdot 1$. These must be the binomial numerical term coefficients.

There are two possible answers:

$$(2x + 1)(x + 3) \quad \text{and} \quad (2x + 3)(x + 1)$$

Multiplying out, we get

$$2x^2 + 7x + 3 \quad \text{and} \quad 2x^2 + 5x + 3$$

Note that both first and last terms are identical. The middle term indicates that $(2x + 3)(x + 1)$ is the answer. Hence,

$$2x^2 + 5x + 3 = \boxed{(2x + 3)(x + 1)}$$ ∎

EXAMPLE 3

Factor $6x^2 + 19x + 10$ completely.

Solution

Note that there is no common monomial to factor from $6x^2 + 19x + 10$. Since there seem to be many possible combinations, we check out the possibilities as follows:

Possible factorizations of 6 are $6 \cdot 1$ and $2 \cdot 3$.

Possible factorizations of 10 are $10 \cdot 1$ and $5 \cdot 2$.

The possible factorizations of $6x^2 + 19x + 10$ are

$$(6x + 5)(x + 2) = 6x^2 + 17x + 10$$
$$(6x + 2)(x + 5) = 6x^2 + 32x + 10*$$
$$(6x + 10)(x + 1) = 6x^2 + 16x + 10*$$
$$(6x + 1)(x + 10) = 6x^2 + 61x + 10$$
$$(2x + 5)(3x + 2) = 6x^2 + 19x + 10$$
$$(2x + 2)(3x + 5) = 6x^2 + 16x + 10*$$
$$(2x + 10)(3x + 1) = 6x^2 + 32x + 10*$$
$$(2x + 1)(3x + 10) = 6x^2 + 23x + 10$$

Each pair of binomials will yield the same first and last term, but only one combination will yield the correct middle term, $19x$:

$$6x^2 + 19x + 10 = \boxed{(2x + 5)(3x + 2)}$$

Note the following:

1. You should stop when you hit the right combination and then check your answer by multiplying.

2. Take a close look at the second possibility, $(6x + 2)(x + 5)$. This possibility can be factored further into $2(3x + 1)(x + 5)$ by factoring 2 from $6x + 2$. If this were the answer, it would imply that 2 is a common factor of $6x^2 + 19x + 10$ (why?). But clearly, there is no common factor of $6x^2 + 19x + 10$, so we can eliminate $(6x + 2)(x + 5)$ as a possibility. For the same reason, we can eliminate the other possibilities that appear with an asterisk (*). ∎

EXAMPLE 4

Factor $12a^3 + 2a^2 - 4a$.

Solution

$12a^3 + 2a^2 - 4a$ *Factor out the common monomial, $2a$, first.*

$= 2a(6a^2 + a - 2)$ *Factor $6a^2 + a - 2$ into $(2a - 1)(3a + 2)$.*

$= \boxed{2a(2a - 1)(3a + 2)}$ ∎

The trial-and-error procedure can be quite laborious—especially when the numbers have numerous factors. If you do not go about checking the factors in a systematic manner, it is very easy to miss the correct factors (and their relative positions) and assume the expression cannot be factored. For this reason, we recommend the *factoring by grouping* method, which we now describe.

Factoring Trinomials by Grouping

Another way to factor trinomials is to use grouping. To factor $Ax^2 + Bx + C$ we would do the following:

1. Find the product, AC.
2. Find two factors of AC that sum to B.
3. Rewrite the middle term as a sum of terms whose coefficients are the factors found in step 2.
4. Factor by grouping.

EXAMPLE 5 Factor $12x^2 - 17x - 5$ by grouping.

Solution
1. Find the product, AC:

$$12(-5) = -60$$

2. Find two factors of -60 that add to -17:

$$-20 \text{ and } +3, \quad \text{since} \quad (-20)(+3) = -60 \text{ and } -20 + 3 = -17$$

Note that we could have also written this as $12x^2 + 3x - 20x - 5$.

3. Rewrite the middle term, $-17x$, as $-20x + 3x$. Hence,

$$12x^2 - 17x - 5 = 12x^2 - 20x + 3x - 5$$

4. Factor by grouping:

$$12x^2 - 20x + 3x - 5$$
$$= 4x(3x - 5) + 1(3x - 5)$$
$$= \boxed{(3x - 5)(4x + 1)} \qquad \blacksquare$$

Although we still have to look for factors (of a number larger than A or C), the process of factoring by grouping is usually a bit more efficient than the trial-and-error process.

EXAMPLE 6 Factor $20a^2 - 7ab - 6b^2$ completely.

Solution Find the product, $20(-6) = -120$.

Which two factors of -120 will yield -7 when added? Answer: -15 and $+8$.

Rewrite $-7ab$ as $-15ab + 8ab$.

Thus,

$$20a^2 - 7ab - 6b^2 = 20a^2 - 15ab + 8ab - 6b^2$$
$$= 5a(4a - 3b) + 2b(4a - 3b)$$
$$= \boxed{(4a - 3b)(5a + 2b)} \qquad \blacksquare$$

EXAMPLE 7 Factor $5x^2 - 13x + 6$ completely.

Solution Since $(5)(6) = 30$, we want factors of 30 that sum to -13. Answer: -10 and -3. Hence,

$$5x^2 - 13x + 6 \qquad \text{\textit{Rewrite} } -13x \text{ \textit{as} } -10x - 3x.$$
$$= 5x^2 - 10x - 3x + 6 \qquad \text{\textit{Factor by grouping.}}$$
$$= 5x(x - 2) - 3(x - 2)$$
$$= \boxed{(x - 2)(5x - 3)} \qquad \blacksquare$$

If there are no pairs of factors of AC that sum to the middle term coefficient, then the trinomial does not factor into two binomials.

EXAMPLE 8

Solution

Factor the following completely.

(a) $5r^2 - 2rs + 10s^2$ (b) $-10z^2 + 11z - 3$

(a) The factors of $5(10) = 50$ are $1 \cdot 50, 2 \cdot 25$, and $5 \cdot 10$. Since there are no pairs of factors of $10(5) = 50$ that sum to -2, the polynomial is

$$\boxed{\text{not factorable}}$$

(b) The factors of $(-10)(-3) = 30$ that sum to 11 are $+6$ and $+5$. Hence,

$$-10z^2 + 11z - 3 = -10z^2 + 6z + 5z - 3$$
$$= -2z(5z - 3) + 1(5z - 3)$$
$$= \boxed{(5z - 3)(-2z + 1)}$$

Another way to solve this problem is to factor -1 from the trinomial first:

$$-10z^2 + 11z - 3 = -[10z^2 - 11z + 3] \qquad \textit{Factor by grouping.}$$
$$= -[10z^2 - 6z - 5z + 3]$$
$$= -[2z(5z - 3) - 1(5z - 3)]$$
$$= -[(5z - 3)(2z - 1)]$$

or simply

$$= \boxed{-(5z - 3)(2z - 1)}$$

Look at the two answers given for this same problem. They actually are the same. If you multiply out $-(2z - 1)$, you will get $-2z + 1$, which is the second factor of the first answer. [Remember that $-(ab) = (-a)(b)$.]   ∎

Factoring Using Special Products

We have discussed factoring $x^2 - 10x + 25$ and $x^2 - 25$ by using trial and error and it took a few steps to arrive at each solution. However, if we had recognized these polynomials as forms of special products, we could have cut down our labor a bit. In this section, we will discuss how to recognize and factor special products without resorting to trial-and-error factoring or factoring by grouping.

First we relist in the box the special products that we have had thus far.

Factoring Special Products	
1. $a^2 - b^2 = (a + b)(a - b)$	*Difference between two squares*
2. $a^2 + 2ab + b^2 = (a + b)^2$	*Perfect square of sum*
3. $a^2 - 2ab + b^2 = (a - b)^2$	*Perfect square of difference*

The first polynomial, $a^2 - b^2$, is called the *difference of two squares;* the difference of squares of two terms can be factored into two binomial conjugates. For example, we could rewrite the binomial

$$4x^2 - 9y^2$$

as the difference of two squares

$$(2x)^2 - (3y)^2$$

which factors into

$$(2x - 3y)(2x + 3y)$$

The last two special products are called *perfect squares* (just as $36 = 6^2$ is a perfect square). Notice that the first and last terms of both perfect square trinomials are perfect squares. For example,

$$9x^2 - 12xy + 4y^2$$
$$= (3x)^2 - 2(3x)(2y) + (2y)^2$$
$$= (3x - 2y)^2$$

If a trinomial is factorable, it can be factored by the methods covered in the previous section. However, if a trinomial can be recognized as a special product, it can be factored quickly and with less effort. For example, when we see a trinomial such as

$$16x^2 - 40xy + 25y^2$$

there are quite a few possible combinations of factors to check if we use trial and error or factoring by grouping. Our experience with special products, however, makes us suspicious when we see two perfect square terms, $16x^2$ and $25y^2$, in the trinomial. We would immediately check to see whether it is a perfect square by choosing

$$(4x - 5y)(4x - 5y)$$

as the first *possible* factorization. Multiplication will confirm our suspicion that this is indeed the proper factorization of $16x^2 - 40xy + 25y^2$.

With regard to the difference of two squares, the only binomials up to this point that factor into two *binomials* are those that are the difference of two squares. Obviously, it is easier to use the difference of squares factorization than to introduce a middle term coefficient of 0 as we did in the previous section using the other factoring methods.

To factor quickly, you must recognize the relationships given in the previous box.

EXAMPLE 9

Factor the following completely.

(a) $x^2 - 6x + 9$ **(b)** $9a^2 + 30a + 25$ **(c)** $4x^2 - 25y^2$

(d) $x^4 - y^4$ **(e)** $x^3 + x^2 - x - 1$

Solution

(a) $x^2 - 6x + 9 = x^2 - 2(3)x + 3^2$ *Note the relationships between terms in a perfect square trinomial.*

$$= \boxed{(x - 3)^2}$$

(b) $9a^2 + 30a + 25 = (3a)^2 + 2(3a)(5) + 5^2$

$$= \boxed{(3a + 5)^2}$$

(c) $4x^2 - 25y^2 = (2x)^2 - (5y)^2$

$$= \boxed{(2x - 5y)(2x + 5y)}$$

(d) $x^4 - y^4$ *There is no common monomial to factor. Rewrite as a difference of two squares.*

$$= (x^2)^2 - (y^2)^2$$ *Factor.*

$$= (x^2 - y^2)(x^2 + y^2)$$ *Do not forget to factor $x^2 - y^2$.*

$$= \boxed{(x - y)(x + y)(x^2 + y^2)}$$

Always check to see whether there is any more factoring to be done.

(e) $x^3 + x^2 - x - 1$ *Factor by grouping.*

$$= x^2(x + 1) - 1(x + 1)$$ *Then factor out $x + 1$.*

$$= (x + 1)(x^2 - 1)$$ *Do not forget to factor $x^2 - 1$.*

$$= \boxed{(x + 1)(x - 1)(x + 1) \quad \text{or} \quad (x - 1)(x + 1)^2}$$ ∎

Here are two more special products that will be useful.

Factoring the Sum and Difference of Cubes	4. $a^3 - b^3 = (a - b)(a^2 + ab + b^2)$ *Difference of two cubes* 5. $a^3 + b^3 = (a + b)(a^2 - ab + b^2)$ *Sum of two cubes*

Note the similarities and differences between factoring the sum and difference of two cubes. Keep in mind that $a^3 - b^3$ is *not* the same as $(a - b)^3$, which when multiplied out will have middle terms. Also note that the right-hand factor, either $a^2 - ab + b^2$ or $a^2 + ab + b^2$, will not have binomial factors. (Do not confuse it with the perfect square $a^2 + 2ab + b^2$, which has binomial factors.)

EXAMPLE 10   Factor the following completely.

(a) $27x^3 - y^3$ (b) $8c^3 + 125b^3$

Solution

(a) $27x^3 - y^3$ *Write as a difference of two cubes.*

$$A^3 - B^3$$
$$= (3x)^3 - y^3 \qquad \text{*Factor.*}$$
$$(A - B)(A^2 + A \cdot B + B^2)$$
$$= (3x - y)[(3x)^2 + (3x)(y) + y^2] \qquad \text{*Simplify inside the brackets.*}$$
$$= \boxed{(3x - y)(9x^2 + 3xy + y^2)}$$

(b) $8c^3 + 125b^3$ *Rewrite as a sum of two cubes.*
$$= (2c)^3 + (5b)^3 \qquad \text{*Factor.*}$$
$$= (2c + 5b)[(2c)^2 - (2c)(5b) + (5b)^2] \qquad \text{*Simplify inside the brackets.*}$$
$$= \boxed{(2c + 5b)(4c^2 - 10cb + 25b^2)}$$

Can you factor $A^2 + B^2$?

Note that although the sum of two *cubes* **does** factor, the sum of two *squares* does **not**. ∎

In general, we offer the following advice for factoring polynomials.

General Advice for Factoring Polynomials	1. Always factor out the greatest common factor first.
	 2. If the polynomial to be factored is a binomial, then it may be a difference of two squares, or a sum or difference of two cubes (remember that a sum of two squares does not factor).
	 3. If the polynomial to be factored is a trinomial, then:
	    (a) If two of the three terms are perfect squares, the polynomial may be a perfect square.
	    (b) Otherwise, the polynomial may be one of the general forms.
	 4. If the polynomial to be factored consists of four or more terms, then try factoring by grouping.

 EXERCISES 5.5

Factor the following completely.

1. $x^2 + 4x - 45$ 2. $x^2 - 10x + 24$

3. $y^2 - 3y - 10$ 4. $a^2 - 8ab - 20b^2$

5. $x^2 - 2xy - 15y^2$

6. $r^2 - rs - 2s^2$

7. $r^2 - 81$

8. $a^2 - 49$

9. $x^2 - xy - 6y^2$

10. $a^2 + 4ab - 21b^2$

11. $x^2 - xy + 6y^2$

12. $a^2 + 4ab + 21b^2$

13. $r^2 - 7rs + 12s^2$

14. $a^2 - 12ab + 20b^2$

15. $r^2 - rs - 12s^2$

16. $a^2 + 12ab - 20b^2$

17. $9x^2 - 49y^2$

18. $4a^2 - 81b^2$

19. $15x^2 + 17x + 4$

20. $9a^2 - 6a - 8$

21. $15x^2 - xy - 6y^2$

22. $10a^2 + 23ab - 12b^2$

23. $15x^2 + xy - 6y^2$

24. $10a^2 - 23ab + 12b^2$

25. $10xy + 3x^2 - 25y^2$

26. $13xy + 6y^2 + 6x^2$

27. $10a^2 + 21ab - 10b^2$

28. $7x^2 + 20xy + 12y^2$

29. $25 - 5y - 2y^2$

30. $21 + 8a - 4a^2$

31. $25 - 5y - y^2$

32. $21 - 8a - 4a^2$

33. $2x^3 + 4x^2 - 16x$

34. $3y^3 + 30y^2 + 63y$

35. $x^3 + 3x^2 - 28x$

36. $y^3 - 5y^2 - 36y$

37. $2x(x - 3) + (x - 1)(x + 2)$

38. $2u(u + 1) + (u + 2)(u - 5)$

39. $18ab - 15abx - 18abx^2$

40. $30y^3 + 25y^2 + 5y$

41. $90y^4 - 114y^3 + 36y^2$

42. $54xy^4 + 45x^2y^3 + 6x^3y^2$

43. $6r^4 - r^2 - 2$

44. $6x^4 - x^2 - 12$

45. $3x^2 - 27$

46. $2x^2 - 50$

47. $20xy^5 + 2x^2y^3 - 8x^3y$

48. $6x^2 + 5xy^2 - 6y^4$

49. $108x^3y + 72x^2y^3 - 15xy^5$

50. $25x^4 + 10x^2y^2 + 15y^4$

51. $12a^7b + a^4b - 6ab$

52. $24a^7b - 20a^4b^3 + 4ab^5$

53. $15a^8 + 19a^4 - 10$

54. $4a^4 + 8a^2 + 3$

55. $16x^2 - 9y^2$

56. $x^2 - 6x + 9$

57. $x^2 + 4xy + 4y^2$

58. $9a^2 + 30ab + 25b^2$

59. $x^2 - 4xy + 4y^2$

60. $9a^2 - 30ab + 25b^2$

61. $x^2 - 4xy - 4y^2$

62. $9a^2 - 30ab - 25b^2$

63. $6x^2y^2 - 5xy + 1$

64. $9r^2 + 42rs + 49s^2$

65. $81r^2s^2 - 16$

66. $25x^2y^2 - 4$

67. $9x^2y^2 - 4z^2$

68. $9a^2b^2 - 4$

69. $25a^2 - 4a^2b^2$

70. $1 - 9a^2$

71. $1 - 14a + 49a^2$

72. $125a^3 + b^3$

73. $8a^3 - b^3$

74. $8a^3 - 343b^3$

75. $x^3 + 125y^3$

76. $9x^4 + 24x^2 + 16$

77. $4x^2 + 25y^2$

78. $9x^4 - 24x^2 - 16$

79. $4y^2 - 20y + 10$

80. $45a^3b - 20ab^3$

81. $12a^3c + 36a^2c^2 + 27ac^3$

82. $18x^5 + 24x^3 + 8x$

83. $4x^4 - 81y^4$

84. $x^8 - y^8$

85. $25a^6 + 10a^3b + b^2$

86. $12y^6 - 27y^2$

87. $12y^6 + 27y^2$

88. $12x^4 - 12y^4$

89. $(a + b)^2 - 4$

90. $(3a + b)^2 - (a + b)^2$

91. $a^2 - 2ab + b^2 - 16$

92. $r^2 - 10r + 25 - x^2$

93. $x^2 + 6x + 9 - r^2$

94. $x^2 + 2xy + y^2 - 81$

95. $a^3 + a^2 - 4a - 4$

96. $r^3 - r^2 - 9r + 9$

97. $x^4 + x^3 - x - 1$

98. $8x^4 - 16x^3 - x + 2$

99. If a race has n entrants, the number of possible different first-, second-, and third-place finishes (excluding ties) is given by the formula $P = n^3 - 3n^2 + 2n$. Factor this polynomial.

100. The volume of a cylindrical shell (see the accompanying figure) is given by the formula $V = \pi R^2 h - \pi r^2 h$. Factor this polynomial.

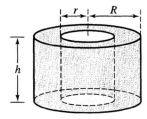

QUESTIONS FOR THOUGHT

101. In this section we mentioned that if a polynomial does *not* have a common factor, we can eliminate any binomial factors that *do* have common factors. For example, the trinomial $6x^2 - 5x - 6$ has no common numerical factors. Why does this imply that $3x - 3$ could not be a binomial factor of $6x^2 - 5x - 6$?

102. Find all k such that:

(a) $x^2 + kx + 10$ is factorable.   (b) $x^2 + kx - 10$ is factorable.

(c) $2x^2 + kx - 3$ is factorable.

103. Find all p such that $x^2 + 3x + p$ is factorable, where $-20 < p < 20$.

104. How would you factor the following?

(a) $3(x + y)^2 - 4(x + y) - 4$ (b) $2a^2 + 4ab + 2b^2 - 7a - 7b + 3$

105. Describe what relationship must exist among terms for a trinomial to factor as a perfect square.

106. Describe the factors of the sum and the differences of two cubes. How do they differ? How are they the same?

107. Discuss the differences between $a^3 - b^3$ and $(a - b)^3$.

108. Factor $x^6 - y^6$ completely.

(a) Begin by using the difference of two squares.

(b) Begin by using the difference of two cubes.

(c) Should the answers to part (a) and (b) be the same? Why or why not?

109. Why is $(a^2b - b)(a + 1)$ *not* a complete factorization of $a^3b + a^2b - ab - b$? What should the answer be?

◇ MINI-REVIEW

110. Find the slope of the line passing through the points $(2, -6)$ and $(3, 5)$.

111. Find the equation of the line passing through the point $(5, 1)$ and perpendicular to the line $x - 6y = 6$.

112. Sketch the graph of $3x - 6y \leq 12$.

113. A shoe manufacturer finds that during the summer there is a linear relationship between the weekly number of pairs of sandals he sells and the average weekly temperature (in °F). If he sells 20 pairs during the week that the temperature averages 74°F, and 40 pairs during the week that the temperature averages 84°F, how many pairs should he expect to sell the week that the temperature averages 90°F?

5.6 Solving Polynomial Equations by Factoring

We have previously learned how to solve first-degree equations in one variable. In fact, these were polynomial equations of degree 1. Polynomial equations of degree 2 are called *quadratic equations*. We define the *standard form* of a quadratic equation as

$$Ax^2 + Bx + C = 0 \quad \text{(where } A \neq 0\text{)}$$

In this standard form, A is the coefficient of the second-degree term, x^2; B is the coefficient of the first-degree term, x; and C is the numerical constant.

As with all other equations, the solutions to quadratic equations are values that when substituted for the variable satisfy the equation. The solutions to a polynomial equation are also called the *roots* of the equation. The factoring techniques we have discussed in this chapter allow us to solve certain quadratic and higher-degree polynomial equations.

We begin by recognizing that if the product of two quantities is 0, then either one or both of the quantities must be 0. Symbolically written, if $a \cdot b = 0$, then $a = 0$, or $b = 0$, or both $a = 0$ and $b = 0$. In mathematics, the word *or* includes the possibility of both. Thus, we can write

The Zero-Product Rule	If $a \cdot b = 0$, then $a = 0$ or $b = 0$.

For example, if we want to find the solution to the equation

$$(x - 2)(x + 3) = 0$$

then either the factor $x - 2$ must equal 0 or the factor $x + 3$ must equal 0. Now we have two first-degree equations:

$$x - 2 = 0 \qquad \text{or} \qquad x + 3 = 0$$
$$\text{Therefore, } x = 2; \qquad \text{Therefore, } x = -3.$$

Hence, our solutions to the equation $(x - 2)(x + 3) = 0$ are $x = 2$ and $x = -3$.

EXAMPLE 1 Solve each of the following equations.

(a) $(3x - 2)(x + 3) = 0$ (b) $y(y + 4) = 0$ (c) $5x(x - 1)(x + 8) = 0$

Solution (a) If $(3x - 2)(x + 3) = 0$, then

$$3x - 2 = 0 \quad \text{or} \quad x + 3 = 0 \qquad \textit{Solve each first-degree equation.}$$
$$3x = 2 \qquad\qquad x = -3$$

Hence, $\boxed{x = \dfrac{2}{3} \quad \text{or} \quad x = -3}$.

Let's check the solution $x = -3$:

$$(3x - 2)(x + 3) = 0 \qquad \text{\textit{Substitute} } -3 \text{ \textit{for} } x.$$

$$[3(-3) - 2](-3 + 3) \overset{?}{=} 0$$

$$\uparrow$$

Note that this arithmetic is not necessary
once we establish that one of the factors is 0.

$$(-11)(0) \overset{\checkmark}{=} 0$$

We leave the other check to the student.

(b)   If $y(y + 4) = 0$, then

$$y = 0 \quad \text{or} \quad y + 4 = 0 \qquad \text{\textit{If the product of factors is} 0, \textit{then}}$$
$$\text{\textit{at least one of the factors must be} 0.}$$

Hence, $\boxed{y = 0 \quad \text{or} \quad y = -4}$.

(c) We can generalize the zero-product rule to more than two factors. We solve the equation $5x(x - 1)(x + 8) = 0$ by setting each factor equal to 0:

$$x = 0 \quad \text{or} \quad x - 1 = 0 \quad \text{or} \quad x + 8 = 0$$

If the product of factors is 0, then at least one of the factors must be 0. We
solve each equation. Note that we can ignore the constant factor 5 since 5   0.

Hence, $\boxed{x = 0, \quad x = 1, \quad \text{or} \quad x = -8}$.

We mentioned that we can ignore the *factor* 5 because $5 \neq 0$. We would arrive at the same conclusion if we were to first divide both sides of the equation by 5.

If we multiply out the left side in part **(a)** of the previous example, we get $3x^2 + 7x - 6 = 0$, which is a quadratic equation in standard form. If the second-degree expression of a quadratic equation (in standard form) factors into two first-degree factors, we can apply the above principle to solve the quadratic equation. This is called the ***factoring method*** of solving quadratic equations.

For example, to solve the second-degree equation $5x^2 - 2 = 3x^2 - x + 4$, we first put the equation in standard form:

$$5x^2 - 2 = 3x^2 - x + 4 \qquad \text{\textit{Put in standard form.}}$$
$$2x^2 + x - 6 = 0 \qquad \text{\textit{Factor the left side.}}$$
$$(2x - 3)(x + 2) = 0 \qquad \text{\textit{Since the product is} 0, \textit{set each factor}}$$
$$\text{\textit{equal to} 0.}$$
$$2x - 3 = 0 \quad \text{or} \quad x + 2 = 0 \qquad \text{\textit{Then solve each first-degree equation.}}$$
$$2x = 3$$
$$x = \frac{3}{2} \quad \text{or} \qquad x = -2$$

We leave it to the student to check these solutions.

EXAMPLE 2

Solve each of the following equations.

(a) $2x^2 - 3x - 1 = 1$ **(b)** $3a^2 = 5a$

Solution   **(a)** Do not try to factor first; $2x^2 - 3x - 1 = 1$ is not in standard form. Remember, the principle upon which the factoring method is based requires the product be equal to 0.

$$2x^2 - 3x - 1 = 1 \qquad \textit{First we put the equation in standard form}$$
$$\textit{(subtract 1 from both sides of the equation).}$$
$$2x^2 - 3x - 2 = 0 \qquad \textit{Then factor.}$$
$$(2x + 1)(x - 2) = 0 \qquad \textit{Then solve each first-degree equation.}$$
$$2x + 1 = 0 \quad \textit{or} \quad x - 2 = 0$$
$$2x = -1 \qquad\qquad x = 2$$

$$\boxed{x = -\frac{1}{2} \quad \text{or} \quad x = 2}$$

(b) Do not make the mistake of dividing both sides of the equation by a; a is a variable that may be 0, and division by 0 is not allowed.

$$3a^2 = 5a \qquad \textit{First put in standard form.}$$
$$3a^2 - 5a = 0 \qquad \textit{Then factor.}$$
$$a(3a - 5) = 0 \qquad \textit{Set each factor equal to 0.}$$
$$a = 0 \quad \textit{or} \quad 3a - 5 = 0$$
$$3a = 5$$

$$\boxed{a = 0 \quad \text{or} \quad a = \frac{5}{3}}$$

The same approach can be applied to polynomials of higher degree if they can be factored.

EXAMPLE 3 Solve for x. $x^3 - 4x^2 = 12x$

Solution This is a third-degree polynomial equation. To use the factoring method, we get one side of the equation to equal to 0, and hope that we can factor.

$$x^3 - 4x^2 = 12x \quad \textit{Subtract 12x from both sides.}$$
$$x^3 - 4x^2 - 12x = 0 \quad \textit{Factor the left side.}$$
$$x(x^2 - 4x - 12) = 0$$
$$x(x - 6)(x + 2) = 0 \quad \textit{We use the zero-product rule and set each factor equal to 0.}$$
$$x = 0 \quad \text{or} \quad x - 6 = 0 \quad \text{or} \quad x + 2 = 0$$

$$\boxed{x = 0 \quad \text{or} \quad x = 6 \quad \text{or} \quad x = -2}$$

The student should check these solutions.

EXAMPLE 4 If $f(x) = 2x^2 + x - 10$, solve each of the following polynomial equations.

(a) $f(x) = 0$ \qquad (b) $f(x) = -9$

Solution (a) Solving the polynomial equation $f(x) = 0$ means we want to find the value x that will make $f(x) = 0$. Since $f(x) = 2x^2 + x - 10$, we solve the equation $2x^2 + x - 10 = 0$:

$$f(x) = 2x^2 + x - 10 \qquad \textit{Substitute } f(x) = 0 \textit{ to get}$$
$$0 = 2x^2 + x - 10 \qquad \textit{Solve for x by factoring.}$$
$$0 = (x - 2)(2x + 5) \qquad \textit{Set each factor equal to 0.}$$
$$0 = x - 2 \quad \text{or} \quad 0 = 2x + 5$$

$$\boxed{x = 2 \quad \text{or} \quad x = -\frac{5}{2}}$$

Hence $f(2) = 0$ and $f\left(-\frac{5}{2}\right) = 0$.

(b) Solving the polynomial equation $f(x) = -9$ means we want to find the value x that will make $f(x) = -9$. Hence we solve the equation $2x^2 + x - 10 = -9$:

$$f(x) = 2x^2 + x - 10 \qquad \textit{Substitute } f(x) = -9 \textit{ to get}$$

$$-9 = 2x^2 + x - 10 \qquad \textit{Put the equation in standard form}$$
$$\textit{(Add 9 to each side.)}$$

$$0 = 2x^2 + x - 1 \qquad \textit{Solve for } x \textit{ by factoring.}$$

$$0 = (x + 1)(2x - 1) \qquad \textit{Set each factor equal to 0.}$$

$$0 = x + 1 \quad \text{or} \quad 0 = 2x - 1$$

$$\boxed{x = -1 \qquad \text{or} \quad x = \frac{1}{2}}$$

Hence $f(-1) = -9$ and $f\left(\dfrac{1}{2}\right) = -9$. ∎

We will discuss more general methods for solving quadratic equations in Chapter 8.

EXAMPLE 5

A rectangle has length 4 inches greater than its width. If its area is 77 sq in., what are the dimensions of the rectangle?

Figure 5.6
Rectangle for Example 5

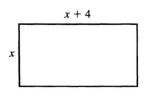

Solution

Draw a diagram and label the sides, as indicated in Figure 5.6. Let

$$x = \text{Width}$$

Then

$$x + 4 = \text{Length} \qquad \textit{Since the length is 4 more than the width}$$

The formula for the area of a rectangle is

$$A = (\text{Length})(\text{Width})$$

$$77 = (x + 4)x$$

Solve:

$$77 = x^2 + 4x$$

$$0 = x^2 + 4x - 77$$

$$0 = (x - 7)(x + 11)$$

$$x = 7 \quad \text{or} \quad x = -11 \qquad \textit{We eliminate the negative answer}$$
$$\textit{since length is never negative.}$$

Thus, $x = 7$ in. (the width) and $x + 4 = 7 + 4 = 11$ in. (the length).

The dimensions are $\boxed{7'' \text{ by } 11''}$. ∎

EXAMPLE 6

A 20′ by 60′ rectangular pool is surrounded by a concrete walkway of uniform width. If the total area of the walkway is 516 sq ft, how wide is the walkway?

Solution

Since the walkway is the same width at all points around the pool, we label this width x and our picture is as shown in Figure 5.7 on page 297.

Figure 5.7
Diagram for Example 6

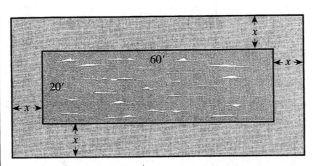

Let's analyze this question carefully, step by step, to develop a strategy for its solution.

THINKING OUT LOUD

What do we need to find?	The width of the walkway
What information are we given?	The dimensions of the pool and the area of the walkway
Is there a connection between what we are given and what we want to find?	From the diagram we see that the area of the outer rectangle equals the area of the pool plus the area of the walkway.
How do we find the area of the outer rectangle?	Since the area of a rectangle is length times width, we need to express the length and width of the outer rectangle in terms of the width x of the walkway.
How do we find x, the width of the walkway?	We can use the area relationship to write an equation and solve for x.

Let's carry out this strategy. We notice that the length of the outer rectangle as you go across from left to right is $x + 60 + x$, which simplifies to $60 + 2x$. Similarly, the width of the outer rectangle from top to bottom is $x + 20 + x$, which simplifies to $20 + 2x$. Thus in terms of x, the area of the outer rectangle (the pool *and* the walkway) is

$$(20 + 2x)(60 + 2x)$$

The area of the inner rectangle (the pool) is $(60)(20) = 1{,}200$ sq ft, and we are given that the area of the walkway itself is 516 sq ft.

Figure 5.7 gives us the following relationship:

Area of outer rectangle = Area of inner rectangle + Area of walkway

$$(20 + 2x)(60 + 2x) = \qquad 1{,}200 \qquad + \qquad 516$$

We solve the quadratic equation:

$$(20 + 2x)(60 + 2x) = 1{,}200 + 516$$

$1{,}200 + 160x + 4x^2 = 1{,}716$	*Put in standard form.*
$4x^2 + 160x - 516 = 0$	*Divide both sides of the equation by 4.*
$\dfrac{4(x^2 + 40x - 129)}{4} = \dfrac{0}{4}$	
$x^2 + 40x - 129 = 0$	*Factor.*
$(x - 3)(x + 43) = 0$	
$x = 3 \quad \text{or} \quad x = -43$	*Eliminate the negative answer. (Why?)*

Hence, $x = 3$.

The width of the walkway is $\boxed{3 \text{ ft}}$. ∎

EXAMPLE 7

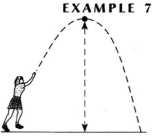

Figure 5.8

Diagram for Example 7

Solution

Jenna throws a ball up into the air. The equation

$$h = h(t) = -16t^2 + 30t + 4$$

gives the height, h (in feet), above the ground that the ball reaches t seconds after she throws it (see Figure 5.8).

(a) How far above the ground is the ball exactly 1 second after she throws it? After $\frac{3}{4}$ of a second?

(b) How many seconds will it take for the ball to hit the ground from the time she throws it?

(a) Since the ball is $h = h(t)$ ft above the ground in t seconds, to find the height of the ball at 1 second, we find $h(1)$:

$$h(t) = -16t^2 + 30t + 4$$
$$h(1) = -16(1)^2 + 30(1) + 4$$
$$= -16 + 30 + 4 = 18$$

The ball is $\boxed{18 \text{ ft above the ground}}$ at 1 second.

At $\frac{3}{4}$ of a second, we find $h\left(\frac{3}{4}\right)$:

$$h(t) = -16t^2 + 30t + 4$$
$$h\left(\tfrac{3}{4}\right) = -16\left(\frac{3}{4}\right)^2 + 30\left(\frac{3}{4}\right) + 4$$
$$= -16\left(\frac{9}{16}\right) + 30\left(\frac{3}{4}\right) + 4$$
$$= -9 + \frac{90}{4} + 4$$
$$= 17\frac{1}{2}$$

Hence, the ball is $\boxed{17\frac{1}{2} \text{ ft above the ground}}$ at $\frac{3}{4}$ of a second.

(b) In this part of the problem, we need to find t, but to find t, we need to know $h(t)$. Since $h(t)$ is the height of the ball above the ground, when the ball hits the ground $h(t)$ must be 0. Hence, we are being asked to find t when $h(t) = 0$.

$$h(t) = -16t^2 + 30t + 4 \qquad \textit{Let } h(t) = 0.$$
$$0 = -16t^2 + 30t + 4 \qquad \textit{Find t: Factor } -2 \textit{ from the right.}$$
$$0 = -2(8t^2 - 15t - 2) \qquad \textit{Divide both sides by } -2.$$
$$\frac{0}{-2} = \frac{-2(8t^2 - 15t - 2)}{-2}$$
$$0 = 8t^2 - 15t - 2$$
$$0 = (8t + 1)(t - 2)$$

$$8t + 1 = 0 \quad \text{or} \quad t - 2 = 0$$
$$8t = -1 \qquad\qquad t = 2$$
$$t = -\frac{1}{8}$$

So $h = 0$ at $t = -\frac{1}{8}$ and at $t = 2$. But $-\frac{1}{8}$ second does not make any sense and we therefore eliminate this answer.

Thus, the ball reaches the ground in $\boxed{2 \text{ seconds}}$.

Note also that at $t = 0$ seconds, the height, $h(t)$ is 4 ft, indicating that the ball actually starts 4 ft above the ground. ∎

In Exercises 1–44, solve the equation.

1. $(x + 2)(x - 3) = 0$

2. $(a - 5)(a + 7) = 0$

3. $0 = (2y - 1)(y - 4)$

4. $0 = (2a + 3)(a - 4)$

5. $x^2 = 25$

6. $a^2 = 81$

7. $x(x - 4) = 0$

8. $y(y + 3) = 0$

9. $12 = x(x - 4)$

10. $15 = y(y + 2)$

11. $5y(y - 7) = 0$

12. $3x(x + 2) = 0$

13. $x^2 - 16 = 0$

14. $a^2 - 225 = 0$

15. $0 = 9c^2 - 16$

16. $0 = 25x^2 - 4$

17. $8a^2 - 18 = 0$

18. $2x^2 = 32$

19. $0 = x^2 - x - 6$

20. $0 = a^2 + 2a - 8$

21. $2y^2 - 3y + 1 = 0$

22. $5a^2 - 14a - 3 = 0$

23. $0 = 8x^2 + 4x - 112$

24. $0 = 6x^2 + 8x - 8$

25. $x^3 + x^2 - 6x = 0$

26. $y^4 - y^2 = 0$

27. $t^4 + 2t^3 + t^2 = 0$

28. $s^3 - s = 0$

29. $20m^3 = 5m$

30. $6b^3 = 9b^4$

31. $x(x - 3) = x^2 - 10$

32. $x(2x - 3) = x^2 + 10$

33. $(t - 4)(t + 1) = (t - 3)(t - 2)$

34. $(a + 2)(a + 5) = (a - 1)(a + 6)$

35. $(2t - 4)(t + 1) = (t - 3)(t - 2)$

36. $(a + 2)(a + 4) = (2a - 1)(a + 6)$

37. $(x + 6)^2 = 16$

38. $(x - 5)^2 = 49$

39. $(3x - 4)^2 = 20 - 24x$

40. $(2x + 3)^2 = 12x + 18$

41. $2(x - 3)(x + 2) = 0$

42. $2(x - 3) + (x + 2) = 0$

43. $2x - 3(x + 2) = 4$

44. $(2x - 3)(x + 2) = 4$

45. If $f(x) = x^2 - 2x - 15$, solve each of the following polynomial equations:
    (a) $f(x) = 0$ (b) $f(x) = 9$

46. If $h(x) = 3x^2 + 5x - 2$, solve each of the following polynomial equations:
    (a) $h(x) = 0$ (b) $h(x) = 20$

Solve each of the following problems algebraically.

47. Five less than the square of a positive number is 1 more than 5 times the number. Find the number.

48. Seven more than the square of a positive number is 1 less than 6 times the number. Find the number(s).

49. The sum of the squares of two positive numbers is 68. If one of the numbers is 8, find the other number.

50. The sum of the squares of two negative numbers is 30. If one of the numbers is -5, find the other number.

51. Find the numbers such that the square of the sum of the number and 6 is 169.

52. Find the numbers such that the square of the sum of the number and 3 is 100.

53. The sum of a number and its reciprocal is $\frac{13}{6}$. Find the number(s).

54. The sum of a number and its reciprocal is $\frac{25}{12}$. Find the number(s).

55. The sum of a number and twice its reciprocal is 3. Find the number(s).

56. The sum of a number and three times its reciprocal is 4. Find the number(s).

57. The profit in dollars (P) made on a concert is related to the price in dollars (d) of a ticket in the following way:

$$P = 10,000(-d^2 + 12d - 35)$$

(a) How much profit is made by selling tickets for $5?

(b) What must the price of a ticket be to make a profit of $10,000?

58. The hourly cost in dollars (C) of producing sofas in a furniture factory is related to the number of sofas (x) produced in the following way:

$$C(x) = -100x^2 + 1,000x - 1,600$$

(a) How much does it cost per hour to produce 4 sofas?

(b) How many sofas must be produced so that the hourly cost is $800?

59. A man jumps off a diving board into a pool. The equation

$$s = s(t) = -16t^2 + 64$$

gives the distance s (in feet) the man is above the pool t seconds after he jumps.

(a) How high above the pool is the diver after the first second?

(b) How long does it take for him to hit the water?

(c) How high is the diving board? [*Hint:* Let $t = 0$.]

60. Alex throws a ball straight up into the air. The equation

$$s = s(t) = -16t^2 + 80t + 44$$

gives the distance s (in feet) the ball is above the ground t seconds after he throws it.

(a) How high is the ball at $t = 2$ seconds?

(b) How long does it take for the ball to hit the ground?

61. Find the dimensions of a rectangle whose area is 80 sq ft and whose length is 2 ft more than its width.

62. Find the dimensions of a rectangle whose area is 108 sq ft and whose length is 3 ft more than its width.

63. A 20′ by 55′ rectangular swimming pool is surrounded by a concrete walkway of uniform width. If the area of the concrete walkway is 400 sq ft, find the width of the walkway.

64. A 21′ by 21′ square swimming pool is surrounded by a path of uniform width. If the area of the path is 184 sq ft, find the width of the path.

❓ QUESTIONS FOR THOUGHT

65. On what property of real numbers is the factoring method based?

66. Discuss what is *wrong* (and why) with the solutions to the following equations:

(a) Problem: Solve $(x - 3)(x - 4) = 7$.

   Solution: $x - 3 = 7$ or $x - 4 = 7$

   $x = 10$ or $x = 11$

(b) Problem: Solve $3x(x - 2) = 0$.

   Solution: $x = 3$, $x = 0$ or $x = 2$

MINI-REVIEW

67. How long will it take a car traveling at a rate of 52 mph to catch up with a car traveling at a rate of 40 mph with an hour head start?

68. Solve for x and graph the solution set on a number line. $-4 \leq 3x - 2 < 5$

69. Find the slope of the line whose equation is $3x - 2y = 8$.

70. Write an equation of the line passing through the points $(-4, 0)$ and $(0, 5)$.

5.7 Polynomial Division

In this section we will discuss division of polynomials—in particular, division by binomials and trinomials. We will discuss division by monomials in Chapter 6 within the context of fractional expressions.

Recall that when we divide numbers using long division, we use the following procedure:

$$
\begin{array}{r}
12 \\
23\overline{)279} \\
23 \\
\hline
49 \\
46 \\
\hline
3
\end{array}
\qquad \text{Which is shorthand for} \qquad
\begin{array}{r}
10 + 2 \\
20 + 3\overline{)200 + 70 + 9} \\
200 + 30 \\
\hline
40 + 9 \\
40 + 6 \\
\hline
3
\end{array}
\qquad
\begin{array}{l}
\textit{We divide } 20 \textit{ into } 200. \\
\\
\textit{We divide } 20 \textit{ into } 40.
\end{array}
$$

First we focus our attention on dividing by 20, but then we multiply the number in the quotient by $20 + 3$, subtract, bring down the next term, and repeat this process. Polynomial division is handled similarly. We will demonstrate by example.

EXAMPLE 1 $(2x^2 + 3x + 3) \div (x + 4)$

Solution

1. Put both polynomials into standard form (arrange terms in descending order of degree).

$$x + 4\overline{)2x^2 + 3x + 3}$$

2. Divide the highest-degree term of the divisor into the highest-degree term of the dividend:

$$\frac{2x^2}{x} = 2x$$

$$
\begin{array}{r}
2x \\
x + 4\overline{)2x^2 + 3x + 3}
\end{array}
$$

3. Multiply the resulting quotient, $2x$, by the whole divisor:

$$2x(x + 4) = 2x^2 + 8x$$

Multiply.
$$
\begin{array}{r}
2x \\
x + 4\overline{)2x^2 + 3x + 3} \\
2x^2 + 8x
\end{array}
$$

4. Subtract the result of step 3 from the dividend:

$$
\begin{array}{r}
2x^2 + 3x \\
-(2x^2 + 8x)
\end{array}
\rightarrow
\begin{array}{r}
2x^2 + 3x \\
-2x^2 - 8x \\
\hline
-5x
\end{array}
$$

Change signs of all terms in $2x^2 + 8x$ and add.

$$
\begin{array}{r}
2x \\
x + 4\overline{)2x^2 + 3x + 3} \\
-(2x^2 + 8x) \\
\hline
-5x
\end{array}
\qquad \textit{Subtract.}
$$

5. Bring down the next term.

$$\begin{array}{r} 2x \\ x+4\overline{)2x^2+3x+3} \\ -(2x^2+8x) \\ \hline -5x+3 \end{array}$$

6. Repeat steps 2–5 until no more terms can be brought down.

   (a) Divide x into $-5x$ to get -5

   (b) Multiply -5 by $x+4$ to get $-5x-20$.

   (c) Subtract $-5x-20$ from $-5x+3$ to get 23.

$$\begin{array}{r} 2x-5 \\ x+4\overline{)2x^2+3x+3} \\ -(2x^2+8x) \\ \hline -5x+3 \\ -(-5x-20) \quad \textit{Subtract.} \\ \hline +23 \end{array}$$

7. The remaining term, $+23$, is the remainder.

$$\begin{array}{r} 2x-5 \\ x+4\overline{)2x^2+3x+3} \\ -(2x^2+8x) \\ \hline -5x+3 \\ -(-5x-20) \\ \hline +23 \end{array}$$

The process ends when the degree of the remainder is less than the degree of the divisor. In this case, the degree of 23 is 0 and the degree of $x+4$ is 1.

Answer: $\boxed{2x-5, \quad \text{Rem. } +23}$

Or, we can rewrite this expression as

$$\boxed{2x-5+\dfrac{23}{x+4}}$$

We should check the answer in the same way we check long division problems with numbers:

$$\text{Dividend} = (\text{Quotient}) \cdot (\text{Divisor}) + \text{Remainder}$$
$$2x^2+3x+3 \overset{?}{=} (2x-5)(x+4)+23 \qquad \textit{Multiply first.}$$
$$\overset{?}{=} 2x^2+3x-20+23$$
$$\overset{\checkmark}{=} 2x^2+3x+3 \qquad\qquad\qquad \blacksquare$$

When writing the dividend in standard form, it is a good idea to leave a space between terms wherever a consecutive power is missing, or fill in the power with a coefficient of 0. This stops you from making the error of combining two different powers of x in a subtraction step.

EXAMPLE 2

$(2x^3+x-18) \div (x-2)$

Solution

$$\begin{array}{r} 2x^2+4x+9 \\ x-2\overline{)2x^3+0x^2+x-18} \\ -(2x^3-4x^2) \\ \hline 4x^2+x \\ -(4x^2-8x) \\ \hline 9x-18 \\ -(9x-18) \\ \hline 0 \end{array}$$

Missing power of x in dividend. Write in power with 0 coefficient.

Answer: $\boxed{2x^2+4x+9}$

Check: $2x^3 + x - 18 \overset{?}{=} (2x^2 + 4x + 9)(x - 2)$

$$\overset{?}{=} 2x^3 + 4x^2 + 9x - 4x^2 - 8x - 18$$

$$\overset{\checkmark}{=} 2x^3 + x - 18$$

∎

EXAMPLE 3

$(a^5 + 3a^3 + a^2 + 3a + 7) \div (a^3 + a + 1)$

Solution

In this example we left a space for the x^4 term rather than writing $0x^4$.

$$
\require{enclose}
\begin{array}{r}
a^2 \qquad\quad + 2 \\
a^3 + a + 1 \enclose{longdiv}{a^5 \qquad\quad + 3a^3 + a^2 + 3a + 7} \\
\underline{-(a^5 \qquad\quad\; + a^3 + a^2)} \\
2a^3 \qquad\; + 3a + 7 \\
\underline{-(2a^3 \qquad\; + 2a + 2)} \\
a + 5
\end{array}
$$

These last two terms must be brought down.

Answer: $\boxed{a^2 + 2, \quad \text{Rem. } a + 5}$ or $\boxed{a^2 + 2 + \dfrac{a + 5}{a^3 + a + 1}}$

Note that the degree of the remainder must be less than the degree of the divisor.

∎

 EXERCISES 5.7

Divide the following using polynomial long division.

1. $(x^2 - x - 20) \div (x - 5)$

2. $(3y^2 + 5y + 7) \div (y + 1)$

3. $(3a^2 + 10a + 8) \div (3a + 4)$

4. $(2x^2 + x - 14) \div (2x - 3)$

5. $(21z^2 + z - 16) \div (3z + 1)$

6. $(5a^2 + 16a + 11) \div (5a + 1)$

7. $(a^3 + a^2 + a - 8) \div (a - 1)$

8. $(x^3 + 2x^2 + 2x + 1) \div (x + 1)$

9. $(3x^3 - 11x^2 - 5x + 12) \div (x - 4)$

10. $(y^3 - 2y^2 + 3y - 2) \div (y - 2)$

11. $(4z^2 - 15) \div (2z + 3)$

12. $(4a^2 - 35) \div (2a - 7)$

13. $(x^4 + x^3 - 4x^2 - 3x - 2) \div (x - 2)$

14. $(y^4 + 4y^3 - 2y^2 - 2y + 3) \div (y + 1)$

15. $(-10 + 2y^2 + 5y - 5y^3 + 3y^4) \div (y - 1)$

16. $(-10x^2 + 12 + 9x - 3x^3 + 6x^4) \div (2x - 1)$

17. $(6 - 5a + 2a^4 + 4a^3) \div (a + 2)$

18. $(10x^4 - 6x - 15 + 5x^3) \div (2x + 1)$

19. $(y^3 - 1) \div (y + 1)$

20. $(8a^3 - 1) \div (2a - 1)$

21. $(8a^3 + 1) \div (2a - 1)$

22. $(y^3 + 1) \div (y + 1)$

23. $(2y^5 + 4 - 3y^4 - y^2 + y) \div (y^2 + 1)$

24. $(5x^4 + 1) \div (x - 1)$

25. $(-10 + 12z + 3z^5 + 3z^2 - 4z^3) \div (z^2 + 2z - 1)$

26. $(5y^6 + 17y^2 - 14 + 7y - 9y^3 - 28y^4 + 15y^5) \div (y^2 + 3y - 5)$

27. $(7x^6 + 1 + x - 3x^2 - 14x^4) \div (x^2 - 2)$

28. $(x^4 - y^4) \div (x - y)$

◇ **MINI-REVIEW**

29. If $f(x) = 5x^2 - 3x + 2$, find $f(4)$ and $f(x^2)$.

CHAPTER 5 SUMMARY

After having completed this chapter you should be able to:

1. Identify the degree and coefficients of the terms in a polynomial, as well as the degree of the polynomial itself (Section 5.1).

   For example: The polynomial $5x^6 - 3x + 8$ has *three* terms:

   The first term, $5x^6$, has coefficient 5 and degree 6.

   The second term, $-3x$, has coefficient -3 and degree 1.

   The constant term, 8, has degree 0.

   The polynomial has degree 6.

2. Combine and simplify polynomial expressions (Section 5.2).

   For example:

   (a) $2(3x^2 - x + 3y) - 3(y - x) - (2x^2 - 3y)$

   $\qquad = 6x^2 - 2x + 6y - 3y + 3x - 2x^2 + 3y$

   $\qquad = 4x^2 + x + 6y$

   (b) $2x^2y(3xy^2 - 6x^3y^2) - 3x(-2xy^2)(-4x^3y) = 6x^3y^3 - 12x^5y^3 - 24x^5y^3$

   $\qquad\qquad\qquad\qquad\qquad\qquad\qquad\qquad = 6x^3y^3 - 36x^5y^3$

3. Multiply polynomials (Section 5.2).

   For example:

   $(2x - y)(x^2 - 3xy - y^2) = 2x^3 - 6x^2y - 2xy^2 - x^2y + 3xy^2 + y^3$

   $\qquad\qquad\qquad\qquad\quad = 2x^3 - 7x^2y + xy^2 + y^3$

4. Multiply polynomials using general forms and special products (Section 5.3).

   For example:

   (a) $(3x - 4)^2 = (3x)^2 - 2(3x)(4) + 4^2$

   $\qquad\qquad\quad = 9x^2 - 24x + 16$

   (b) $[(x - y) - 7][(x - y) + 7] = (x - y)^2 - 7^2$

   $\qquad\qquad\qquad\qquad\qquad = x^2 - 2xy + y^2 - 49$

5. Factor various types of polynomials (Sections 5.4, 5.5).

   For example:

   Common monomial factoring: (a) $2x^2 + 7x = x(2x + 7)$

   Factoring by grouping: (b) $x^2 - 3x - xy + 3y$

   $\qquad\qquad\qquad\qquad\qquad\qquad = x(x - 3) - y(x - 3)$

   $\qquad\qquad\qquad\qquad\qquad\qquad = (x - 3)(x - y)$

   General forms: (c) $y^2 - 10y + 21 = (y - 7)(y - 3)$

   $\qquad\qquad\qquad\qquad\qquad$ (d) $2x^2 + 7x + 6 = (2x + 3)(x + 2)$

   $\qquad\qquad\qquad\qquad\qquad$ (e) $6x^5 - 15x^3y + 9xy^2$

   $\qquad\qquad\qquad\qquad\qquad\qquad = 3x(2x^4 - 5x^2y + 3y^2)$

   $\qquad\qquad\qquad\qquad\qquad\qquad = 3x(2x^2 - 3y)(x^2 - y)$

   Using special products: (f) $16m^2 - 9n^2 = (4m - 3n)(4m + 3n)$ *Difference of two squares*

   $\qquad\qquad\qquad\qquad\qquad$ (g) $25x^2 - 60x + 36 = (5x - 6)^2$ *Perfect square*

   $\qquad\qquad\qquad\qquad\qquad$ (h) $x^3 - 8 = x^3 - 2^3$ *Difference of two cubes*

   $\qquad\qquad\qquad\qquad\qquad\qquad = (x - 2)(x^2 + 2x + 4)$

   $\qquad\qquad\qquad\qquad\qquad$ (i) $t^2 + 6t + 9 - u^2 = (t + 3)^2 - u^2$ *Group the first three terms.*

   $\qquad\qquad\qquad\qquad\qquad\qquad = (t + 3 - u)(t + 3 + u)$ *Difference of two squares*

6. Use the factoring method to solve polynomial equations (Section 5.6).

   For example: To solve the equation $2x^2 - 30 = 7x$, we proceed as follows:

   $2x^2 - 30 = 7x$ *Write the quadratic equation in standard form.*

   $2x^2 - 7x - 30 = 0$ *Factor the left side.*

   $(2x + 5)(x - 6) = 0$ *Using the zero-product rule, we set each factor equal to 0.*

   $2x + 5 = 0$ or $x - 6 = 0$

        $x = -\dfrac{5}{2}$ or $x = 6$

7. Use long division to divide polynomials (Section 5.7).

   For example: $(8x^3 - 28x + 19) \div (2x - 3)$

   Solution:

   $$
   \begin{array}{r}
   4x^2 + 6x - 5 \\
   2x - 3 \overline{)\, 8x^3 + 0x^2 - 28x + 19} \\
   \underline{-(8x^3 - 12x^2)} \\
   12x^2 - 28x \\
   \underline{-(12x^2 - 18x)} \\
   -10x + 19 \\
   \underline{-(-10x + 15)} \\
   4
   \end{array}
   $$

   Answer: $4x^2 + 6x - 5 + \dfrac{4}{2x - 3}$

8. Solve applications using polynomial equations (Sections 5.1 and 5.6).

CHAPTER 5   REVIEW EXERCISES

In Exercises 1–26, perform the operations and simplify.

1. Subtract the sum of $2x^2 - 3x + 4$ and $5x^2 - 3$ from $2x^3 - 4$.

2. Subtract $2x^3 - 3x^2 - 2$ from the sum of $2x^3 - 3x + 4$ and $3x^2 - 5x + 9$.

3. $3x^2(2xy - 3y + 1)$

4. $5rs^2(3r^2s - 2rs^2 - 3)$

5. $3ab(2a - 3b) - 2a(3ab - 4b^2)$

6. $3xy(2x - 3y + 4) - 2x(5xy - 3y) - 2xy^2$

7. $3x - 2(x - 3) - [x - 2(5 - x)]$

8. $5x - 4\{3 - 2[x - (2 - x)]\}$

9. $(x - 3)(x + 2)$

10. $(x - 5)(x - 8)$

11. $(3y - 2)(2y - 1)$

12. $(5y - 3a)(5y + 3a)$

13. $(3x - 4y)^2$

14. $(5a + 3b)(a - 2b)$

15. $(4x^2 - 5y)^2$

16. $(4a - 3b^2)(4a + 3b^2)$

17. $(7x^2 - 5y^3)(7x^2 + 5y^3)$

18. $(2x - 5)(3x^2 - 2x + 1)$

19. $(5y^2 - 3y + 7)(2y - 3)$

20. $(7x^2 + 3xy - 2y^2)(3x - 2y)$

21. $(2x + 3y + 4)(2x + 3y - 5)$

22. $[(a + b) + (x - y)][(a + b) - (x - y)]$

23. $[(x - y) + 5]^2$

24. $(x - 3 + y)(x - 3 - y)$

25. $(a + b - 4)^2$

26. $(x + y + 5)^2$

In Exercises 27–72, factor the expression completely.

27. $6x^2y - 12xy^2 + 9xy$

28. $15a^2b^2 - 10ab^4 + 5ab^2$

29. $3x(a + b) - 2(a + b)$

30. $5y(y - 1) + 3(y - 1)$

31. $2(a - b)^2 + 3(a - b)$

32. $4(a - b)^2 + 7(a - b)$

33. $5ax - 5a + 3bx - 3b$

34. $2xa + 2xb + 3a + 3b$

35. $5y^2 - 5y + 3y - 3$

36. $14a^2 - 7ab + 6ab - 3b^2$

37. $a^2 + a(a - 10)$

38. $t^3 + t(t - 6)$

39. $2t(t + 2) - (t - 2)(t + 4)$

40. $3m(m - 1) - (2m + 1)(m - 2)$

41. $x^2 - 2x - 35$

42. $a^2 + 5a - 36$

43. $a^2 + 5ab - 14b^2$

44. $y^4 + x^2y^2 - 6x^4$

45. $35a^2 + 17ab + 2b^2$

46. $x^2 - 6xy + 9y^2$

47. $a^2 - 6ab^2 + 9b^4$

48. $2x^3 + 6x^2 - 54x$

49. $3a^3 - 21a^2 + 30a$

50. $5a^3b + 5a^2b^2 - 30ab^3$

51. $2x^3 - 50xy^2$

52. $3y^3 + 24y^2 + 48y$

53. $6x^2 + 5x - 6$

54. $25y^2 - 5y - 12$

55. $8x^3 + 125y^3$

56. $x^3 - 27$

57. $6a^2 - 17ab - 3b^2$

58. $12x^2 + 16xy^2 + 5y^4$

59. $21a^4 + 41a^2b^2 + 10b^4$

60. $54a^4 - 16ab^3$

61. $25x^4 - 40x^2y^2 + 16y^4$

62. $18x^3 + 15x^2y - 18xy^2$

63. $20x^3y - 60x^2y^2 + 45xy^3$

64. $4a^4 - 9b^4$

65. $6a^4b - 8a^3b^2 - 8a^2b^3$

66. $28x^4y - 63x^2y^3$

67. $6x^5 - 10x^3 - 4x$

68. $30x^5y - 85x^3y^2 + 25xy^3$

69. $(a - b)^2 - 4$

70. $(3x - 2)^2 - (5y + 3)^2$

71. $9y^2 + 30y + 25 - 9x^2$

72. $25x^4 - y^2 - 8y - 16$

In Exercises 73–76, find the quotient using long division.

73. $(3x^3 - 4x^2 + 7x - 5) \div (x - 2)$

74. $(x^4 - x - 1) \div (x + 1)$

75. $(8a^3 - 27) \div (2a - 3)$

76. $(y^6 + y^5 + y^4 + y^3 + y^2 + y + 1) \div (y^2 + y + 1)$

In Exercises 77–82, solve the given equation by factoring.

77. $x(x + 5)(3x - 4) = 0$

78. $x^2 - 20 = 8x$

79. $x^4 = 25x^2$

80. $x^3 + 10x^2 - 24x = 0$

81. $(x + 6)(x - 3) = (4x - 2)(x + 4)$

82. $(x + 7)^2 = x + 19$

In Exercises 83–86, given $f(x) = 2x^2 - 5x + 3$ and $g(x) = 3x - 1$, find

83. $f(x)g(x)$

84. $f(x) + g(x)$

85. $f(x + 1)$

86. $g(x) - g(2)$

87. The sum of the squares of the first n natural numbers is given by the formula

$$S(n) = 1^2 + 2^2 + 3^2 + \cdots + n^2 = \tfrac{1}{6}(2n^3 + 3n^2 + n). \text{ Factor } S(n).$$

88. The sum of the cubes of the first n natural numbers is given by the formula

$$S(n) = 1^3 + 2^3 + 3^3 + \cdots + n^3 = \tfrac{1}{4}(n^4 + 2n^3 + n^2).$$ Factor $S(n)$.

89. A particular company knows that if the price of an item is c dollars, then it can sell $20{,}000 - 1{,}000c^2$ items.

   (a) Express the revenue, R, as a function of c.

   (b) Use the function R to compute the revenue when the price of an item is \$1, \$2, and \$4.

90. The daily profit, P, made on selling a small toy is related to the price, x, of the toy in the following way:

$$P = P(x) = -1{,}000x^2 + 11{,}000x - 24{,}000$$

   (a) How much daily profit is made selling the toy for \$5?

   (b) What must the price of the toy be to make a daily profit of \$4,000?

 CHAPTER 5 PRACTICE TEST

Perform the operations and simplify the following.

1. $(9a^2 + 6ab + 4b^2)(3a - 2b)$

2. $(x - 3)(x + 3) - (x - 3)^2$

3. $(x - y - 2)(x - y + 2)$

4. $(3x + y^2)^2$

Factor the following completely:

5. $10x^3y^2 - 6x^2y^3 + 2xy$

6. $6ax + 15a - 2bx - 5b$

7. $x^2 + 11xy - 60y^2$

8. $10x^2 - 11x - 6$

9. $2x^2 - 3x + 7$

10. $3a^3b - 3ab^3$

11. $r^3s - 10r^2s^2 + 25rs^3$

12. $8a^3 - 1$

13. $(2x + y)^2 - 64$

14. $a^3 + 4a^2 - a - 4$

15. Find the quotient using long division: $(x^3 + 7x - 8) \div (x - 3)$

16. Solve for x.
   (a) $2x^3 + 8x^2 - 24x = 0$
   (b) $(2x - 7)(x - 4) = (4x - 19)(x - 2)$

17. An object is thrown straight up into the air. The equation

$$s = s(t) = -16t^2 + 32t + 48$$

gives the distance, s (in feet), the object is above the ground t seconds after it is thrown.

   (a) How high above the ground is the object at $t = 2$ seconds?

   (b) How long does it take for the ball to hit the ground?

18. Given $f(x) = x^2 - 3x + 2$, find
   (a) $f(5)$ (b) $f(x + 5)$

We will return to this function in Example 4 of this section.

An environmental consultant for a large factory finds that the cost C (in thousands of dollars) to remove p percent of the pollutants released by the factory can be approximated by the function

$$C(p) = \frac{70p}{100 - p}$$

Understanding how this function behaves would be very useful in determining the monetary investment necessary to make specific improvements in the amount of pollution removed. This cost function $C(p)$ is called a *rational function,* and will be investigated further later in this section.

6.1 Rational Functions

In Chapter 1 we defined the set of rational numbers, Q, in the following way:

$$Q = \left\{ \frac{a}{b} \,\middle|\, a, b \in Z, b \neq 0 \right\}$$

which means that a rational number is any number that can be represented as the quotient of two integers, provided that the denominator is not 0.

Similarly, we define a ***rational expression*** as a quotient of two polynomials, provided the denominator is not the ***zero polynomial.*** (Remember that the zero polynomial is simply the number 0.) A ***rational function*** is defined to be a quotient of two polynomial functions.

DEFINITION	A ***rational function*** is a function of the form $$f(x) = \frac{p(x)}{q(x)} \qquad \text{where } p(x) \text{ and } q(x) \text{ are polynomials and } q(x) \neq 0$$

But even if the denominator of a rational expression is not the zero polynomial, we must still be careful about division by 0; a nonzero polynomial could have a value of 0 when certain values are substituted for the variable. For example, the rational expression $\frac{3x - 4}{x - 5}$ has the nonzero polynomial $x - 5$ as its denominator. However, since $x - 5$ is equal to 0 when $x = 5$,

$$\frac{3x - 4}{x - 5} \quad \text{is not defined for } x = 5$$

Alternatively, we can say that the ***domain*** of the rational function $f(x) = \frac{3x - 4}{x - 5}$ is the set of all real numbers *excluding* $x = 5$.

A word about terminology is in order here. While a rational expression is a quotient of polynomials, a ***fraction*** is *any* quotient of expressions. For example, the following are all examples of fractions:

$$\frac{2x^3 - 3x + 7}{2x^2 + 5}, \qquad \frac{3x - 5}{2x^2 + 8}, \qquad \frac{3x^2 + 2x}{\sqrt{2x - 5}}, \qquad \frac{(2x^2 - 3x + 5)^{1/3}}{2x - 1}$$

The first two fractions are rational expressions. The last two fractions are not rational expressions because they contain expressions that are not polynomials.

EXAMPLE 1 Which value(s) of x must be excluded for each of the following rational expressions?

(a) $\dfrac{6}{2x - 1}$ (b) $\dfrac{x - 4}{5}$

Solution Essentially, we need to eliminate those values of x that make the denominator equal to 0, and hence the fraction undefined.

(a) $\dfrac{6}{2x - 1}$ is undefined when $2x - 1 = 0$.

Hence $\boxed{\text{we exclude } x = \dfrac{1}{2}}$.

(b) $\dfrac{x - 4}{5}$ $\boxed{\text{is defined for all values of } x}$ because the *denominator* is never equal to 0.

Remember that it is permissible for the *numerator* of a fraction to equal 0. If $x = 4$, the fraction becomes $\frac{4 - 4}{5} = \frac{0}{5}$, which is equal to 0. ∎

EXAMPLE 2 Find the domain of $f(x) = \dfrac{2x + 1}{x^2 - 2x - 8}$.

Solution Remember that the domain of a function is the set of all values of x that make $f(x)$ defined and real. Hence we want to find and eliminate the values of x that make the denominator equal to 0 and therefore $f(x)$ undefined. Since $f(x) = \dfrac{2x + 1}{x^2 - 2x - 8}$ is undefined when the denominator is 0, we solve the equation $x^2 - 2x - 8 = 0$:

$$x^2 - 2x - 8 = 0 \qquad \textit{Solve by factoring.}$$
$$(x - 4)(x + 2) = 0 \qquad \textit{Set each factor equal to 0.}$$
$$x - 4 = 0 \quad \text{or} \quad x + 2 = 0$$
$$x = 4 \quad \text{or} \qquad x = -2$$

Hence the domain of $f(x)$ is $\boxed{\text{all real numbers except } x = 4 \text{ and } x = -2}$. We can write this domain alternatively as $\{x \mid x \neq 4, x \neq -2\}$. ∎

Just as the integer p may be regarded as a rational number by rewriting it as $\dfrac{p}{1}$, polynomials may also be considered as rational expressions since they can be represented as a quotient of the polynomial and 1.

Let's examine a few situations in which we can use a rational function as a mathematical model.

EXAMPLE 3 The area of a rectangle is 4 sq meters.

(a) Express the length of the rectangle as a function of its width.

(b) Use this function to explain how the length and width for this rectangle are related.

Solution (a) The area of a rectangle is *length* $\times$ *width*. Since the area of the rectangle is 4, we have

$$4 = lw \qquad \textit{Where } l = \textit{length and } w = \textit{width}$$

Since we want to express the length as a function of the width, we solve for l to get

$$l = \frac{4}{w} \qquad \textit{We can rewrite this using function notation, replacing } l \textit{ with}$$
$$\qquad \qquad L(w) \textit{ (since the length is a function of the width) as}$$

$$L(w) = \frac{4}{w}$$

(b) Let's begin by examining this function algebraically: What does the equation tell us in general about the relationship between the length and width of this rectangle? Consider the equation $L(w) = \dfrac{4}{w}$. What happens to $L(w)$ if we keep changing the numerical value of w, allowing w to get larger and larger? If the denominator of the fraction $\frac{4}{w}$ gets larger and larger, the fraction itself gets smaller and smaller. As w becomes smaller and smaller, the fraction gets larger and larger. Let's construct a table of values for $L(w)$.

Recall from arithmetic that $4 \div \frac{1}{4} = 4 \cdot \frac{4}{1} = 16$. Or you can use your calculator and compute $4 \div \frac{1}{4}$ as $4 \div 0.25$.

Width	Length
w	$\dfrac{4}{w} = L(w)$
$\dfrac{1}{4}$	$\dfrac{4}{\frac{1}{4}} = 16$
$\dfrac{1}{2}$	$\dfrac{4}{\frac{1}{2}} = 8$
1	$\dfrac{4}{1} = 4$
2	$\dfrac{4}{2} = 2$
4	$\dfrac{4}{4} = 1$
8	$\dfrac{4}{8} = \dfrac{1}{2}$
16	$\dfrac{4}{16} = \dfrac{1}{4}$

Note that when $w = 0$, $L(w)$ is undefined (that is, $L(0)$ does not exist), since we are dividing by 0. Observe that as w becomes larger and larger, $L(w)$ becomes smaller and smaller. This table confirms the algebraic relationship we suggested earlier.

Using the table above, we can also plot points and graph this equation to get a "picture" of this relationship (see Figure 6.1).

Figure 6.1
The graph of $L(w) = \dfrac{4}{w}$

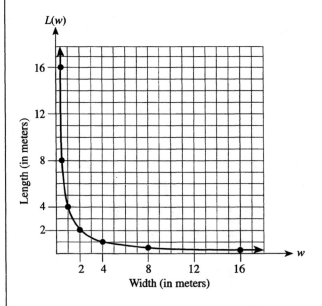

The graph shows that as w gets bigger and bigger (moving to the right), the $L(w)$ values get smaller and smaller ($L(w)$ gets closer and closer to 0). On the other hand, note that as w gets closer and closer to 0 (moving to the left), the $L(w)$ values get larger and larger ($L(w)$ keeps growing). ∎

EXAMPLE 4

An environmental consultant for a large factory finds that the cost C (in thousands of dollars) to remove p percent of the pollutants released by the factory can be approximated by the function

$$C(p) = \frac{60p}{100 - p}$$

(a) What is the domain of this function?

(b) Create a table of values for this function, and explain what these values mean.

(c) Sketch a graph of this function. Describe the behavior of this cost function. (What is happening to the cost as we get closer and closer to removing 100% of the pollutants?)

Solution

(a) First note that for this function to make sense, p, the percent of pollutants being removed, cannot be less than 0 or greater than 100. We can also see from the equation that p cannot equal 100. (Why?) Hence the domain is $0 \leq p < 100$.

(b) The table below shows $C(p)$ for various values of p. $C(p)$ is the cost of removing p percent of the pollutants. For example, $C(50) = 60$ means it costs $60,000 to remove 50% of the pollutants.

(c) The graph is shown in Figure 6.2.

p	$C(p) = \dfrac{60p}{100 - p} = cost\ (in\ thousands)$
10	$C(10) = \dfrac{60(10)}{100 - 10} = 6.67$
30	$C(30) = \dfrac{60(30)}{100 - 30} = 25.71$
50	$C(50) = \dfrac{60(50)}{100 - 50} = 60$
70	$C(70) = \dfrac{60(70)}{100 - 70} = 140$
75	$C(75) = \dfrac{60(75)}{100 - 75} = 180$
80	$C(80) = \dfrac{60(80)}{100 - 80} = 240$
90	$C(90) = \dfrac{60(90)}{100 - 90} = 540$
95	$C(95) = \dfrac{60(95)}{100 - 95} = 1{,}140$

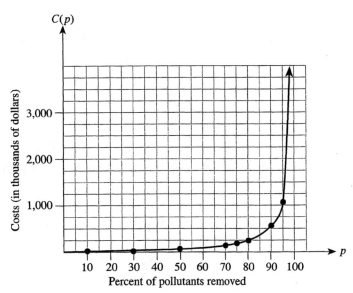

Figure 6.2

We can see that as p, the percent of pollutants removed, increases, the cost to remove this level of pollutants also increases. However, what is interesting to note is that as p increases, the cost increases more and more rapidly. In particular, as p approaches 100, the cost increases enormously. For example, $C(75) = 180$, which means that it costs $180,000 to remove 75% of the pollutants, and $C(80) = 240$, which means that it costs $240,000 to remove 80% of the pollutants. Thus, if the factory is already removing 75% of the pollutants, in order to remove an additional 5% of pollutants the factory would require an additional $60,000.

However, $C(90) = 540$ and $C(95) = 1{,}140$, which means that if the factory is already removing 90% of the pollutants, in order to remove an additional 5% of pollutants, the factory would require an additional $600,000! The graph shows us that as p approaches 100%, the cost of each additional percent removed is increasing enormously. ∎

Note that as the percentage of pollutants removed approaches 100%, *the cost becomes prohibitive.*

EXERCISES 6.1

In Exercises 1–8, what values of the variable(s) should be excluded for the fraction?

1. $\dfrac{x}{x-2}$

2. $\dfrac{x+2}{3y+2}$

3. $\dfrac{3xy^2}{2}$

4. $\dfrac{3x^2z}{5}$

5. $\dfrac{a+b}{5x}$

6. $\dfrac{x^2}{y}$

7. $\dfrac{3xy}{3x-y}$

8. $\dfrac{5ab}{2a-b}$

In Exercises 9–16, find the domain of the given function.

9. $f(x) = \dfrac{3x}{x-8}$

10. $g(x) = \dfrac{x-7}{x+2}$

11. $h(x) = \dfrac{2x+1}{5x-8}$

12. $g(x) = \dfrac{3x-1}{7x-9}$

13. $f(x) = \dfrac{3x-2}{x^2-25}$

14. $h(x) = \dfrac{x-9}{x^2-16}$

15. $f(x) = \dfrac{2x+1}{x^2-x-6}$

16. $g(x) = \dfrac{3x-1}{2x^2-9x-5}$

17. The area of a rectangle is 20 square feet.

   (a) Express the length of the rectangle as a function of its width.

   (b) Use this function to find the length of this rectangle when the width is 0.5, 1, 2, 4, 5, 10, 15, and 20 feet. Explain how the length and width for this rectangle are related.

18. The area of a rectangle is 100 square feet.

   (a) Express the length of the rectangle as a function of its width.

   (b) Use this function to find the length of this rectangle when the width is 0.5, 1, 20, 40, 60, 80, 100, and 200 feet. Explain how the length and width for this rectangle are related.

19. A manufacturer finds that the cost C (in dollars) to produce x items is given by $C = 0.4x + 8,000$. It then follows that the average cost per item to produce x items is given by

$$A(x) = \frac{0.4x + 8,000}{x}$$

   (a) Compute $A(5)$, the average per item cost to produce 5 items. Compute $A(10)$, $A(50)$, $A(100)$, $A(200)$, and $A(300)$.

   (b) Use the points found in part (a) to sketch a rough graph of this function. Use the graph or a table to explain how the number of items produced is related to the average cost per item.

20. An entomologist uses the function

$$n(d) = \frac{500(d+4)}{0.4d+2}$$

to model the number n of insects present in a colony d days after the initial formation of the colony.

   (a) How many insects are present after 1, 5, 10, 20, 30, 60, and 90 days?

   (b) Use the points found in part (a) to sketch a rough graph of this function. Use the graph or a table to explain how the number of insects in the colony changes as time goes by.

21. An ecological study group suggests that under certain conditions the following function relates the number n of deer that can be realistically supported on a acres of foraging land:

$$n(a) = \frac{40a}{0.4a + 8} \qquad \text{for } 0 \leq a \leq 200$$

   (a) Compute $n(1)$, $n(10)$, $n(50)$, and $n(100)$, and explain what each of these values means.

   (b) Use the points found in part (a) to sketch a rough graph of this function. Use the graph or a table to explain how the number of deer sustained is related to the number of acres of foraging land.

22. A pharmaceutical company finds that when a certain drug is administered to a patient the concentration c of the drug in the bloodstream (in milligrams per liter) h hours after the drug was administered is given by

$$c(h) = \frac{50h}{h^2 + 1}$$

   (a) Compute $c(0.25)$, $c(0.5)$, $c(1)$, $c(2)$, $c(6)$, and $c(24)$, and explain what each of these values means.

   (b) Use the points found in part (a) to sketch a rough graph of this function. Use the graph or a table to explain how the concentration of the drug in the bloodstream changes as time passes by.

23. Suppose that a manufacturer finds that the cost C of managing and storing g gallons of a certain chemical is given by the function

$$C = C(g) = 2g + \frac{5,000}{g}$$

   (a) What can the domain of this function be?

   (b) Compute $C(1)$, $C(5)$, $C(10)$, $C(20)$, $C(40)$, $C(100)$, $C(200)$, and $C(300)$, and explain what each of these values means.

   (c) Use the points found in part (a) to sketch a rough graph of this function. Describe the behavior of this cost function.

24. Suppose that a company finds that the cost C per unit of producing x units is given by the function

$$C = C(x) = 325 + \frac{750}{x^2}$$

   (a) What can the domain of this function be?

   (b) Compute $C(1)$, $C(3)$, $C(7)$, $C(12)$, $C(15)$, $C(20)$, and $C(30)$, and explain what each of these values means.

   (c) Use the points found in part (a) to sketch a rough graph of this function. Describe the behavior of this cost function. What is happening to the cost per unit as the company manufactures more and more units?

6.2 Equivalent Fractions

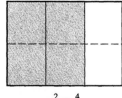

$$\frac{2}{3} = \frac{4}{6}$$

We know from previous experience with rational expressions that two expressions may look different but may actually be equivalent or represent the same amount. With numerical fractions we can draw pictures to demonstrate that $\frac{2}{3}$ and $\frac{4}{6}$ are equivalent.

On the other hand, how do we determine whether $\frac{35x^2}{14x}$, $\frac{5x}{2}$, and $\frac{5x^4}{2x^3}$ are equivalent?

With variables involved, we primarily use the Fundamental Principle of Fractions.

The Fundamental Principle of Fractions	$\dfrac{a \cdot k}{b \cdot k} = \dfrac{a}{b}$ $b, k \neq 0$

This principle says that if we *divide* or *multiply* the numerator and denominator of a fraction by the same nonzero expression, we obtain an equivalent fraction. In the boxed equation, moving from left to right is called ***reducing fractions to lower terms;*** moving from right to left is called ***building fractions to higher terms.***

Reducing Fractions

A fraction ***reduced to lowest terms*** or ***written in simplest form*** is a fraction that has no factors (other than ±1) common to both its numerator and denominator. This requires us to factor both numerator and denominator and then divide out factors common to the numerator and denominator. It is usually quicker to factor out the greatest common factor.

EXAMPLE 1

Express the following in simplest form:

(a) $\dfrac{56}{98}$ (b) $\dfrac{33x^4y^2}{15xy^5}$ (c) $\dfrac{x + y}{x - y}$

Solution

(a) $\dfrac{56}{98} = \dfrac{7 \cdot 2 \cdot 2 \cdot 2}{7 \cdot 7 \cdot 2}$ *For convenience, we cross out the factors common to the numerator and denominator and then rewrite the fraction in reduced form.*

$= \boxed{\dfrac{4}{7}}$

Instead of factoring the numerator and denominator completely, we could factor out the greatest common factor and then reduce:

$$\dfrac{56}{98} = \dfrac{4 \cdot 14}{7 \cdot 14}$$ *The greatest common factor is 14.*

$$= \boxed{\dfrac{4}{7}}$$

(b) $\dfrac{33x^4y^2}{15xy^5} = \dfrac{11 \cdot 3 \cdot x \cdot x \cdot x \cdot x \cdot y \cdot y}{5 \cdot 3 \cdot x \cdot y \cdot y \cdot y \cdot y \cdot y} = \dfrac{11x^3}{5y^3}$

or

$$\dfrac{33x^4y^2}{15xy^5} = \dfrac{11x^3 \cdot 3xy^2}{5y^3 \cdot 3xy^2} = \boxed{\dfrac{11x^3}{5y^3}}$$

(c) $\dfrac{x + y}{x - y}$ $\boxed{\text{cannot be reduced}}$.

Remember that the Fundamental Principle of Fractions refers only to common factors. We can divide out common factors but not common terms.   ■

We can now apply the factoring techniques we studied in Chapter 5.

EXAMPLE 2

Express the following in simplest form:

(a) $\dfrac{x^2 - y^2}{(x - y)^2}$ (b) $\dfrac{x - 8}{x^2 - 5x - 24}$

(c) $\dfrac{4x^2 - 4x - 3}{2x^2 - x - 3}$ (d) $\dfrac{16 - x^2}{x^2 - x - 12}$

Solution

(a) $\dfrac{x^2 - y^2}{(x - y)^2} = \dfrac{(x - y)(x + y)}{(x - y)(x - y)}$ *First factor; then reduce.*

$= \dfrac{(x - y)(x + y)}{(x - y)(x - y)}$

$= \boxed{\dfrac{x + y}{x - y}}$

(b) $\dfrac{x - 8}{x^2 - 5x - 24} = \dfrac{x - 8}{(x - 8)(x + 3)}$ *First factor; then reduce.*

$= \dfrac{x - 8}{(x - 8)(x + 3)}$

$= \boxed{\dfrac{1}{x + 3}}$ *Remember that* $\dfrac{x - 8}{x^2 - 5x - 24} = \dfrac{1}{x + 3}$

for all values of x except 8 and −3. Why?

(c) $\dfrac{4x^2 - 4x - 3}{2x^2 - x - 3} = \dfrac{(2x - 3)(2x + 1)}{(2x - 3)(x + 1)}$ *Factor and reduce.*

$= \dfrac{(2x - 3)(2x + 1)}{(2x - 3)(x + 1)}$

$= \boxed{\dfrac{2x + 1}{x + 1}}$ *For all values of x except* $\frac{3}{2}$ *and −1*

(d) $\dfrac{16 - x^2}{x^2 - x - 12} = \dfrac{(4 - x)(4 + x)}{(x - 4)(x + 3)}$ *Factor.*

At first glance it appears that there are no common factors, but as we discussed in Chapter 5, $4 - x$ is the negative of $x - 4$; that is,

$$-(x - 4) = -x + 4 = 4 - x$$

Thus, we could factor −1 from *either* $4 - x$ or $x - 4$:

$$\dfrac{(4 - x)(4 + x)}{(x - 4)(x + 3)} = \dfrac{(-1)(x - 4)(4 + x)}{(x - 4)(x + 3)}$$

$$= \dfrac{-1(4 + x)}{x + 3} \quad \text{or} \quad \boxed{\dfrac{-x - 4}{x + 3}} \qquad \blacksquare$$

A reminder: When we state that two rational expressions or functions are equal, it is always understood these expressions are equal only for values of x where both expressions are defined. Thus, in Example 4(b), $\dfrac{x - 8}{x^2 - 5x - 24}$ and $\dfrac{1}{x + 3}$ are equivalent for all values of x *except* $x = 8$ and $x = -3$.

Building Fractions to Higher Terms

In the process of adding fractions with different denominators, we will have to use the Fundamental Principle of Fractions to do the opposite of reducing: ***building to higher terms.*** We demonstrate by example.

EXAMPLE 3

Fill in the question mark to make the two fractions equivalent.

(a) $\dfrac{3x}{5y^2 z} = \dfrac{?}{20xy^4 z^2}$ **(b)** $\dfrac{2x - 3}{x^2 - 25} = \dfrac{?}{(x - 5)(x + 5)^2}$

Solution

The Fundamental Principle of Fractions says that two fractions are equivalent if one is obtained by multiplying the denominator and the numerator of the other by the same (nonzero) expression. Thus, all we need to do is to look at what additional factors appear in the denominator of the second fraction and multiply the numerator of the first fraction by these same factors.

(a)
$$\frac{3x}{5y^2z} = \frac{?}{20xy^4z^2}$$

*To make $5y^2z$ into $20xy^4z^2$, we need to multiply by $4xy^2z$. Therefore, we must multiply the **numerator** by $4xy^2z$ as well.*

$$\frac{3x(4xy^2z)}{5y^2z(4xy^2z)} = \frac{12x^2y^2z}{20xy^4z^2}$$

The answer is $\boxed{12x^2y^2z}$.

(b)
$$\frac{2x - 3}{x^2 - 25} = \frac{?}{(x - 5)(x + 5)^2}$$

Factor the denominator of the left fraction.

$$\frac{(2x - 3)}{(x - 5)(x + 5)} = \frac{?}{(x - 5)(x + 5)^2}$$

Looking at the denominators and moving from left to right, we see that we are missing a factor of $x + 5$.

$$\frac{(2x - 3)(x + 5)}{(x - 5)(x + 5)(x + 5)} = \frac{(2x - 3)(x + 5)}{(x - 5)(x + 5)^2}$$

*Thus, we must also multiply the **numerator** by $(x + 5)$.*

The answer is $\boxed{(2x - 3)(x + 5) \quad \text{or} \quad 2x^2 + 7x - 15}$. ∎

Signs of Fractions

In a rational expression, a sign may precede any of the following: the numerator, the denominator, or the entire fraction. In general,

$$\frac{a}{b} = -\frac{a}{-b} = -\frac{-a}{b} = \frac{-a}{-b}$$

and

$$-\frac{a}{b} = \frac{-a}{b} = \frac{a}{-b} = -\frac{-a}{-b}$$

You may check that these are equal by letting $a = 6$ and $b = 3$. Note that if you change *exactly* two of the three signs of a fraction, the result will be an equivalent fraction.

Of the three equivalent forms,

$$-\frac{x}{3} = \frac{-x}{3} = \frac{x}{-3}$$

the first two are usually the preferred forms.

 EXERCISES 6.2

In Exercises 1–36, reduce to lowest terms.

1. $\dfrac{3x^2y}{15xy}$

2. $\dfrac{24a^3b^2}{36ab^4}$

3. $\dfrac{16x^2y^3a}{18xy^4a^3}$

4. $\dfrac{87a^2b^3}{57a^5b^9}$

5. $\dfrac{(x - 5)(x + 4)}{(x - 3)(x + 4)}$

6. $\dfrac{(x - 2)(x + 1)}{(x - 2)(x + 3)}$

7. $\dfrac{(2x - 3)(x - 5)}{(2x + 3)(x + 3)}$

8. $\dfrac{(5y - 1)(2y - 7)}{(5y + 1)(3y + 2)}$

9. $\dfrac{(2x - 3)(x - 5)}{(2x - 3)(5 - x)}$

10. $\dfrac{(5y - 1)(3y + 2)}{(1 - 5y)(3y + 2)}$

11. $\dfrac{3x^2 - 3x}{6x^2 + 18x}$

12. $\dfrac{6a^2 - 3a}{15a^2 - 15a}$

13. $\dfrac{x^2 - 9}{x^2 - 6x + 9}$

14. $\dfrac{x^2 - 6x + 9}{x^2 - 9}$

15. $\dfrac{w^2 - 8wz + 7z^2}{w^2 + 8wz + 7z^2}$

16. $\dfrac{x^2 - 4xy + 4y^2}{x^2 + 4xy + 4y^2}$

17. $\dfrac{x^2 + x - 12}{x - 3}$

18. $\dfrac{a^2 + 2a - 63}{a - 7}$

19. $\dfrac{x^2 + x - 12}{3 - x}$

20. $\dfrac{a^2 + 2a - 63}{7 - a}$

21. $\dfrac{3a^2 - 13a - 30}{15a^2 + 28a + 5}$

22. $\dfrac{3a^2 - a - 2}{2a^2 + a - 3}$

23. $\dfrac{2x^3 - 2x^2 - 12x}{3x^2 - 6x}$

24. $\dfrac{10a^3 - 45a^2 - 25a}{2a^2 - 10a}$

25. $\dfrac{2x^2}{3x^2 - 6}$

26. $\dfrac{5a^2}{2a^2 - 10}$

27. $\dfrac{3a^2 - 7a - 6}{3 + 5a - 2a^2}$

28. $\dfrac{2x^2 - 3x - 2}{2 + 5x - 3x^2}$

29. $\dfrac{6r^2 - r - 2}{2 + r - 6r^2}$

30. $\dfrac{15y^2 - y - 2}{2 + y - 15y^2}$

31. $\dfrac{a^3 + b^3}{(a + b)^3}$

32. $\dfrac{a^3 + b^3}{a^2 + b^2}$

33. $\dfrac{ax + bx - 2ay - 2by}{4xy - 2x^2}$

34. $\dfrac{4x^2 - 8x + 3}{4x^2 - 6x + 2xy - 3y}$

35. $\dfrac{(a + b)^2 - (x + y)^2}{a + b + x + y}$

36. $\dfrac{x - 1}{x^3 + x^2 - x - 1}$

In Exercises 37–48, fill in the missing expression.

37. $\dfrac{2x}{3y} = \dfrac{?}{9x^2y}$

38. $\dfrac{5a}{3b} = \dfrac{?}{21a^2b}$

39. $\dfrac{5}{3a^2b} = \dfrac{?}{15a^4b^2}$

40. $\dfrac{8}{5x^2y} = \dfrac{?}{20x^3y^3}$

41. $\dfrac{3x}{x - 5} = \dfrac{?}{(x - 5)(x + 5)}$

42. $\dfrac{2z}{z - 6} = \dfrac{?}{(z - 6)^2}$

43. $\dfrac{a - b}{x + y} = \dfrac{?}{x^2 + 2xy + y^2}$

44. $\dfrac{x - y}{a - b} = \dfrac{?}{a^2 - b^2}$

45. $\dfrac{y - 2}{2y - 3} = \dfrac{?}{12 - 5y - 2y^2}$

46. $\dfrac{x + 1}{2x - 5} = \dfrac{?}{15 - x - 2x^2}$

47. $\dfrac{x - y}{a^2 - b^2} = \dfrac{?}{a^2x + a^2y - b^2x - b^2y}$

48. $\dfrac{5x + y}{r - s} = \dfrac{?}{r^2a + r^2b - s^2a - s^2b}$

ⓠ QUESTIONS FOR THOUGHT

49. Discuss what is **wrong** (if anything) with the following:

   (a) $\dfrac{\cancel{a}2 + \cancel{b}2}{\cancel{a} + \cancel{b}} \overset{?}{=} a + b$ (b) $\dfrac{\cancel{a^3 + b^3}}{\cancel{(a + b)^3}} \overset{?}{=} 1$

   (c) $\dfrac{ax + bx + 2ay + 2by}{a + b} \overset{?}{=} \dfrac{(a + b)x + (a + b)2y}{a + b}$

   $\overset{?}{=} \dfrac{\cancel{(a + b)}x + (a + b)2y}{\cancel{a + b}}$

   $\overset{?}{=} x + (a + b)2y$

50. Evaluate both of the following expressions for $y = 0, 1, 2, 3,$ and 4.

   $$\dfrac{2y^2 - y - 6}{y^2 - y - 2} \quad \text{and} \quad \dfrac{2y + 3}{y + 1}$$

   How do the values compare for each expression?

◇ **MINI-REVIEW**

51. *Solve for x.* $10(x + 24) - 6x = 400$

52. Write an equation of the line that passes through the point $(-5, 3)$ and is perpendicular to the line whose equation is $4x - 5y = 7$.

53. Given $f(x) = 2x^3 - x^2 + 3$, find $f(x^2)$.

6.3   Multiplication and Division of Rational Expressions

Multiplication

Now that we have some experience with rational expressions, we can examine the arithmetic operations with these expressions. We begin with multiplication and division, since performing these operations is more straightforward than addition and subtraction.

We define multiplication as follows:

Multiplication of Fractions	$\dfrac{a}{b} \cdot \dfrac{c}{d} = \dfrac{a \cdot c}{b \cdot d}$ $b, d \neq 0$

The product of fractions is defined as the product of the numerators divided by the product of the denominators, provided neither denominator is 0. For example:

$$\frac{3x}{y} \cdot \frac{4x^2}{7y^3} = \frac{(3x)(4x^2)}{(y)(7y^3)} = \frac{12x^3}{7y^4}$$

$$\frac{x - y}{2x + y} \cdot \frac{3x - 2y}{x + y} = \frac{(x - y)(3x - 2y)}{(2x + y)(x + y)} = \frac{3x^2 - 5xy + 2y^2}{2x^2 + 3xy + y^2}$$

Now that we have defined multiplication, we can take another look at the Fundamental Principle of Fractions. By the multiplicative identity property, we have

$$\frac{a}{b} = \frac{a}{b} \cdot 1 \qquad \textit{Multiplication by 1 does not change the value of an expression.}$$

$$= \frac{a}{b} \cdot \frac{k}{k} \qquad \textit{Since } \frac{k}{k} = 1 \quad (k \neq 0)$$

$$= \frac{a \cdot k}{b \cdot k}$$

which is the Fundamental Principle of Fractions. Thus, the Fundamental Principle of Fractions can be viewed as simply stating that multiplying by 1 does not change the value of an expression.

In the previous section we required that our final answer be reduced to lowest terms. In the process of multiplication, factors of each numerator remain in the numerator of the product and factors of each denominator remain in the denominator of the product. Therefore, it is much more efficient to reduce by any common factors before we actually carry out the multiplication.

EXAMPLE 1   Perform the operations. Express your answer in simplest form.

(a) $\dfrac{24x^2y}{13a^3b^2} \cdot \dfrac{26ab^3}{3xy^2}$ (b) $\dfrac{x + 2y}{x - y} \cdot \dfrac{y - x}{x - 2y}$

(c) $\left(\dfrac{x^2 + x}{x^2 - 1}\right)\left(\dfrac{x}{x + 2}\right)(x^2 + x - 2)$

Solution

(a) $\dfrac{24x^2y}{13a^3b^2} \cdot \dfrac{26ab^3}{3xy^2} = \dfrac{\overset{8}{\cancel{24}}\overset{x}{\cancel{x^2}}\cancel{y}}{\underset{a^2}{\cancel{13}\cancel{a^3}b^2}} \cdot \dfrac{\overset{2}{\cancel{26}}a\overset{b}{\cancel{b^3}}}{\underset{y}{3\cancel{x}\cancel{y^2}}}$

$= \boxed{\dfrac{16bx}{a^2y}}$

(b) $\dfrac{x + 2y}{x - y} \cdot \dfrac{y - x}{x - 2y} = \dfrac{x + 2y}{x - y} \cdot \dfrac{(-1)(x - y)}{x - 2y}$ *Since $y - x = (-1)(x - y)$*

$= \dfrac{x + 2y}{\cancel{x - y}} \cdot \dfrac{-1\cancel{(x - y)}}{x - 2y}$ *Then reduce.*

$= \boxed{\dfrac{-(x + 2y)}{x - 2y}}$ or $\boxed{\dfrac{-x - 2y}{x - 2y}}$ or $\boxed{-\dfrac{x + 2y}{x - 2y}}$

(c) $\left(\dfrac{x^2 + x}{x^2 - 1}\right)\left(\dfrac{x}{x + 2}\right)(x^2 + x - 2)$ *Factor and reduce.*

$= \dfrac{x\cancel{(x + 1)}}{\cancel{(x + 1)}\cancel{(x - 1)}} \cdot \dfrac{x}{\cancel{x + 2}} \cdot \dfrac{\cancel{(x + 2)}\cancel{(x - 1)}}{1}$ *Note the 1 in the denominator.*

$= \dfrac{x^2}{1} = \boxed{x^2}$ ∎

Writing in the understood denominator of 1 helps you to avoid errors in reducing fractions.

Division

We can now proceed to formulate the rule for division of fractions. Just as subtraction is the inverse of addition, division is the inverse operation of multiplication. That is, $38 \div 2$ is 19 because $19 \cdot 2 = 38$. Thus,

$$38 \div 2 = 19 \quad \text{because} \quad 19 \cdot 2 = 38$$

and

$$\dfrac{a}{b} \div \dfrac{c}{d} = \dfrac{ad}{bc} \quad \text{because} \quad \dfrac{ad}{bc} \cdot \dfrac{c}{d} = \dfrac{a}{b}$$

We rewrite

$$\dfrac{ad}{bc} \quad \text{as} \quad \dfrac{a}{b} \cdot \dfrac{d}{c}$$

Hence, we have the rule for division given in the next box.

Division of Fractions	$\dfrac{a}{b} \div \dfrac{c}{d} = \dfrac{a}{b} \cdot \dfrac{d}{c}$ $b, c, d \neq 0$

Recall from Chapter 1 that the multiplicative inverse of a number is called its *reciprocal*. We usually define reciprocal as follows:

DEFINITION	If $x \neq 0$, the **reciprocal** of x is $\dfrac{1}{x}$.

Thus, the reciprocal of 5 is $\dfrac{1}{5}$.

The reciprocal of $x^2 + 2$ is $\dfrac{1}{x^2 + 2}$.

The reciprocal of $\dfrac{a}{b}$ is $\dfrac{1}{\dfrac{a}{b}}$, which is $1 \div \dfrac{a}{b}$, and, by definition of division,

$$1 \div \dfrac{a}{b} = 1 \cdot \dfrac{b}{a} = \dfrac{b}{a}$$

Hence, if $a \neq 0$ and $b \neq 0$, the reciprocal of $\dfrac{a}{b}$ is $\dfrac{b}{a}$.

We can state the rule for division as follows:

To divide **by** *a fraction, multiply by its reciprocal.*

EXAMPLE 2

Perform the operations. Express your answer in simplest form.

(a) $\dfrac{16x^3}{9y^4} \div \dfrac{32x^6}{27y^3}$ **(b)** $\dfrac{3x^2 - 5xy + 2y^2}{2x^2 + 3xy + y^2} \div \dfrac{x - y}{x^2 + xy}$

Solution

(a) $\dfrac{16x^3}{9y^4} \div \dfrac{32x^6}{27y^3}$ *Dividing by $\dfrac{32x^6}{27y^3}$ means multiplying by $\dfrac{27y^3}{32x^6}$.*

$= \dfrac{16x^3}{9y^4} \cdot \dfrac{27y^3}{32x^6}$ *Reduce.*

$= \dfrac{\overset{}{16x^3}}{\underset{y}{9y^4}} \cdot \dfrac{\overset{3}{27y^3}}{\underset{2\,x^3}{32x^6}}$

$= \boxed{\dfrac{3}{2x^3y}}$

(b) $\dfrac{3x^2 - 5xy + 2y^2}{2x^2 + 3xy + y^2} \div \dfrac{x - y}{x^2 + xy}$ *Multiply by the reciprocal of the divisor (the expression you are dividing by).*

$= \dfrac{3x^2 - 5xy + 2y^2}{2x^2 + 3xy + y^2} \cdot \dfrac{x^2 + xy}{x - y}$ *Then factor and reduce.*

$= \dfrac{(3x - 2y)(x - y)}{(2x + y)(x + y)} \cdot \dfrac{x(x + y)}{x - y}$

$= \boxed{\dfrac{x(3x - 2y)}{2x + y}}$ or $\boxed{\dfrac{3x^2 - 2xy}{2x + y}}$ ∎

Just as operations on polynomials can be applied to polynomial functions, so too operations on rational expressions can be applied to rational functions.

EXAMPLE 3

Given $f(x) = \dfrac{x + 1}{x - 1}$ and $g(x) = x^2 - 1$. Find

(a) $f(x) \cdot g(x)$ **(b)** $f(x) \div g(x)$

Solution

(a) $f(x) \cdot g(x) = \dfrac{x + 1}{x - 1} \cdot (x^2 - 1)$ *Factor and reduce.*

$= \dfrac{x + 1}{x - 1} \cdot \dfrac{(x + 1)(x - 1)}{1}$

$= \boxed{(x + 1)^2}$

(b) $f(x) \div g(x) = \dfrac{x + 1}{x - 1} \div (x^2 - 1)$ *Follow the rule for division and factor.*

$= \dfrac{x + 1}{x - 1} \cdot \dfrac{1}{(x + 1)(x - 1)}$

$= \boxed{\dfrac{1}{(x - 1)^2}}$ ∎

EXERCISES 6.3

Perform the indicated operations. Reduce all answers to lowest terms.

1. $\dfrac{10a^2b}{3xy^3} \cdot \dfrac{9xy^4}{5a^4b^7}$

2. $\dfrac{32a^2}{7xb^2} \cdot \dfrac{21x^2b^4}{8a^3}$

3. $\dfrac{17a^2b^3}{18yx} \div \dfrac{34a^2}{9xy}$

4. $\dfrac{38xy^2z}{81a^2b^3} \div \dfrac{19ac^2}{27y^2}$

5. $\dfrac{16x^3b}{9a} \cdot 24a^2b^3$

6. $24a^2b^3 \cdot \dfrac{16x^3b}{9a}$

7. $\dfrac{32r^2s^3}{12a^2b} \cdot \left(\dfrac{15ab^2}{16r} \cdot \dfrac{24rs^2}{5ab} \right)$

8. $\dfrac{32x^2c}{12a^2b} \cdot \left(\dfrac{17a^2x^2}{34b^2c} \cdot \dfrac{16x}{9a} \right)$

9. $\dfrac{32r^2s^3}{12a^2b} \div \left(\dfrac{15ab^2}{16r} \cdot \dfrac{24rs^2}{5ab} \right)$

10. $\dfrac{32x^2c}{12a^2b} \div \left(\dfrac{17a^2x^2}{34b^2c} \cdot \dfrac{16x}{9a} \right)$

11. $\dfrac{x^2 - x - 2}{x + 3} \div \dfrac{3x + 9}{2x + 2}$

12. $\dfrac{4x + 8}{3x - 6} \cdot \dfrac{6x - 12}{8x + 16}$

13. $\dfrac{x^2 - x - 2}{x + 3} \cdot \dfrac{3x + 9}{2x + 2}$

14. $\dfrac{4x + 8}{3x - 6} \div \dfrac{6x - 12}{8x +16}$

15. $\dfrac{5a^3 - 5a^2b}{3a^2 + 3ab} \cdot (a + b)$

16. $\dfrac{x - 3}{2x^2 - 5x - 3} \cdot (8x + 4)$

17. $\dfrac{5a^3 - 5a^2b}{3a^2 + 3ab} \div (a + b)$

18. $(8x + 4) \div \dfrac{x - 3}{2x^2 - 5x - 3}$

19. $\dfrac{2x^2 + 3x - 5}{2x + 5} \cdot \dfrac{1}{1 - x}$

20. $\dfrac{2y^2 - 9y - 5}{2y + 1} \cdot \dfrac{1}{5 - y}$

21. $\dfrac{2a^2 - 7a + 6}{4a^2 - 9} \cdot \dfrac{4a^2 + 12a + 9}{a^2 - a - 2}$

22. $\dfrac{2x^2 - 5x - 12}{3x^2 - 11x - 4} \cdot \dfrac{3x^2 - 14x - 5}{2x^2 - 7x - 15}$

23. $\dfrac{x^2 - y^2}{(x + y)^3} \cdot \dfrac{(x + y)^2}{(x - y)^2}$

24. $\dfrac{2r^2 + rs - 3s^2}{r^2 - s^2} \cdot \dfrac{2r - 2s}{2r^2 + 5rs + 3s^2}$

25. $\dfrac{9x^2 + 3x - 2}{6x^2 - 2x} \div \dfrac{3x + 2}{6x^2}$

26. $\dfrac{2a^2 - 5a - 3}{4a^2 + 2a} \div \dfrac{2a + 1}{4a}$

27. $\dfrac{2x^2 + x - 3}{x^2 - 1} \div \dfrac{2x^2 + 5x + 3}{2 - 2x}$

28. $\dfrac{9x^2 - 9x + 2}{2x - 6x^2} \cdot \dfrac{6x^3}{3x - 2}$

29. $\dfrac{6q^2 - q - 2}{8q^2 + 4q} \cdot \dfrac{8q^2}{6q^2 - 4q}$

30. $\dfrac{4a^2 - 4a - 3}{8a + 4a^2} \cdot \dfrac{16a^2}{4a^2 - 6a}$

31. $\dfrac{m^2 - 10m + 25}{m^2 - 25} \div (5m^2 - 25m)$

32. $\dfrac{2c^3 - 18c^2}{9c^2} \cdot (3c^2 - 9c)$

33. $\left(\dfrac{2t^2 + 3t + 1}{3t^2 - t - 2} \right) \cdot \left(\dfrac{t - 1}{2t - 1} \right) \cdot \left(\dfrac{3t + 2}{t + 1} \right)$

34. $\left(\dfrac{6x^2 + x - 2}{4x^2 - 8x + 3} \right) \cdot \left(\dfrac{x - 1}{3x + 2} \cdot \dfrac{8x - 12}{2x - 2} \right)$

35. $\dfrac{9a^2 + 9a + 2}{3a^2 - 2a - 1} \cdot \left(\dfrac{a - 1}{3a^2 + 4a + 1} \div \dfrac{3a + 2}{a + 1} \right)$

36. $\dfrac{9a^2 + 9a + 2}{3a^2 - 2a - 1} \div \left(\dfrac{a - 1}{3a^2 + 4a + 1} \cdot \dfrac{3a + 2}{a + 1} \right)$

37. $\dfrac{2r^2 - 5r - 3}{6r - 2} \div \left(\dfrac{r - 3}{2} \div \dfrac{3r - 1}{2r + 1} \right)$

38. $\left(\dfrac{2r^2 - 5r - 3}{6r - 2} \div \dfrac{r - 3}{2} \right) \div \dfrac{3r - 1}{2r + 1}$

39. $\dfrac{x^2 - y^2}{y^3x - x^3y} \div (x^2 + 2xy + y^2)$

40. $\dfrac{x^2 - y^2}{y^3x - x^3y} \cdot (x^2 + 2xy + y^2)$

In Exercises 41–46, use $f(x) = \dfrac{x+2}{x-3}$, $g(x) = 2x^2 - 2x - 12$, *and* $h(x) = \dfrac{1}{3x^2 + 6x}$.

41. $f(x) \cdot g(x)$ **42.** $f(x) \cdot h(x)$

43. $f(x) \div g(x)$ **44.** $g(x) \div f(x)$

45. $h(x) \div f(x) \cdot g(x)$ **46.** $xh(x) \cdot g(x)$

 MINI-REVIEW

47. *Solve the following system of equations.*

$$\begin{cases} 6x - 2y = 7 \\ 16x + 3y = 2 \end{cases}$$

48. Express the area of the shaded region of the figure in terms of x.

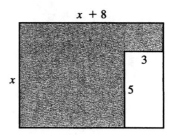

49. What is the degree of the polynomial $-4x^3 + 6x^2 - 5x + 2$?

50. *Solve for x.* $|2x - 3| = |3x + 4|$

6.4 Sums and Differences of Rational Expressions

The process of adding and subtracting fractions with the same or *common denominators* can be demonstrated by using the distributive property along with the definition of rational multiplication as follows:

$$\frac{a}{c} + \frac{b}{c} = a\left(\frac{1}{c}\right) + b\left(\frac{1}{c}\right) \qquad \textit{Rational multiplication}$$

$$= (a + b)\left(\frac{1}{c}\right) \qquad \textit{The distributive property}$$

$$= \frac{a + b}{c} \qquad \textit{Rational multiplication}$$

Hence, we have the rules stated in the box.

Addition and Subtraction of Rational Expressions	$\dfrac{a}{c} + \dfrac{b}{c} = \dfrac{a+b}{c}$ and $\dfrac{a}{c} - \dfrac{b}{c} = \dfrac{a-b}{c}$

In combining fractions with common denominators, we simply combine the numerators and place this result over the common denominator.

EXAMPLE 1 | Perform the operations.

     (a) $\dfrac{5y}{x} + \dfrac{3}{x}$ (b) $\dfrac{2x - 3}{x - 2} - \dfrac{x - 1}{x - 2}$

     (c) $\dfrac{4x^2 - 33x}{x^2 + x - 2} + \dfrac{2x - 6}{x^2 + x - 2} - \dfrac{(3x - 2)(x - 7)}{x^2 + x - 2}$

Solution

(a) $\dfrac{5y}{x} + \dfrac{3}{x} = \boxed{\dfrac{5y + 3}{x}}$

(b) $\dfrac{2x - 3}{x - 2} - \dfrac{x - 1}{x - 2}$ *Remember, we are subtracting the **quantity** $x - 1$ and therefore **must** include parentheses.*

$= \dfrac{2x - 3 - (x - 1)}{x - 2}$ *Remove parentheses.*

$= \dfrac{2x - 3 - x + 1}{x - 2}$ *Observe the signs of the terms in the numerator. Combine terms in the numerator.*

$= \dfrac{x - 2}{x - 2}$ *Then reduce.*

$= \boxed{1}$

(c) $\dfrac{4x^2 - 33x}{x^2 + x - 2} + \dfrac{2x - 6}{x^2 + x - 2} - \dfrac{(3x - 2)(x - 7)}{x^2 + x - 2}$ *Combine numerators.*

$= \dfrac{4x^2 - 33x + (2x - 6) - (3x - 2)(x - 7)}{x^2 + x - 2}$ *Remember that you are subtracting a product; find the product first.*

$= \dfrac{4x^2 - 33x + 2x - 6 - (3x^2 - 23x + 14)}{x^2 + x - 2}$ *Then subtract.*

$= \dfrac{4x^2 - 33x + 2x - 6 - 3x^2 + 23x - 14}{x^2 + x - 2}$ *Next, combine terms.*

$= \dfrac{x^2 - 8x - 20}{(x - 1)(x + 2)}$ *Factor.*

$= \dfrac{\cancel{(x + 2)}(x - 10)}{(x - 1)\cancel{(x + 2)}}$ *Reduce.*

$= \boxed{\dfrac{x - 10}{x - 1}}$ ∎

Our last step should be to reduce the answer to lowest terms. Also, keep in mind that we can reduce a fraction only by common factors, *not* common terms.

The next type of problem to consider is one in which the denominators are different. If the denominators are different, we use the fundamental principle of fractions to build new fractions. The new fractions must be equivalent to the original fractions and all have the same denominator. Once the denominators are the same, we can add the fractions as we did before. The idea is to find an expression that can serve as a common denominator.

This new denominator must be divisible by the original denominators and, for convenience, it should be the "smallest" expression divisible by the original denominators. By "smallest" we mean having the least number of factors. Hence, we call the smallest expression divisible by all denominators in question the ***least common denominator,*** or **LCD.** To find the LCD, we follow the procedure outlined in the accompanying box.

Procedure for Finding the LCD	1. Factor each denominator *completely.* 2. The LCD consists of the product of each *distinct* factor the *maximum* number of times it appears in any *one* denominator.

EXAMPLE 2

Find the LCD of the following:

(a) $\dfrac{3}{14x^3}$, $\dfrac{5}{21x^2y^4}$, $\dfrac{1}{12x^4y^3}$ (b) $\dfrac{3}{x^2-9}$, $\dfrac{x+1}{x^2+6x+9}$

Solution

(a) The LCD of $\dfrac{3}{14x^3}$, $\dfrac{5}{21x^2y^4}$, and $\dfrac{1}{12x^4y^3}$ is found in the following way:

1. Factor each denominator as completely as possible.

$$14x^3 = 7 \cdot 2xxx$$
$$21x^2y^4 = 7 \cdot 3xxyyyy$$
$$12x^4y^3 = 2 \cdot 2 \cdot 3xxxxyyy$$

2. Write each factor the *maximum* (not the total) number of times it appears in any one denominator.

The LCD is $7 \cdot 2 \cdot 2 \cdot 3xxxxyyyy = \boxed{84x^4y^4}$.

7   appears *once* in the first two denominators.

2   appears *twice* in the third denominator, and once in the first denominator.

3   appears *once* in the second and third denominators.

x appears *four* times in the third denominator, three times in the first denominator, and twice in the second denominator.

y appears *four* times in the second denominator, and three times in the third denominator.

Looking at the LCD and the denominators in factored form, note that all three denominators appear within the LCD. This means that the LCD is divisible by all three denominators. Also note that each factor in the LCD is necessary. For example, we cannot drop a factor of y or else $21x^2y^4$ will not divide into the LCD; we cannot drop a factor of x or $12x^4y^3$ will not divide into the LCD. The fact that there are no "extra" factors makes it the *least* common denominator.

(b) The LCD of $\dfrac{3}{x^2-9}$ and $\dfrac{x+1}{x^2+6x+9}$ is found as follows:

1. Factor each denominator completely.

$$x^2 - 9 = (x+3)(x-3)$$
$$x^2 + 6x + 9 = (x+3)(x+3)$$

That is, $x - 3$ appears once in the first denominator and $x + 3$ appears twice in the second denominator.

2. Write each factor the maximum number of times it appears in any one denominator.

The LCD is $(x-3)(x+3)(x+3) = \boxed{(x-3)(x+3)^2}$. ∎

Now let's see how we can use the LCD and the Fundamental Principle of Fractions to add or subtract fractions with unlike denominators. We can add fractions with unlike denominators by following four general steps.

To Combine Fractions with Different Denominators	1. Find the LCD. 2. Build each fraction to higher terms with the LCD in each denominator. 3. Combine, as with fractions with common denominators. 4. Simplify if possible.

EXAMPLE 3

Perform the indicated operations.

(a) $\dfrac{3}{5x^2y} - \dfrac{2}{3xy^2} + x$ (b) $\dfrac{3x}{x^2-9} + \dfrac{5}{2x^3-6x^2}$ (c) $\dfrac{5x-10}{x-4} + \dfrac{3x-2}{4-x}$

Solution

(a) First find the LCD:

$$\text{LCD:} \quad 5 \cdot 3 \cdot x^2 y^2$$

Build fractions to higher terms with the LCD, $5 \cdot 3 \cdot x^2 y^2$, in each denominator. Look at $5 \cdot 3 \cdot x^2 y^2$ and determine what factors are missing.

$$\frac{3}{5x^2 y} = \frac{3 \ (3y)}{5x^2 y \ (3y)}$$

Multiply numerator and denominator by the missing factors to make $5x^2 y$ into $5 \cdot 3 \cdot x^2 y^2$.

$$\frac{2}{3xy^2} = \frac{2 \ (5x)}{3xy^2 \ (5x)}$$

Multiply numerator and denominator by the missing factors to make $3xy^2$ into $5 \cdot 3 \cdot x^2 y^2$.

$$\frac{x}{1} = \frac{x \ (5 \cdot 3 \cdot x^2 y^2)}{1 \ (5 \cdot 3 \cdot x^2 y^2)}$$

Rewrite x as $\frac{x}{1}$ and fill in the missing factors to make 1 into $5 \cdot 3 \cdot x^2 y^2$.

$$\frac{3}{5x^2 y} - \frac{2}{3xy^2} + x = \frac{3(3y) - 2(5x) + x(5 \cdot 3 \cdot x^2 y^2)}{5 \cdot 3 \cdot x^2 y^2}$$

Place numerators over the LCD and combine.

$$= \boxed{\frac{9y - 10x + 15x^3 y^2}{15x^2 y^2}}$$

Your last step should be to simplify (reduce) your answer. In this case, the answer is already in simplest form.

(b) The LCD is found by factoring the denominators and writing each factor the maximum number of times it appears in any denominator:

$$x^2 - 9 = (x - 3)(x + 3)$$
$$2x^3 - 6x^2 = 2x^2(x - 3)$$

Thus, the LCD is $2x^2(x - 3)(x + 3)$.

$$\frac{3x}{x^2 - 9} + \frac{5}{2x^3 - 6x^2}$$

Build fractions by filling in missing factors.

$$= \frac{3x(2x^2)}{(x - 3)(x + 3)(2x^2)} + \frac{5(x + 3)}{2x^2(x - 3)(x + 3)}$$

Combine, as with like fractions.

$$= \frac{6x^3 + 5(x + 3)}{2x^2(x - 3)(x + 3)}$$

*At this point you may be tempted to reduce the x^2 with x^3 and/or the $(x + 3)$ in the numerator with the $(x + 3)$ in the denominator. However, neither x^3 nor $(x + 3)$ is a **factor** of the numerator and thus we cannot reduce the fraction at this point. Therefore the final answer is*

$$= \boxed{\frac{6x^3 + 5x + 15}{2x^2(x - 3)(x + 3)}}$$

(c) $$\frac{5x - 10}{x - 4} + \frac{3x - 2}{4 - x}$$

Note: Since $x - 4$ is the negative of $4 - x$, we multiply the numerator and denominator of the second fraction by -1.

$$= \frac{5x - 10}{x - 4} + \frac{(3x - 2)(-1)}{(4 - x)(-1)}$$

$$= \frac{5x - 10}{x - 4} + \frac{(3x - 2)(-1)}{x - 4}$$

Now the denominators are the same.

$$= \frac{5x - 10 + (3x - 2)(-1)}{x - 4} \qquad \text{\textit{Combine numerators; place results above the common denominator.}}$$

$$= \frac{5x - 10 - 3x + 2}{x - 4} = \frac{2x - 8}{x - 4} = \frac{2(x - 4)}{x - 4} \qquad \text{\textit{Factor and reduce.}}$$

$$= \boxed{2} \qquad\qquad\qquad\qquad\qquad \blacksquare$$

EXAMPLE 4

Perform the indicated operations. $\dfrac{3}{x^2 - 9} - \dfrac{x + 1}{x^2 + 6x + 9}$

Solution

We found the LCD of these two rational expressions previously in Example 2(b).

$$\frac{3}{x^2 - 9} - \frac{x + 1}{x^2 + 6x + 9} = \frac{3}{(x + 3)(x - 3)} - \frac{x + 1}{(x + 3)(x + 3)} \qquad \text{\textit{The LCD is}}$$

The LCD is $(x - 3)(x + 3)^2$. Build fractions by filling in missing factors.

$$= \frac{3(x + 3)}{(x - 3)(x + 3)^2} - \frac{(x + 1)(x - 3)}{(x - 3)(x + 3)^2} \qquad \text{\textit{Combine.}}$$

$$= \frac{3(x + 3) - (x + 1)(x - 3)}{(x - 3)(x + 3)^2} \qquad \text{\textit{Simplify the numerator.}}$$

$$= \frac{(3x + 9) - (x^2 - 2x - 3)}{(x - 3)(x + 3)^2}$$

$$= \frac{3x + 9 - x^2 + 2x + 3}{(x - 3)(x + 3)^2}$$

$$= \boxed{\frac{-x^2 + 5x + 12}{(x - 3)(x + 3)^2}} \qquad\qquad \blacksquare$$

EXAMPLE 5

If $f(x) = \dfrac{2}{x + 1}$, find and simplify $f(x + h) - f(x)$.

Solution

We begin by finding $f(x + h)$:

$$f(x) = \frac{2}{x + 1} \qquad \text{\textit{$f(x + h)$ is found by substituting $x + h$ for x.}}$$

$$f(x + h) = \frac{2}{x + h + 1} \qquad \text{\textit{Next we write out the expression $f(x + h) - f(x)$.}}$$

$$f(x + h) - f(x) = \frac{2}{x + h + 1} - \frac{2}{x + 1} \qquad \text{\textit{Next, find the LCD and build the fractions. LCD $= (x + h + 1)(x + 1)$}}$$

$$= \frac{2(x + 1)}{(x + h + 1)(x + 1)} - \frac{2(x + h + 1)}{(x + h + 1)(x + 1)} \qquad \text{\textit{Combine the numerators.}}$$

$$= \frac{2(x + 1) - 2(x + h + 1)}{(x + h + 1)(x + 1)}$$

$$= \frac{2x + 2 - 2x - 2h - 2}{(x + h + 1)(x + 1)}$$

$$= \boxed{\frac{-2h}{(x + h + 1)(x + 1)}} \qquad\qquad \blacksquare$$

Dividing a Polynomial by a Monomial

We discussed polynomial division in Chapter 5 and postponed discussing division by monomials until now because the process typically requires us to rewrite the quotient as a fraction.

EXAMPLE 6   Find the quotient. $(6x^5y^2 - 9x^3y + 12x^2) \div 6x^2y$

Solution   Division by monomials can be accomplished in two ways, depending on what type of answer is being sought. Both methods require us to rewrite the quotient as a fraction.

Method 1:   Just as we can combine several fractions that have the same denominator into a single fraction, we can also write a single fraction with several terms in the numerator as a sum or difference of several fractions.

$$\frac{6x^5y^2 - 9x^3y + 12x^2}{6x^2y} = \frac{6x^5y^2}{6x^2y} - \frac{9x^3y}{6x^2y} + \frac{12x^2}{6x^2y} \qquad \text{\textit{Notice that we are doing the}}$$
$$\text{\textit{reverse of combining fractions.}}$$

$$= \frac{\overset{x^3y}{\cancel{6x^5y^2}}}{\cancel{6x^2y}} - \frac{\overset{3x}{\cancel{9x^3y}}}{\underset{2}{\cancel{6x^2y}}} + \frac{\overset{2}{\cancel{12x^2}}}{6x^2y} \qquad \text{\textit{Reduce each fraction.}}$$

$$= \boxed{x^3y - \frac{3x}{2} + \frac{2}{y}}$$

Method 2:   An alternative approach is to reduce the fraction as discussed in Section 6.2:

$$\frac{6x^5y^2 - 9x^3y + 12x^2}{6x^2y} \qquad \text{\textit{Factor and reduce.}}$$

$$= \frac{3x^2(2x^3y^2 - 3xy + 4)}{\underset{2}{\cancel{6x^2y}}}$$

$$= \boxed{\frac{2x^3y^2 - 3xy + 4}{2y}}$$

The answers obtained by the two methods may look different but they are in fact equal. Try combining the fractions in the answer obtained by method 1 into a single fraction and see whether you get the answer produced by method 2.   ■

 EXERCISES 6.4

Perform the indicated operations. Express your answer in simplest form.

1. $\dfrac{x+2}{x} - \dfrac{2-x}{x}$

2. $\dfrac{x-4}{2x} + \dfrac{x+4}{2x}$

3. $\dfrac{10a}{a-b} - \dfrac{10b}{a-b}$

4. $\dfrac{5x}{x+2} + \dfrac{10}{x+2}$

5. $\dfrac{3a}{3a^2+a-2} - \dfrac{2}{3a^2+a-2}$

6. $\dfrac{x}{3x^2+x-2} + \dfrac{1}{3x^2+x-2}$

7. $\dfrac{x^2}{x^2-y^2} + \dfrac{y^2}{x^2-y^2} - \dfrac{2xy}{x^2-y^2}$

8. $\dfrac{a^2}{a^2-b^2} + \dfrac{b^2}{a^2-b^2} + \dfrac{2ab}{b^2-a^2}$

9. $\dfrac{5x}{x+3} + \dfrac{3x}{x+3} + 4$

10. $\dfrac{3t}{t-2} + \dfrac{2}{t-2} + 3t$

11. $\dfrac{3x}{2y^2} - \dfrac{4x^2}{9y}$

12. $\dfrac{24}{5x^2 y} + \dfrac{14}{45xy^3}$

13. $\dfrac{7y}{6x^2} - \dfrac{8x^2}{9y^2}$

14. $\dfrac{5a}{4b^2} - \dfrac{16b}{25a^2}$

15. $\dfrac{7y}{6x^2} \cdot \dfrac{8x^2}{9y^2}$

16. $\dfrac{5a}{4b^2} \div \dfrac{16b}{24a^2}$

17. $\dfrac{36a^2}{b^2 c} + \dfrac{24}{bc^3} - \dfrac{3}{7bc}$

18. $\dfrac{3x}{2a^2 b} + \dfrac{2y}{3ab^2} - \dfrac{3}{a^3 b^2}$

19. $\dfrac{3}{x} + \dfrac{x}{x + 2}$

20. $\dfrac{5}{y} + \dfrac{y}{y - 3}$

21. $\dfrac{a}{a - b} - \dfrac{b}{a}$

22. $\dfrac{2}{x - 7} - \dfrac{7}{x}$

23. $\dfrac{5}{x + 7} - \dfrac{2}{x - 3}$

24. $\dfrac{3}{x - 2} + \dfrac{4}{x + 5}$

25. $\dfrac{2}{x - 7} + \dfrac{3x + 1}{x + 2}$

26. $\dfrac{3}{a + 4} + \dfrac{5a + 1}{a - 2}$

27. $\dfrac{2r + s}{r - s} - \dfrac{r - 2s}{r + s}$

28. $\dfrac{3x + y}{x + y} - \dfrac{2x + y}{x - y}$

29. $\dfrac{4}{x - 4} + \dfrac{x}{4 - x}$

30. $\dfrac{a}{a - b} + \dfrac{b}{b - a}$

31. $\dfrac{7a + 3}{2a - 1} + \dfrac{5a + 4}{1 - 2a}$

32. $\dfrac{3x + 1}{x - 2} + \dfrac{2x + 3}{2 - x}$

33. $\dfrac{a}{a - b} - \dfrac{b}{a^2 - b^2}$

34. $\dfrac{x}{x - y} + \dfrac{y}{(x - y)^2}$

35. $\dfrac{a}{a - b} \div \dfrac{b}{a^2 - b^2}$

36. $\dfrac{x}{x - y} \cdot \dfrac{y}{(x - y)^2}$

37. $\dfrac{2y + 1}{y + 2} + \dfrac{3y}{y + 3} + y$

38. $\dfrac{2x + 1}{x + 3} + \dfrac{3x}{x - 2} + 2x$

39. $\dfrac{5x + 1}{x + 2} + \dfrac{2x + 6}{x^2 + 5x + 6}$

40. $\dfrac{2a + 3}{a^2 - 2a - 8} - \dfrac{a - 5}{a - 4}$

41. $\dfrac{5x + 1}{x + 2} \div \dfrac{2x + 6}{x^2 + 5x + 6}$

42. $\dfrac{2a + 3}{a^2 - 2a - 8} \div \dfrac{a - 5}{a - 4}$

43. $\dfrac{x + 1}{x^2 - 3x} + \dfrac{x - 2}{x^2 - 6x + 9}$

44. $\dfrac{x - 2}{3x^2 - 12x} - \dfrac{3}{x^2 - 8x + 16}$

45. $\dfrac{a + 3}{a - 3} + \dfrac{a}{a + 4} - \dfrac{3}{a^2 + a - 12}$

46. $\dfrac{x + 6}{x - 3} + \dfrac{x}{x + 2} - \dfrac{10}{x^2 - x - 6}$

47. $\dfrac{y + 7}{y + 5} - \dfrac{y}{y - 3} + \dfrac{16}{y^2 + 2y - 15}$

48. $\dfrac{3x + 4}{x + 4} + \dfrac{3x}{x - 2} + \dfrac{4}{x^2 + 2x - 8}$

49. $\dfrac{3x - 4}{x - 5} + \dfrac{4x}{10 + 3x - x^2}$

50. $\dfrac{2r - 5}{r - 2} + \dfrac{3r}{6 - r - r^2}$

51. $\dfrac{2a - 1}{a^2 + a - 6} + \dfrac{a + 2}{a^2 - 2a - 15} - \dfrac{a + 1}{a^2 - 7a + 10}$

52. $\dfrac{3y + 2}{y^2 - 2y + 1} - \dfrac{7y - 3}{y^2 - 1} + \dfrac{5}{y + 1}$

53. $\dfrac{5a}{3a - 1} + \dfrac{2a + 1}{5a + 2} + 5a + 1$

54. $\dfrac{3x}{x - 1} + \dfrac{x + 3}{x - 2} + 2x - 3$

55. $\dfrac{2r + xs}{r + s} + \dfrac{2s + xr}{r + s}$

56. $\dfrac{ax + ay}{a + b} + \dfrac{bx + by}{a + b}$

6.5 Mixed Operations and Complex Fractions

Now we are in the position to perform mixed operations with fractions.

EXAMPLE 1 Perform the indicated operations and simplify.

$$\left(\frac{x+6}{x+2} - \frac{4}{x}\right) \div \frac{x^2 - 16}{x^2 - 4}$$

Solution $\left(\dfrac{x+6}{x+2} - \dfrac{4}{x}\right) \div \dfrac{x^2 - 16}{x^2 - 4}$ *Combine fractions in parentheses. The LCD is $x(x+2)$.*

$= \left(\dfrac{x(x+6)}{x(x+2)} - \dfrac{4(x+2)}{x(x+2)}\right) \div \dfrac{x^2 - 16}{x^2 - 4}$

$= \left(\dfrac{x(x+6) - 4(x+2)}{x(x+2)}\right) \div \dfrac{x^2 - 16}{x^2 - 4}$

$= \left(\dfrac{x^2 + 6x - 4x - 8}{x(x+2)}\right) \div \dfrac{x^2 - 16}{x^2 - 4}$

$= \left(\dfrac{x^2 + 2x - 8}{x(x+2)}\right) \div \dfrac{x^2 - 16}{x^2 - 4}$ *Next we follow the rule for division.*

$= \dfrac{x^2 + 2x - 8}{x(x+2)} \cdot \dfrac{x^2 - 4}{x^2 - 16}$ *Factor and reduce.*

$= \dfrac{(x+4)(x-2)}{x(x+2)} \cdot \dfrac{(x+2)(x-2)}{(x+4)(x-4)}$

$= \boxed{\dfrac{(x-2)^2}{x(x-4)}}$ or $\boxed{\dfrac{x^2 - 4x + 4}{x^2 - 4x}}$ ∎

Another way of expressing a quotient of fractions is to use a large fraction bar instead of the quotient sign, ÷. Thus, we can rewrite

$$\frac{a}{b} \div \frac{c}{d} \quad \text{as} \quad \frac{\dfrac{a}{b}}{\dfrac{c}{d}}$$

Quotients written this way (fractions within fractions) are called **complex fractions**. This notation is often more convenient than using the quotient sign. It allows us to demonstrate that the "multiply by the reciprocal of the divisor" rule is simply an application of the Fundamental Principle of Fractions:

$\dfrac{\dfrac{a}{b}}{\dfrac{c}{d}} = \dfrac{\dfrac{a}{b} \cdot \dfrac{d}{c}}{\dfrac{c}{d} \cdot \dfrac{d}{c}}$ *Multiply numerator and denominator of the complex fraction by $\dfrac{d}{c}$ (Fundamental Principle of Fractions).*

$= \dfrac{\dfrac{a}{b} \cdot \dfrac{d}{c}}{\dfrac{c}{d} \cdot \dfrac{d}{c}} = \dfrac{\dfrac{a}{b} \cdot \dfrac{d}{c}}{1}$ *Reduce.*

$= \dfrac{a}{b} \cdot \dfrac{d}{c}$

57. $\dfrac{r^2}{r^3 - s^3} + \dfrac{rs}{r^3 - s^3} + \dfrac{s^2}{r^3 - s^3}$

58. $\dfrac{a^2}{a^3 + 8b^3} - \dfrac{2ab}{a^3 + 8b^3} + \dfrac{4b^2}{a^3 + 8b^3}$

59. $\dfrac{2s + t}{s^3 - t^3} + \dfrac{3s}{s^2 + st + t^2}$

60. $\dfrac{3x + 1}{x^3 + 8} + \dfrac{2x + 1}{x^2 - 2x + 4}$

In Exercises 61–66, find the quotient by each of the following methods:

(a) *Express as a single fraction reduced to lowest terms.*

(b) *Rewrite the fraction as sums or differences of fractions with the same denominator (and then simplify each fraction).*

61. $\dfrac{x^2 + 4x}{4x}$

62. $\dfrac{a^3 - 6a^2}{3a}$

63. $\dfrac{15x^3y^2 - 10x^2y^3}{5x^2y^2}$

64. $\dfrac{18r^2s^6 + 24r^3s^4}{6r^2s^3}$

65. $\dfrac{6m^2n - 4m^3n^2 - 9mn}{15mn^2}$

66. $\dfrac{10u^2v^3 - 15u^4v + 20uv^3}{25u^2v^3}$

In Exercises 67–74, use $f(x) = \dfrac{x - 2}{x + 2}$, $g(x) = \dfrac{2x}{x^2 - 4}$, and $h(x) = \dfrac{x}{x - 2}$.

67. $f(x) + g(x)$

68. $f(x) \cdot g(x)$

69. $f(x) \cdot h(x)$

70. $f(x) - h(x)$

71. $g(x) + h(x)$

72. $g(x) \div h(x)$

73. $h(x) \div g(x)$

74. $f(x) - g(x) + h(x)$

In Exercises 75–78, find and simplify $f(x + h) - f(x)$.

75. $f(x) = \dfrac{3}{x}$

76. $f(x) = \dfrac{1}{x - 6}$

77. $f(x) = \dfrac{x}{x - 3}$

78. $f(x) = \dfrac{2x}{x + 4}$

? QUESTION FOR THOUGHT

79. Use the calculator to evaluate the following for $x = -1, -\frac{1}{2}, 0, \frac{1}{2}, 1$, and 2; discuss your results.

$$\dfrac{3x + 5}{x - 1} + \dfrac{x + 7}{1 - x}$$

MINI-REVIEW

80. *Solve for x.* $\dfrac{x}{3} - \dfrac{x}{4} = 4$

81. Find the slope of the line passing through the points $(-4, 2)$ and $(5, -2)$.

82. *Simplify.* $(x - 3)^2 - (x + 3)^2$

83. Sketch the graph of the solution set of $2x - 3y \geq 12$.

Thus, an expression such as

$$\frac{\dfrac{3a^2b}{2xy^3}}{\dfrac{9ab^2}{8x^2y}}$$

can be rewritten as

$$\frac{3a^2b}{2xy^3} \div \frac{9ab^2}{8x^2y} = \frac{3a^2b}{2xy^3} \cdot \frac{8x^2y}{9ab^2}$$

$$= \frac{\overset{a}{\cancel{3}\cancel{a^2}b}}{\underset{y^2}{\cancel{2}\cancel{xy^3}}} \cdot \frac{\overset{4x}{\cancel{8}\cancel{x^2y}}}{\underset{3\quad b}{\cancel{9}\cancel{ab^2}}} = \frac{4ax}{3by^2}$$

EXAMPLE 2

Solution

If $f(x) = \dfrac{2-x}{x+1}$, find $f\left(\dfrac{2}{3}\right)$.

$$f\left(\frac{2}{3}\right) = \frac{2 - \dfrac{2}{3}}{\dfrac{2}{3} + 1}$$

This is a complex fraction that needs to be simplified. We offer two methods of solution. The first method treats the complex fraction as a multiple-operation problem similar to Example 1. That is, we treat the complex fraction as if it were written as

$$\left(2 - \frac{2}{3}\right) \div \left(\frac{2}{3} + 1\right)$$

Hence, we combine the fractions in the numerator of the complex fraction, combine the fractions in the denominator of the complex fraction, and then we will have a quotient of two fractions.

Method 1: $\dfrac{2 - \dfrac{2}{3}}{\dfrac{2}{3} + 1}$ *Combine the fractions in the numerator and denominator of the complex fraction. The LCD in both cases is 3.*

$$= \frac{\dfrac{6}{3} - \dfrac{2}{3}}{\dfrac{2}{3} + \dfrac{3}{3}}$$

$$= \frac{\dfrac{4}{3}}{\dfrac{5}{3}}$$ *We now have the quotient of two fractions. We follow the rule for division; multiply by the reciprocal of the divisor.*

$$= \frac{4}{\cancel{3}} \cdot \frac{\cancel{3}}{5} = \boxed{\frac{4}{5}}$$

The second method attempts to immediately clear the denominators *within* the complex fraction. To do this, we apply the Fundamental Principle by multiplying the numerator and denominator of the complex fraction by the LCD of *all* the simple fractions in the complex fraction.

Method 2:

$$\frac{2 - \dfrac{2}{3}}{\dfrac{2}{3} + 1}$$

Find the LCD of all the simple fractions, which is 3. Next multiply the numerator and denominator of the complex fraction by 3.

$$= \frac{\left(2 - \dfrac{2}{3}\right) \cdot \dfrac{3}{1}}{\left(\dfrac{2}{3} + 1\right) \cdot \dfrac{3}{1}}$$

Now use the distributive property in the numerator and denominator.

$$= \frac{2 \cdot 3 - \dfrac{2}{\cancel{3}} \cdot \dfrac{\cancel{3}}{1}}{\dfrac{2}{\cancel{3}} \cdot \dfrac{\cancel{3}}{1} + 1 \cdot 3}$$

Reduce where appropriate.

$$= \frac{6 - 2}{2 + 3} = \boxed{\dfrac{4}{5}}$$

Either method can be used to simplify any complex fraction. There are situations for which method 1 is simpler and others for which method 2 is simpler.

It is a worthwhile exercise to compute the value of this complex fraction using a calculator. You may find that doing this computation with a calculator is not quite as easy as you might think. ∎

EXAMPLE 3

Express the following as a simple fraction reduced to lowest terms:

$$\frac{1 - \dfrac{2}{x}}{1 + \dfrac{2}{x} - \dfrac{8}{x^2}}$$

Solution

We again illustrate both methods.

Method 1:

$$\frac{1 - \dfrac{2}{x}}{1 + \dfrac{2}{x} - \dfrac{8}{x^2}}$$

Combine the fractions in the numerator and denominator of the complex fraction.

The LCD for the numerator is x; the LCD for the denominator is x^2.

$$= \frac{\dfrac{x}{x} - \dfrac{2}{x}}{\dfrac{x^2}{x^2} + \dfrac{2x}{x^2} - \dfrac{8}{x^2}}$$

$$= \frac{\dfrac{x - 2}{x}}{\dfrac{x^2 + 2x - 8}{x^2}}$$

We now have the quotient of two fractions. Now follow the rule for division: Multiply by the reciprocal of the divisor.

$$= \frac{x - 2}{x} \cdot \frac{x^2}{x^2 - 2x - 8}$$

Factor and reduce.

$$= \frac{\cancel{x - 2}}{\cancel{x}} \cdot \frac{\cancel{x^2}^{x}}{(x + 4)(\cancel{x - 2})}$$

$$= \boxed{\dfrac{x}{x + 4}}$$

Method 2: $\dfrac{1 - \dfrac{2}{x}}{1 + \dfrac{2}{x} - \dfrac{8}{x^2}}$ *We multiply the numerator and denominator of the complex fraction by the LCD of **all** denominators of the simple fractions, which is x^2.*

$$= \frac{\left(1 - \dfrac{2}{x}\right) \cdot \dfrac{x^2}{1}}{\left(1 + \dfrac{2}{x} - \dfrac{8}{x^2}\right) \cdot \dfrac{x^2}{1}}$$ *Next, use the distributive property in numerator and denominator.*

$$= \frac{x^2 - \dfrac{2}{x} \cdot \dfrac{x^2}{1}}{x^2 + \dfrac{2}{x} \cdot \dfrac{x^2}{1} - \dfrac{8}{x^2} \cdot \dfrac{x^2}{1}}$$

$$= \frac{x^2 - 2x}{x^2 + 2x - 8}$$ *Factor and reduce.*

$$= \frac{x(x - 2)}{(x + 4)(x - 2)} = \boxed{\frac{x}{x + 4}} \qquad \blacksquare$$

EXAMPLE 4   If $f(x) = \dfrac{3}{x}$, simplify $\dfrac{f(x + 5) - f(x)}{5}$.

Solution   Looking carefully at the given expression, we recognize that we are simply computing the difference between two expressions, $f(x + 5)$ and $f(x)$, and then dividing this difference by 5. Since we are given $f(x)$, our first step is to find $f(x + 5)$:

$$f(x) = \frac{3}{x}$$ *To find $f(x + 5)$, substitute $x + 5$ for x in $\dfrac{3}{x}$.*

$$f(x + 5) = \frac{3}{x + 5}$$

Now that we have $f(x + 5)$, we can find $\dfrac{f(x + 5) - f(x)}{5}$:

$$\frac{f(x + 5) - f(x)}{5} = \frac{\overbrace{\dfrac{3}{x + 5}}^{f(x + 5)} - \overbrace{\dfrac{3}{x}}^{f(x)}}{5}$$ *We choose to simplify the complex fraction using method 2. We multiply the numerator and denominator of thee complex fraction by the LCD of all the simple fractions, which is $x(x + 5)$.*

$$= \frac{\left(\dfrac{3}{x + 5} - \dfrac{3}{x}\right) \dfrac{x(x + 5)}{1}}{5 \cdot x(x + 5)}$$

$$= \frac{\dfrac{3}{x + 5} \cdot \dfrac{x(x + 5)}{1} - \dfrac{3}{x} \cdot \dfrac{x(x + 5)}{1}}{5 \cdot x(x + 5)}$$ *Simplify.*

$$= \frac{3x - 3(x + 5)}{5x(x + 5)}$$ *Note the necessary parentheses around $x + 5$. Also note that you cannot reduce by a factor of $(x + 5)$ because it is not a factor of the numerator. Now simplify the numerator and reduce the fraction.*

$$= \frac{3x - 3x - 15}{5x(x + 5)} = \frac{-15}{5x(x + 5)} = \boxed{\frac{-3}{x(x + 5)}} \qquad \blacksquare$$

Express each of the following as a simple fraction reduced to lowest terms.

1. $\dfrac{\dfrac{3}{xy^2}}{\dfrac{15}{x^2y}}$

2. $\dfrac{\dfrac{5}{3a^2b}}{\dfrac{25}{9ab^2}}$

3. $\dfrac{\dfrac{3}{x-y}}{\dfrac{x-y}{3}}$

4. $\dfrac{\dfrac{5}{x+y}}{\dfrac{5}{x-y}}$

5. $\dfrac{a-\dfrac{1}{3}}{\dfrac{9a^2-1}{3a}}$

6. $\dfrac{1-\dfrac{1}{x^2}}{\dfrac{x-1}{x}}$

7. $\dfrac{x+\dfrac{2}{x^2}}{\dfrac{1}{x}+2}$

8. $\left(\dfrac{1}{x}+\dfrac{1}{y}\right)\div\dfrac{3}{xy^2}$

9. $\left(1-\dfrac{4}{x^2}\right)\div\left(\dfrac{1}{x}-\dfrac{2}{x^2}\right)$

10. $\dfrac{x-\dfrac{3}{y^2}}{\dfrac{2}{x}-\dfrac{3}{y^2}}$

11. $\dfrac{1-\dfrac{5}{y}}{y+3-\dfrac{40}{y}}$

12. $\dfrac{3+\dfrac{9}{x}}{x-7-\dfrac{30}{x}}$

13. $\dfrac{1-\dfrac{4}{z}+\dfrac{4}{z^2}}{\dfrac{1}{z^2}-\dfrac{2}{z^3}}$

14. $\dfrac{2+\dfrac{3}{x}-\dfrac{2}{x^2}}{\dfrac{2}{x^2}-\dfrac{1}{x^3}}$

15. $\dfrac{\dfrac{4}{y^2}-\dfrac{12}{xy}+\dfrac{9}{x^2}}{\dfrac{4}{y^2}-\dfrac{9}{x^2}}$

16. $\dfrac{\dfrac{9}{t}+\dfrac{12}{s}+\dfrac{4t}{s^2}}{\dfrac{9}{t}+\dfrac{9}{s}+\dfrac{2t}{s^2}}$

17. $\dfrac{\dfrac{2x}{y}+7+\dfrac{5y}{x}}{3x+2y-\dfrac{y^2}{x}}$

18. $\dfrac{\dfrac{6a}{b}-5-\dfrac{6b}{a}}{2-\dfrac{3b}{a}}$

19. $\dfrac{1-\dfrac{3}{x}-\dfrac{10}{x^2}}{4+\dfrac{8}{x}}$

20. $\dfrac{5+\dfrac{35}{x}}{1+\dfrac{3}{x}-\dfrac{28}{x^2}}$

21. $\dfrac{9-\dfrac{25}{t^2}}{6+\dfrac{10}{t}}$

22. $\dfrac{16-\dfrac{49}{v^2}}{12+\dfrac{21}{v}}$

23. $\dfrac{\dfrac{1}{x-3}-\dfrac{1}{x}}{3}$

24. $\dfrac{\dfrac{1}{a+5}-\dfrac{1}{a}}{5}$

25. $\dfrac{\dfrac{h}{h+1}-\dfrac{h}{h-1}}{2}$

26. $\dfrac{\dfrac{y+4}{y+2}-\dfrac{y}{y-2}}{4}$

27. $\left(3+\dfrac{1}{2x-1}\right)\div\left(5+\dfrac{x}{2x-1}\right)$

28. $\left(a+\dfrac{2a}{a-1}\right)\div\left(a-\dfrac{2a}{a-1}\right)$

29. $\dfrac{\dfrac{4}{x+3}-\dfrac{4}{x}}{3}$

30. $\dfrac{\dfrac{7}{x+h}-\dfrac{7}{x}}{h}$

In Exercises 31–44, use $f(x)=\dfrac{2x}{x-3}$, $g(x)=-\dfrac{1}{x}$, *and* $h(x)=\dfrac{x+2}{x}$ *to find and simplify the given expression.*

31. $f\left(\tfrac{2}{3}\right)$

32. $g\left(\tfrac{3}{4}\right)$

33. $g\left(\tfrac{2}{x}\right)$

34. $f\left(\tfrac{3}{x}\right)$

35. $\dfrac{f(x+3)-f(x)}{3}$

36. $\dfrac{g(x-4)-g(x)}{4}$

37. $\dfrac{h(x-2)-h(x)}{2}$

38. $\dfrac{g(x)-g(5)}{x-5}$

39. $\dfrac{f(x)+g(x)}{h(x)}$

40. $\dfrac{g(x)+h(x)}{f(x)}$

41. $\dfrac{g(x)+1}{h(x)}$

42. $\dfrac{h(x)-1}{g(x)}$

43. $\dfrac{f(x)-h(x)}{3}$

44. $\dfrac{g(x)-f(x)}{3}$

 MINI-REVIEW

45. *Solve for x.* $(x-4)(x+1)=(x-3)(x-2)$

46. *Solve for x.* $(2x-4)(x+1)=(x-3)(x-2)$

47. Write an equation of the line passing through the point $(-4, 5)$ that is parallel to the line whose equation is $3x-2y=5$.

48. *Simplify.* $x-[5-3(x-5)]$

6.6 Fractional Equations and Inequalities

Up to now we have been concerned with performing operations with fractional expressions. In this section we will discuss how to approach fractional equations and inequalities.

In Chapter 2 we developed a strategy for solving first-degree equations. In Section 6.4 we discussed the idea of the least common denominator (LCD). Our method for solving fractional equations and inequalities will use both of these ideas, as illustrated in the following examples.

EXAMPLE 1 | Solve for x. $\dfrac{x}{4} - \dfrac{x-3}{3} = \dfrac{x+3}{6}$

Solution | Rather than solve this equation directly, we would much prefer to solve an equivalent equation without fractions. The idea of an LCD that we used in Section 6.4 can be used to accomplish this.

Since we are dealing with an equation, we can multiply both sides of the equation by any nonzero quantity we choose. If we multiply the entire equation by a number that is divisible by 3, 4, and 6, we will "eliminate" the denominators. The LCD is exactly the smallest such quantity. This process is called **clearing the denominators.**

We multiply both sides of the equation by LCD of all the denominators in the equation, which is 12.

$$\frac{x}{4} - \frac{x-3}{3} = \frac{x+3}{6}$$

$$12\left(\frac{x}{4} - \frac{x-3}{3}\right) = 12\left(\frac{x+3}{6}\right) \qquad \textit{Each fraction is multiplied by 12.}$$

$$\frac{12}{1}\cdot\frac{x}{4} - \frac{12}{1}\cdot\frac{x-3}{3} = \frac{12}{1}\cdot\frac{x+3}{6} \qquad \textit{Reduce.}$$

$$\frac{\overset{3}{\cancel{12}}}{1}\cdot\frac{x}{4} - \frac{\overset{4}{\cancel{12}}}{1}\cdot\frac{x-3}{3} = \frac{\overset{2}{\cancel{12}}}{1}\cdot\frac{x+3}{6}$$

$$3x - 4(x-3) = 2(x+3) \qquad \textit{Note that the parentheses around } x-3$$

$$3x - 4x + 12 = 2x + 6 \qquad \textit{and } x+3 \textit{ are necessary.}$$

$$-x + 12 = 2x + 6$$

$$6 = 3x$$

$$\boxed{2 = x}$$

The check is left to the student. ∎

EXAMPLE 2 | Solve for x. $\dfrac{4}{x} + \dfrac{5}{2} = \dfrac{8}{x}$

Solution | We follow the procedure described in Example 1.

$$\frac{4}{x} + \frac{5}{2} = \frac{8}{x} \qquad \textit{Multiply both sides of the equation by the LCD,}$$
$$\textit{which is } 2x.$$

$$2x\left(\frac{4}{x} + \frac{5}{2}\right) = 2x\left(\frac{8}{x}\right)$$

$$\frac{2x}{1}\cdot\frac{4}{x} + \frac{2x}{1}\cdot\frac{5}{2} = \frac{2x}{1}\cdot\frac{8}{x} \qquad \textit{We clear the denominators.}$$

$$\frac{2\cancel{x}}{1}\cdot\frac{4}{\cancel{x}} + \frac{2x}{1}\cdot\frac{5}{2} = \frac{2\cancel{x}}{1}\cdot\frac{8}{\cancel{x}}$$

$$8 + 5x = 16$$

$$5x = 8$$

You should continue to check all solutions.

$$\boxed{x = \frac{8}{5} = 1.6}$$

∎

When a variable does not appear in any denominator, clearing the denominators is the first step to take in solving fractional inequalities as well.

EXAMPLE 3 | Solve for q. $\dfrac{q}{5} + \dfrac{5-q}{3} \le 2$

Solution | We clear the denominators by multiplying both sides of the inequality by the LCD, which is $5 \cdot 3 = 15$.

$$\frac{15}{1} \cdot \frac{q}{5} + \frac{15}{1} \cdot \frac{5-q}{3} \le 15 \cdot 2$$

$$\frac{\cancel{15}^3}{1} \cdot \frac{q}{\cancel{5}} + \frac{\cancel{15}^5}{1} \cdot \frac{5-q}{\cancel{3}} \le 15 \cdot 2$$

$$3q + 5(5-q) \le 30$$

$$3q + 25 - 5q \le 30$$

$$25 - 2q \le 30$$

$$-2q \le 5$$

$$\boxed{q \ge -\frac{5}{2}}$$

Do not forget to reverse the inequality symbol when dividing by a negative number. ■

EXAMPLE 4 | Solve for a. $\dfrac{5}{2a} + \dfrac{3}{a-2} = \dfrac{7}{10a}$

Solution | We clear the denominator by multiplying both sides of the equation by the LCD, which is $10a(a-2)$.

$$\frac{5}{2a} + \frac{3}{a-2} = \frac{7}{10a}$$

Each fraction is multiplied by the LCD.

$$\left(\frac{10a(a-2)}{1}\right)\frac{5}{2a} + \left(\frac{10a(a-2)}{1}\right)\frac{3}{a-2} = \left(\frac{10a(a-2)}{1}\right)\frac{7}{10a}$$

Reduce.

$$\frac{\overset{5}{\cancel{10a}}(a-2)}{1} \cdot \frac{5}{2\cancel{a}} + \frac{10a(\cancel{a-2})}{1} \cdot \frac{3}{\cancel{a-2}} = \frac{\cancel{10a}(a-2)}{1} \cdot \frac{7}{\cancel{10a}}$$

$$25(a-2) + 30a = 7(a-2)$$

$$25a - 50 + 30a = 7a - 14$$

$$55a - 50 = 7a - 14$$

$$48a = 36$$

$$a = \frac{36}{48} = \boxed{\frac{3}{4}}$$
■

Use your calculator to check your answer.

As the next example shows, solving fractional equations requires some care.

EXAMPLE 5 | Solve for x. $\dfrac{7}{x+5} + 2 = \dfrac{2-x}{x+5}$

Solution | Again we clear the denominator by multiplying both sides of the equation by the LCD, which is $x+5$:

$$\frac{7}{x+5} + 2 = \frac{2-x}{x+5}$$

First multiply both sides of the equation by $x+5$ and reduce.

$$(\cancel{x+5})\left(\frac{7}{\cancel{x+5}}\right) + 2(x+5) = (\cancel{x+5})\left(\frac{2-x}{\cancel{x+5}}\right)$$

$$7 + 2(x+5) = 2 - x$$

237

$$7 + 2x + 10 = 2 - x$$
$$2x + 17 = 2 - x$$
$$3x = -15$$
$$x = -5$$

Check: $x = -5$: $\dfrac{7}{x + 5} + 2 = \dfrac{2 - x}{x + 5}$

$$\dfrac{7}{-5 + 5} + 2 \overset{?}{=} \dfrac{2 - (-5)}{-5 + 5}$$

$$\dfrac{7}{0} + 2 \neq \dfrac{7}{0}$$

Since we are never allowed to divide by 0, $\frac{7}{0}$ is undefined. Therefore, $x = -5$ is *not* a solution.

Have we made an error? No. As we pointed out in Chapter 2, if we multiply an equation by 0 we may no longer have an equivalent equation (that is, an equation with the same solution set). This is exactly what has happened here.

We multiplied the original equation by $x + 5$ to clear the denominators, but if $x = -5$, then $x + 5$ is equal to 0, and so we have multiplied the original equation by 0. The resulting equation, for which $x = -5$ is a solution, is not equivalent to the original equation, for which $x = -5$ is not even an allowable value.

Our logic tells us that $x = -5$ is the only possible solution. Since $x = -5$ does not satisfy the original equation, the original equation has

$$\boxed{\text{no solutions}}$$ ■

Example 5 shows that when we multiply an equation by a variable quantity that might be equal to 0, we *must* check our answer(s) in the original equation. This check is not optional, but rather a necessary step in the solution. We are not checking for errors—we are checking to see whether we have obtained a valid solution.

Another way of saying this is that we look at our original equation in Example 5 and ask, "What are the possible replacement values for x?" We must disqualify $x = -5$ from the outset since it requires division by 0, which is undefined.

EXAMPLE 6   Solve for t. $\dfrac{4}{t} - \dfrac{5}{t + 3} = 1$

Solution   We will use the LCD, which is $t(t + 3)$ to clear the denominators.

$$\dfrac{4}{t} - \dfrac{5}{t + 3} = 1$$ *Note that $t = 0$ and $t = -3$ must be excluded.*

$$t(t + 3) \cdot \dfrac{4}{t} - t(t + 3) \cdot \dfrac{5}{t + 3} = t(t + 3) \cdot 1$$

$$4(t + 3) - 5t = t(t + 3)$$
$$4t + 12 - 5t = t^2 + 3t$$
$$-t + 12 = t^2 + 3t$$ *We recognize this as a quadratic equation. We get the equation into standard form.*

$$0 = t^2 + 4t - 12$$
$$0 = (t + 6)(t - 2)$$
$$t + 6 = 0 \quad \text{or} \quad t - 2 = 0$$
$$\boxed{t = -6 \quad \text{or} \quad t = 2}$$

The check is left to the student.   ■

EXAMPLE 7

Solve for t. $\dfrac{5}{t+3} - \dfrac{4}{3t} = \dfrac{7}{t^2 + 3t}$

Solution

We will use the LCD to clear the denominators. To find the LCD we want each denominator in factored form.

$$\frac{5}{t+3} - \frac{4}{3t} = \frac{7}{t(t+3)} \qquad LCD = 3t(t+3)$$

$$3t(t+3) \cdot \frac{5}{t+3} - 3t(t+3) \cdot \frac{4}{3t} = 3t(t+3) \cdot \frac{7}{t(t+3)}$$

$$15t - 4(t+3) = 21$$

$$15t - 4t - 12 = 21$$

$$11t - 12 = 21$$

$$11t = 33$$

$$\boxed{t = 3}$$

The check is left to the student. ■

EXAMPLE 8

Combine and simplify. $\dfrac{2}{t} + \dfrac{3}{t+2} - \dfrac{4}{5t}$

Solution

It is very important to recognize the difference between this example and the previous one. Example 7 was an equation. The multiplication property of *equality* allowed us to "clear the denominators." This example, on the other hand, is an expression, *not* an equation. Therefore, the multiplication property of equality does not apply; we cannot "clear the denominators."

Instead, we are being asked to combine three fractions. We will use the LCD again in this example, but this time to *build* the fractions. Following the outline used in Section 6.4, we proceed as follows:

$$\frac{2}{t} + \frac{3}{t+2} - \frac{4}{5t} \qquad LCD = 5t(t+2)$$

$$= \frac{2 \cdot 5(t+2)}{5t(t+2)} + \frac{3 \cdot 5t}{5t(t+2)} - \frac{4(t+2)}{5t(t+2)}$$

$$= \frac{10(t+2) + 15t - 4(t+2)}{5t(t+2)}$$

$$= \frac{10t + 20 + 15t - 4t - 8}{5t(t+2)} = \boxed{\frac{21t + 12}{5t(t+2)}} \qquad ■$$

 EXERCISES 6.6

In each of the following, if the exercise is an equation or inequality, solve it. If it is an expression, perform the indicated operations and simplify.

1. $\dfrac{x}{3} - \dfrac{x}{2} + \dfrac{x}{4} = 1$

2. $\dfrac{a}{4} - \dfrac{a}{5} - \dfrac{a}{10} = 1$

3. $\dfrac{t}{3} + \dfrac{t}{5} < \dfrac{t}{6} - 11$

4. $\dfrac{n}{6} - \dfrac{n}{9} > \dfrac{n}{3} - 5$

5. $\dfrac{a-1}{6} + \dfrac{a+1}{10} = a - 3$

6. $\dfrac{w-3}{8} + \dfrac{w+4}{12} = w - 4$

7. $\dfrac{y-5}{2} = \dfrac{y-2}{5}$

8. $\dfrac{z-2}{7} = \dfrac{z-7}{2}$

9. $\dfrac{y-5}{2} \le \dfrac{y-2}{5} + 3$

10. $\dfrac{z-2}{7} \ge \dfrac{z-7}{2} - 5$

11. $\dfrac{x-3}{4} - \dfrac{x-4}{3} = 2$

12. $\dfrac{x-3}{5} - \dfrac{x+2}{6} = 1$

13. $\dfrac{x-3}{4} - \dfrac{x-4}{3} \ge 2$

14. $\dfrac{x-3}{5} - \dfrac{x+2}{6} \le 1$

15. $\dfrac{3x+11}{6} - \dfrac{2x+1}{3} = x+5$

16. $\dfrac{7x+1}{4} - \dfrac{3x+1}{8} = \dfrac{x+2}{2}$

17. $\dfrac{x-3}{5} - \dfrac{3x+1}{4} < 8$

18. $\dfrac{5x+1}{2} - \dfrac{x+1}{4} > 2$

19. $\dfrac{5}{x} - \dfrac{1}{2} = \dfrac{3}{x}$

20. $\dfrac{4}{3x} + \dfrac{9}{x} - \dfrac{6}{5}$

21. $\dfrac{4}{x} - \dfrac{1}{5} + \dfrac{7}{2x}$

22. $\dfrac{2}{x} + \dfrac{1}{3} = \dfrac{5}{x}$

23. $\dfrac{1}{t-3} + \dfrac{2}{t} = \dfrac{5}{3t}$

24. $\dfrac{2}{y+2} + \dfrac{3}{y} = \dfrac{5}{2y}$

25. $\dfrac{6}{a-3} - \dfrac{3}{8} = \dfrac{21}{4a-12}$

26. $\dfrac{5}{z-1} - \dfrac{7}{z} = \dfrac{3}{2z-2}$

27. $\dfrac{7}{x-5} + 2 = \dfrac{x+2}{x-5}$

28. $\dfrac{9}{x+2} - 3 = \dfrac{x+11}{x+2}$

29. $\dfrac{4}{y^2-2y} - \dfrac{3}{2y} = \dfrac{17}{6y}$

30. $\dfrac{3}{z^2-4z} + \dfrac{7}{4z} - \dfrac{3}{8}$

31. $\dfrac{2x}{x-5} - \dfrac{2x+1}{x+2} = \dfrac{3}{x+2}$

32. $\dfrac{3a}{a-4} - \dfrac{3a+1}{a+3} = \dfrac{12}{a-4}$

33. $\dfrac{5}{y^2+3y} - \dfrac{4}{3y} + \dfrac{1}{2}$

34. $\dfrac{9}{z^2+5z} + \dfrac{6}{5z} = \dfrac{3}{10z}$

35. $\dfrac{9}{x^2+4x} = \dfrac{6}{x^2+2x}$

36. $\dfrac{6}{t^2-3t} = \dfrac{12}{t^2-9t}$

37. $x + \dfrac{1}{x} = 2$

38. $a - \dfrac{2}{a} = \dfrac{7}{3}$

39. $\dfrac{3x+2}{x^2-4x-5} + \dfrac{x-4}{x+1} = \dfrac{x}{x-5}$

40. $\dfrac{3x+2}{x^2-4x-5} + \dfrac{x-4}{x+1} - \dfrac{x}{x-5}$

41. $\dfrac{5x+1}{x^2-4} - \dfrac{2x+3}{x+2} + \dfrac{2x+3}{x-2}$

42. $\dfrac{2x-3}{x+2} - \dfrac{5x+1}{x^2-4} = \dfrac{2x+3}{x-2}$

43. $\dfrac{1}{x^2-x-2} + \dfrac{2}{x^2-1} = \dfrac{1}{x^2-3x+2}$

44. $\dfrac{3}{a^2+3a-10} + \dfrac{12}{a^2-2a} = \dfrac{4}{a^2+5a}$

45. $\dfrac{1}{x-4} - \dfrac{5}{x+2} = \dfrac{6}{x^2-2x-8}$

46. $\dfrac{3}{3x-2} - \dfrac{7}{x+1} = \dfrac{5}{3x^2+x-2}$

47. $\dfrac{n}{3n+2} + \dfrac{6}{9n^2-4} - \dfrac{2}{3n-2}$

48. $\dfrac{n}{2n-3} + \dfrac{2}{2n+3} - \dfrac{5n}{4n^2-9}$

49. $\dfrac{1}{3n + 4} + \dfrac{8}{9n^2 - 16} = \dfrac{1}{3n - 4}$

50. $\dfrac{5}{2n + 1} + \dfrac{3}{2n - 1} = \dfrac{22}{4n^2 - 1}$

51. $\dfrac{4}{2x - 1} + \dfrac{2}{x + 3} = \dfrac{5}{2x^2 + 5x - 3}$

52. $\dfrac{7}{3a + 2} + \dfrac{4}{a + 5} = \dfrac{8}{3a^2 + 17a + 10}$

53. $\dfrac{6}{x} - \dfrac{2}{x - 1} = 1$

54. $\dfrac{8}{x + 3} + \dfrac{14}{x} = 1$

55. $\dfrac{x}{x - 1} = \dfrac{2x}{x + 1}$

56. $\dfrac{3x}{x + 5} = \dfrac{x}{x + 3}$

57. $\dfrac{2x}{x + 2} = x - 1$

58. $\dfrac{2}{x - 1} = 4 - x$

59. $\dfrac{5}{x} + \dfrac{9}{x + 2} = 4$

60. $\dfrac{3}{x - 2} - \dfrac{7}{x} = 6$

61. $\dfrac{6}{3a + 5} - \dfrac{2}{a - 4} = \dfrac{10}{3a^2 - 7a - 20}$

62. $\dfrac{5}{y - 2} - \dfrac{3}{2y - 1} = \dfrac{4}{2y^2 - 5y + 2}$

63. $\dfrac{2x + 3}{x^2 - x - 2} - \dfrac{x + 4}{x^2 + 3x + 2} = \dfrac{x}{x^2 - 4}$

64. $\dfrac{3x - 1}{x^2 - 3x - 10} - \dfrac{1}{x + 5} = \dfrac{2x + 1}{x^2 - 3x - 10}$

65. $\dfrac{3}{x^2 - x - 6} + \dfrac{2}{2x^2 - 5x - 3} = \dfrac{5}{2x^2 + 5x + 2}$

66. $\dfrac{10}{2a^2 - a - 15} - \dfrac{5}{3a^2 - 4a - 15} = \dfrac{3}{6a^2 + 25a + 25}$

67. $\dfrac{2x + 1}{x^2 + x - 2} + \dfrac{4x}{x^2 - 1} = \dfrac{15x - 1}{x^2 + 3x + 2}$

68. $\dfrac{x + 1}{x^2 - 2x - 15} - \dfrac{x + 2}{x^2 - 25} + \dfrac{1}{x - 5}$

69. $\dfrac{4}{4x^2 - 9} - \dfrac{5}{4x^2 - 8x + 3} = \dfrac{8}{4x^2 + 4x - 3}$

70. $\dfrac{6}{9y^2 - 1} - \dfrac{4}{9y^2 + 9y + 2} = \dfrac{9}{9y^2 + 3y - 2}$

In Exercises 71–76, given $f(x) = \dfrac{3x + 1}{(x - 2)^2}$ *and* $g(x) = \dfrac{x + 5}{x - 2}$, *express the following as a single simplified fraction.*

71. $f(x) + g(x)$

72. $f(x) - g(x)$

73. $2f(x) - 3g(x)$

74. $3f(x) + 2g(x)$

75. $\dfrac{f(x)}{g(x)}$

76. $\dfrac{g(x)}{f(x)}$

◇ **MINI-REVIEW**

77. *Simplify.* $3x^2y(2x^3y^2)$

78. *Simplify.* $3x^2y(2x^3 + y^2)$

79. Give an example of a function $f(x)$ for which $f(x + 2) \neq f(x) + f(2)$.

80. Find the domain of $f(x) = \dfrac{1}{\sqrt{3x - 5}}$.

6.7 Literal Equations

In this section we elaborate on literal equations, which we first discussed in Section 1.5.

A literal equation that has a "real-life" interpretation is often called a *formula.* For instance, the area, A, of a trapezoid (see Figure 6.3 on page 344) is given by the formula

$$A = \frac{1}{2}h(b_1 + b_2)$$

Figure 6.3
Trapezoid

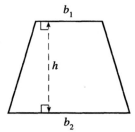

This formula is quite useful if we are given h, b_1, and b_2 and want to compute A. However, if we are given A, h, and b_1 and we want to compute b_2, we would much prefer to have a formula solved explicitly for b_2.

EXAMPLE 1   Solve explicitly for b_2. $A = \frac{1}{2}h(b_1 + b_2)$

Solution   We offer two approaches to illustrate a point.

Method 1: $A = \frac{1}{2}h(b_1 + b_2)$ *Multiply the equation by 2 to clear the denominator.*

$2A = h(b_1 + b_2)$ *Apply the distributive property.*

$2A = hb_1 + hb_2$ *Then isolate b_2 (subtract hb_1 from both sides).*

$2A - hb_1 = hb_2$ *Divide both sides by h.*

$$\frac{2A - hb_1}{h} = \frac{hb_2}{h}$$

$$\boxed{\frac{2A - hb_1}{h} = b_2}$$

Method 2: $A = \frac{1}{2}h(b_1 + b_2)$ *Again clear the denominator.*

$2A = h(b_1 + b_2)$ *Divide both sides by h.*

$$\frac{2A}{h} = \frac{h(b_1 + b_2)}{h}$$

$$\frac{2A}{h} = b_1 + b_2$$ *Isolate b_2 (subtract b_1 from both sides).*

$$\boxed{\frac{2A}{h} - b_1 = b_2}$$

Both methods are equally correct. What is important is that you recognize that the two answers are equivalent. If we combine the second answer into a single fraction we get

$$\frac{2A}{h} - b_1 = \frac{2A}{h} - \frac{hb_1}{h} = \frac{2A - hb_1}{h}$$

which is the first answer. Keep this in mind when you check your answers with those in the answer key in the back of the book.   ∎

The same procedure can be applied to solving literal *inequalities* as well.

EXAMPLE 2   Solve explicitly for a. $a - 2c \le 6a + 7d$

Solution $a - 2c \le 6a + 7d$ *Add $2c$ to both sides of the inequality.*

$a - 2c \; +2c \; \le 6a + 7d \; +2c$

$$a \leq 6a + 7d + 2c$$

$$a \boxed{-6a} \leq 6a + 7d + 2c \boxed{-6a}$$

*Do not stop here! The variable **a** must appear on only one side of the inequality.*

$$-5a \leq 7d + 2c$$

$$\downarrow$$

$$\frac{-5a}{-5} \geq \frac{7d + 2c}{-5}$$

*Remember that when we divide both sides of an inequality by a negative number, we **reverse** the inequality symbol.* ∎

$$\boxed{a \geq \frac{7d + 2c}{-5}}$$

EXAMPLE 3 Solve for t. $at + 9 = 3t + b$

Solution We want to get the t terms on one side of the equation and the non-t terms on the other side.

$$at + 9 = 3t + b$$

First add $-3t$ to both sides of the equation.

$$at + 9 \boxed{-3t} = 3t + b \boxed{-3t}$$

$$at - 3t + 9 = b$$

Then subtract 9 from both sides.

$$at - 3t + 9 \boxed{-9} = b \boxed{-9}$$

$$at - 3t = b - 9$$

To isolate t, we factor out the t on the left side.

$$t(a - 3) = b - 9$$

Then divide both sides by $a - 3$.

$$\frac{t(a - 3)}{a - 3} = \frac{b - 9}{a - 3}$$

$$\boxed{t = \frac{b - 9}{a - 3}}$$

Since we cannot divide by 0, this solution assumes that $a \neq 3$. ∎

Notice that in Example 3 we had to factor out t from $at - 3t$. This may seem like a new step that we have not seen before, but actually this step was implicit in the equations we solved prior to this section. For example, in solving

$$7t - 9 = 3t + 8$$

we subtract $3t$ from both sides and add 9 to both sides so our equation would look like this:

$$7t - 9 \boxed{-3t + 9} = 3t + 8 \boxed{-3t + 9}$$

$$7t - 3t = 8 + 9$$

We normally combine like terms, $7t - 3t = 4t$ and $8 + 9 = 17$, and simplify our equation:

$$4t = 17$$

If you think back to how we are allowed to combine terms (by the distributive property), you will see that the factoring step is implicit in combining terms:

$$7t - 3t = (7 - 3)t \quad \text{\textit{Distributive property}}$$

$$= 4t$$

So this procedure was not new; you have actually been doing it all along.

EXAMPLE 4

Solve for u. $y = \dfrac{u + 1}{u + 2}$

Solution

$$y = \frac{u + 1}{u + 2}$$

Begin by multiplying both sides by $u + 2$ to clear the denominator.

$$(u + 2)y = \frac{u + 1}{u + 2} \cdot \frac{u + 2}{1}$$

$$(u + 2)y = u + 1$$

Apply the distributive property.

$$uy + 2y = u + 1$$

We collect all the u terms on one side, non-u terms on the other side.

$$uy + 2y \; -u - 2y = u + 1 \; -u - 2y$$

$$uy - u = 1 - 2y$$

Factor out u on the left side.

$$u(y - 1) = 1 - 2y$$

Then divide both sides of the equation by $y - 1$.

$$\frac{u(y - 1)}{y - 1} = \frac{1 - 2y}{y - 1}$$

$$\boxed{u = \frac{1 - 2y}{y - 1}}$$

This solution assumes that $y \neq 1$ and $u \neq -2$. Why? ■

EXERCISES 6.7

Solve each of the following equations or inequalities explicitly for the indicated variable.

1. $5x + 7y = 4$ for x

2. $5x + 7y = 4$ for y

3. $2x - 9y = 11$ for y

4. $2x - 9y = 11$ for x

5. $w + 4z - 1 = 2w - z + 3$ for w

6. $w + 4z - 1 = 2w - z + 3$ for z

7. $2(6r - 5t) > 5(2r + t)$ for r

8. $2(6r - 5t) > 5(2r + t)$ for t

9. $3m - 4n + 6p = 5n + 2p - 8$ for n

10. $3m - 4n + 6p = 5n + 2p - 8$ for m

11. $\dfrac{a}{5} - \dfrac{b}{3} = \dfrac{a}{2} - \dfrac{b}{6}$ for a

12. $\dfrac{c}{12} - \dfrac{d}{8} = \dfrac{c}{4} - \dfrac{d}{6}$ for d

13. $\dfrac{x + y}{3} - \dfrac{x}{2} + \dfrac{y}{6} = 3(x - y)$ for x

14. $\dfrac{w - z}{10} - \dfrac{w}{5} + \dfrac{z}{4} = 2(z + w)$ for z

15. $ax + b = cx + d$ for x

16. $p - rz = q - tz$ for z

17. $3x + 2y - 5 = ax + by + 1$ for x

18. $3x + 2y - 5 = ax + by + 1$ for y

19. $(x + 3)(y + 7) = a$ for x

20. $(3x - 2)(2y - 1) = b$ for y

21. $y = \dfrac{u - 1}{u + 1}$ for u

22. $z = \dfrac{w - 2}{w + 3}$ for w

23. $x = \dfrac{2t - 3}{3t - 2}$ for t

24. $u = \dfrac{3y - 4}{2y - 3}$ for y

Each of the following is a formula from mathematics or the physical or social sciences. Solve each formula for the indicated variable.

25. $A = \dfrac{1}{2}bh$ for b

26. $A = \dfrac{1}{2}bh$ for h

27. $A = \dfrac{1}{2}h(b_1 + b_2)$ for b_1

28. $A = \dfrac{1}{2}h(b_1 + b_2)$ for h

29. $A = P(1 + rt)$ for r

30. $A = P(1 + rt)$ for P

31. $C = \dfrac{5}{9}(F - 32)$ for F

32. $F = \dfrac{9}{5}C + 32$ for C

33. $\dfrac{P_1}{V_1} = \dfrac{P_2}{V_2}$ for P_2

34. $\dfrac{P_1}{V_1} = \dfrac{P_2}{V_2}$ for V_2

35. $S = s_0 + v_0 t + \dfrac{1}{2}gt^2$ for g

36. $S = s_0 + v_0 t + \dfrac{1}{2}gt^2$ for v_0

37. $\dfrac{x - \mu}{s} < 1.96$ for x (assume $s > 0$)

38. $\dfrac{x - \mu}{s} < 1.96$ for μ (assume $s > 0$)

39. $\dfrac{1}{f} = \dfrac{1}{f_1} + \dfrac{1}{f_2}$ for f_1

40. $\dfrac{1}{f} = \dfrac{1}{f_1} + \dfrac{1}{f_2}$ for f

41. $S = 2\pi r^2 + 2\pi rh$ for h

42. $S = 2LH + 2LW + 2WH$ for W

◇ **MINI-REVIEW**

43. *Solve for x.* $(x - 3)^2 = 4$

44. *Multiply and simplify.* $(x - 2)^3$

45. An auto repair shop spends a total of $940 on 18 car batteries. Some were heavy-duty batteries costing $60 each and the rest were regular batteries costing $50 each. How many of each were bought?

46. Use the following graph of $f(x)$ to determine its domain and range, and find $f(-3)$.

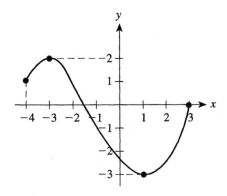

6.8 Applications: Rational Functions and Equations as Mathematical Models

As we have seen on numerous occasions, functions and equations can be used to model real-life situations. In this section, we pay particular attention to situations that give rise to functions and equations that involve rational expressions.

The outline suggested in Chapter 2 for solving verbal problems applies equally well to problems that give rise to fractional equations and inequalities. We will repeat this advice in the next box for your reference.

Outline of Strategy for Solving Verbal Problems	1. *Read the problem carefully,* as many times as is necessary to understand what the problem is saying and what it is asking. 2. *Use diagrams* whenever you think it will make the given information clearer. 3. *Find the underlying relationship or formula* relevant to the given problem. Ask whether there is some underlying relationship or formula you need to know. If not, then the words of the problem themselves give the required relationship. 4. Clearly *identify the unknown quantity* (or quantities) in the problem, and label it (them) using one variable. 5. By using the underlying formula or relationship in the problem, *write an equation* involving the unknown quantity (or quantities). 6. *Solve* the equation. 7. *Answer the question.* Make sure you have answered the question that was asked. 8. *Check* the answer(s) in the original words of the problem.

EXAMPLE 1

Gary drove from his house to Elaine's house. He had driven over the speed limit for one-third of the distance, when he was stopped and given a ticket for speeding. He then drove under the speed limit for one-half the total distance until his car ran out of gas. He walked the remaining 5 miles to Elaine's house. What is the distance from Gary's to Elaine's house?

Solution

At first glance, this may look like a distance–rate problem, but actually the problem involves only distance. First, draw a picture to represent the distances traveled and label the distances, as shown in Figure 6.4.

Figure 6.4
Diagram for Example 1

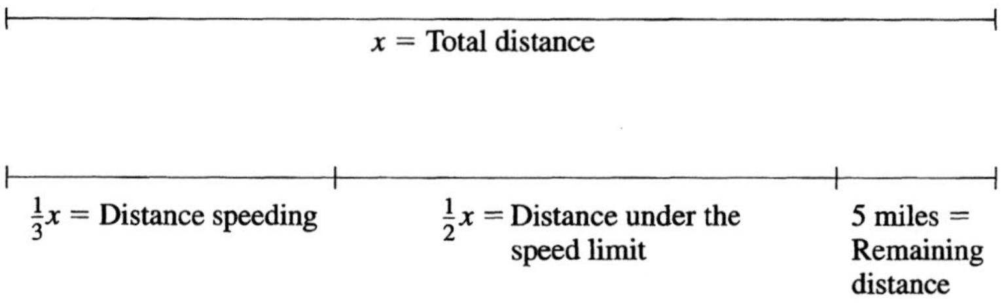

x = Total distance

$\frac{1}{3}x$ = Distance speeding $\frac{1}{2}x$ = Distance under the speed limit   5 miles = Remaining distance

The figure illustrates the relationships among the distances traveled under each condition. It gives us the following equation:

$$\frac{1}{3}x + \frac{1}{2}x + 5 = x$$

We solve this equation by first multiplying the equation by the LCD of the fractions, which is 6:

$$\overset{2}{\cancel{6}}\left(\frac{1}{3}x\right) + \overset{3}{\cancel{6}}\left(\frac{1}{2}x\right) + 6 \cdot 5 = 6 \cdot x$$

$$2x + 3x + 30 = 6x$$

$$5x + 30 = 6x \qquad \textit{Subtract 5x from both sides.}$$

$$30 = x$$

$$x = \boxed{30 \text{ miles}}$$

Check: One-third the distance speeding $= \frac{1}{3}(30) = 10$ miles

One-half the distance under the limit $= \frac{1}{2}(30) = 15$ miles

Remaining distance $= 5$ miles

Total $= 30$ miles

An alternative, shorter way to solve the same problem is to consider the fact that Gary has already traveled $\frac{1}{2} + \frac{1}{3}$, or $\frac{5}{6}$ of the distance before he runs out of gas. So he still has $\frac{1}{6}$ the total distance to walk. This remaining distance is given as 5 miles. Hence, we have

$$\frac{1}{6} \text{ the total distance} = 5 \text{ miles} \quad \text{or} \quad \frac{1}{6}x = 5$$

Multiplying both sides of the equation by 6, we have

$$x = 30 \text{ miles} \qquad \blacksquare$$

Ratio and proportion problems are fairly straightforward to set up, as long as you remember to match up the corresponding units.

EXAMPLE 2

In a local district, the ratio of Democrats to Republicans is 5 to 7. If there are 2,100 Republicans in the district, how many Democrats are there?

Solution

First, you should realize that the ratio of a to b is simply the fraction $\frac{a}{b}$ reduced to lowest terms. Hence, to *find* the ratio of the number of Democrats to the number of Republicans, we would create the fraction

$$\frac{\text{Number of Democrats}}{\text{Number of Republicans}}$$

and reduce it to get $\frac{5}{7}$.

We let $x =$ number of Democrats and set up our equation with two fractions, being careful to match up the units:

$$\frac{5 \text{ Democrats}}{7 \text{ Republicans}} = \frac{x \text{ Democrats}}{2,100 \text{ Republicans}} \quad \text{or} \quad \frac{5}{7} = \frac{x}{2,100}$$

Multiply both sides of the equation by 2,100 to get

$$1,500 = x$$

Hence, there are $\boxed{1,500 \text{ Democrats}}$ in that district. $\qquad \blacksquare$

EXAMPLE 3

If 1 kilogram is 2.2 pounds, how many kilograms are in 106 pounds?

Solution

Again, we match up the units to check that the fractions are set up properly. Let $x =$ the number of kg in 106 lb.

$$\frac{x \text{ kg}}{106 \text{ lb}} = \frac{1 \text{ kg}}{2.2 \text{ lb}}$$

$$\frac{x}{106} = \frac{1}{2.2}$$

Since we are solving for x, we multiply both sides of the equation by 106:

$$x = \frac{106}{2.2} = \boxed{48.18 \text{ kg}} \quad \text{(rounded to two decimal places)} \qquad \blacksquare$$

EXAMPLE 4

If the ratio of Republicans to Democrats in a district is 4 to 9, and there is a total of 2,210 Republicans and Democrats in that district, how many Republicans are there?

Solution

Let x = number of Republicans. Then

$$2,210 - x = \text{Number of Democrats} \qquad \textit{Total minus part = remainder}$$

Hence, our equation becomes

$$\frac{4}{9} = \frac{x}{2,210 - x}$$

Multiplying both sides of the equation by $9(2,210 - x)$, we get

$$\cancel{9}(2,210 - x)\left(\frac{4}{\cancel{9}}\right) = \left(\frac{x}{\cancel{2,210 - x}}\right)(9)\cancel{(2,210 - x)}$$
$$4(2,210 - x) = 9x$$
$$8,840 - 4x = 9x$$
$$8,840 = 13x$$
$$680 = x$$

Thus, there are $\boxed{680 \text{ Republicans}}$ in the district.

We leave the check to the student. ∎

EXAMPLE 5

How many liters each of 35%* and 60% alcohol solutions must be mixed together to make 40 liters of a 53% alcohol solution?

Solution

We offer both a one- and a two-variable approach.

One-Variable Approach:

We can let x = amount of 35% solution.

Then $40 - x$ = amount of 60% solution. Why?

We can visualize this problem as shown in Figure 6.5.

Figure 6.5
Diagram for Example 5

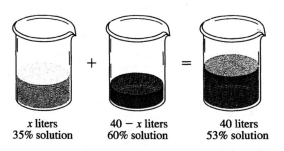

x liters   40 − x liters   40 liters
35% solution   60% solution   53% solution

To write an equation to solve this problem, we need to differentiate between the amount of *solution* we have and the amount of *actual alcohol* in the solution. For instance, if we have 100 liters of a 30% alcohol solution, the amount of actual alcohol is

$$0.30(100) = 30 \text{ liters}$$

The basic relationship we use in this example is that the amounts of alcohol in each solution add up to the total amount of alcohol in the final solution.

*In this text, when we refer to percent we mean percent by volume.

Thus, our equation is

$$0.35x \quad + \quad 0.60(40 - x) \quad = \quad 0.53(40)$$

Amount of alcohol $+$ Amount of alcohol $=$ Total amount of alcohol
in the 35% solution   in the 60% solution   in final solution

Since $0.35 = \frac{35}{100}$, $0.60 = \frac{60}{100}$, and $0.53 = \frac{53}{100}$, we multiply both sides of the equation by 100 to clear the decimals:

$$35x + 60(40 - x) = 53(40)$$
$$35x + 2,400 - 60x = 2,120$$
$$-25x + 2,400 = 2,120$$
$$-25x = -280$$
$$x = \frac{-280}{-25} = 11.2$$

We must mix
$40 - 11.2 =$

11.2 liters of 35% alcohol solution with
28.8 liters of 60% alcohol solution

Check: $11.2 + 28.8 \overset{\checkmark}{=} 40$ $0.35(11.2) + 0.60(28.8) \overset{?}{=} 0.53(40)$
$$3.92 + 17.28 \overset{\checkmark}{=} 21.2$$

Two-Variable Approach: We can also visualize the problem as indicated in Figure 6.6.

Let $x =$ amount of 35% alcohol solution
Let $y =$ amount of 60% alcohol solution

Figure 6.6
Diagram for two-variable approach

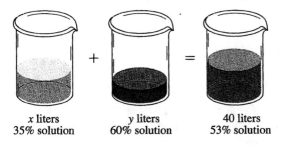

x liters y liters   40 liters
35% solution   60% solution   53% solution

We create two equations—one relating the amounts of *solution,* the other relating the amounts of *pure alcohol.* We obtain the following system of equations:

$$\begin{cases} x + y = 40 & \text{Amounts of solution} \\ 0.35x + 0.60y = 0.53(40) & \text{Amounts of pure alcohol} \end{cases}$$

We rewrite the first equation, solving for y to get $y = 40 - x$. We then substitute $y = 40 - x$ into the second equation and get

$$0.35x + 0.60(40 - x) = 0.53(40)$$

This is exactly the same equation we obtained using the one-variable approach. The rest of the solution is as it appears for the one-variable approach. ∎

EXAMPLE 6   Mrs. Stone invests a certain amount of money in a bank account paying 5.1% interest per year, and $3,500 more than this amount in a mutual fund paying 8.2% interest per year. If the annual income from the two investments is $905.45, how much is invested at each rate?

Solution

The amount of interest, I, earned in 1 year if P dollars is invested at a rate of r% per year is computed as

$$I = P \cdot r \qquad Interest = (Principal)(Rate)$$

where r is written as a decimal. For instance, if \$1,000 is invested at 8% per year, then the interest earned in 1 year is

$$I = (1000)(0.08) = \$80$$

Based on the information given in this example, let

$$x = \text{Amount invested at } 5.1\%$$

Then

$$x + 3,500 = \text{Amount invested at } 8.2\%$$

Our equation is

5.1% written as a decimal is 0.051; 8.2% is 0.082.

$$\underbrace{0.051x}_{} + \underbrace{0.082(x + 3,500)}_{} = \underbrace{905.45}_{}$$

| Interest received from the 5.1% investment | + | Interest received from the 8.2% investment | = | Total interest received from both investments |

Multiplying both sides of the equation by 1,000 clears the decimals:

$$51x + 82(x + 3,500) = 905,450$$
$$51x + 82x + 287,000 = 905,450$$
$$133x = 618,450$$
$$x = 4,650$$

Thus, there is

$$\boxed{\$4,650 \text{ invested at } 5.1\%}$$

and \$3,500 more, or

$$\boxed{\$8,150 \text{ invested at } 8.2\%}$$

Using a calculator gives us the advantage of skipping the step of "clearing decimals." But you still need to write down the equation steps as you proceed to solve the equation. That is, we can start with

$$0.051x + 0.082(x + 3,500) = 905.45 \qquad \textit{Simplify the left side using your}$$
$$0.051x + 0.082x + 287 = 905.45 \qquad \textit{calculator.}$$
$$0.133x + 287 = 905.45 \qquad \textit{Isolate x using the calculator for}$$
$$0.133x = 618.45 \qquad \textit{your computations.}$$
$$x = 4,650$$

Check: $8,150 \overset{\checkmark}{=} 4,650 + 3,500 \qquad 0.051(4,650) + 0.082(8,150) \overset{?}{=} 905.45$

$$237.15 + 668.30 \overset{\checkmark}{=} 905.45$$

The computations in the check above can easily be done by calculator. ∎

EXAMPLE 7

Greg can paint a house in 20 hours, whereas Mark can paint the same house in 40 hours. How long will it take them to paint the house if they work together?

Solution

To solve this problem algebraically we need to assume that Greg and Mark work in a totally cooperative manner and that they work at a constant rate.

This example is similar to the work problem in Section 2.2 (Example 11), where we were given a rate and needed to know the time it took to get a certain amount done. In general we know that the relationship between the amount of work done and the rate at which the work is being done is

Amount of work done = (Work rate) · (time)   or $W = rt$

What makes this example slightly different from the version in Section 2.2 is that the rates are stated differently in this problem. We can rewrite the rates given in this problem as follows: To say that it takes Greg 20 hours to paint a house means that Greg can complete $\frac{1}{20}$ of a house in 1 hour, or that his rate is $\frac{1}{20}$ of a house per hour.

Notice that $\frac{1}{20}$ house per hour means that in 3 hours Greg paints $\frac{3}{20}$ of a house, and in 20 hours, he completes $\frac{20}{20} = 1$ house. In general, the portion of the job completed = (rate) × (time).

Since Mark can paint the same house in 40 hours, his rate is $\frac{1}{40}$ of a house per hour. Now that we have the rates in more familiar form, we can approach this example as we did Exercise 11 of Section 2.2.

$$\begin{pmatrix} \text{Portion of the job} \\ \text{completed by Greg} \end{pmatrix} + \begin{pmatrix} \text{Portion of the job} \\ \text{completed by Mark} \end{pmatrix} = \begin{pmatrix} 1 \text{ complete} \\ \text{job} \end{pmatrix}$$

(Greg's rate) · (Greg's time) + (Mark's rate) · (Mark's time) = 1 complete house

We are given Greg's and Mark's rates. Since Greg and Mark are working the same amount of time, we can let x = number of hours Greg works = number of hours Mark works. Thus the equation becomes

$$\frac{1}{20} \cdot x \qquad + \qquad \frac{1}{40} \cdot x \qquad = 1$$

or

$$\frac{x}{20} + \frac{x}{40} = 1$$

Multiply by the LCD, which is 40:

$$\frac{40}{1} \cdot \frac{x}{20} + \frac{40}{1} \cdot \frac{x}{40} = 40 \cdot 1$$

$$2x + x = 40$$

$$3x = 40$$

$$x = \frac{40}{3} = 13\frac{1}{3} \text{ hours} = \boxed{13 \text{ hours and } 20 \text{ minutes}}$$

The check is left to the student. ∎

EXAMPLE 8   It takes Nadia 8 hours to complete a particular job. Suppose Victor begins working on the job with Nadia, and he then quits after 2 hours. Nadia takes 3 more hours to complete the job working alone. How long would it take Victor to do the job by himself?

Solution   This problem is similar to Example 7, but requires more analysis.

Since Nadia can complete the job in 8 hours, her rate is $\frac{1}{8}$ of a job per hour. Similarly, if we let x = the amount of time it takes Victor to complete the job, then his rate is $\frac{1}{x}$ of a job per hour.

They start by working together for 2 hours. This means that for the first 2 hours, Nadia completes

$$W = r \cdot t$$

$$W = \left(\frac{1}{8}\right)(2) = \frac{1}{4} \text{ of the job}$$

For the same first 2 hours, Victor completes

$$W = r \cdot t$$

$$W = \left(\frac{1}{x}\right)(2) = \frac{2}{x} \text{ of the job}$$

Hence after the first 2 hours $\frac{1}{4} + \frac{2}{x}$ of the job is complete.

After Victor quits, it takes Nadia 3 hours to complete the job working alone. Since her rate is $\frac{1}{8}$ of a job per hour, during the last 3 hours she completes

$$W = rt$$

$$W = \left(\frac{1}{8}\right)(3) = \frac{3}{8} \text{ of the job}$$

We can now add the portions of the job completed by each person over each period of time:

$$\underbrace{\frac{1}{4}}_{} \quad + \quad \underbrace{\frac{2}{x}}_{} \quad + \quad \underbrace{\frac{3}{8}}_{} \quad = \quad \underbrace{1}_{}$$

Portion completed   *Portion completed*   *Portion completed*   *1 complete job*
by Nadia during   *by Victor during*   *by Nadia during*
the first 2 hours   *the first 2 hours*   *the last 3 hours*

We solve for x:

$$\frac{1}{4} + \frac{2}{x} + \frac{3}{8} = 1 \qquad \textit{Multiply both sides by the LCD, } 8x.$$

$$8x\left(\frac{1}{4} + \frac{2}{x} + \frac{3}{8}\right) = 8x \cdot 1 \qquad \textit{Perform the operations on each side and simplify.}$$

$$8x \cdot \frac{1}{4} + 8x \cdot \frac{2}{x} + 8x \cdot \frac{3}{8} = 8x$$

$$2x + 16 + 3x = 8x$$

$$5x + 16 = 8x \qquad \textit{Solve for x to get}$$

$$16 = 3x$$

$$\frac{16}{3} = x$$

Hence working alone, it would take Victor $\frac{16}{3} = 5\frac{1}{3}$ hours.   ■

EXAMPLE 9

A train can make a 480-km trip in the same time that a car can make a 320-km trip. If the train travels 40 kph faster than the car, how long does it take the car to make its trip?

Solution

We will use the relationship $d = r \cdot t$ in the form $t = \frac{d}{r}$. Since we are told that the times for the train and car are the same, we have

$$t_{\text{train}} = t_{\text{car}}$$

$$\frac{d_{\text{train}}}{r_{\text{train}}} = \frac{d_{\text{car}}}{r_{\text{car}}}$$

Let r = rate for car. Then $r + 40$ = rate for train. Thus, our equation is

$$\frac{480}{r + 40} = \frac{320}{r} \qquad LCD = r(r + 40)$$

$$r(r + 40) \cdot \frac{480}{r + 40} = r(r + 40) \cdot \frac{320}{r}$$

$$480r = 320(r + 40)$$
$$480r = 320r + 12{,}800$$
$$160r = 12{,}800$$
$$r = 80$$

Keep in mind that the problem asks for the *time* it takes the car to make the 320-km trip, which is

$$t = \frac{320}{80} = \boxed{4 \text{ hours}}$$

Check: The rate of the train is $80 + 40 = 120$ kph.
The time for the train to make its 480-km trip is

$$t = \frac{480}{120} = 4 \text{ hours}$$ ∎

Let's return to the situation described at the beginning of this chapter.

EXAMPLE 10

An environmental consultant for a large factory finds that the cost C (in thousands of dollars) to remove p percent of the pollutants released by the factory can be approximated by the function

$$C(p) = \frac{60p}{100 - p}$$

(a) What is the cost of removing 70% of the pollutants?

(b) If the company determines that it can afford to allocate $200,000 to remove pollutants for the factory, what percentage of the pollutants can be removed?

(c) Suppose the company puts A (in thousands) toward removing pollutants. Express the percentage of pollutants that can be removed as a function (in terms of) A, and use this function to answer part (b).

Solution

(a) We are given the percentage p of pollutants to be removed, so we simply substitute for p in the given cost function. In other words, we are being asked to compute $C(70)$.

$$C(p) = \frac{60p}{100 - p} \qquad \textit{Substitute } p = 70.$$

$$= \frac{60(70)}{100 - 70} = \frac{60(70)}{30} = 140$$

Thus the cost of removing 70% of the pollutants is $140,000.

(b) We are given the cost, $C(p)$, and want to find p. Since $C(p)$ is the cost in thousands, we have $C(p) = 200$. Hence we need to solve the *rational equation* $C(p) = 200$:

$$C(p) = \frac{60p}{100 - p} \qquad \textit{Set } C(p) = 200 \textit{ and find } p.$$

$$200 = \frac{60p}{100 - p} \qquad \textit{Multiply both sides of the equation by } 100 - p.$$

$$(100 - p)200 = \frac{60p}{100 - p}(100 - p)$$

$$200(100 - p) = 60p$$

$$20{,}000 - 200p = 60p$$

$$20{,}000 = 260p$$

$$\frac{20{,}000}{260} \approx 76.92 = p$$

Hence, rounding to the nearest tenth, 76.9% of the pollutants can be removed for $200,000.

(c) Since $C(p)$ and A are both expressed in thousands, we have $C(p) = A$.

$$C(p) = \frac{60p}{100 - p} \qquad \text{Set } C(p) = A \text{ and solve for } p:$$

$$A = \frac{60p}{100 - p} \qquad \text{Multiply both sides of the equation by } 100 - p.$$

$$(100 - p)A = \frac{60p}{100 - p}(100 - p)$$

$$A(100 - p) = 60p \qquad \text{Distribute } A.$$

$$100A - pA = 60p \qquad \text{Collect terms containing } p.$$

$$100A = pA + 60p \qquad \text{Factor out } p.$$

$$100A = p(A + 60) \qquad \text{Isolate } p: \text{ Divide both sides by } A + 60.$$

$$\frac{100A}{A + 60} = p$$

Hence, $p = p(A) = \dfrac{100A}{A + 60}$ gives us the percent of pollutants that can be removed for A thousand dollars.

We can use this function to computer the answer to part **(b)** by substituting $A = 200$ in the function $p(A)$.

$$p = p(A) = \frac{100A}{A + 60} \qquad \text{Substitute } A = 200.$$

$$= \frac{100(200)}{200 + 60} \approx 76.92 \qquad \text{Which agrees with our answer to part } \mathbf{(b)} \qquad \blacksquare$$

 EXERCISES 6.8

Solve each of the following problems algebraically. That is, set up an equation or inequality and solve it. Be sure to label clearly what the variable represents.

1. If three-fourths of a number is 7 less than two-fifths of the number, what is the number?

2. If 5 more than five-sixths of a number is 3 less than two-thirds of the number, what is the number?

3. The ratio of men to women in a certain mathematics class is 7 to 9. If there are 810 women in the class, how many men are in the class?

4. In a certain town, the ratio of dogs to cats is 8 to 11. If there is a total of 2,812 cats and dogs, how many cats are there?

5. The ratio of two positive numbers is 5 to 12. Find the two numbers, if one number is 21 less than the other.

6. The ratio of two positive numbers is 7 to 9. Find the two numbers, if one number is 4 more than the other.

7. If 1 inch is 2.54 cm, how many inches are there in 52 cm? (Round your answer to two decimal places.)

8. If 1 kilogram is 2.2 lb, how many pounds are there in 17 kg? (Round your answer to two decimal places.)

9. On planet G, the units of currency are the droogs, the dreeps, and the dribbles. If 5 droogs are equivalent to 4 dreeps, and 7 dreeps are equivalent to 25 dribbles, how many dribbles are in 28 droogs?

10. On planet P, length is measured in wings, wongs, and wytes. If 14 wings are equivalent to 9 wytes, and 9 wongs are equivalent to 7 wings, how many wongs make a wyte?

11. The first side of a triangle is one-half the second side; the third side is two cm more than the second side. If the perimeter is 22 cm, find the lengths of the sides.

12. The width of a rectangle is three-fifths the length. If the perimeter is 80 in., find the dimensions of the rectangle.

13. The perimeter of a rectangle is 50 cm. If its length is $2\frac{1}{2}$ times its width, find its dimensions.

14. The shortest side of a triangle is two-thirds its medium side, and the longest side is 5 feet longer than the shortest side. If the perimeter is $23\frac{2}{3}$ ft, find the length of each side.

15. Mike was walking home from the ballfield when one-quarter of the way home he decided to take a cab. If he was 6 miles from his home when he decided to take a cab, how far is the home from the ballfield?

16. Half the height of a radio tower is painted blue and $\frac{1}{5}$ the height is painted red. If 22 feet remain unpainted, how tall is the tower?

17. Valerie walks from her home to her school. One-fifth of the way there she finds a nickel. One-quarter of the rest of the way she finds a dime. If she is still 2 blocks from school when she finds the dime, how many blocks did she walk from her home to school? (Assume that all blocks are equal in length.)

18. Raju walks from his home to his school. One-fifth of the way there he finds a nickel. One quarter of the rest of the way there he finds a dime. If he is still 3 blocks from school when he finds the dime, how far did he walk from his home to his school? (Assume that all blocks are equal in length.)

19. A law of physics states that if an electrical circuit has three resistors in parallel, then the reciprocal of the total resistance of the circuit is the sum of the reciprocals of the individual resistances. As a formula, we have

$$\frac{1}{R} = \frac{1}{R_1} + \frac{1}{R_2} + \frac{1}{R_3}$$

where R_1, R_2, and R_3 are the individual resistances measured in ohms, and R is the total resistance measured in ohms (see the accompanying figure).

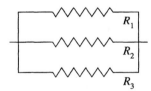

In such a circuit, the total resistance is $1\frac{1}{4}$ ohms, and two of the resistors are 2 ohms and 5 ohms. What is the third resistance?

20. Einstein's theory of relativity states that velocities must be added according to the formula

$$v = \frac{v_1 + v_2}{1 + \frac{v_1 v_2}{c^2}}$$

where v is the resulting velocity, v_1 and v_2 are the velocities to be added, and c is the speed of light. If v_1 and v_2 are both one-half the speed of light, what is the resultant velocity?

21. Cindy has invested in two interest-bearing investments: a certificate of deposit that yields 6% interest per year, and a bond that yields 10% interest. She invested $3,000 more in the certificate than in the bond. If she receives a total of $580 in annual interest, how much is invested in each venture?

22. Nick invested his money in two money-market certificates: One yields 4% interest per year and the other, higher-risk, certificate yields 8% per year. He invested $3,520 more in the certificate yielding 4% than in the other certificate. How much did he invest in each certificate if he receives a total of $1,100.80 in annual interest from the two certificates?

23. Arthur has a total of $25,000 saved in two banks: One bank gives $5\frac{1}{2}\%$ yearly interest, and the other gives 7% interest. If his total yearly interest from both banks is $1,465, how much was saved in each bank?

24. Patrick has invested $15,000 in two bonds: One bond yields 9% annual interest and the other yields $8\frac{3}{4}\%$ annual interest. How much is invested in each certificate if the combined yearly interest from both bonds is $1,340?

25. Lew wants to invest $18,000 in two bonds. One yields $8\frac{1}{2}\%$ annual interest and the other yields 11% annual interest. How much should he invest in each bond if he wants to receive a combined annual interest rate of 10%?

26. Joan saved $21,000 in two banks. One bank gives $4\frac{3}{4}\%$ annual interest, and the other gives $5\frac{1}{2}\%$ annual interest. How much did she save in each bank if she received a combined annual interest rate of 5% on her savings?

27. It takes Carol 3 hours to paint a small room and it takes John 5 hours to paint the same room. Working together, how long would it take for them to finish the room?

28. Pipe A can fill a pool with water in 3 days, and pipe B can fill the same pool in 2 days. If both pipes were used, how long would it take to fill the pool?

29. The Quickie Cleaning Service can clean a certain office building in 30 hours, while the Super-Quickie Cleaning Service can do the same job in 20 hours. If the two services work together, how long will it take to get the building clean?

30. The Echo brand candy corn machine can make enough candy corn to fill a supermarket order in 16 hours. On the other hand, the newer Echo 2 machine can make enough to fill the same order in 13 hours. How many hours would it take to make enough candy corn to fill the supermarket order if both machines were working together?

31. A bricklayer can complete a wall in $2\frac{2}{3}$ days, whereas his assistant can do the same size wall in 5 days. Working together, how long will it take for them to complete the wall?

32. A clerk can process 500 forms in $1\frac{2}{5}$ days. It takes $2\frac{1}{2}$ days for another clerk to process the same 500 forms. If both clerks work together, how long will it take them to process the 500 forms?

33. Repeat Exercise 29 if the Quickie Cleaning Service works alone for 10 hours and is then replaced by the Super-Quickie Cleaning Service.

34. Repeat Exercise 29 if the Super-Quickie Cleaning Service works alone for 10 hours and is then replaced by the Quickie Cleaning Service.

35. When a bathtub faucet is turned on (and the drain is shut), it can fill a tub in 10 minutes; when the drain is open, a full tub can *empty* in 15 minutes. How long would it take for the bathtub to fill if the water were turned on with the drain left open? [*Hint:* Let the rate at which the bathtub drains be negative.]

36. How long would it take for the bathtub of Exercise 35 to fill if a full tub can empty in 6 minutes when the drain is opened?

37. Aaron takes 10 hours to complete a particular job, and Kimberly takes 8 hours to complete the same job. Aaron begins work on the job by himself at noon. At 3 P.M. Kimberly joins him. What time do they complete the job?

38. It takes 4 hours for David and Malika to complete a particular job working together. If David could have completed the job himself in 8 hours, how long would it have taken Malika to complete the job working alone?

39. Lori takes 6 hours to mow her lawn alone. Suppose she starts the job at 10 A.M. and an hour later Megan shows up with her mower and helps her finish at 1 P.M. How long would it have taken Megan to do the job by herself?

40. What time would Megan and Lori of Exercise 39 finish mowing the lawn if they both started at 10 A.M.?

41. Bill can ride 10 km in the same time that Jill can ride 15 km. If Jill rides 10 kph faster than Bill, how fast does Bill ride?

42. A car can make a 200-mile trip in the same time that a bike can make a 60-mile trip. If the car travels 35 mph faster than the bike, how long does it take the bike to make its trip?

43. Marla drove 600 miles on an interstate highway. Her speed was 50 mph except on a part of the highway under construction, where her speed was 20 mph. If her total driving time was 14 hours, how many miles did she drive at the slower speed?

44. Susan decided to run to the store, which is 8 km from her house. She ran at a rate of 7 kph for part of the way and then walked at a rate of 3 kph the rest of the way. If the total trip took 2 hours, how many km did she run?

45. How many ounces of a 20% solution of alcohol must be mixed with 5 ounces of a 50% solution to get a mixture of 30% alcohol?

46. How many ounces of a 35% solution of sulfuric acid (and distilled water) must be mixed with 12 ounces of a 20% solution to get a 30% solution of sulfuric acid?

47. A chemist has a 30% solution of alcohol and a 75% solution of alcohol. How much of each should be mixed together to get 80 ml of a 50% mixture?

48. A chemist has a 45% mixture of hydrochloric acid and an 80% mixture of the same acid. How much of each should be mixed together to get 60 ml of a 60% solution of hydrochloric acid?

49. Two alloys, one 40% iron and the other 60% iron, are to be melted down to form another alloy. How much of each alloy should be melted down and mixed to form 80 tons of an alloy that is 55% iron?

50. Two alloys, one 28% iron and the other 82% iron, are to be melted down to form another alloy. How much of each alloy should be melted down and mixed to form 108 tons of an alloy that is 40% iron?

51. Abner has 2 liters of a 60% solution of alcohol. How much pure alcohol must he add to have an 80% solution?

52. Susan has 2 liters of a 60% solution of alcohol. How much pure water should she add to have a 40% solution?

53. Jack's radiator has a 3-gallon capacity. His radiator is filled to capacity with a 30% mixture of antifreeze and water. He drains off some of the old solution and refills the radiator to capacity with pure water to get a 20% mixture. How much did he drain off?

54. Jack's car radiator has a 3-gallon capacity. His radiator is filled to capacity with a 30% mixture of antifreeze and water. He drains off some of the old solution and refills the radiator to capacity with pure antifreeze to get a 45% mixture. How much did he drain off?

55. Advance tickets were sold at a concert for $25.00 each. At the door, tickets were $30.50 each. How many advance tickets were sold if 3,600 tickets were sold, netting $97,700?

56. Children's tickets at a movie sold for $4.50, whereas adult tickets sold for $7.25. On a single weekday the movie *Spiders* took in $15,650. If 2,500 tickets were sold that day, how many of each type were sold?

57. Sam had a bunch of nickels, dimes, and quarters totaling $20. If he had five more dimes than nickels and twice as many quarters as nickels, how many of each coin did he have?

58. Jake had 205 coins, consisting of nickels, dimes, and quarters. If the total value of the coins was $22 and there were three times as many dimes as nickels, how many of each coin did he have?

59. Orchestra seating at a play sold for $25.00, balcony tickets sold for $20.50, and general admission tickets sold for $16.00. For a single showing, there were twice as many general admission tickets sold as orchestra tickets. If there were 900 tickets sold and the total gross for the showing was $17,325, how many of each ticket were sold?

60. April saved a total of $19,000 in three banks: the First National Bank, the First Federal Bank, and the Fidelity Bank. The First National Bank gave $4\frac{3}{4}\%$ yearly interest, First Federal gave 5% yearly interest, and Fidelity gave $5\frac{1}{2}\%$ yearly interest. April had twice as much money saved in First Federal as she had saved in Fidelity. How much did she have saved in each bank if she received $932.50 in yearly interest for all her savings combined?

61. Ari's math teacher assigns course grades in the following way: Two exams are given, each worth 20% of the course grade; quizzes and homework together are worth 20% of the course grade; and the final exam is worth 40% of the course grade. Ari received a grade of 85 on the first exam, 65 on the second exam, and had a quiz and homework combined average of 72. What score must he get on the final exam to receive a grade of at least 80 for the course?

62. Repeat Exercise 61 if Ari received the same exam and quiz and homework scores but wanted to find the score he would need on the final exam to receive a grade of at least 70 for the course.

63. Tamara had $20,000 to invest. She decided to invest part of it in a high-risk bond that yields 8.2% annual interest, and the rest in a savings bank yielding 3.9% per year. What is the least amount she should invest in the high-risk bond if she wants to receive at least $1,000 interest per year?

64. Repeat Exercise 63 if Tamara wants to receive at least $2,000 a year interest.

65. A teacher assigns course grades in the following way: Each of three exams is worth 20%, and the final exam is worth 40%. If Chen's exam grades are 85, 92, and 86, what is the lowest he could score on the final exam for him to have an average of at least 90?

66. Repeat Exercise 65 if Chen receives the same exam grades, but wants to find the lowest he could score on the final exam and still have a course average of at least 80.

67. When two resistors, one of 6 ohms and one of x ohms, are connected in parallel, the resulting circuit has a combined resistance R given by

$$R(x) = \frac{6x}{6 + x}$$

(a) What should the resistance of x be for the resultant circuit to have a combined resistance of 3 ohms?

(b) What should the resistance of x be for the resultant circuit to have a combined resistance of A ohms?

68. It takes Tamika 2 hours to complete a job. If it takes x hours for Juan to do the same job alone, then the number of hours T it takes for the job to be completed when both Tamika and Juan work together is given by

$$T(x) = \frac{2 + x}{2x}$$

(a) How long would it take Juan to complete the job working alone if together they could complete the job in $1\frac{1}{2}$ hours?

(b) How long would it take Juan to complete the job working alone if together they could complete the job in 1 hour?

69. A manufacturer finds that the cost C (in dollars) to produce x items is given by $C = 0.2x + 6,000$. It then follows that the average cost per unit to produce x items is given by

$$A(x) = \frac{0.2x + 6,000}{x}$$

(a) The manufacturer determines that the most profit can be made if the average cost per unit is $100. How many items should be produced if the average per unit cost is $100?

(b) How many items should be produced if the average per unit cost is T?

70. A state environmental control department finds that the function

$$C(p) = \frac{180p}{100 - p}$$

serves as a good model for the cost C (in millions of dollars) to remove pollutants in the state's lakes and rivers.

(a) If the state allocates $20,000,000 to remove pollutants from its rivers and lakes, what percentage of the pollutants can be removed?

(b) Suppose the state allocates A (in millions) toward removing pollutants. Express the percentage of pollutants that can be removed as a function (in terms) of A.

? QUESTION FOR THOUGHT

71. The distance from Philadelphia to State College is 200 miles. Joe wants to travel the distance in 4 hours, and therefore he figures that he must average 50 mph for the trip. His car develops problems, however, so he can travel only 25 mph. Halfway there, the problem suddenly disappears. Joe now figures that for him to make the total trip within the 4-hour limit, he must average 75 mph for the rest of the trip. What is wrong with this logic?

MINI-REVIEW

72. *Simplify.* $5 - \{2x - 3[x - 2(x - 3)]\}$

73. *Factor completely.* $3x^3y - 6x^2y^2 + 3xy^3$

74. *Factor completely.* $(x - a)^2 - 9$

75. *Solve for x and graph the solution set.* $|2x + 8| \leq 10$

CHAPTER 6   SUMMARY

After having completed this chapter you should be able to:

1. Identify a rational function and its domain (Section 6.1).

   For example: The function $f(x) = \dfrac{3x - 7}{2 - 5x}$ is a rational function with domain
   $x \neq \frac{2}{5}$.

2. Apply the Fundamental Principle of Fractions to reduce fractions (Section 6.2).

   For example: $\dfrac{2x^2 - 8x}{x^2 - 16} = \dfrac{2x(x - 4)}{(x + 4)(x - 4)} = \dfrac{2x}{x + 4}$

3. Multiply and divide rational expressions (Section 6.3).

   For example:

   (a) $\dfrac{x^2 - 3x + 2}{4x - 8} \cdot \dfrac{8x}{x^3 - x^2} = \dfrac{(x - 2)(x - 1)}{4(x - 2)} \cdot \dfrac{8x}{x^2(x - 1)}$

   $$= \dfrac{(x - 2)(x - 1)}{4(x - 2)} \cdot \dfrac{8x}{x^2(x - 1)} = \dfrac{2}{x}$$

   (b) $\dfrac{x^3 y - xy^3}{4x + 4y} \div (x^2 - xy) = \dfrac{x^3 y - xy^3}{4x + 4y} \cdot \dfrac{1}{x^2 - xy}$ *Use the rule for division.*
   Factor and reduce.

   $$= \dfrac{xy(x + y)(x - y)}{4(x + y)} \cdot \dfrac{1}{x(x - y)}$$

   $$= \dfrac{xy(x + y)(x - y)}{4(x + y)} \cdot \dfrac{1}{x(x - y)}$$

   $$= \dfrac{y}{4}$$

4. Find the least common denominator for several fractions (Section 6.4).

   For example: Find the LCD of

   $$\dfrac{5}{2x^2}, \quad \dfrac{3}{x^2 + 2x}, \quad \dfrac{2}{x^2 - 4}$$

   Factor each denominator: $2x^2, \quad x(x + 2), \quad (x + 2)(x - 2)$

   The distinct factors are $2, \quad x, \quad x + 2, \quad x - 2$

   The LCD is $2x^2(x + 2)(x - 2)$.

5. Use the Fundamental Principle to combine fractions with unlike denominators (Section 6.4).

   For example:

   $$\dfrac{5}{2x^2} - \dfrac{3}{x^2 + 2x} + \dfrac{2}{x^2 - 4}$$

   $$= \dfrac{5}{2x^2} - \dfrac{3}{x(x + 2)} + \dfrac{2}{(x + 2)(x - 2)} \qquad LCD: = 2x^2(x + 2)(x - 2)$$

   $$= \dfrac{5(x + 2)(x - 2)}{2x^2(x + 2)(x - 2)} - \dfrac{3(2x)(x - 2)}{2x^2(x + 2)(x - 2)} + \dfrac{2(2x^2)}{2x^2(x + 2)(x - 2)}$$

   $$= \dfrac{5(x^2 - 4) - 6x(x - 2) + 4x^2}{2x^2(x + 2)(x - 2)}$$

   $$= \dfrac{5x^2 - 20 - 6x^2 + 12x + 4x^2}{2x^2(x + 2)(x - 2)}$$

   $$= \dfrac{3x^2 + 12x - 20}{2x^2(x + 2)(x - 2)}$$

6. Simplify complex fractions (Section 6.5).

For example:

$$\frac{\dfrac{1}{s} + \dfrac{6}{t}}{\dfrac{1}{s^2} - \dfrac{36}{t^2}} = \frac{\left(\dfrac{1}{s} + \dfrac{6}{t}\right)(s^2 t^2)}{\left(\dfrac{1}{s^2} - \dfrac{36}{t^2}\right)(s^2 t^2)}$$

Multiply numerator and denominator by the LCD of all simple fractions: $s^2 t^2$.

$$= \frac{st^2 + 6s^2 t}{t^2 - 36s^2}$$

$$= \frac{st(t + 6s)}{(t - 6s)(t + 6s)}$$

$$= \frac{st}{t - 6s}$$

7. Use the LCD to solve fractional equations (Section 6.6).

For example: Solve for x.

$$\frac{6}{x + 3} - \frac{3}{x + 6} = \frac{4}{x + 3}$$

Multiply both sides of the equation by $(x + 3)(x + 6)$.

$$(x + 3)(x + 6) \cdot \frac{6}{x + 3} - (x + 3)(x + 6) \cdot \frac{3}{x + 6} = (x + 3)(x + 6) \cdot \frac{4}{x + 3}$$

$$6(x + 6) - 3(x + 3) = 4(x + 6)$$

$$6x + 36 - 3x - 9 = 4x + 24$$

$$3x + 27 = 4x + 24$$

$$3 = x$$

Be sure to check that the solution is valid.

Check: $\dfrac{6}{3 + 3} - \dfrac{3}{3 + 6} \overset{?}{=} \dfrac{4}{3 + 3}$

$$\frac{6}{6} - \frac{3}{9} \overset{?}{=} \frac{4}{6}$$

$$1 - \frac{1}{3} \overset{\checkmark}{=} \frac{2}{3}$$

8. Solve a literal equation explicitly for a specified variable (Section 6.7).

For example: Solve for t.

$$3t - 7s = at - xs + 1$$

Collect t terms on one side and non-t terms on the other side of the equation.

$$3t - 7s \;\; - at \;\; = at - xs + 1 \;\; - at$$

Subtract at from both sides.

$$3t - at - 7s = -xs + 1$$

Add 7s to both sides.

$$3t - at - 7s \;\; + 7s \;\; = -xs + 1 \;\; + 7s$$

$$3t - at = 7s - xs + 1$$

Factor t from the left side.

$$t(3 - a) = 7s - xs + 1$$

Divide both sides of the equation by $3 - a$.

$$t = \frac{7s - xs + 1}{3 - a}$$

$$a \neq 3$$

9. Solve verbal problems that give rise to fractional equations (Section 6.8).

For example: A clerk can complete a job in 4 hours. If another clerk can complete the same job in 2 hours, how long would it take them to complete the job if they both worked together?

Let x be the number of hours it takes them to complete the job together.

Then $\frac{x}{4}$ represents the portion of the job completed by the first clerk in x hours.

$\frac{x}{2}$ represents the portion of the job completed by the second clerk in x hours.

Therefore, our equation is

$$\frac{x}{4} + \frac{x}{2} = 1 \qquad \textit{Multiply both sides of the equation by 4.}$$

$$x + 2x = 4$$

$$3x = 4$$

$$x = \frac{4}{3} = 1\frac{1}{3}$$

Hence, working together, they will complete the job in $1\frac{1}{3}$ hours or 1 hour and 20 minutes.

CHAPTER 6 REVIEW EXERCISES

In Exercises 1–4, find the domain of the given function.

1. $f(x) = \dfrac{2x - 1}{x + 5}$

2. $g(x) = \dfrac{x - 6}{3x + 4}$

3. $h(x) = \dfrac{1}{3x^2 - 11x - 4}$

4. $g(x) = \dfrac{x - 4}{2x^2 + 13x - 7}$

In Exercises 5–12, reduce to lowest terms.

5. $\dfrac{4x^2y^3}{16xy^5}$

6. $\dfrac{12a^2b^4}{16a^5bc^2}$

7. $\dfrac{x^2 + 2x - 8}{x^2 + 3x - 10}$

8. $\dfrac{6x^2 - 7x - 3}{(2x - 3)^2}$

9. $\dfrac{x^4 - 2x^3 + 3x^2}{x^2}$

10. $\dfrac{12a^3b^4 - 16ab^3 + 18a}{4a^2b}$

11. $\dfrac{5xa - 7a + 5xb - 7b}{3xa - 2a + 3xb - 2b}$

12. $\dfrac{8a^3 - b^3}{4a^2 + 2ab + b^2}$

In Exercises 13–54, perform the indicated operations. Express your answer in simplest form.

13. $\dfrac{4x^2y^3z^2}{12xy^4} \cdot \dfrac{24xy^5}{16xy}$

14. $\dfrac{4x^2y^3z^2}{12xy^4} \div \dfrac{24xy^5}{16xy}$

15. $\dfrac{5}{3x^2y} + \dfrac{1}{3x^2y}$

16. $\dfrac{3}{2a^2b} - \dfrac{3a}{2a^3b}$

17. $\dfrac{3x}{x - 1} + \dfrac{3}{x - 1}$

18. $\dfrac{2a}{a - 3} - \dfrac{6}{a - 3}$

19. $\dfrac{2x^2}{x^2 + x - 6} + \dfrac{2x}{x^2 + x - 6} - \dfrac{12}{x^2 + x - 6}$

20. $\dfrac{3a^2}{a^2 - a - 6} - \dfrac{3a}{a^2 - a - 6} - \dfrac{18}{a^2 - a - 6}$

21. $\dfrac{5}{3a^2b} - \dfrac{7}{4ab^4}$

22. $\dfrac{7}{3xy^2} + \dfrac{2}{5xy} - \dfrac{4}{30xy}$

23. $\dfrac{3x + 1}{2x^2} - \dfrac{3x - 2}{5x}$

24. $\dfrac{7x - 1}{3x} + \dfrac{5x + 2}{6x^2}$

25. $\dfrac{x - 7}{5 - x} + \dfrac{3x + 3}{x - 5}$

26. $\dfrac{3a + 1}{a - 4} + \dfrac{2a + 3}{4 - a}$

27. $\dfrac{x^2 + x - 6}{x + 4} \cdot \dfrac{2x^2 + 8x}{x^2 + x - 6}$

28. $\dfrac{a^2 + 2a - 15}{4a^2 + 8a} \cdot \dfrac{2a^2 + 4a}{a + 5}$

29. $\dfrac{a^2 - 2ab + b^2}{a + b} \div \dfrac{(a - b)^3}{a + b}$

30. $\dfrac{r^2 - rs - 2s^2}{2r - s} \div \dfrac{12r^2 - 24rs}{8r^2 - 4rs}$

31. $\dfrac{3x}{2x + 3} - \dfrac{5}{x - 4}$

32. $\dfrac{5a}{a - 1} + \dfrac{3a}{2a + 1}$

33. $\dfrac{3x - 2}{2x - 7} + \dfrac{5x + 2}{2x - 3}$

34. $\dfrac{7x + 1}{x + 3} - \dfrac{2x + 3}{x - 2}$

35. $\dfrac{5a}{a^2 - 3a} + \dfrac{2}{4a^3 + 4a^2}$

36. $\dfrac{3}{x^2 + 2x - 8} - \dfrac{5}{x^2 - x - 2}$

37. $\dfrac{5}{x^2 - 4x + 4} + \dfrac{3}{x^2 - 4}$

38. $\dfrac{3}{a^2 - 6a + 9} - \dfrac{5}{a^2 - 9}$

39. $\dfrac{2x}{7x^2 - 14x - 21} + \dfrac{2x}{14x - 42}$

40. $\dfrac{5}{x - y} + \dfrac{3}{y^2 - x^2}$

41. $\dfrac{5x}{x - 2} + \dfrac{3x}{x + 2} - \dfrac{2x + 3}{x^2 - 4}$

42. $\dfrac{2x}{x - 5} - \dfrac{3x}{x + 5} + \dfrac{x + 1}{x^2 - 25}$

43. $\left(\dfrac{2x + y}{5x^2y - xy^2}\right)\left(\dfrac{25x^2 - y^2}{10x^2 + 3xy - y^2}\right)\left(\dfrac{5x^2 - xy}{5x + y}\right)$

44. $\left(\dfrac{3a + 2b}{2a^2 + 3ab}\right)\left(\dfrac{2a^2 + ab - 3b^2}{9a^2 - 4b^2}\right)\left(\dfrac{3a^2b^2 - 2ab^3}{a - b}\right)$

45. $\dfrac{4x + 11}{x^2 + x - 6} - \dfrac{x + 2}{x^2 + 4x + 3}$

46. $\dfrac{2x + 1}{2x^2 + 13x + 15} - \dfrac{x - 1}{2x^2 - 3x - 9}$

47. $\dfrac{5x}{x^2 - x - 2} + \dfrac{4x + 3}{x^3 + x^2} - \dfrac{x - 6}{x^3 - 2x^2}$

48. $\dfrac{2r}{r^2 - rs - 2s^2} + \dfrac{2s}{r^2 - 3rs + 2s^2} + \dfrac{3}{r^2 - s^2}$

49. $\dfrac{4x^2 + 12x + 9}{8x^3 + 27} \cdot \dfrac{12x^3 - 18x^2 + 27x}{4x^2 - 9}$

50. $\dfrac{4x^2 - 12x + 9}{8x^3 - 27} \div \dfrac{4x^2 - 9}{12x^3 + 18x^2 + 27x}$

51. $4x \div \left(\dfrac{8x^2 - 8xy}{2ax + bx - 2ay - by} \div \dfrac{2ax + 2bx + 3ay + 3by}{2a^2 + 3ab + b^2}\right)$

52. $\left(\dfrac{8x^2 - 8xy}{2ax + bx - 2ay - by} \cdot \dfrac{2a^2 + 3ab + b^2}{2ax + 2bx + 3ay + 3by}\right) \div 4x$

53. $\left(\dfrac{x}{2} + \dfrac{3}{x}\right) \cdot \dfrac{x + 1}{x}$

54. $\left(\dfrac{x}{y} - \dfrac{y}{x}\right) \div \dfrac{x^2 - y^2}{x^2y^2}$

In Exercises 55–60, express the complex fraction as a simple fraction reduced to lowest terms.

55. $\dfrac{\dfrac{3x^2y}{2ab}}{\dfrac{9x}{16a^2}}$

56. $\dfrac{\dfrac{x}{x-y}}{\dfrac{y}{x-y}}$

57. $\dfrac{\dfrac{3}{a}-\dfrac{2}{a}}{\dfrac{5}{a}}$

58. $\dfrac{\dfrac{2}{x^2}+\dfrac{1}{x}}{\dfrac{4}{x^2}-1}$

59. $\dfrac{\dfrac{3}{b+1}+2}{\dfrac{2}{b-1}+b}$

60. $\dfrac{\dfrac{z}{z-2}+\dfrac{1}{z+1}}{\dfrac{3z}{z^2-z-2}}$

In Exercises 61–64, let $f(x) = \dfrac{x+3}{x-2}$ and $g(x) = \dfrac{1}{x-4}$.

61. Find (and simplify) $f(x) - g(x)$.

62. Find (and simplify) $g(x + h) - g(x)$.

63. Evaluate $g\left(\frac{2}{3}\right)$.

64. Evaluate $f\left(\frac{3}{5}\right)$.

In Exercises 65–82, solve the equations or inequalities.

65. $\dfrac{x}{3} + \dfrac{x-1}{2} = \dfrac{7}{6}$

66. $\dfrac{x}{2} - \dfrac{1}{3} = \dfrac{2x+3}{6}$

67. $\dfrac{x}{5} - \dfrac{x+1}{3} < \dfrac{1}{3}$

68. $\dfrac{x}{2} - \dfrac{1}{3} \geq \dfrac{2x+3}{6}$

69. $\dfrac{5}{x} - \dfrac{1}{3} = \dfrac{11}{3x}$

70. $\dfrac{7}{x} - \dfrac{3}{2x} = 5$

71. $\dfrac{x+1}{3} - \dfrac{x}{2} > 4$

72. $\dfrac{2-x}{14} \leq \dfrac{x+1}{7} + 2$

73. $-\dfrac{7}{x} + 1 = -13$

74. $\dfrac{3}{x-1} + 4 = \dfrac{5}{x-1}$

75. $\dfrac{5}{x-2} - 1 = 0$

76. $\dfrac{2}{x-3} + 1 = 3$

77. $\dfrac{x-2}{5} - \dfrac{3-x}{15} > \dfrac{1}{9}$

78. $\dfrac{2x+1}{3} + \dfrac{x}{4} \leq \dfrac{5}{6}$

79. $\dfrac{7}{x-1} + 4 = \dfrac{x+6}{x-1}$

80. $\dfrac{3}{x-2} + 5 = \dfrac{1+x}{x-2}$

81. $\dfrac{4x+1}{x^2-x-6} = \dfrac{2}{x-3} + \dfrac{5}{x+2}$

82. $\dfrac{5}{x+3} + \dfrac{2}{x} = \dfrac{x-12}{x^2+3x}$

In Exercises 83–92, solve the equations explicitly for the given variable.

83. $5x - 3y = 2x + 7y$ for x

84. $5x - 3y = 2x + 7y$ for y

85. $3xy = 2xy + 4$ for y

86. $5ab - 2a = 3ab + 2b$ for b

87. $\dfrac{2x+1}{y} = x$ for y

88. $\dfrac{ax+b}{c} = a$ for a

89. $\dfrac{ax+b}{cx+d} = y$ for x

90. $\dfrac{2s+3}{3s-2} = r$ for s

91. $\dfrac{1}{a} + \dfrac{1}{b} + \dfrac{1}{c} = \dfrac{1}{d}$ for b

92. $\dfrac{a}{c} - \dfrac{b}{d} = e$ for c

Solve each of the following problems algebraically.

93. If 1 inch is 2.54 centimeters, how many inches are there in 1 centimeter?

94. The ratio of Democrats to Republicans in a district is 4 to 3. If there is a total of 1,890 Democrats and Republicans, how many Democrats are there?

95. Carol walked from her aunt's to her father's house. Halfway there she picked up her brother Arnold and one-third of the rest of the way there she picked up her sister Julie. The three of them walked a distance of $1\frac{1}{2}$ miles before arriving at their father's house. How far did Carol walk?

96. José takes the same amount of time to walk 3 miles as it takes Carlos to ride his bike 5 miles. If Carlos travels 5 miles per hour faster than José, what is Carlos' rate of speed?

97. It takes Charles $2\frac{1}{2}$ days to refinish a room and it takes Ellen $2\frac{1}{3}$ days to refinish the same room. How long would it take them to refinish the room if they worked together?

98. It takes Jerry twice as long as Sue to clean up the kitchen. If Sue can clean up the kitchen in $\frac{1}{3}$ hour, how long would it take to clean up the kitchen if she works together with Jerry?

99. Tali takes 6 hours to complete a particular job. Suppose she and John begin working on the job together, and after 2 hours Tali leaves. If John completes the job himself an hour later, how long would it have taken John to complete the same job if he worked alone?

100. It takes 3 hours for two people to complete a particular job working together. If one of them could have completed the job alone in 8 hours, how long would it take the other to complete the job working alone?

101. How much of a 35% solution of alcohol should a chemist mix with 5 liters of a 70% alcohol solution to get a solution that is 60% alcohol?

102. How much pure water should be added to 3 liters of a 65% solution of sulfuric acid to dilute it to 30%?

103. Children's tickets at a movie theater sold for $3.50, and adult tickets sold for $6.25. On a single weekday the movie *Fred* took in $4,970. If 980 tickets were sold that day, how many of each type were sold?

104. Peg has 82 coins in pennies, nickels, and dimes, totaling $3.32. If she has 4 times as many nickels as dimes, how many of each coin does she have?

105. A pharmaceutical company finds that when a certain drug is administered to a patient, the concentration c of the drug in the bloodstream (in milligrams per liter) h hours after the drug was administered is given by

$$c(h) = \frac{30.4h}{h^2 + 2}$$

(a) Compute $c(0.25)$, $c(0.5)$, $c(1)$, $c(2)$, $c(4)$, and $c(10)$, and explain what each of these values means.

(b) Use the points found in part (a) to sketch a rough graph of the function. Use the graph or a table to explain how the concentration of the drug in the bloodstream changes as time passes.

106. A manufacturer finds that the cost C (in dollars) to produce x items is given by $C = 0.3x + 2,500$. It then follows that the average cost per unit $A(x)$ to produce x items is given by

$$A(x) = \frac{0.3x + 2,500}{x}$$

(a) The manufacturer determines that the most profit can be made if the average cost per unit is $12.50. How many items should be produced if the average per unit cost is $12.50?

(b) How many items should be produced if the average per unit cost is $A?

CHAPTER 6 PRACTICE TEST

1. Find the domain of $f(x) = \dfrac{3x + 5}{2x + 5}$.

2. Express the following in simplest form.

   (a) $\dfrac{24x^2y^4}{64x^3y}$

   (b) $\dfrac{x^2 - 9}{x^2 - 6x + 9}$

   (c) $\dfrac{6x^3 - 9x^2 - 6x}{5x^3 - 10x^2}$

3. Perform the indicated operations and express your answer in simplest form.

   (a) $\dfrac{4xy^3}{5ab^4} \cdot \dfrac{15}{16x^4y^5}$

   (b) $\dfrac{3x}{18y^2} + \dfrac{5}{8x^2y}$

   (c) $\dfrac{r^2 - rs - 2s^2}{2s^2 + 4rs} \div \dfrac{r - 2s}{4s^2 + 8rs}$

   (d) $\dfrac{9x - 2}{4x - 3} + \dfrac{x + 4}{3 - 4x}$

   (e) $\dfrac{3x}{x^2 - 4} + \dfrac{4}{x^2 - 5x + 6} - \dfrac{2x}{x^2 - x - 6}$

   (f) $\left(\dfrac{3}{x} - \dfrac{2}{x + 1}\right) \div \dfrac{1}{x + 1}$

4. Express as a simple fraction reduced to lowest terms.

$$\dfrac{\dfrac{3}{x + 1} - 2}{\dfrac{5}{x} + 1}$$

5. If $f(x) = \dfrac{3x + 1}{x + 4}$, evaluate $f\left(-\tfrac{3}{5}\right)$.

6. Solve the following:

   (a) $\dfrac{2x - 4}{6} - \dfrac{5x - 2}{3} < 5$

   (b) $\dfrac{3}{x - 8} = 2 - \dfrac{5 - x}{x - 8}$

   (c) $\dfrac{3}{2x + 1} + \dfrac{4}{2x - 1} = \dfrac{29}{4x^2 - 1}$

7. Solve explicitly for x:

$$y = \dfrac{x - 2}{2x + 1}$$

8. How much of a 30% alcohol solution must be mixed with 8 liters of a 45% solution to get a mixture that is 42% alcohol?

9. It takes Jackie $3\tfrac{1}{2}$ hours to complete a job and it takes 2 hours for Eleanor to do the same job. How long would it take for them to complete the job working together?

10. A manufacturer finds that the cost C (in dollars) to produce x items is given by $C = 0.25x + 3{,}200$. It then follows that the average cost per unit $A(x)$ to produce x items is given by

$$A(x) = \dfrac{0.25x + 3{,}200}{x}$$

   The manufacturer determines that the most profit can be made if the average cost per unit is \$18. How many items should be produced if the average per unit cost is \$18?

CHAPTERS 4–6 CUMULATIVE REVIEW

In Exercises 1–4, sketch the graph of each equation in a rectangular coordinate system.

1. $3y - 5x + 9 = 0$

2. $y = -\dfrac{2}{3}x - 1$

3. $y = -5$

4. $x = -5$

5. On the same coordinate system, sketch the graphs of the lines with slopes 2 and -2 passing through the point $(2, 3)$.

6. On the same coordinate system, sketch the graphs of the lines with slopes $\frac{3}{4}$ and $-\frac{3}{4}$ passing through the point $(3, 2)$.

In Exercises 7–12, find the slope of the line satisfying the given condition(s).

7. Passing through points $(2, -3)$ and $(3, 5)$

8. Passing through points $(5, -4)$ and $(-2, 3)$

9. Equation is $y = 5x - 8$

10. Equation is $3x - 2y = 11$

11. Parallel to the line passing through the points $(2, -1)$ and $(6, 4)$

12. Perpendicular to the line passing through the points $(2, -3)$ and $(4, 2)$

*In Exercises 13–14, find the values of **a** satisfying the given condition(s).*

13. The line through the points $(2, a)$ and $(a, -2)$ has slope 3.

14. The line through the points $(a, 2)$ and $(1, 3)$ is parallel to the line through the points $(4, -1)$ and $(5, 1)$.

In Exercises 15–22, find the equation of the line satisfying the given conditions.

15. The line passes through the point $(-2, 7)$ and has slope 3.

16. The line passes through the point $(2, 5)$ and has slope -2.

17. The line passes through the points $(2, 7)$ and $(3, 1)$.

18. The line passes through the points $(3, 5)$ and $(4, 5)$.

19. The line has y-intercept 2 and slope 4.

20. The line has x-intercept 3 and slope -1.

21. The line passes through the point $(2, -3)$ and is parallel to the line $3x + 5y = 4$.

22. The line passes through the point $(2, -3)$ and is perpendicular to the line $2y = 4x + 1$.

23. Estimate the equation of the line given in the figure.

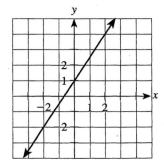

24. The owner of a clothing store found that the relationship between his daily profit on bathing suits (P) and the daily temperature (T) during the summer months is linear. If he makes $450 when the temperature is 86°F and $325 when the temperature is 80°F, write an equation relating P to T, and predict his daily profit on a 90°F day.

In Exercises 25–32, solve the given system of equations.

25. $\begin{cases} 3x - 2y = 8 \\ 5x + y = 9 \end{cases}$

26. $\begin{cases} 4x - 3y = 2 \\ 6x - 5y = 3 \end{cases}$

27. $\begin{cases} 7u + 5v = 23 \\ 8u + 9v = 23 \end{cases}$

28. $\begin{cases} -10s + 7t = -6 \\ -4s + 6t = -4 \end{cases}$

29. $\begin{cases} 2m = 3n - 5 \\ 3n = 2m - 5 \end{cases}$

30. $\begin{cases} 5w = 4v + 7 \\ 4v = 5w - 7 \end{cases}$

31. $\begin{cases} \dfrac{2}{3}y - \dfrac{1}{2}x = 6 \\ \dfrac{4}{5}y - \dfrac{3}{4}x = 6 \end{cases}$

32. $\begin{cases} \dfrac{x}{4} + \dfrac{5y}{6} = -\dfrac{11}{12} \\ \dfrac{5x}{3} + \dfrac{y}{2} = 4 \end{cases}$

In Exercises 33–36, graph the inequality on the rectangular coordinate system.

33. $2x + 3y \geq 18$

34. $7x - y < 14$

35. $2y < 5x - 20$

36. $2y \leq 4$

In Exercises 37–38, identify the degree of the polynomial.

37. $5xy^2 - 2x^2y^3 + 2$

38. 3

In Exercises 39–50, perform the operations and express your answer in simplest form.

39. $(3x^2 + 2x - 4) - (2x^2 - 3x + 5)$

40. $-3x(2x - 5y + 4)$

41. $(x - y)(x - 3y)$

42. $(3x - 2y)(x - y)$

43. $(x + y - 2)(x + y)$

44. $(2a + b)(4a^2 - 2ab + b^2)$

45. $(3x - 5y)^2$

46. $(2m + 3n)(2m - 3n)$

47. $(3x - 5y)(3x + 5y)$

48. $(2m + 3n)^2$

49. $(2x + y - 3)(2x + y + 3)$

50. $(x - 2y + 3)^2$

In Exercises 51–72, factor as completely as possible.

51. $x^2 - 5x - 24$

52. $y^2 - 4x^2$

53. $y^2 - 12xy + 35x^2$

54. $10a^2 - 3ab - b^2$

55. $4y^2 + 16yz + 15z^2$

56. $9x^2 - 25z^2$

57. $25a^2 + 20ab + 4b^2$

58. $4x^2 - 12x - 9$

59. $36x^2 - 9$

60. $25x^2 - 30xz + 9z^2$

61. $25a^2 + 20ab - 4b^2$

62. $12y^3 - 16y^2 - 3y$

63. $3y^3 + 5y^2 - 2y$

64. $25a^4 + 10a^2b^2 - 8b^4$

65. $49a^4 - 14a^2z - 3z^2$

66. $18a^5b - 9a^3b^2 - 2ab^3$

67. $(x - y)^2 - 16$

68. $(a - 2b)^2 - 25$

69. $16a^4 - b^4$

70. $(x + y)^2 + 3(x + y) + 2$

71. $8a^3 + 125b^3$

72. $x^3 - 25x - x^2 + 25$

In Exercises 73–78, solve the given equation.

73. $x^2 - x = 12$

74. $2t^2 + 5 = 7t$

75. $(a + 3)(a - 5) = 9$

76. $(3c + 1)(2c - 5) = (6c - 1)(c + 2)$

77. $(r + 4)^2 = 36$

78. $3x^2 = 5x$

For Exercises 79–80, if $f(x) = x^2 - 5x + 4$, solve the given polynomial equation.

79. $f(x) = 0$

80. $f(x) = 4$

In Exercises 81–84, find the quotients.

81. $(x^2 + 2x + 3) \div (x + 4)$

82. $(2x^2 + 7x - 1) \div (2x + 1)$

83. $(4x^3 + 3x + 1) \div (2x + 3)$

84. $(x^4 + 2) \div (x^2 + 2x + 1)$

In Exercises 85–86, find the domain of the function.

85. $f(x) = \dfrac{3x - 1}{2x + 3}$

86. $g(x) = \dfrac{x - 7}{3x^2 - 5x - 2}$

In Exercises 87–90, reduce to lowest terms.

87. $\dfrac{18a^3b^2}{16a^5b}$

88. $\dfrac{x^2 - 9y^2}{x^2 - 6xy + 9y^2}$

89. $\dfrac{2a^3 - 5a^2b - 3ab^2}{a^4 - 2a^3b - 3a^2b^2}$

90. $\dfrac{27x^3 - y^3}{18x^2 + 6xy + 2y^2}$

In Exercises 91–100, perform the operations. Express your answer in simplest terms.

91. $\dfrac{3xy^2}{5a^3b} \div \dfrac{21x^3y}{25ab^3}$

92. $\dfrac{2x^2 - xy - y^2}{x + y} \cdot \dfrac{x^2 - y^2}{x - y}$

93. $\dfrac{3x}{2y} + \dfrac{2y}{3x}$

94. $\dfrac{6}{x - 2} - \dfrac{3x}{x - 2}$

95. $\left(\dfrac{2x^3 - 2x^2 - 24x}{x + 2}\right)\left(\dfrac{x + 2}{4x^2 + 12x}\right)$

96. $\dfrac{9a^2 - 6ab + b^2}{3a + b} \div \dfrac{3a^2 - 4ab + b^2}{3a^2 - 2ab - b^2}$

97. $\dfrac{2}{x - 5} - \dfrac{3}{x - 2}$

98. $\dfrac{3}{2x^2 - 5xy - 3y^2} - \dfrac{5}{x^2 - 2xy - 3y^2}$

99. $\dfrac{x^3 + x^2y}{2x^2 + xy} \div \left[\left(\dfrac{x^2 + 2xy - 3y^2}{2x^2 - xy - y^2}\right)(x + y)\right]$

100. $\dfrac{x}{x - 5y} - \dfrac{2y}{x + 5y} - \dfrac{20y^2}{x^2 - 25y^2}$

In Exercises 101–102, write as a simple fraction reduced to lowest terms.

101. $\dfrac{x - \dfrac{2}{x}}{\dfrac{1}{2} - x}$

102. $\dfrac{\dfrac{x}{x + y} - \dfrac{4y}{x + 4y}}{\dfrac{x - 2y}{x + y} + 1}$

In Exercises 103–104, given $f(x) = \dfrac{x + 4}{2x + 1}$ and $g(x) = \dfrac{3}{x + 1}$, find and simplify the following.

103. $f\left(\dfrac{2}{3}\right)$

104. $g(x + h) - g(x)$

In Exercises 105–110, solve the equations or inequalities.

105. $\dfrac{2}{x} - \dfrac{1}{2} = 2 - \dfrac{1}{x}$

106. $\dfrac{4}{x + 4} - 2 = 0$

107. $\dfrac{x}{2} - \dfrac{x + 1}{3} > \dfrac{2}{3}$

108. $\dfrac{3}{x - 2} + 3 = \dfrac{x + 1}{x - 2}$

109. $\dfrac{3}{x - 2} + \dfrac{5}{x + 1} = \dfrac{1}{x^2 - x - 2}$

110. $\dfrac{x + 3}{4} - \dfrac{2x + 1}{3} \le \dfrac{1}{2}$

In Exercises 111–114, solve for the given variable.

111. $2a + 3b = 5b - 4a$ (for a)

112. $3xy - 2y = 5x + 3y$ (for y)

113. $\dfrac{x - y}{y} = x$ (for y)

114. $\dfrac{2x + 3}{x - 2} = y$ (for x)

In Exercises 115–119, solve algebraically.

115. The ratio of foreign-made cars to American-made cars in a town is 5 to 6. If there are 1,200 American-made cars in the town, how many cars are there altogether?

116. How much of a 20% solution of alcohol should be mixed with 8 liters of a 35% solution of alcohol to get a solution that is 30% alcohol?

117. Carmen can paint a room in 4 hours, and Judy can paint the same room in $4\frac{1}{2}$ hours. How long would it take for them to paint the room working together?

118. Megan takes 5 hours to complete a particular job. Suppose she starts the job at 8 A.M. and two hours later Jason shows up and helps her finish at 11 A.M. How long would it have taken Jason to do the job by himself?

119. General admission tickets at a theater sold for $3.50, and reserved seats sold for $4.25. If 505 tickets were sold for a performance that took in $1,861.25, how many of each type of ticket were sold?

120. A company finds that the cost C per unit of producing x units is given by the function

$$C = C(x) = 325 + \dfrac{750}{x^2}$$

(a) Compute $C(5)$, $C(10)$, $C(50)$, $C(100)$, $C(300)$, $C(500)$, and $C(1,000)$, and explain what each of these values means.

(b) Use the points found in part (a) to sketch a rough graph of this function. Describe the behavior of this cost function. What is happening to the cost per item as the company manufactures more and more items?

1. Perform the operations and simplify:
   (a) $(2x^2 - 3xy + 4y^2) - (5x^2 - 2xy + y^2)$
   (b) $(3a - 2b)(5a + 3b)$
   (c) $(2x^2 - y)(2x^2 + y)$
   (d) $(3y - 2z)^2$
   (e) $(x + y - 3)^2$

2. Factor the following completely:
   (a) $a^2 - 9a + 14$
   (b) $6r^2 - 5rs - 6s^2$
   (c) $10a^4 - 9a^2y - 9y^2$
   (d) $4a^4 - 12a^2b^2 + 9b^4$
   (e) $(a + 2b)^2 - 25$
   (f) $125x^3 - 1$

3. If $f(x) = (x - 3)(x + 9)$, solve the polynomial equation $f(x) = 0$.

4. Solve the following.
   (a) $2x^2 + 3x - 2 = 0$
   (b) $(x - 3)(x + 4) = 8$

5. Find the quotient. $(2x^3 + 6x + 5) \div (x + 2)$

6. Find the domain of the rational function $f(x) = \dfrac{2x}{(3x - 2)(x + 1)}$.

7. Perform the indicated operations and express your answer in simplest form.
   (a) $\left(\dfrac{25x^2 - 9y^2}{x - y}\right)\left(\dfrac{2x^2 + xy - 3y^2}{10x^2 + 9xy - 9y^2}\right)$
   (b) $\dfrac{2y}{2x - y} + \dfrac{4x}{y - 2x}$
   (c) $\dfrac{3x}{x^2 - 10x + 21} - \dfrac{2}{x^2 - 8x + 15}$

8. Write as a simple fraction reduced to lowest terms.
$$\frac{\dfrac{1}{x} - 2}{3 + \dfrac{1}{x + 1}}$$

9. If $f(x) = \dfrac{x}{2x + 1}$, find and simplify $f(x + h) - f(x)$.

10. Solve the following:
    (a) $\dfrac{2}{x + 1} + \dfrac{3}{2x} = \dfrac{6}{x^2 + x}$
    (b) $\dfrac{x}{3} - \dfrac{x + 2}{7} < 4$
    (c) $\dfrac{5}{x + 3} + 2 = \dfrac{x + 8}{x + 3}$

11. Solve for a.
$$y = \frac{a}{a + 1}$$

12. Carol can process 80 forms in 6 hours, whereas Joe can process the same 80 forms in $5\frac{1}{2}$ hours. How long would it take them to process the same forms if they work together?

13. Sketch the graph of the equation $y = -\dfrac{3}{4}x + 6$ using the intercept method.

14. Find the slope of a line passing through the points $(2, -3)$ and $(3, -4)$.

15. Find the equations of the line passing through the point $(2, -3)$ and
    (a) Parallel to the line $3y - 2x = 4$
    (b) Perpendicular to the line $3y - 2x = 4$

16. There is a perfect linear relationship between the scores on two tests, test A and test B. Anyone scoring 40 on test A will score 30 on test B; anyone scoring 60 on test A will score 25 on test B. What score on test B should a person get if he or she scored 48 on test A?

17. Solve the following system of equations:

$$\begin{cases} 5x + 2y = 4 \\ 2x - 3y = 13 \end{cases}$$

18. Sketch a graph of $3x + 6y > 18$ on a rectangular coordinate system.

Although we have dealt with exponents in previous chapters, in this chapter we will engage in a more formal treatment of exponents. Beginning with the definition of *natural number* exponents, we will discuss the rules for multiplying and dividing simple expressions. Then we will examine what happens when we allow exponents to take on integer and rational values.

7.1 Natural Number and Integer Exponents

Natural Number Exponents

First, recall the definition of exponential notation:

$x^n = x \cdot x \cdot x \cdot \cdots \cdot x$ where the factor x occurs n times in the product.

Observe that for this definition to make sense, n must be a natural number. (How can you have -3 factors of x?) With this definition of exponents, and the suitable properties of the real number system, we will state the first three rules of natural number exponents:

Rules of Natural Number Exponents	1. $x^n \cdot x^m = x^{n+m}$ 2. $(x^n)^m = x^{nm}$ 3. $(xy)^n = x^n y^n$

As we stated in Chapter 1, rule 1 is a matter of counting x's:

$$x^n \cdot x^m = \underbrace{(x \cdot x \cdot x \cdot \cdots \cdot x)}_{n\ times}\underbrace{(x \cdot x \cdot x \cdot \cdots \cdot x)}_{m\ times} = \underbrace{x \cdot x \cdot x \cdot x \cdot \cdots \cdot x}_{n\ +\ m\ times} = x^{n+m}$$

Rule 2 is derived by applying rule 1:

$$(x^n)^m = \underbrace{x^n \cdot x^n \cdot \cdots \cdot x^n}$$

x^n occurs m times in the product.

$$= x^{n+n+\cdots+n} \qquad \textit{By rule 1 the exponent n is added m times.}$$
$$= x^{nm}$$

Rule 1 and rule 2 are often confused (when do I add exponents and when do I multiply?). Keep the differences in mind: Rule 1 states that when *two powers of the same base are to be multiplied,* the exponents are *added;* rule 2 states that when *a power is raised to a power,* the exponents are *multiplied.*

Rule 3 is derived from the associative and commutative properties of multiplication:

$$(xy)^n = \underbrace{(xy) \cdot (xy) \cdot \cdots \cdot (xy)}_{n\ times} \qquad \textit{Reorder and regroup by the associative and commutative properties of multiplication.}$$

$$= \underbrace{(x \cdot x \cdot \cdots \cdot x)}_{n\ times}\underbrace{(y \cdot y \cdot \cdots \cdot y)}_{n\ times}$$
$$= x^n y^n$$

EXAMPLE 1

Perform the indicated operations and simplify.

(a) $x^7 \cdot x^6$ (b) $3^8 \cdot 3^2$ (c) $(x^7)^6$

(d) $(3xy)^4$ (e) $(-3x^3)^2(-2x^2)^5$ (f) $(x^2 + y^3)^2$

Solution

(a) $x^7 \cdot x^6$ *Apply rule 1.*

$= x^{7+6} = \boxed{x^{13}}$

(b) $3^8 \cdot 3^2$ *Multiply using rule 1.*

$= 3^{8+2} = \boxed{3^{10}}$ *Note that the answer is **not** 9^{10}.*

(c) $(x^7)^6$ *Apply rule 2.*

$= x^{7 \cdot 6} = \boxed{x^{42}}$

(d) $(3xy)^4$ *Apply rule 3:*

$= 3^4 x^4 y^4$ *Each **factor** is raised to the 4th power.*

$= \boxed{81x^4 y^4}$

(e) $(-3x^3)^2(-2x^2)^5$ *First apply rule 3.*

$= (-3)^2(x^3)^2(-2)^5(x^2)^5$ *Note that the sign is part of the coefficient and is raised to the given power. Then use rule 2.*

$= 9x^6(-32)x^{10}$ *Multiply using rule 1.*

$= \boxed{-288x^{16}}$

(f) $(x^2 + y^3)^2 = (x^2 + y^3)(x^2 + y^3)$

$= \boxed{x^4 + 2x^2 y^3 + y^6}$

*We cannot apply rule 2 for exponents in this case since rule 2 applies only to **factors** and **not terms**. We use polynomial multiplication instead.* ∎

Up until now we have concentrated on developing rules for exponential expressions involving multiplication. Let's now examine division. We consider the expression $\dfrac{x^n}{x^m}$ (we assume $x \neq 0$):

Case (i): $n > m$

Case (ii): $n < m$

Case (iii): $n = m$

Since $n = m$, we have $x^n = x^m$.

Hence, $\dfrac{x^n}{x^m}$ is a fraction with the numerator identical to the denominator. Thus,

$$\frac{x^n}{x^m} = \frac{x^n}{x^n} = 1$$

We summarize this discussion as follows:

Rule 4 of Natural Number Exponents	If $x \neq 0$, $$\frac{x^n}{x^m} = \begin{cases} x^{n-m} & \text{if } n > m \\ \dfrac{1}{x^{m-n}} & \text{if } n < m \\ 1 & \text{if } n = m \end{cases}$$

We had to split rule 4 into three cases to ensure natural number values for the exponents. Shortly, when we allow integer values for exponents, we will consolidate these three cases into one.

The next and final rule for natural number exponents is a result of the associative and commutative properties of rational multiplication.

We consider the expression $\left(\dfrac{x}{y}\right)^n$.

$$\left(\frac{x}{y}\right)^n = \overbrace{\left(\frac{x}{y}\right)\left(\frac{x}{y}\right) \cdots \left(\frac{x}{y}\right)}^{n \text{ times}} = \frac{\overbrace{x \cdot x \cdots x}^{n \text{ times}}}{\underbrace{y \cdot y \cdots y}_{n \text{ times}}} = \frac{x^n}{y^n}$$

Thus, we have:

Rule 5 of Natural Number Exponents	If $y \neq 0$, $$\left(\frac{x}{y}\right)^n = \frac{x^n}{y^n}$$

For convenience, we assume that all values of the variable are nonzero and real numbers.

EXAMPLE 2

Perform the indicated operations and simplify.

(a) $\dfrac{x^7}{x^4}$ 　　　　(b) $\dfrac{x^4}{x^7}$ 　　　　(c) $\left(\dfrac{r^5}{s^2}\right)^4$

Solution

These expressions require straightforward applications of rules 4 and 5.

(a) $\dfrac{x^7}{x^4}$ 　　*Divide using rule 4, case (i).*

$$= x^{7-4} = \boxed{x^3}$$

(b) $\dfrac{x^4}{x^7}$ 　　*Divide using rule 4, case (ii).*

$$= \frac{1}{x^{7-4}} = \boxed{\frac{1}{x^3}}$$

(c) $\left(\dfrac{r^5}{s^2}\right)^4 = \dfrac{(r^5)^4}{(s^2)^4}$ *Apply rule 5, then raise to a power using rule 2.*

$= \boxed{\dfrac{r^{20}}{s^8}}$

■

Let's examine problems requiring us to combine the use of several of the rules of natural number exponents.

EXAMPLE 3 Perform the indicated operations and simplify.

(a) $\left(\dfrac{a^2a^5}{a^6}\right)^4$ (b) $\dfrac{(3a^2)^4(2a)^2}{(-2a^3)^5}$

Solution (a) We will show two ways to approach this problem.

First applying rule 1 inside parentheses:

$\left(\dfrac{a^2a^5}{a^6}\right)^4 = \left(\dfrac{a^7}{a^6}\right)^4$ *Then rule 4*

$= (a)^4$

$= \boxed{a^4}$

Applying rule 5 first:

$\left(\dfrac{a^2a^5}{a^6}\right)^4 = \dfrac{(a^2a^5)^4}{(a^6)^4}$ *Then rule 3*

$= \dfrac{(a^2)^4(a^5)^4}{(a^6)^4}$ *Then rule 2*

$= \dfrac{a^8a^{20}}{a^{24}}$ *Then rule 1*

$= \dfrac{a^{28}}{a^{24}}$ *Then rule 4*

$= \boxed{a^4}$

Experience will teach you which approach is more efficient.

(b) $\dfrac{(3a^2)^4(2a)^2}{(-2a^3)^5} = \dfrac{3^4(a^2)^4 2^2a^2}{(-2)^5(a^3)^5}$ *Apply rule 3, then rule 2*

$= \dfrac{81a^8(4)a^2}{-32a^{15}}$ *Then rule 1*

$= \dfrac{81 \cdot 4a^{10}}{-2a^{15}}$ *Then rule 4*

$= \dfrac{(81)(4)}{-32a^5}$ *Reduce.*

$= \boxed{-\dfrac{81}{8a^5}}$

■

Integer Exponents

We originally defined x^n as the product of n x's. Based on that definition, it does not make sense for n to be negative or 0. Hence, the exponents we discussed were natural numbers. Now we would like to allow exponents to take on any *integer* values, and determine what it means when exponents have nonpositive integer values. This is called extending the definition of exponents to the integers.

In previous discussions, our understanding of the definition of a positive integer exponent led quite naturally to the five rules for exponents. To define negative and zero exponents, we will work the other way around. Since we want the exponent rules developed previously to continue to apply, we assume that the exponent rules developed for natural number exponents will still be valid for integer exponents. We then will use these rules to show us how to define integer exponents.

Let's assume x^0 exists and $x \neq 0$; see what happens when we find the product $x^0 \cdot x^n$ by applying the first rule of exponents:

$$x^0 \cdot x^n = x^{0+n} \qquad Rule\ 1$$
$$= x^n$$

Hence, $x^0 \cdot x^n = x^n$. Verbally stated, multiplying an expression by x^0 does not change the expression. Thus, x^0 has the same property as 1, the multiplicative identity. Since 1 is the only number that has this property, it would be convenient to have $x^0 = 1$. We therefore make the following definition:

DEFINITION	A zero exponent is defined as follows: $$x^0 = 1 \qquad (x \neq 0)$$ Note that $\mathbf{0^0}$ *is* ***undefined.***

For example (assume all variables are nonzero and real numbers):

$$5^0 = 1$$
$$(xy^3)^0 = 1$$

$(-165)^0 = 1$ *Even if the base is negative, raising to the zero power still yields* $+1$.

$\left(\dfrac{x^2y^5z^2}{xy^4z^9}\right)^0 = 1$ *Look carefully before simplifying an expression.*

Now let's examine x^{-n} when n is a natural number and $x \neq 0$. What does it mean to have a negative exponent? We assume x^{-n} exists and will examine what happens when we find the product $x^n \cdot x^{-n}$ by applying rule 1 again:

$$x^{-n} \cdot x^n = x^{-n+n} \qquad Rule\ 1$$
$$= x^0$$
$$= 1 \qquad Definition\ of\ zero\ exponent$$

Hence, $x^{-n} \cdot x^n = 1$.   *Dividing both sides of the equation above by x^n, we get*

$$x^{-n} = \frac{1}{x^n}$$

We therefore make the following definition:

DEFINITION	Negative exponents are defined as follows: If n is a natural number and $x \neq 0$, then $$x^{-n} = \frac{1}{x^n}$$

Verbally stated, an expression with a negative exponent is the reciprocal of the same expression with the exponent made positive. Thus,

$$x^{-3} = \frac{1}{x^3} \qquad 5^{-4} = \frac{1}{5^4} \qquad 10^{-5} = \frac{1}{10^5}$$

Let's examine what happens when there is a negative exponent in the denominator of a fraction:

$$\frac{1}{x^{-n}} = \frac{1}{\frac{1}{x^n}} \qquad \text{\textit{Definition of negative exponents}}$$

$$= 1 \cdot \frac{x^n}{1} \qquad \text{\textit{Rule for dividing fractions}}$$

$$= x^n$$

Hence, $\frac{1}{x^{-n}} = x^n$. Thus we have

$$x^{-n} = \frac{1}{x^n} \quad \text{and} \quad \frac{1}{x^{-n}} = x^n$$

In words, this says that x^{-n} is the reciprocal of x^n, and x^n is the reciprocal of x^{-n}. For example,

$$\frac{1}{x^{-4}} = \frac{x^4}{1} = x^4 \qquad\qquad \frac{1}{2^{-2}} = \frac{2^2}{1} = 4$$

$$x^{-2} = \frac{1}{x^2} \qquad\qquad \frac{1}{(-2)^{-3}} = (-2)^{+3} = -8$$

Do not confuse the sign of an exponent with the sign of the base. For example, -2 is a number 2 units to the left of 0 on the number line, whereas $2^{-1} = \frac{1}{2}$ is a positive number, one-half unit to the right of 0, as shown in the figure:

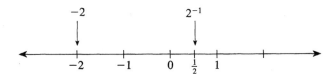

EXAMPLE 4

Using a calculator, evaluate 3^{-6}.

(a) Find the answer rounded to six decimal places.

(b) Find the answer exactly.

Solution

(a) To evaluate 3^{-6} as a decimal, we would press the following sequence of keys: $\boxed{3}\ \boxed{y^x}\ \boxed{6}\ \boxed{+/-}\ \boxed{=}$ to get

$$\boxed{0.001372}$$

rounded to six decimal places.

(b) To find the answer exactly, we would have to rewrite 3^{-6} as $\frac{1}{3^6}$. We can use the calculator to evaluate 3^6 as follows: $\boxed{3}\ \boxed{y^x}\ \boxed{6}\ \boxed{=}$ to get $\boxed{729}$. The exact answer is then

$$\boxed{\frac{1}{729}}$$

∎

It is important to note that our definitions of zero and negative exponents are consistent with the five exponent rules we have been using, so we are free to use the exponent rules for expressions involving both positive and negative integer exponents.

Since we need not be concerned whether the exponents are integers, we can now consolidate rule 4 for natural number exponents.

Rule 4 for Integer Exponents	$\dfrac{x^n}{x^m} = x^{n-m} \qquad (x \neq 0)$

For example,

According to natural number exponent rule 4:	According to integer exponent rule 4:
$\dfrac{x^3}{x^3} = 1$	$\dfrac{x^3}{x^3} = x^{3-3} = x^0 = 1$
$\dfrac{x^2}{x^6} = \dfrac{1}{x^{6-2}} = \dfrac{1}{x^4}$	$\dfrac{x^2}{x^6} = x^{2-6} = x^{-4}$
	$= \dfrac{1}{x^4}$ *By definition of negative exponents*

Definitions and Rules for Integer Exponents	Rule 1: $\quad x^n x^m = x^{n+m}$
	Rule 2: $\quad (x^n)^m = x^{nm}$
	Rule 3: $\quad (xy)^n = x^n y^n$
	Rule 4: $\quad \dfrac{x^n}{x^m} = x^{n-m} \qquad (x \neq 0)$
	Rule 5: $\quad \left(\dfrac{x}{y}\right)^n = \dfrac{x^n}{y^n} \qquad (y \neq 0)$
	Definition: $\quad a^0 = 1 \qquad (a \neq 0)$
	Definition: $\quad a^{-n} = \dfrac{1}{a^n} \qquad (a \neq 0)$

The only difference between the rules for integer and natural number exponents is the consolidation of rule 4.

Let's now examine some expressions involving integer exponents.

EXAMPLE 5 Perform the indicated operations and simplify. Express your answers with positive exponents only.

(a) $y^{-4}y^8 y^{-6}$ (b) $\dfrac{x^{-6}}{x^{-8}}$ (c) $(x^{-4})^{-6}$

(d) $(a^{-2}b^3 c^{-2})^2$ (e) $\left(\dfrac{r^{-3}}{r^0}\right)^{-2}$ (f) $\left(\dfrac{2}{3}\right)^{-1}$ (g) $\dfrac{c^{-4}d^6}{c^5 d^{-3}}$

Solution We *could* simplify all these expressions by using the definition of negative exponents and changing all negative exponents to positive exponents by substituting reciprocals. For example:

(a) $y^{-4}y^8 y^{-6} = \left(\dfrac{1}{y^4}\right)(y^8)\left(\dfrac{1}{y^6}\right)$ *Definition of negative exponents*

$= \dfrac{1}{y^4} \cdot \dfrac{y^8}{1} \cdot \dfrac{1}{y^6}$

$= \dfrac{y^8}{y^4 y^6}$ *Apply rule 1 for **natural number exponents**.*

$$= \frac{y^8}{y^{10}} \qquad \textit{Apply rule 4 for \textbf{natural number exponents}.}$$

$$= \boxed{\frac{1}{y^2}}$$

A more efficient method would be to apply the rules for integer exponents first, and then use the definition, if needed, to express the final answer with positive exponents.

Alternative Solution for Part (a):

$$y^{-4}y^8y^{-6} \qquad \textit{Apply rule 1 for \textbf{integer exponents}.}$$

$$= y^{-4 + 8 +(-6)}$$

$$= y^{-2} \qquad \textit{Apply the definition of negative exponents.}$$

$$= \boxed{\frac{1}{y^2}}$$

When simplifying an expression with exponents it is easier, in general, to use the exponent rules rather than using the definition, if you have a choice.

(b) $\dfrac{x^{-6}}{x^{-8}} = x^{-6-(-8)}$ *We have applied rule 4 for **integer exponents**. Note: Numerator exponent minus denominator exponent*

$$= x^{-6+8} \qquad \textit{Remember that you are subtracting a negative exponent.}$$

$$= \boxed{x^2}$$

(c) $(x^{-4})^{-6} = x^{(-6)(-4)} = \boxed{x^{24}}$ *Rule 2*

(d) $(a^{-2}b^3c^{-2})^2$ *This is a product raised to a power: Apply rule 3.*

$$= (a^{-2})^2(b^3)^2(c^{-2})^2 \qquad \textit{This is a power of a power: Apply rule 2.}$$

$$= a^{-4}b^6c^{-4} \qquad \textit{Apply the definition of negative exponents.}$$

$$= \left(\frac{1}{a^4}\right)(b^6)\left(\frac{1}{c^4}\right)$$

$$= \boxed{\frac{b^6}{a^4c^4}}$$

(e) $\left(\dfrac{r^{-3}}{r^0}\right)^{-2} = \left(\dfrac{r^{-3}}{1}\right)^{-2}$ *Definition of zero exponent*

$$= (r^{-3})^{-2} \qquad \textit{Apply rule 2.}$$

$$= \boxed{r^6}$$

In general, x^{-n} is the reciprocal of x^n. For example, $\left(\dfrac{2}{3}\right)^{-5} = \left(\dfrac{3}{2}\right)^5$

(f) $\left(\dfrac{2}{3}\right)^{-1}$ *Since x^{-1} is the reciprocal of x (remember that x^{-n} is the reciprocal of x^n)*

$$= \left(\frac{3}{2}\right)^1$$

$$= \boxed{\frac{3}{2}}$$

(g) $\dfrac{c^{-4}d^6}{c^5d^{-3}} = c^{-4-5}d^{6-(-3)}$ *Rule 4*

$$= c^{-9}d^9 = \boxed{\frac{d^9}{c^9}} \qquad \blacksquare$$

EXAMPLE 6

Perform the indicated operations and simplify. Express your answers with positive exponents only.

(a) $(5x^{-2}y^{-1})^{-2}$ (b) $(5x^{-2} + y^{-1})^{-2}$

(c) $\dfrac{a^{-2}b^{-2}}{a^{-1}b^{-1}}$ (d) $\dfrac{a^{-2} - b^{-2}}{a^{-1} + b^{-1}}$

Solution

(a) $(5x^{-2}y^{-1})^{-2}$ *A product raised to a power: Apply rule 3.*

$\quad = 5^{-2}(x^{-2})^{-2}(y^{-1})^{-2}$ *Now apply rule 2 to x and y.*

$\quad = 5^{-2}(x^4)(y^2)$ *Apply the definition of negative exponents to 5^{-2}.*

$\quad = \left(\dfrac{1}{5^2}\right)(x^4y^2) = \boxed{\dfrac{x^4y^2}{25}}$

Note the differences between parts (a) and (b).

(b) Do not try to apply rule 3 in this problem; x^{-2} and y^{-1} are *terms*, not factors. Rule 3 applies to *factors only*.

$(5x^{-2} + y^{-1})^{-2} = \left(\dfrac{5}{x^2} + \dfrac{1}{y}\right)^{-2}$ *By the definition of negative exponents. Note that 5 remains in the numerator of the first fraction. Now add fractions in parentheses; the LCD is x^2y.*

$\quad = \left(\dfrac{5y + x^2}{x^2y}\right)^{-2}$ *Now we can change the sign of the exponent outside the parentheses and rewrite the entire fraction as its reciprocal.*

$\quad = \left(\dfrac{x^2y}{5y + x^2}\right)^{+2}$

$\quad = \dfrac{(x^2y)^2}{(5y + x^2)^2} = \boxed{\dfrac{x^4y^2}{(5y + x^2)^2}}$

(c) $\dfrac{a^{-2}b^{-2}}{a^{-1}b^{-1}}$ *Apply rule 4.*

$\quad = a^{-2-(-1)}b^{-2-(-1)} = a^{-1}b^{-1} = \boxed{\dfrac{1}{ab}}$

Note the differences between parts (c) and (d).

(d) $\dfrac{a^{-2} - b^{-2}}{a^{-1} + b^{-1}}$ *We rewrite each **term** in the numerator and denominator using the definition of negative exponents.*

$\quad = \dfrac{\dfrac{1}{a^2} - \dfrac{1}{b^2}}{\dfrac{1}{a} + \dfrac{1}{b}}$ *A complex fraction. Multiply the numerator and denominator of the complex fraction by a^2b^2. Why?*

$\quad = \dfrac{\left(\dfrac{1}{a^2} - \dfrac{1}{b^2}\right)a^2b^2}{\left(\dfrac{1}{a} + \dfrac{1}{b}\right)a^2b^2}$

$\quad = \dfrac{b^2 - a^2}{ab^2 + a^2b}$ *Factor and reduce.*

$\quad = \dfrac{(b - a)\cancel{(b + a)}}{ab\cancel{(b + a)}} = \boxed{\dfrac{b - a}{ab}}$ ∎

EXAMPLE 7

Perform the indicated operations and simplify. Express your answer with positive exponents only.

$$\dfrac{9^{-3} \cdot 3^{-4}}{3^{-2} \cdot 9^2}$$

Solution

$$\frac{9^{-3} \cdot 3^{-4}}{3^{-2} \cdot 9^2}$$ *If we notice that everything can be expressed as a power of 3, we can proceed as follows.*

$$= \frac{(3^2)^{-3} \cdot 3^{-4}}{3^{-2}(3^2)^2}$$

$$= \frac{3^{-6} \cdot 3^{-4}}{3^{-2} \cdot 3^4}$$

$$= \frac{3^{-10}}{3^2}$$

$$= 3^{-10-2}$$

$$= 3^{-12}$$

$$= \boxed{\frac{1}{3^{12}}}$$

■

 EXERCISES 7.1

In Exercises 1–46, perform the indicated operations and simplify. Assume that all variables represent nonzero real numbers. Express your answers with positive exponents only.

1. $(x^2x^5)(x^3x)$

2. $(a^2b^5)(a^4b^7)$

3. $(-2a^2b^3)(3a^5b^7)$

4. $(-4r^3s)(-2rst^3)$

5. $(a^2)^5$

6. $(y^3)^8$

7. $\left(\frac{2}{3}\right)^2$

8. $\left(\frac{3}{2}\right)^3$

9. $(x + y^3)^2$

10. $(a^2b)^2$

11. $(xy^3)^2$

12. $(a^2 + b)^2$

13. $(2^3 \cdot 3^2)^2$

14. $(5^2 \cdot 2^3)^2$

15. $(x^4y^3)^5(x^3y^2)^2$

16. $(a^2a^3)^5(a^3a)^6$

17. $(-2a^2)^3(ab^2)^4$

18. $(r^2s^3)^2(-rs^4)^3$

19. $(r^2st)^3(-2rs^2t)^4$

20. $(-2x^2y)^2(2xy^3)^3$

21. $\frac{x^5}{x^2}$

22. $\frac{x^2}{x^5}$

23. $\frac{x^3y^2}{xy^4}$

24. $\frac{a^7b^4}{a^7b^4}$

25. $\frac{5^4 \cdot 2^2}{25^2 \cdot 4^2}$

26. $\frac{2^2 \cdot 3^4}{9^2 \cdot 4^3}$

27. $\frac{a^5b^9c}{a^4bc^5}$

28. $\frac{2^2x^2y^3}{2^4xy^3}$

29. $\frac{(-3)^2xy^4}{-3^2xy^5}$

30. $\frac{(-2)^2xy^5}{-2^2xy^5}$

31. $\frac{3^2(-2)^3}{(-9^2)(-4)^2}$

32. $\frac{(-9)^2(-4)^3}{-3^3 \cdot 2^4}$

33. $\left(\frac{y^5}{y^8}\right)^3$

34. $\left(\frac{x^5}{x^4}\right)^5$

35. $\left(\frac{y^2y^7}{y^4}\right)^3$

36. $\left(\frac{x^5}{x^3x^9}\right)^4$

37. $\frac{(3r^2s)^3(-2rs^2)^4}{(-18rs)^2}$

38. $\frac{(2xy^2)^3(-2xy)^2}{(-2x)^3}$

39. $\left(\frac{2x^2y^3}{xy^4}\right)^2\left(\frac{3xy^2}{6}\right)^3$

40. $\left(\frac{x^2x^3}{x}\right)^4\left(\frac{x^2x^5}{x^3}\right)^2$

41. $\left(\frac{(6ab^2)^2}{-3ab}\right)^3$

42. $\left(\frac{(-5b^2c)^2}{-10b^2c^3}\right)^3$

43. $\left(\frac{-2a^2b^3}{ab}\right)^3(-3xy^2)^3$

44. $\left(\frac{(3ab^2)^3(5a^2b)}{9ab}\right)^3$

45. $[(r^3s^2)^3(rs^2)^4]^2$

46. $[(-3rs^2)^2(-2st^2)^3]^3$

In Exercises 47–50, use a calculator to evaluate the following to six decimal places.

47. 5^{-8}

48. -3^{-5}

49. $-2 \cdot 5^{-3} + 8$

50. $4 \cdot 2^{-6} - 4$

In Exercises 51–104, perform the indicated operations and simplify. Express your answers with positive exponents only. (Assume that all variables represent nonzero real numbers.)

51. $x^{-2}x^4x^{-3}$

52. $a^2a^{-3}b^2$

53. $(x^5y^{-4})(x^{-3}y^2x^0)$

54. $(a^{-1}b^2)(a^3b^{-4})$

55. $(3^{-2})^{-3}$

56. $(2^{-3})^{-2}$

57. $(a^{-2}b^{-3})^2$

58. $(x^{-5}y^{-3}x^0)^{-2}$

59. $(r^{-3}s^2)^{-4}(r^2)^{-3}$

60. $(a^{-2}b^3)^{-5}(a^3)^{-2}$

61. -2^{-2}

62. $(-2)^{-2}$

63. $(-3)^{-2}$

64. -3^{-2}

65. $(2^{-2})^{-3}(3^{-3})^2$

66. $(3^{-2})^4(2^{-4})^{-3}$

67. $(3^{-2}s^3)^4(9s^{-3})^{-2}$

68. $(2r^2s)^{-2}(4r)^3$

69. $\dfrac{x^4}{x^{-2}}$

70. $\dfrac{x^{-2}}{x^4}$

71. $\dfrac{x^{-3}y^2}{x^{-5}y^0}$

72. $\dfrac{a^{-2}b^2}{a^{-3}b^4a^0}$

73. $\left(\dfrac{1}{2}\right)^{-1}$

74. $\left(-\dfrac{3}{4}\right)^{-1}$

75. $\left(-\dfrac{3}{5}\right)^{-3}$

76. $\left(\dfrac{5}{8}\right)^{-3}$

77. $\dfrac{x^{-1}xy^{-2}}{x^4y^{-3}y}$

78. $\dfrac{a^{-4}b^{-3}}{a^{-2}b^{-4}}$

79. $\dfrac{(a^{-2}b^2)^{-3}}{ab^{-2}}$

80. $\dfrac{(2r^{-4}s^{-2})^{-3}}{2r^2s^3}$

81. $\left(\dfrac{x^{-1}x^{-3}}{x^{-2}}\right)^{-3}$

82. $\left(\dfrac{a^{-2}a^3}{a^{-1}}\right)^{-2}$

83. $\dfrac{2^{-2}\cdot 3^2}{6^{-2}}$

84. $\dfrac{3^{-5}\cdot 9^{-1}}{27^2}$

85. $\dfrac{(3x)^{-2}(2xy^{-1})^0}{(2x^{-2}y^3)^{-2}}$

86. $\dfrac{(2xy^2)^0(3x^2y^{-1})^{-1}}{(3x^{-1}y)^{-1}}$

87. $\left(\dfrac{x^{-3}y^{-4}}{x^{-5}y^{-7}}\right)^{-3}$

88. $\left(\dfrac{a^{-2}b^3}{a^3b^{-4}}\right)^{-2}$

89. $\dfrac{(-3a^{-4}b^{-2})(-4ab^{-3})^{-1}}{(12ab^2)^{-1}}$

90. $\dfrac{(-2a^2b^{-1})^{-2}(-5ab^2)^{-1}}{(50a^{-2}b)^{-1}}$

91. $(x^2y^{-3})^{-1}$

92. $(a^3b^{-2})^{-2}$

93. $(x^2+y^{-3})^{-1}$

94. $(a^3+b^{-2})^{-2}$

95. $(x^{-2}+y^{-2})^{-2}$

96. $(x^{-2}+y^{-2})(x^{-2}-y^{-2})$

97. $\left(\dfrac{x^{-4}y^{-7}z^{-6}}{x^{-24}y^{-16}}\right)^0$

98. $\left(\dfrac{x^{-2}+y^{-5}}{x^{-6}-y^{-4}}\right)^0$

99. $\dfrac{x^{-1}+y^{-1}}{xy^{-1}}$

100. $\dfrac{a^{-1}-b^{-1}}{(ab)^{-1}}$

101. $\dfrac{r^{-2}+s^{-1}}{r^{-1}+s^{-2}}$

102. $\dfrac{c^{-2}-d^{-3}}{c^{-3}-d^{-2}}$

103. $\dfrac{2a^{-1}+b^{-2}}{a^{-2}+b}$

104. $\dfrac{3x^{-2}-y^{-3}}{x+y^{-1}}$

 QUESTIONS FOR THOUGHT

105. Discuss what is ***wrong*** (if anything) in each of the following.

(a) $x^2x^3 \overset{?}{=} x^6$

(b) $(x^2)^3 \overset{?}{=} x^5$

(c) $(x^2y^2)^3 \stackrel{?}{=} x^6y^6$

(d) $(x^2 + y^2)^3 \stackrel{?}{=} x^6 + y^6$

(e) $\dfrac{6x^6}{2x^2} \stackrel{?}{=} 3x^3$

106. Fill in the operation(s) that makes the following true for all n:

$$(x \ ? \ y)^n = x^n \ ? \ y^n$$

107. Why do we have to separate rule 4 of natural number exponents into cases?

108. Describe what is **wrong** (if anything) with the following:

(a) $8^{-1} \stackrel{?}{=} -8$

(b) $8^{-1} \stackrel{?}{=} \dfrac{1}{8}$

(c) $(-2)^{-3} \stackrel{?}{=} +8$

(d) $(-2)^{-3} \stackrel{?}{=} +6$

(e) $(-2)^{-3} \stackrel{?}{=} \dfrac{1}{-8}$

(f) $\dfrac{x^{16}}{x^{-5}} \stackrel{?}{=} x^{11}$

(g) $xy^{-1} \stackrel{?}{=} \dfrac{1}{xy}$

(h) $xy^{-1} \stackrel{?}{=} \dfrac{x}{y}$

109. Suppose that we allow exponents to be fractions and that the rules of integer exponents still hold. Notice that if we square $9^{1/2}$, we get

$$(9^{1/2})^2 = 9^{2/2} = 9^1 = 9$$

Hence,

$$(9^{1/2})^2 = 9$$

What does this imply about the value of $9^{1/2}$?

110. Consider the equation $y = 2^x$.

(a) Construct a table of values for y for $x = -3, -2, -1, 0, 1, 2,$ and 3.

(b) Plot the points (x, y) on the rectangular coordinate system. You should arrive at the graph shown in Figure 7.1 Check that your graph agrees with the figure.

Figure 7.1

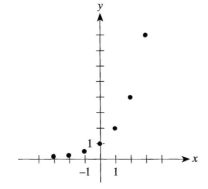

(c) Use the figure to discuss how changes in the value of x affect the value of y. (If x changes by 1 unit, how will this affect y? Will y always change by the same amount?) Is y growing quickly or slowly? Is y ever negative?

 MINI-REVIEW

111. *Solve for x.* $-2 \le 5 - 2x < 11$

112. The length of a rectangular area is 5 meters less than twice its width. If the rectangular area is to be carpeted at a cost of $14 per square meter, express the cost of carpeting this area in terms of the width, w.

113. Write an equation of the line passing through the points $(0, -4)$ and $(6, 0)$.

114. Given $f(x) = 2x^2 - 5x - 1$, compute $f(3) + f(2)$ and $f(5)$.

7.3 Rational Exponents and Radical Notation

Our original definition of exponents required natural number exponents. We then let the exponent rules tell us how to extend the definition of exponents to include integer exponents. Next we will extend the definition even further to define rational number exponents. We will approach this task in the same way we did in Section 7.1, except that we will primarily use rule 2 for exponents to extend our definition to include rational number exponents. Remember that a rational number is a number of the form $\frac{p}{q}$, where p and q are integers and $q \neq 0$.

We will start with the simplest case: $a^{1/2}$. How do we define $a^{1/2}$ in general? Let's examine $9^{1/2}$. First observe that if we apply rule 2 and square $9^{1/2}$ we get

$$(9^{1/2})^2 = 9^{2/2} = 9^1 = 9$$

So $9^{1/2}$ is a number that, *when squared*, yields 9. There are two possible answers:

$$3 \quad \text{since } 3^2 = 9 \quad \text{and} \quad -3 \text{ since } (-3)^2 = 9$$

Therefore, we create the following definition to avoid ambiguity:

DEFINITION	$a^{1/2}$ (called the ***principal square root*** of a) is the *nonnegative* quantity that, when squared, yields a.

Thus, $9^{1/2} = 3$.

EXAMPLE 1 Evaluate the following:

(a) $16^{1/2}$ (b) $-16^{1/2}$ (c) $(-16)^{1/2}$

Solution

(a) $16^{1/2} = \boxed{4}$ *Since $4^2 = 16$ and is nonnegative*

(b) $-16^{1/2} = \boxed{-4}$ *Note: We want the negative of $16^{1/2}$.*

Can you find a real number whose square is –16? Why not?

(c) $(-16)^{1/2}$ is $\boxed{\text{not a real number}}$.   *Since **no** real number squared will yield a negative number* ∎

We arrive at the definition of $a^{1/3}$ in the same way we did for $a^{1/2}$. For example, if we cube $8^{1/3}$, we get

$$(8^{1/3})^3 = 8^{3/3} = 8^1 = 8$$

Thus, $8^{1/3}$ is the number that, *when cubed,* yields 8.

Since $2^3 = 8$, we have $8^{1/3} = 2$.

DEFINITION	$a^{1/3}$ (called the ***cube root*** of a) is the quantity that, when cubed, yields a.

Hence,

$$27^{1/3} = 3 \quad \text{since } 3^3 = 27$$
$$(-125)^{1/3} = -5 \quad \text{since } (-5)^3 = -125$$

Let's examine one more root before we generalize our findings. We will look at $a^{1/4}$. Let's raise $16^{1/4}$ to the fourth power:

$$(16^{1/4})^4 = 16^{4/4} = 16^1 = 16$$

Thus, $16^{1/4}$ is a number that, when raised to the fourth power, yields 16. As with the square root, we have two possible answers:

$$2 \quad \text{since } 2^4 = 16 \qquad \text{and} \qquad -2 \quad \text{since } (-2)^4 = 16$$

Again, to avoid ambiguity, we define $a^{1/4}$ as follows:

DEFINITION	$a^{1/4}$ (called the ***principal fourth root*** of a) is the *nonnegative* quantity that, when raised to the fourth power, yields a.

Looking at the discussion preceding each of the definitions above, you will notice that there is a possibility for ambiguity when the root is even. That is, there are two possible answers. To eliminate this ambiguity, we inserted the word *nonnegative* in our definitions of the square root and fourth root. On the other hand, for odd roots (such as cube roots), there is only one real-number answer, so we need not be concerned with ambiguity. This leads us to the following general definition.

DEFINITION	$a^{1/n}$ (*called the **principal nth root of a***) is the real number (positive when n is even) that, when raised to the nth power, yields a. We can write this symbolically as: $$a^{1/n} = \begin{cases} b & \text{if } n \text{ is odd and } b^n = a \\ |b| & \text{if } n \text{ is even, } a \geq 0, b^n = a \end{cases}$$

Earlier we pointed out that the square root of –16 is not a real number, since no real number squared will yield a negative number. In general, raising any real number to an even power will always yield a nonnegative number. Therefore, the even root of a negative number is not a real number.

We can summarize the various types of roots as indicated in the box.

	n is even	*n is odd*
$a > 0$	$a^{1/n}$ is the positive nth root of a	$a^{1/n}$ is the nth root of a
$a < 0$	$a^{1/n}$ is not a real number	$a^{1/n}$ is the nth root of a
$a = 0$	$0^{1/n} = 0$	$0^{1/n} = 0$

EXAMPLE 2

Evaluate the following:

(a) $(-32)^{1/5}$ **(b)** $(-64)^{1/6}$ **(c)** $(-8)^{1/3}$ **(d)** $\left(\dfrac{1}{81}\right)^{1/4}$

Solution

(a) $(-32)^{1/5} = \boxed{-2}$ *Since* $(-2)^5 = -32$

(b) $(-64)^{1/6}$ $\boxed{\text{is not a real number.}}$ *What number raised to the sixth power will yield -64?*

(c) $(-8)^{1/3} = \boxed{-2}$ *Since* $(-2)^3 = -8$

(d) $\left(\dfrac{1}{81}\right)^{1/4} = \boxed{\dfrac{1}{3}}$ *Since* $\left(\dfrac{1}{3}\right)^4 = \dfrac{1}{81}$ ∎

We will often have occasion to use an alternate notation for fractional exponents, called *radical notation:*

$$x^{1/n} \quad \text{is also written as} \quad \sqrt[n]{x}$$

For example:

$$x^{1/5} = \sqrt[5]{x}$$
$$x^{1/7} = \sqrt[7]{x}$$

In particular,

$$x^{1/2} \quad \text{is written as} \quad \sqrt{x}$$

Thus far we have defined $a^{1/n}$ where n is a natural number. With some help from rule 2 for exponents, we can define the expression $a^{m/n}$ where n and m are natural numbers.

DEFINITION

If $a^{1/n}$ is a real number, then

$$a^{m/n} = (a^{1/n})^m$$

That is, $a^{m/n}$ is the nth root of a raised to the mth power.

We define $a^{-m/n}$ as follows:

DEFINITION

$$a^{-m/n} = \frac{1}{a^{m/n}} \quad (a \neq 0).$$

Now that we have defined rational exponents, we assert that the *rules for integer exponents hold for rational exponents as well, provided the root is a real number* (that is, provided we avoid even roots of negative numbers). For example, to use the rule $(a^r)^s = a^{rs}$ where r and s are rational, it is necessary that both a^r and a^s be defined.

Since $a^{\frac{m}{n}} = a^{m \cdot \frac{1}{n}} = (a^m)^{1/n}$, we find that $(a^{1/n})^m = (a^m)^{1/n}$. Hence, we can interpret $a^{m/n}$ in two ways, as indicated in the next box.

If $a^{1/n}$ is a real number, then
$$a^{m/n} = (a^{1/n})^m = (a^m)^{1/n}$$

EXAMPLE 3

Evaluate each of the following:

(a) $27^{2/3}$ (b) $16^{3/4}$ (c) $(-64)^{2/3}$ (d) $-64^{2/3}$

(e) $36^{-1/2}$ (f) $(-125)^{-1/3}$ (g) $\left(\dfrac{1}{125}\right)^{-1/3}$

Solution

In general, you will find it easier to find the root *before* raising to a power.

(a) $27^{2/3} = (27^{1/3})^2 = 3^2 = \boxed{9}$

(b) $16^{3/4} = (16^{1/4})^3 = 2^3 = \boxed{8}$

We could have done this same problem in the following way:
$$16^{3/4} = (16^3)^{1/4} = (4{,}096)^{1/4} = 8$$

But this approach requires more multiplication and finding a difficult root.

(c) $(-64)^{2/3} = [(-64)^{1/3}]^2 = [-4]^2 = \boxed{+16}$

(d) $-64^{2/3} = -[(64)^{1/3}]^2 = -[4]^2 = \boxed{-16}$ *Note the difference between this problem and part (c).*

(e) $36^{-1/2} = \dfrac{1}{36^{1/2}}$ *Begin by changing the negative exponent into a positive exponent by using the definition of a negative rational exponent.*

$= \boxed{\dfrac{1}{6}}$

(f) $(-125)^{-1/3} = \dfrac{1}{(-125)^{1/3}}$ *Definition of negative rational exponent*

$= \dfrac{1}{-5} = \boxed{-\dfrac{1}{5}}$

Note that *the sign of the exponent has no effect on the sign of the base.*

(g) We will approach this problem a bit differently, using the fact that an exponent of -1 turns an expression into its reciprocal.

$$\left(\frac{1}{125}\right)^{-1/3} = \left[\left(\frac{1}{125}\right)^{-1}\right]^{1/3}$$

$$= \left[\frac{125}{1}\right]^{1/3} \quad \textit{Since the reciprocal of } \frac{1}{125} \textit{ is } \frac{125}{1}$$

$$= 125^{1/3} = \boxed{5} \qquad\blacksquare$$

As we stated earlier, the rules for integer exponents are also valid for rational exponents. Thus, we simplify expressions involving rational exponents by following the same procedures we used for integer exponents. The main difficulty in simplifying rational exponent expressions is the fractional arithmetic involved.

One point of confusion that frequently arises involves the difference between negative exponents and fractional exponents. *Negative exponents involve* **reciprocals** *of the base.* For example,

$$x^{-4} = \frac{1}{x^4} \quad \text{or} \quad 16^{-4} = \frac{1}{16^4} = \frac{1}{65{,}536}$$

On the other hand, *fractional exponents yield **roots** of the base.* For example,

$$x^{1/4} = \text{the fourth root of } x \quad \text{or} \quad 16^{1/4} = 2$$

As with integer exponents, when we are asked to simplify an expression, the bases and exponents should appear as few times as possible. Unless otherwise noted, we assume all variables represent positive real numbers.

EXAMPLE 4

Perform the operations and simplify. Express your answer with positive exponents only.

(a) $x^{1/2}x^{2/3}x^{3/4}$ (b) $\dfrac{x^{2/5}}{x^{3/4}}$ (c) $(y^{2/3}y^{-1/2})^2$

(d) $\dfrac{a^{1/2}a^{-2/3}}{a^{1/4}}$ (e) $\left(\dfrac{x^{-1/2}y^{-1/4}}{x^{1/4}}\right)^{-4}$

Solution

We apply the rules of rational exponents.

(a) $x^{1/2}x^{2/3}x^{3/4}$ *Since all factors have the same base, we apply rule 1 and add the exponents.*

$= x^{1/2+2/3+3/4}$ *Leave the exponent as an improper fraction (reduced).*

$= x^{6/12+8/12+9/12}$

$= \boxed{x^{23/12}}$

(b) $\dfrac{x^{2/5}}{x^{3/4}}$ *Use rule 4: Subtract the exponents.*

$= x^{2/5\,-3/4}$

$= x^{8/20\,-15/20}$

$= x^{-7/20}$ *Use the definition of negative exponents.*

$= \boxed{\dfrac{1}{x^{7/20}}}$

(c) $(y^{2/3}y^{-1/2})^2$ *Make sure you can follow the arithmetic. Apply rule 1.*

$= (y^{2/3+(-1/2)})^2$

$= (y^{1/6})^2$ *Next rule 2: Multiply exponents.*

$= y^{2/6}$ *Reduce the exponent.*

$= \boxed{y^{1/3}}$

(d) $\dfrac{a^{1/2}a^{-2/3}}{a^{1/4}}$

$= \dfrac{a^{1/2+(-2/3)}}{a^{1/4}}$ *Rule 1*

$= \dfrac{a^{-1/6}}{a^{1/4}}$ *Apply rule 4.*

$= a^{-1/6-1/4}$

$= a^{-5/12}$

$= \boxed{\dfrac{1}{a^{5/12}}}$

(e) This example is a lot easier if we bring in the outside exponent by rules 5 and 3.

$$\left(\frac{x^{-1/2}y^{-1/4}}{x^{1/4}}\right)^{-4} \qquad \textit{First rule 5}$$

$$= \frac{(x^{-1/2}y^{-1/4})^{-4}}{(x^{1/4})^{-4}} \qquad \textit{Next rule 3}$$

$$= \frac{(x^{-1/2})^{-4}(y^{-1/4})^{-4}}{(x^{1/4})^{-4}} \qquad \textit{Now rule 2}$$

$$= \frac{x^2 y^1}{x^{-1}}$$

$$= x^{2-(-1)}y = \boxed{x^3 y} \qquad \blacksquare$$

Again, keep in mind that rules 3 and 5 for exponents apply to *factors*, not terms.

EXAMPLE 5 Perform the indicated operations and simplify the following:

(a) $(x^{1/2} + 2x^{1/2})x^{-1/3}$ (b) $(5a^{1/2} + 3b^{1/2})^2$

Solution (a) $(x^{1/2} + 2x^{1/2})x^{-1/3}$ *Combine like terms in parentheses.*

$\qquad = (3x^{1/2})x^{-1/3}$ *Then apply rule 1.*

$\qquad = 3x^{1/2+(-1/3)}$

$\qquad = \boxed{3x^{1/6}}$

(b) For squaring a binomial, we can use the perfect square special product.

$$(5a^{1/2} + 3b^{1/2})^2 = (5a^{1/2})^2 + 2(5a^{1/2})(3b^{1/2}) + (3b^{1/2})^2$$

$$= 5^2 a^{2/2} + 30a^{1/2}b^{1/2} + 3^2 b^{2/2}$$

$$= \boxed{25a + 30a^{1/2}b^{1/2} + 9b} \qquad \blacksquare$$

Radicals

In Chapter 1, we stated that the real numbers consist of rational and irrational numbers. Recall that irrational numbers are defined as real numbers that cannot be expressed as a quotient of two integers. Some of the examples of irrational numbers given included expressions such as $\sqrt{2}$, $\sqrt{3}$, and $\sqrt{7}$, which are also examples of square root expressions. Here we will examine the more general radical expression, $\sqrt[n]{a}$.

Recall that radicals are an alternative way of writing an expression with fractional exponents. That is, we have the following definition:

DEFINITION $\sqrt[n]{a} = a^{1/n}$ where n is a positive integer.

$\sqrt[n]{a}$ is called the principal **nth root of a.**

In $\sqrt[n]{a}$, n is called the **index** of the radical, the symbol $\sqrt{}$ is called the **radical** or radical sign, and the expression, a, under the radical is called the **radicand.** Thus,

$\sqrt[4]{3} = 3^{1/4}$ is called the **fourth root** of 3.

$\sqrt[5]{9} = 9^{1/5}$ is called the **fifth root** of 9.

$\sqrt[3]{x} = x^{1/3}$ is usually called the **cube root** of x.

$\sqrt{y} = y^{1/2}$ is usually called the **square root** of y.

Note that we usually drop the index for square roots and write $\sqrt{a}$ rather than $\sqrt[2]{a}$.

Thus, $\sqrt[n]{a}$ is that quantity (nonnegative when n is even) that, when raised to the nth power, yields a.

Symbolically, we define the nth root for n a positive odd integer as follows:

> For $a \in R$ and n a positive *odd* integer,
> $$\sqrt[n]{a} = b \quad \text{if and only if} \quad b^n = a.$$

Thus,

$$\sqrt[3]{64} = 4 \quad \text{since} \quad 4^3 = 64.$$
$$\sqrt[5]{-32} = -2 \quad \text{since} \quad (-2)^5 = -32.$$

When the index of the radical is *even*, we require the root to be *positive:*

> For $a \in R$, and n a positive *even* integer,
> $$\sqrt[n]{a} = b \quad \text{if } b^n = a \text{ and } b \geq 0$$

In either case, where n is odd or even, if $\sqrt[n]{a}$ is real, $\sqrt[n]{a}$ is called the **principal nth root** of a. Keep in mind that when n is even, the principal nth root cannot be negative.

$\sqrt{9} = 3 \quad$ since $3^2 = 9 \qquad$ *Note that even though $(-3)^2 = 9$, we are interested only in the principal or positive square root.*

$\sqrt[4]{16} = 2 \quad$ since $2^4 = 16$

$\sqrt[6]{-64} \quad$ is not a real number since no real number when raised to the sixth power will yield a negative number.

As with rational exponents, we summarize the various types of roots as follows:

	n is even	*n is odd*
$a > 0$	$\sqrt[n]{a}$ is the positive nth root of a	$\sqrt[n]{a}$ is the nth root of a
$a < 0$	$\sqrt[n]{a}$ is not a real number	$\sqrt[n]{a}$ is the nth root of a
$a = 0$	$\sqrt[n]{0} = 0$	$\sqrt[n]{0} = 0$

EXAMPLE 6

Evaluate the following.

(a) $\sqrt[4]{81}$ (b) $\sqrt[5]{-243}$ (c) $\sqrt{-81}$ (d) $\sqrt[3]{0}$

Solution

(a) $\sqrt[4]{81} = \boxed{3} \qquad$ *Because $(3)^4 = 81$ (principal root only)*

(b) $\sqrt[5]{-243} = \boxed{-3} \qquad$ *Because $(-3)^5 = -243$*

(c) $\sqrt{-81} \quad \boxed{\text{is not a real number}}$.   *Since the radicand is negative **and** the index is even*

(d) $\sqrt[3]{0} = \boxed{0}$

■

By defining $\sqrt[n]{a} = a^{1/n}$, we can rewrite $a^{m/n}$ in terms of radicals, assuming $a^{1/n}$ is a real number.

Using exponent rule 2, we have

$$a^{m/n} = (a^m)^{1/n} = \sqrt[n]{a^m}$$

Or, again by exponent rule 2, we can equivalently write

$$a^{m/n} = (a^{1/n})^m = (\sqrt[n]{a})^m$$

Hence, we have the property stated in the box.

If $\sqrt[n]{a}$ is a real number and m and n are positive integers, then

$$\sqrt[n]{a^m} = (\sqrt[n]{a})^m$$

EXAMPLE 7

Rewrite the following using radical notation.

(a) $a^{1/6}$ (b) $b^{2/3}$ (c) $(8)^{4/9}$ (d) $5x^{1/3}$ (e) $x^{-3/4}$

Solution

(a) $a^{1/6} = \boxed{\sqrt[6]{a}}$

(b) $b^{2/3} = \boxed{\sqrt[3]{b^2} \quad \text{or} \quad (\sqrt[3]{b})^2}$

(c) $(8)^{4/9} = \boxed{\sqrt[9]{8^4} \quad \text{or} \quad (\sqrt[9]{8})^4}$

(d) $5x^{1/3} = \boxed{5\sqrt[3]{x}}$ *Note that the exponent applies only to x and not to 5.*

(e) $x^{-3/4}$ *Change to positive exponents first.*

$$= \frac{1}{x^{3/4}}$$

$$= \boxed{\frac{1}{\sqrt[4]{x^3}} \quad \text{or} \quad \frac{1}{(\sqrt[4]{x})^3}}$$ ∎

EXAMPLE 8

Express in radical form.

(a) $x^{5/8}$ (b) $(x^2 + y^2)^{3/2}$

Solution

(a) $x^{5/8} = \boxed{(\sqrt[8]{x})^5} \quad \text{or} \quad \boxed{\sqrt[8]{x^5}}$

Note: It is standard practice to leave a radical in the form $\sqrt[8]{x^5}$ rather than the form $(\sqrt[8]{x})^5$.

(b) $(x^2 + y^2)^{3/2} = \boxed{\sqrt{(x^2 + y^2)^3}}$ ∎

As with rational exponents, depending on the problem, you may find one form more convenient to use than another. Using the form $(\sqrt[n]{a})^m$, or finding the root first, is most useful when evaluating a number. For example, to evaluate $27^{2/3}$, we *could* interpret this as $\sqrt[3]{27^2}$. Then

$$\sqrt[3]{27^2} = \sqrt[3]{729} = 9$$

which requires quite a bit of multiplication and being able to figure out that the cube root of 729 is 9.

On the other hand, if we interpret $27^{2/3}$ as $(\sqrt[3]{27})^2$, then

$$27^{2/3} = (\sqrt[3]{27})^2 = (3)^2 = 9$$

which is obviously much less work.

When we evaluate numerical expressions it is preferable to use the form that finds the root first. The form $\sqrt[n]{a^m}$ will be most useful when we simplify radical expressions with variables, as we will discuss in the next section.

Let's examine $\sqrt[n]{a^n}$. It is tempting to say that $\sqrt[n]{a^n} = a$. However, if a is negative and n is even, this causes a problem. For example,

$$\sqrt[4]{(-2)^4} = \sqrt[4]{+16} = 2 \qquad \textit{Note that the answer is \textbf{not} --2.}$$

Regardless of the sign of a, if n is even, a^n is always nonnegative and therefore its root always exists. In addition, by definition, an even root is always nonnegative. We therefore have the following.

For $a \in R$ and n an even positive integer,
$$\sqrt[n]{a^n} = |a|$$

On the other hand, if n is an odd positive integer, we *do* find the following:

For $a \in R$ and n an odd positive integer,
$$\sqrt[n]{a^n} = a$$

EXAMPLE 9

Evaluate the following:

(a) $\sqrt[3]{5^3}$ (b) $\sqrt{(-2)^2}$ (c) $\sqrt[7]{(-8)^7}$ (d) $\sqrt[4]{(-3)^4}$

Solution

(a) $\sqrt[3]{5^3} = \boxed{5}$

(b) $\sqrt{(-2)^2} = |-2| = \boxed{2}$ *Note that the answer is **not** --2.*

(c) $\sqrt[7]{(-8)^7} = \boxed{-8}$

(d) $\sqrt[4]{(-3)^4} = |-3| = \boxed{3}$ *Note:* $\sqrt[4]{(-3)^4} = \sqrt[4]{81} = 3$

*Also note that $\left(\sqrt[4]{-3}\right)^4$ is **not** equal to $\sqrt[4]{(-3)^4}$ since $\sqrt[4]{-3}$ is not a real number.* ∎

Up until now we have restricted our discussion to numbers that are perfect nth powers (the nth root is a rational number). Consider the two numbers $\sqrt{9}$ and $\sqrt{21}$. They are numerically different, but conceptually, they are the same: $\sqrt{9}$ is the positive number that when squared yields 9; $\sqrt{21}$ is the positive number that when squared yields 21. The only difference is that $\sqrt{9}$ turns out to be a nice rational number but $\sqrt{21}$ does not.

Keep in mind that decimal representations of irrational numbers must be approximations since the decimal neither terminates nor repeats. When we write approximations, we usually use the symbol "$\approx$." Thus, we can state

$\sqrt{21} \approx 4.58$ if we want an approximate value of $\sqrt{21}$ rounded to the nearest hundredth.

$\sqrt{21} \approx 4.583$ if we want the value rounded to the nearest thousandth.

On occasion we need to do computations involving roots that are irrational numbers. In these situations, when we need to approximate the value of a radical expression, we are expected to use a calculator.

EXERCISES 7.3

In Exercises 1–46, evaluate the expression if possible.

1. $8^{1/3}$
2. $16^{1/4}$
3. $(-32)^{1/5}$
4. $(-64)^{1/3}$

5. $-100^{1/2}$
6. $(-100)^{1/2}$
7. $\sqrt[3]{64}$
8. $\sqrt[6]{64}$

9. $\sqrt[4]{81}$
10. $\sqrt{-81}$
11. $\sqrt[8]{-1}$
12. $\sqrt[3]{-125}$

13. $-\sqrt[9]{-1}$
14. $\sqrt[10]{0}$
15. $\sqrt[3]{-343}$
16. $\sqrt[6]{-78}$

17. $-\sqrt[4]{1,296}$
18. $-\sqrt[5]{-243}$
19. $\sqrt[8]{256}$
20. $\sqrt[3]{-729}$

21. $\sqrt[7]{78,125}$
22. $-\sqrt[3]{343}$
23. $(-32)^{3/5}$
24. $(-243)^{3/5}$

25. $32^{-1/5}$
26. $27^{-1/3}$
27. $(-32)^{-1/5}$
28. $(-27)^{-1/3}$

29. $-(81)^{-1/2}$
30. $-(16)^{-1/4}$
31. $(-64)^{-2/3}$
32. $(-81)^{-3/4}$

33. $\sqrt{(-16)^2}$
34. $\sqrt{-16^2}$
35. $\left(\sqrt{-16}\right)^2$
36. $\sqrt{(-3)^4}$

37. $-\left(\sqrt{16}\right)^2$
38. $\left(\sqrt{-3}\right)^4$
39. $\sqrt[n]{3^{2n}}$
40. $\sqrt[n]{2^n}$

41. $\left(\dfrac{64}{27}\right)^{1/3}$
42. $\left(\dfrac{16}{81}\right)^{1/4}$
43. $\left(\dfrac{81}{16}\right)^{-1/4}$
44. $\left(\dfrac{27}{64}\right)^{-1/3}$

45. $\left(-\dfrac{1}{32}\right)^{-4/5}$
46. $\left(-\dfrac{1}{243}\right)^{-4/5}$

In Exercises 47–70, perform the operations and simplify. Express your answers with positive exponents only. Assume that all variables represent positive real numbers.

47. $x^{1/2}x^{2/3}$
48. $x^{1/3}x^{-2/5}$
49. $(a^{-1/2})^{-3/4}$
50. $(s^{-1/3})^{2/5}$

51. $(2^{-1} \cdot 4^{1/2})^{-2}$
52. $(3^2 \cdot 27^{-1/3})^{-2}$
53. $(r^{1/2}r^{-2/3}s^{1/2})^{-2}$
54. $(a^{1/2}b^{-1/3})^{-1/2}$

55. $(r^{-1}s^{1/2})^{-2}(r^{-1/2}s^{1/3})^2$
56. $(a^{1/3}b^{-2})^{-2}(a^{2/3}b^{-2})^3$
57. $\dfrac{x^{-1/2}}{x^{-1/3}}$
58. $\dfrac{x^{1/2}}{x^{-1/4}}$

59. $\dfrac{a^{-1/2}b^{1/3}}{a^{1/4}b^{1/5}}$
60. $\dfrac{x^{1/2}y^{-1/3}}{x^{1/3}y^{1/5}}$
61. $\left(\dfrac{x^{1/2}x^{-1}}{x^{1/3}}\right)^{-6}$
62. $\left(\dfrac{x^{-1/3}x^{1/5}}{x}\right)^{-15}$

63. $\dfrac{(4^{-1/2} \cdot 16^{3/4})^{-2}(64^{5/6})}{(-64)^{1/3}}$
64. $\left(\dfrac{9^{-1/2} \cdot 27^{2/3} \cdot 81^{1/4}}{(-3)^{-1} \cdot 81^{3/4}}\right)^{-2}$

65. $\dfrac{(x^{1/2}y^{1/3})^{-2}(x^{1/3}y^{1/4})^{-12}}{xy^{1/4}}$
66. $\dfrac{(a^{1/2}b^{1/3})^{-6}(a^{1/3}b^{-1/2})^2}{a^{-1/3}b}$

67. $(x^{1/2} + x)x^{1/2}$
68. $(x^{1/2} + x^{3/2})x^{1/2}$

69. $(x^{1/2} - 2x^{-1/2})^2$
70. $4x(x^{1/2} + 1)^2$

In Exercises 71–84, change to exponential form.

71. $\sqrt[3]{xy}$
72. $\sqrt[4]{x^3y^2}$
73. $\sqrt{x^2 + y^2}$
74. $\sqrt[3]{x^3 - y^3}$

75. $\sqrt[5]{5a^2b^3}$
76. $3\sqrt[5]{2x^2y^3}$
77. $2\sqrt[3]{3xyz^4}$
78. $2\sqrt[3]{ab}$

79. $5\sqrt[3]{(x - y)^2}$
80. $3\sqrt[7]{(x - y)^2(x + y)^3}$
81. $\sqrt[n]{x^n - y^n}$
82. $\sqrt[n]{x^{2n}y^{3n}}$

83. $\sqrt[n]{x^{5n+1}y^{2n-1}}$
84. $\sqrt[n]{x^{2n-3}y^{4n}}$

In Exercises 85–98, change to radical form.

85. $x^{1/3}$

86. $a^{3/5}$

87. $mn^{1/3}$

88. $(mn)^{1/3}$

89. $(-a)^{2/3}$

90. $(-x)^{3/4}$

91. $-a^{2/3}$

92. $-x^{3/4}$

93. $(a^2b)^{1/3}$

94. $(x^3y^2)^{3/5}$

95. $(x^2 + y^2)^{1/2}$

96. $(x^3 - y^3)^{1/3}$

97. $(x^n - y^n)^{1/2}$

98. $(x^2 - y)^{1/n}$

In Exercises 99–102, use your calculator to evaluate the following to four decimal places.

99. $36^{-1/2}$

100. $64^{-2/3}$

101. $3 - 18^{-3/4}$

102. $12 - 28^{2/5}$

 QUESTIONS FOR THOUGHT

103. Explain what is *wrong* (if anything) with each of the following:

(a) $8^{1/3} \stackrel{?}{=} \dfrac{1}{8^3}$ (b) $8^{-3} \stackrel{?}{=} -512$ (c) $8^{-1/3} \stackrel{?}{=} -2$

104. What is the difference between a negative exponent and a fractional exponent?

105. What are the differences among the rules of exponents for rational, integer, and natural number exponents?

106. Discuss the similarities and differences among 9^{-2}, $9^{1/2}$, and $9^{-1/2}$.

107. Prove the following using the rules of rational exponents, assuming all roots are real numbers:

$$\sqrt[m]{\sqrt[n]{a}} = \sqrt[mn]{a}$$

[*Hint:* Change the radicals to rational exponents.]

108. Given the result of Exercise 107, rewrite the following as a single radical:

(a) $\sqrt[3]{\sqrt[4]{6}}$ (b) $\sqrt{\sqrt[3]{x^2y}}$ (c) $\sqrt[4]{\sqrt[3]{\sqrt{x}}}$

109. Explain why the following is *wrong:*

$$\sqrt{(-4)^2} \stackrel{?}{=} (\sqrt{-4})^2$$

◇ **MINI-REVIEW**

110. *Solve.* $2x^2 = 3x$

111. Use the following graph of $y = f(x)$ to find

(a) $f(4)$

(b) $f(-3)$

(c) $f(0)$

(d) $f(2)$

(e) the zeros of $f(x)$

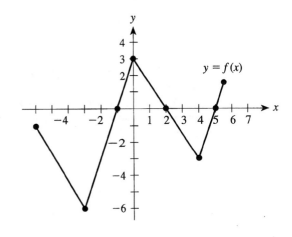

112. *Combine.* $\dfrac{x}{3} - \dfrac{x}{2} + 4$

113. *Solve.* $\dfrac{x}{3} - \dfrac{x}{2} = 4$

7.4 Simplifying Radical Expressions

Now that we have defined radicals, our next step is to determine what constitutes simplified form. Along with the definition of a radical, the following three properties of radicals will provide us with much of what we will need to simplify radicals:

Properties of Radicals	If $\sqrt[n]{a}$ and $\sqrt[n]{b}$ are real numbers, then
	1. $\sqrt[n]{ab} = \sqrt[n]{a}\sqrt[n]{b}$
	2. $\sqrt[n]{\dfrac{a}{b}} = \dfrac{\sqrt[n]{a}}{\sqrt[n]{b}}$ $(b \neq 0)$
	3. $\sqrt[np]{a^{mp}} = \sqrt[n]{a^m}$ $(a \geq 0)$

Properties 1 and 2 are actually forms of rules 3 and 5 of rational exponents, whereas property 3 is a result of reducing a fractional exponent.

Property 1: $\sqrt[n]{ab} = (ab)^{1/n} = a^{1/n}b^{1/n} = \sqrt[n]{a}\sqrt[n]{b}$

Property 2: $\sqrt[n]{\dfrac{a}{b}} = \left(\dfrac{a}{b}\right)^{1/n} = \dfrac{a^{1/n}}{b^{1/n}} = \dfrac{\sqrt[n]{a}}{\sqrt[n]{b}}$

Property 3: $\sqrt[np]{a^{mp}} = a^{(mp)/(np)} = a^{m/n} = \sqrt[n]{a^m}$

Our goal in this section is to write expressions in simplest radical form. We *define* simplest radical form in the accompanying box.

An expression is in **simplest radical form** if:

1. All factors of the radicand have exponents less than the index.

   For example, $\sqrt[3]{y^5}$ violates this condition.

2. There are no fractions under the radical.

   For example, $\sqrt{\dfrac{3}{5}}$ violates this condition.

3. There are no radicals in the denominator of a fraction.

   For example, $\dfrac{4}{\sqrt[3]{x}}$ violates this condition.

4. The greatest common factor of the index and the exponents of all the radicand factors is 1.

   For example, $\sqrt[8]{x^4}$ violates this condition.

To simplify matters, from this point on, all variables will represent positive real numbers.

Given the definition of a radical and the three properties of radicals, we can simplify many radical expressions according to the criteria given in the box. Here are a few examples of how we would use the properties to simplify radicals:

1. $\sqrt{18} = \sqrt{9 \cdot 2} = \sqrt{3^2 \cdot 2}$ *Factor out the greatest perfect square. Then apply property 1.*

   $= \sqrt{3^2}\sqrt{2}$

   $= 3\sqrt{2}$ *Since $\sqrt{3^2} = 3$*

2. $\sqrt[5]{64} = \sqrt[5]{2^6}$ *Factor out the greatest perfect fifth power.*

     $= \sqrt[5]{2^5 \cdot 2}$ *Then apply property 1.*

     $= \sqrt[5]{2^5}\sqrt[5]{2}$

     $= 2\sqrt[5]{2}$ *Since $\sqrt[5]{2^5} = 2$*

3. $\sqrt[4]{\dfrac{81}{16}} = \dfrac{\sqrt[4]{81}}{\sqrt[4]{16}}$ *Property 2*

     $= \dfrac{3}{2}$

4. $\sqrt[8]{x^6}$ *Factor the greatest common factor from the index and the exponent of the radicand. Then apply property 3.*

     $= \sqrt[4\cdot2]{x^{3\cdot2}}$

     $= \sqrt[4]{x^3}$

An alternative way to simplify this last expression is to first convert the radical expression to rational exponents:

$$\sqrt[8]{x^6} = x^{6/8} = x^{3/4} = \sqrt[4]{x^3}$$

EXAMPLE 1

Express the following in simplest radical form. Assume all variables are positive numbers.

(a) $\sqrt{25x^8y^6}$ (b) $\sqrt[3]{\dfrac{27}{y^{18}}}$

Solution

(a) $\sqrt{25x^8y^6}$ *Apply property 1*

     $= \sqrt{25}\sqrt{x^8}\sqrt{y^6}$

     $= \boxed{5 \cdot x^4 \cdot y^3}$ *Since $5^2 = 25$, $(x^4)^2 = x^8$, and $(y^3)^2 = y^6$*

(b) $\sqrt[3]{\dfrac{27}{y^{18}}} = \dfrac{\sqrt[3]{27}}{\sqrt[3]{y^{18}}}$ *Property 2*

     $= \boxed{\dfrac{3}{y^6}}$ *Since $3^3 = 27$ and $(y^6)^3 = y^{18}$*   ■

EXAMPLE 2

Express the following in simplest radical form. Assume all variables are positive numbers.

(a) $\sqrt{x^{10}}$ (b) $\sqrt[3]{y^{18}}$ (c) $\sqrt[4]{x^{12}}$ (d) $\sqrt[7]{x^{21}}$

Solution

(a) $\sqrt{x^{10}} = \boxed{x^5}$ *Since $(x^5)^2 = x^{10}$*

(b) $\sqrt[3]{y^{18}} = \boxed{y^6}$ *Since $(y^6)^3 = y^{18}$*

(c) $\sqrt[4]{x^{12}} = \boxed{x^3}$ *Since $(x^3)^4 = x^{12}$*

(d) $\sqrt[7]{x^{21}} = \boxed{x^3}$ *Since $(x^3)^7 = x^{21}$*   ■

For a power to be a perfect nth power, the exponent must be divisible by n. In all cases of Example 2, the factors were perfect nth powers, where n was the index of the radical. Let's examine how to simplify radicals with radicand factors that are not perfect nth powers. In these cases we try to factor the greatest perfect nth power from the expression.

EXAMPLE 3

Express the following in simplest radical form:

(a) $\sqrt{x^7}$ (b) $\sqrt[6]{x^{17}}$ (c) $\sqrt[3]{24}$ (d) $\sqrt[4]{64a^{11}c^{24}}$

Solution

(a) $\sqrt{x^7}$ *Factor the greatest perfect square factor of x^7, which is x^6, from the radicand.*

$= \sqrt{x^6 \cdot x}$

$= \sqrt{x^6}\,\sqrt{x}$

$= \boxed{x^3\sqrt{x}}$ $\sqrt{x^6} = x^3$ *because* $(x^3)^2 = x^6$.

(b) $\sqrt[6]{x^{17}}$ *The greatest perfect sixth-power factor of x^{17} is x^{12}. Thus, we factor x^{12} from x^{17}.*

$= \sqrt[6]{x^{12} \cdot x^5}$

$= \sqrt[6]{x^{12}}\,\sqrt[6]{x^5}$

$= \boxed{x^2\sqrt[6]{x^5}}$ $\sqrt[6]{x^{12}} = x^2$ *because* $(x^2)^6 = x^{12}$.

Note that the exponent of x under the radical is less than the index, thereby satisfying criterion 1 for simplifying radicals.

(c) $\sqrt[3]{24} = \sqrt[3]{8 \cdot 3}$

$= \sqrt[3]{8}\sqrt[3]{3} = \boxed{2\sqrt[3]{3}}$

(d) $\sqrt[4]{64a^{11}c^{24}}$ *Factor the greatest perfect fourth power from each factor.*

$= \sqrt[4]{(16 \cdot 4)(a^8 \cdot a^3)(c^{24})}$

$= \sqrt[4]{(16a^8c^{24})(4a^3)}$

$= \sqrt[4]{16}\,\sqrt[4]{a^8}\,\sqrt[4]{c^{24}}\,\sqrt[4]{4a^3}$ *By property 1*

$= \boxed{2a^2c^6\sqrt[4]{4a^3}}$

Again, note that all exponents of factors under the radical are less than the index. ∎

EXAMPLE 4

Express in simplest radical form.

(a) $\sqrt[5]{(x^2 + 2)^5}$ (b) $\sqrt[3]{x^3 + y^3}$

Solution

(a) $\sqrt[5]{(x^2 + 2)^5} = x^2 + 2$ *Remember that $\sqrt[5]{a^5} = a$.*

(b) $\sqrt[3]{x^3 + y^3}$ $\boxed{\text{cannot be simplified.}}$ *Remember, $x^3 + y^3$ is not the same as $(x + y)^3$.* ∎

The properties of radicals can also be used to simplify products and quotients of radicals. When the first two properties of radicals are read from right to left, they state that *if the indices are the same,* the product (quotient) of radicals is the radical of the product (quotient).

EXAMPLE 5

Perform the operations and simplify.

(a) $\sqrt{3a^2b}\,\sqrt{6ab^3}$ (b) $(ab\sqrt[3]{2a^2b})(2a\sqrt[3]{4ab})$

Solution

(a) We could simplify each radical first, but after we multiply, it may be necessary to simplify again. It is often better to multiply radicands first.

$$\sqrt{3a^2b}\sqrt{6ab^3} = \sqrt{(3a^2b)(6ab^3)}$$
$$= \sqrt{18a^3b^4} \quad \textit{Then simplify.}$$
$$= \sqrt{9a^2b^4}\sqrt{2a}$$
$$= \boxed{3ab^2\sqrt{2a}}$$

(b) Since this is all multiplication, we use the associative and commutative properties to reorder and regroup variables, and then use radical property 1 to multiply the radicals.

$$\left(ab\sqrt[3]{2a^2b}\right)\left(2a\sqrt[3]{4ab}\right) = (ab)(2a)\sqrt[3]{(2a^2b)(4ab)}$$
$$= 2a^2b\sqrt[3]{8a^3b^2} \qquad \textit{Then simplify the radical.}$$
$$= 2a^2b\left(\sqrt[3]{8a^3}\sqrt[3]{b^2}\right)$$
$$= 2a^2b\left(2a\sqrt[3]{b^2}\right) \qquad \textit{Multiply the expressions}$$
$$= \boxed{4a^3b\sqrt[3]{b^2}} \qquad \textit{outside the radical.}$$

Next we examine radicals of quotients. ∎

EXAMPLE 6

Express in simplest radical form. $\sqrt{\dfrac{32s^9}{4s^{17}}}$

Solution

$\sqrt{\dfrac{32s^9}{4s^{17}}}$ *Do not apply property 2 without thinking—try to simplify the fraction first.*

$= \sqrt{\dfrac{8}{s^8}}$ *Then apply property 2.*

$= \dfrac{\sqrt{8}}{\sqrt{s^8}}$ *We simplify the numerator and denominator.*

$= \boxed{\dfrac{2\sqrt{2}}{s^4}}$ ∎

Rationalizing the Denominator

A radical in the denominator of a fraction violates criterion 3 for simplifying radicals. In such a case we may have to *rationalize,* or eliminate the radical, in the denominator. To do this, we apply the Fundamental Principle of Fractions, as shown in Example 7.

EXAMPLE 7

Simplify. $\sqrt{\dfrac{2}{5}}$

Solution

$\sqrt{\dfrac{2}{5}}$ *This violates criterion 2 of simplified form for radicals. We apply property 2.*

$= \dfrac{\sqrt{2}}{\sqrt{5}}$ *This violates criterion 3 (a radical in the denominator).*

We apply the Fundamental Principle of Fractions and multiply the numerator and denominator by $\sqrt{5}$. Why $\sqrt{5}$? We choose $\sqrt{5}$ because the product of $\sqrt{5}$ and the denominator will yield the square root of a perfect square, which yields a rational expression. Thus,

$$\frac{\sqrt{2}}{\sqrt{5}} = \frac{\sqrt{2}\cdot\sqrt{5}}{\sqrt{5}\cdot\sqrt{5}} = \frac{\sqrt{2\cdot 5}}{\sqrt{5^2}} = \boxed{\frac{\sqrt{10}}{5}}$$

∎

In rationalizing a denominator, what we try to do is to multiply the numerator *and* the denominator of the fraction by the expression that will make the denominator the nth root of a perfect nth power.

EXAMPLE 8

Simplify. $\sqrt[3]{\dfrac{1}{y}}$

Solution

$$\sqrt[3]{\frac{1}{y}} = \frac{\sqrt[3]{1}}{\sqrt[3]{y}} = \frac{1}{\sqrt[3]{y}}$$

We multiply the numerator and denominator by $\sqrt[3]{y^2}$. Why $\sqrt[3]{y^2}$? Because multiplying $\sqrt[3]{y^2}$ by the original denominator, $\sqrt[3]{y}$, will yield $\sqrt[3]{y^3}$, the cube root of a perfect cube. Thus,

$$\sqrt[3]{\frac{1}{y}} = \frac{1}{\sqrt[3]{y}} = \frac{1 \cdot \sqrt[3]{y^2}}{\sqrt[3]{y}\sqrt[3]{y^2}}$$

$$= \frac{\sqrt[3]{y^2}}{\sqrt[3]{y \cdot y^2}}$$

$$= \frac{\sqrt[3]{y^2}}{\sqrt[3]{y^3}} \qquad \textit{Since } \sqrt[3]{y^3} = y$$

$$= \boxed{\frac{\sqrt[3]{y^2}}{y}} \qquad \textit{Notice that we no longer have a radical in the denominator.} \qquad \blacksquare$$

EXAMPLE 9

Express the following in simplest radical form:

(a) $\sqrt{\dfrac{3}{2x^2}}$ (b) $\sqrt[3]{\dfrac{3}{2x^2}}$

Solution

(a) $\sqrt{\dfrac{3}{2x^2}}$ *Apply property 2.*

$$= \frac{\sqrt{3}}{\sqrt{2x^2}} \qquad \textit{Simplify the denominator by property 1:} \quad \sqrt{2x^2} = x\sqrt{2}$$

$$= \frac{\sqrt{3}}{x\sqrt{2}} \qquad \textit{To make the denominator contain the square root of a perfect square, multiply the numerator and denominator by } \sqrt{2}.$$

$$= \frac{\sqrt{3} \cdot \sqrt{2}}{x\sqrt{2} \cdot \sqrt{2}} \qquad \textit{Note } \sqrt{2}\sqrt{2} = 2.$$

$$= \boxed{\frac{\sqrt{6}}{2x}}$$

(b) $\sqrt[3]{\dfrac{3}{2x^2}}$ *Apply property 2.*

$$= \frac{\sqrt[3]{3}}{\sqrt[3]{2x^2}} \qquad \textit{To change } \sqrt[3]{2x^2} \textit{ into the cube root of a perfect cube, we can multiply the numerator and denominator by } \sqrt[3]{4x}.$$

$$= \frac{\sqrt[3]{3}\sqrt[3]{4x}}{\sqrt[3]{2x^2}\sqrt[3]{4x}} \qquad \textit{Then } \sqrt[3]{2x^2}\ \sqrt[3]{4x} = \sqrt[3]{8x^3}.$$

$$= \frac{\sqrt[3]{12x}}{\sqrt[3]{8x^3}} \qquad \textit{Now the radicand in the denominator is a perfect cube.}$$

$$= \boxed{\frac{\sqrt[3]{12x}}{2x}} \qquad\qquad\qquad \blacksquare$$

EXAMPLE 10

Express the following in simplest radical form. $\dfrac{2x\sqrt{24xy^3}}{5x^2y\sqrt{12xy}}$

Solution

We could simplify each radical first, but after simplifying, multiplying, and reducing, we may have to simplify again. Since this expression is a quotient, we can use property 2 to collect all radicands under one radical.

$$\frac{2x\sqrt{24xy^3}}{5x^2y\sqrt{12xy}}$$

$$= \frac{2x}{5x^2y}\sqrt{\frac{24xy^3}{12xy}} \qquad \textit{Then reduce fractions inside and outside the radicals.}$$

$$= \frac{2}{5xy}\sqrt{2y^2} \qquad \textit{Now simplify the radical expression.}$$

$$= \frac{2}{5xy}(y\sqrt{2}) \qquad \textit{Then reduce again.}$$

$$= \boxed{\dfrac{2\sqrt{2}}{5x}} \qquad\qquad\qquad\qquad\qquad\qquad\qquad\qquad\blacksquare$$

The last criterion for simplifying radical expressions requires us to factor the greatest common factor of the index and all the exponents of factors of the radicand; this requires property 3 for radicals:

$$\sqrt[np]{a^{mp}} = \sqrt[n]{a^m} \qquad \textit{We can factor out the greatest common factor of the index and the exponent of the radicand.}$$

For example, $\sqrt[3]{x}$ and $\sqrt[6]{x^2}$ are identical (assuming $x \geq 0$). If we convert to exponential notation, we can see that

$$\sqrt[6]{x^2} = x^{2/6} = x^{1/3} = \sqrt[3]{x}$$

Thus, we can find $\sqrt[6]{27^2}$ by the following:

$$\sqrt[6]{27^2} = \sqrt[6]{729} = 3$$

Or we can recognize that $\sqrt[6]{27^2} = \sqrt[3]{27} = 3$, which takes less effort to evaluate.

We can use property 3 to "reduce the index with the exponent of the radicand" or we can convert to fractional exponents, reduce the fractional exponent, and then rewrite the answer in radical form.

Property 3 is also used to find products and quotients of radicals with different indices. (Keep in mind that properties 1 and 2 require that the indices be the same.)

EXAMPLE 11

Simplify. $\sqrt[3]{x^2}\,\sqrt[5]{x^4}$

Solution

$\sqrt[3]{x^2}\,\sqrt[5]{x^4} \qquad \textit{The indices are not the same; thus, we cannot use property 1.}$

The least common multiple of the indices, 5 and 3, is 15. We change the radicals using property 3 as follows:

$$\sqrt[3]{x^2}\,\sqrt[5]{x^4} = \sqrt[3\cdot5]{x^{2\cdot5}}\,\sqrt[5\cdot3]{x^{4\cdot3}}$$

$$= \sqrt[15]{x^{10}}\,\sqrt[15]{x^{12}} \qquad \textit{Since the indices are the same we can now apply property 1.}$$

$$= \sqrt[15]{x^{22}}$$

$$= \sqrt[15]{x^{15}\cdot x^7} \qquad \textit{Don't forget to simplify the radical.}$$

$$= \boxed{x\sqrt[15]{x^7}}$$

303

Actually, it is more instructive to change radicals into rational exponents and to simplify the problem as follows:

$$\sqrt[3]{x^2}\ \sqrt[5]{x^4} = x^{2/3}x^{4/5}$$
$$= x^{2/3\,+\,4/5}$$
$$= x^{10/15\,+\,12/15}$$
$$= x^{22/15} \qquad \textit{Change back to radical notation.}$$
$$= \sqrt[15]{x^{22}} = \boxed{x\sqrt[15]{x^7}} \qquad\qquad\qquad \blacksquare$$

EXERCISES 7.4

Simplify the following. Assume that all variables represent positive real numbers.

1. $\sqrt{56}$

2. $\sqrt{45}$

3. $\sqrt{48}$

4. $\sqrt{54}$

5. $\sqrt[5]{64}$

6. $\sqrt[4]{243}$

7. $\sqrt{8}\ \sqrt{18}$

8. $\sqrt{12}\ \sqrt{75}$

9. $\sqrt{64x^8}$

10. $\sqrt[4]{64x^8}$

11. $\sqrt[4]{81x^{12}}$

12. $\sqrt{81x^{12}}$

13. $\sqrt{128x^{60}}$

14. $\sqrt[3]{128x^{60}}$

15. $\sqrt[4]{128x^{60}}$

16. $\sqrt[6]{128x^{60}}$

17. $\sqrt[5]{128x^{60}}$

18. $\sqrt[7]{128x^{60}}$

19. $\sqrt[3]{x^3y^6}$

20. $\sqrt{x^4y^8}$

21. $\sqrt{32a^2b^4}$

22. $\sqrt{54x^6y^{12}}$

23. $\sqrt[5]{a^{35}b^{75}}$

24. $\sqrt[6]{x^{36}y^{72}}$

25. $\sqrt{x^3y}\ \sqrt{xy^3}$

26. $\sqrt{6ab}\ \sqrt{6a^5b^5}$

27. $\sqrt{\dfrac{1}{2}}$

28. $\sqrt{\dfrac{2}{7}}$

29. $\dfrac{\sqrt{x}}{\sqrt{5}}$

30. $\dfrac{\sqrt{5}}{\sqrt{a}}$

31. $\sqrt{\dfrac{45}{4}}$

32. $\sqrt{\dfrac{8}{9}}$

33. $\dfrac{1}{\sqrt{75}}$

34. $\sqrt{\dfrac{3}{8}}$

35. $\sqrt{64x^5y^8}$

36. $\sqrt{12a^3b^9}$

37. $\sqrt[3]{81x^8y^7}$

38. $\sqrt[3]{24a^5b^2}$

39. $\sqrt[3]{54y^2}\ \sqrt[3]{48y^4}$

40. $\sqrt[3]{20ab^5}\ \sqrt[3]{50b^4}$

41. $\sqrt[6]{(x+y^2)^6}$

42. $\sqrt[6]{(a^2+b)^6}$

43. $\sqrt[4]{x^4-y^4}$

44. $\sqrt[3]{x^3-y^3}$

45. $\left(2s\sqrt{6t}\right)\left(5t\sqrt{3s}\right)$

46. $\left(4a\sqrt{10b}\right)\left(3b\sqrt{2a}\right)$

47. $\left(3a\sqrt[3]{2b^4}\right)\left(2a^2\sqrt[3]{4b^2}\right)$

48. $\left(3a\sqrt[3]{5b^2a}\right)\left(2b\sqrt[3]{25a^2b}\right)$

49. $\sqrt[3]{\dfrac{x^3y^6}{8}}$

50. $\sqrt[5]{\dfrac{r^{10}s^{15}}{32}}$

51. $\sqrt[4]{\dfrac{32x^9}{y^{12}}}$

52. $\sqrt[3]{\dfrac{32x^9}{y^{12}}}$

53. $\dfrac{\sqrt{54xy}}{\sqrt{2xy}}$

54. $\dfrac{\sqrt[6]{6x^2y}}{\sqrt{3xy}}$

55. $\dfrac{\sqrt[4]{x^2y^{17}}}{\sqrt[4]{x^{14}y}}$

56. $\dfrac{\sqrt[3]{a^{13}b^2}}{\sqrt[3]{a^4b^5}}$

57. $\sqrt{\dfrac{3xy}{5x^2y}}$

58. $\sqrt{\dfrac{5ab}{3a^2b}}$

59. $\sqrt{\dfrac{3x^2y}{x^3y^4}}$

60. $\sqrt{\dfrac{2a^2b^3}{a^5b^{18}}}$

61. $\sqrt[3]{\dfrac{3}{2}}$

62. $\sqrt[3]{\dfrac{2}{3}}$

63. $\sqrt[3]{\dfrac{9}{4}}$

64. $\sqrt[3]{\dfrac{4}{9}}$

65. $\sqrt[4]{\dfrac{9}{4}}$

66. $\sqrt[4]{\dfrac{4}{9}}$

67. $\sqrt[3]{\dfrac{81x^2y^4}{2x^3y}}$

68. $\sqrt[3]{\dfrac{64a^2b^5}{9a^4b^2}}$

69. $\dfrac{3a^2\sqrt{a^2x^5}}{9a^5\sqrt{a^6x}}$

70. $\dfrac{5x^2\sqrt{a^3b^2}}{4y^2\sqrt{a^7b^3}}$

71. $\dfrac{-3r^2s\sqrt{32r^2s^5}}{2r\sqrt{2r^5}}$

72. $\dfrac{-7a^2b\sqrt{81a^2b}}{14a\sqrt{9a^7}}$

73. $\sqrt[12]{a^6}$ 74. $\sqrt[6]{x^4}$ 75. $(\sqrt[3]{x})(\sqrt[4]{x^3})$ 76. $(\sqrt[3]{x^2})(\sqrt{x^3})$

77. $\dfrac{\sqrt[3]{a^2}}{\sqrt{a}}$ 78. $\dfrac{\sqrt[3]{a}}{\sqrt[4]{a^2}}$ 79. $\sqrt[n]{x^{5n}y^{3n}}$ 80. $\sqrt[n]{x^{2n}y^{4n}}$

QUESTION FOR THOUGHT

81. Discuss what is **wrong** (if anything) with each of the following:

(a) $(\sqrt{-2})^2 \overset{?}{=} \sqrt{(-2)^2} \overset{?}{=} \sqrt{4} \overset{?}{=} 2$ (b) $2 \overset{?}{=} \sqrt[6]{64} \overset{?}{=} \sqrt[6]{(-8)^2} \overset{?}{=} \sqrt[3]{-8} \overset{?}{=} -2$

(c) $\sqrt{x^2 - y^2} \overset{?}{=} x - y$ (d) $(a^5 + b^5)^{1/5} \overset{?}{=} a + b$

◇ MINI-REVIEW

82. *Factor as completely as possible.* $2x^2 + 7x - 15$.

83. *Divide.* $\dfrac{x^3 - 2x + 3}{x + 4}$

7.5   Adding and Subtracting Radical Expressions

We combine terms with the radical factors in the same way we combined terms with variable factors—through the use of the distributive property. Just as we can combine

$$3x + 4x = (3 + 4)x \qquad \textit{Distributive property}$$
$$= 7x$$

we can also combine

$$3\sqrt{2} + 4\sqrt{2} = (3 + 4)\sqrt{2} \qquad \textit{Distributive property}$$
$$= 7\sqrt{2}$$

EXAMPLE 1   Simplify.

(a) $7\sqrt{3} - 4\sqrt{3} + 6\sqrt{3}$ (b) $5\sqrt{2} - 8\sqrt{3} - (\sqrt{2} - 7\sqrt{3})$

Solution   (a) $7\sqrt{3} - 4\sqrt{3} + 6\sqrt{3}$

$$= (7 - 4 + 6)\sqrt{3} \qquad \textit{Apply the distributive property.}$$

$$= \boxed{9\sqrt{3}}$$

(b) $5\sqrt{2} - 8\sqrt{3} - (\sqrt{2} - 7\sqrt{3})$ *First remove parentheses.*

$$= 5\sqrt{2} - 8\sqrt{3} - \sqrt{2} + 7\sqrt{3}$$

$$= (5 - 1)\sqrt{2} + (-8 + 7)\sqrt{3}$$

$$= \boxed{4\sqrt{2} - \sqrt{3}} \qquad\qquad\blacksquare$$

We may encounter an expression where, at first glance, it may seem that the radicals cannot be combined, as in the following case:

Simplify. $\sqrt{18x^3} - x\sqrt{32x}$

However, if we simplify each radical term first, we may find that we *can* combine the two radicals:

$$\sqrt{18x^3} - x\sqrt{32x} = \sqrt{9x^2}\sqrt{2x} - x\sqrt{16}\sqrt{2x}$$
$$= 3x\sqrt{2x} - 4x\sqrt{2x}$$
$$= (3 - 4)x\sqrt{2x}$$
$$= -x\sqrt{2x}$$

Thus, our first step should be to simplify each radical expression.

EXAMPLE 2

Simplify each of the following.

(a) $\sqrt{27} - \sqrt{81} + \sqrt{12}$ (b) $5\sqrt{4x^3} + 7x\sqrt{8x} - 2x\sqrt{9x} + \sqrt{2x}$

(c) $3x\sqrt[3]{24x^2} + 4x\sqrt[3]{54x^5} - 2\sqrt[3]{81x^5}$

Solution

(a) $\sqrt{27} - \sqrt{81} + \sqrt{12}$ *Simplify each term first.*

    $= 3\sqrt{3} - 9 + 2\sqrt{3}$ *Then combine where possible.*

    $= \boxed{5\sqrt{3} - 9}$

Note that we cannot combine $5\sqrt{3} - 9$, just as we cannot combine $5x - 9$.

(b) $5\sqrt{4x^3} + 7x\sqrt{8x} - 2x\sqrt{9x} + \sqrt{2x}$

    $= 5(\sqrt{4x^2}\sqrt{x}) + 7x(\sqrt{4}\sqrt{2x}) - 2x(\sqrt{9}\sqrt{x}) + \sqrt{2x}$

    $= 5(2x\sqrt{x}) + 7x(2\sqrt{2x}) - 2x(3\sqrt{x}) + \sqrt{2x}$

    $= 10x\sqrt{x} + 14x\sqrt{2x} - 6x\sqrt{x} + \sqrt{2x}$

    $= \boxed{4x\sqrt{x} + 14x\sqrt{2x} + \sqrt{2x}}$

(c) $3x\sqrt[3]{24x^2} + 4x\sqrt[3]{54x^5} - 2\sqrt[3]{81x^5}$ *Simplify each radical.*

    $= 3x(\sqrt[3]{8}\sqrt[3]{3x^2}) + 4x(\sqrt[3]{27x^3}\sqrt[3]{2x^2}) - 2(\sqrt[3]{27x^3}\sqrt[3]{3x^2})$

    $= 3x(2\sqrt[3]{3x^2}) + 4x(3x\sqrt[3]{2x^2}) - 2(3x\sqrt[3]{3x^2})$

    $= 6x\sqrt[3]{3x^2} + 12x^2\sqrt[3]{2x^2} - 6x\sqrt[3]{3x^2}$ *Then combine where possible.*

    $= \boxed{12x^2\sqrt[3]{2x^2}}$ ∎

EXAMPLE 3

Perform the indicated operations and simplify.

(a) $\sqrt{3} + \dfrac{6}{\sqrt{3}}$ (b) $5\sqrt{\dfrac{x}{y}} + \dfrac{\sqrt{xy}}{y}$

Solution

(a) $\sqrt{3} + \dfrac{6}{\sqrt{3}}$ *Rationalize the denominator.*

    $= \sqrt{3} + \dfrac{6\sqrt{3}}{\sqrt{3}\sqrt{3}} = \sqrt{3} + \dfrac{6\sqrt{3}}{3}$ *Reduce.*

                  $= \sqrt{3} + 2\sqrt{3}$ *Combine.*

                  $= \boxed{3\sqrt{3}}$

(b) $5\sqrt{\dfrac{x}{y}} - \dfrac{\sqrt{xy}}{y}$ *Apply property 2.*

    $= \dfrac{5}{1} \cdot \dfrac{\sqrt{x}}{\sqrt{y}} - \dfrac{\sqrt{xy}}{y}$

$$= \frac{5\sqrt{x}}{\sqrt{y}} - \frac{\sqrt{xy}}{y} \qquad \textit{Rationalize the first denominator.}$$

$$= \frac{5\sqrt{x}\sqrt{y}}{\sqrt{y}\sqrt{y}} - \frac{\sqrt{xy}}{y}$$

$$= \frac{5\sqrt{xy}}{y} - \frac{\sqrt{xy}}{y} \qquad \textit{Combine fractions.}$$

$$= \frac{5\sqrt{xy} - \sqrt{xy}}{y} = \boxed{\frac{4\sqrt{xy}}{y}} \qquad \blacksquare$$

 EXERCISES 7.5

Perform the indicated operations. Express your answers in simplest radical form. Assume that all variables represent positive real numbers.

1. $5\sqrt{3} - \sqrt{3}$

2. $8\sqrt{7} - 2\sqrt{7}$

3. $2\sqrt{5} - 4\sqrt{5} - \sqrt{5}$

4. $9\sqrt{2} - \sqrt{2} - 12\sqrt{2}$

5. $8\sqrt{3} - (4\sqrt{3} - 2\sqrt{6})$

6. $6\sqrt{5} - (3\sqrt{7} - \sqrt{5})$

7. $2\sqrt{3} - 2\sqrt{5} - (\sqrt{3} - \sqrt{5})$

8. $\sqrt{6} - 2\sqrt{2} - (\sqrt{2} - \sqrt{6})$

9. $2\sqrt{x} - 5\sqrt{x} + 3\sqrt{x}$

10. $5\sqrt{ab} - 7\sqrt{ab} + 3\sqrt{a}$

11. $5a\sqrt{b} - 3a^3\sqrt{b} + 2a\sqrt{b}$

12. $3xy - 2\sqrt{y} - 5x\sqrt{y}$

13. $3x\sqrt[3]{x^2} - 2\sqrt[3]{x^2} + 6\sqrt[3]{x^2}$

14. $6 - 4x\sqrt[3]{x^2} + 3\sqrt[3]{x^2} - 8$

15. $(7 - 3\sqrt[3]{a}) - (6 - \sqrt[3]{a})$

16. $(2 - 5\sqrt[3]{x}) - (6 + \sqrt[3]{x})$

17. $\sqrt{12} - \sqrt{27}$

18. $\sqrt{18} - \sqrt{8} + \sqrt{32}$

19. $\sqrt{24} - \sqrt{27} + \sqrt{54}$

20. $\sqrt{12} + \sqrt{18} + \sqrt{24}$

21. $6\sqrt{3} - 4\sqrt{81}$

22. $5\sqrt{2} - 6\sqrt{16}$

23. $3\sqrt{24} - 5\sqrt{48} - \sqrt{6}$

24. $3\sqrt{8} - 5\sqrt{32} + 2\sqrt{27}$

25. $3\sqrt[3]{24} - 5\sqrt[3]{48} - \sqrt[3]{6}$

26. $3\sqrt[3]{8} - 5\sqrt[3]{32} + 2\sqrt[3]{27}$

27. $2a\sqrt{ab^2} - 3b\sqrt{a^2b} - ab\sqrt{ab}$

28. $x\sqrt{x^3y} + y\sqrt{xy^3}$

29. $\sqrt[3]{x^4} - x\sqrt[3]{x}$

30. $3\sqrt[3]{16x} - 5\sqrt[3]{2x} - 3x\sqrt[3]{2}$

31. $\sqrt{20x^9y^8} + 2xy\sqrt{5x^7y^6}$

32. $2b^2\sqrt{48a^7b^6} - 5a\sqrt{27a^5b^{10}}$

33. $5\sqrt[3]{9x^5} - 3x\sqrt[3]{x^2} + 2x\sqrt[3]{72x^2}$

34. $3a\sqrt[3]{ab^4} - 5b\sqrt[3]{8a^4b} - ab\sqrt[3]{2ab}$

35. $4\sqrt[4]{16x} - 7\sqrt[4]{x^5} + x\sqrt[4]{81x}$

36. $5\sqrt[4]{32x^5} - 3x\sqrt[4]{2x} + 7\sqrt[4]{x^5}$

37. $\frac{1}{\sqrt{5}} + 2$

38. $\frac{1}{\sqrt{3}} - 3$

39. $\frac{12}{\sqrt{6}} - 2\sqrt{6}$

40. $\frac{15}{\sqrt{3}} - 3\sqrt{3}$

41. $\sqrt{\frac{1}{2}} + \sqrt{2}$

42. $\sqrt{\frac{2}{7}} - \sqrt{7}$

43. $\sqrt{\frac{5}{2}} + \sqrt{\frac{2}{5}}$

44. $\sqrt{\frac{3}{5}} - \sqrt{\frac{5}{3}}$

45. $\sqrt{\frac{1}{7}} - 3\sqrt{\frac{1}{5}}$

46. $2\sqrt{\frac{1}{5}} + \sqrt{\frac{2}{3}}$

47. $\frac{1}{\sqrt[3]{2}} - 6\sqrt[3]{4}$

48. $\frac{1}{\sqrt[3]{5}} - 4\sqrt[3]{25}$

49. $\sqrt{\frac{1}{x}} + \sqrt{\frac{1}{y}}$

50. $\sqrt{\frac{1}{x}} - \sqrt{y}$

51. $\frac{1}{\sqrt[3]{9}} - \frac{3}{\sqrt[3]{3}}$

52. $\frac{5}{\sqrt[3]{25}} - \frac{15}{\sqrt[3]{5}}$

53. $3\sqrt{\frac{2}{49}} + 3\sqrt{7}$

54. $2\sqrt{2} - 3\sqrt{\frac{5}{4}}$

55. $3\sqrt{10} - \frac{4}{\sqrt{10}} + \frac{2}{\sqrt{10}}$

56. $2\sqrt{30} - \frac{5}{\sqrt{30}} + \frac{1}{\sqrt{30}}$

57. $6\sqrt[3]{25} - \frac{15}{\sqrt[3]{5}} + 5\sqrt[3]{\frac{1}{5}}$

58. $2\sqrt[3]{49} - \frac{14}{\sqrt[3]{7}} + 5\sqrt[3]{\frac{1}{7}}$

59. $\frac{1}{2\sqrt{x-1}} + \sqrt{x-1}$

60. $3\sqrt{x^2-2} - \frac{2}{\sqrt{x^2-2}}$

MINI-REVIEW

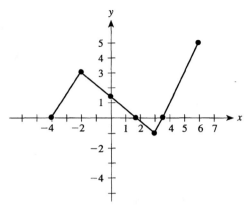

61. Use the accompanying graph of $y = f(x)$ to find

    (a) the domain

    (b) the range

    (c) where $f(x)$ is increasing

    (d) where $f(x)$ is decreasing

62. *Factor as completely as possible.* $3x^3 - 75x$

63. Sketch the graph of the equation $y = \dfrac{2x - 3}{5}$. Label the intercepts.

7.6   Multiplying and Dividing Radical Expressions

As with multiplying polynomials, we use the distributive property to multiply expressions with more than one radical term. For example,

$$\sqrt{2}(\sqrt{2} - \sqrt{3}) = \sqrt{2}\sqrt{2} - \sqrt{2}\sqrt{3} \qquad \textit{Distributive property}$$
$$= 2 - \sqrt{6}$$

EXAMPLE 1   Perform the indicated operations.

    (a) $(2\sqrt{3} - 5\sqrt{2})(2\sqrt{3} - \sqrt{2})$ **(b)** $(2\sqrt{x} - 3\sqrt{y})(2\sqrt{x} + 3\sqrt{y})$

Solution   We apply what we have learned about multiplying polynomials. Each term in the first set of parentheses multiplies each term in the second set.

    (a) $(2\sqrt{3} - 5\sqrt{2})(2\sqrt{3} - \sqrt{2})$

$$= (2\sqrt{3})(2\sqrt{3}) - (2\sqrt{3})(\sqrt{2}) - (5\sqrt{2})(2\sqrt{3}) + (5\sqrt{2})(\sqrt{2})$$
$$= 4 \cdot 3 - 2\sqrt{6} - 10\sqrt{6} + 5 \cdot 2$$
$$= 12 - 12\sqrt{6} + 10 = \boxed{22 - 12\sqrt{6}}$$

    (b) $(2\sqrt{x} - 3\sqrt{y})(2\sqrt{x} + 3\sqrt{y})$ *This is a difference of squares.*

$$= (2\sqrt{x})^2 - (3\sqrt{y})^2 \qquad \textit{Square each term.}$$
$$= 2^2(\sqrt{x})^2 - 3^2(\sqrt{y})^2$$
$$= \boxed{4x - 9y}$$ ■

EXAMPLE 2   Perform the indicated operations.

    (a) $(\sqrt{x + y})^2 - (\sqrt{x} + \sqrt{y})^2$ **(b)** $(\sqrt[3]{x} - \sqrt[3]{y})(\sqrt[3]{x^2} + \sqrt[3]{xy} + \sqrt[3]{y^2})$

Solution   **(a)** $(\sqrt{x + y})^2 - (\sqrt{x} + \sqrt{y})^2$

$$= x + y - [(\sqrt{x})^2 + 2\sqrt{x}\sqrt{y} + (\sqrt{y})^2] \qquad \begin{array}{l}\textit{Note the difference in the}\\ \textit{way we handle } (\sqrt{x + y})^2 \\ \textit{and } (\sqrt{x} + \sqrt{y})^2.\end{array}$$

$$= x + y - [x + 2\sqrt{xy} + y]$$
$$= x + y - x - 2\sqrt{xy} - y = \boxed{-2\sqrt{xy}}$$

    (b) $(\sqrt[3]{x} - \sqrt[3]{y})(\sqrt[3]{x^2} + \sqrt[3]{xy} + \sqrt[3]{y^2})$

$$= \sqrt[3]{x}\sqrt[3]{x^2} + \sqrt[3]{x}\sqrt[3]{xy} + \sqrt[3]{x}\sqrt[3]{y^2} - \sqrt[3]{y}\sqrt[3]{x^2} - \sqrt[3]{y}\sqrt[3]{xy} - \sqrt[3]{y}\sqrt[3]{y^2}$$
$$= \sqrt[3]{x^3} + \sqrt[3]{x^2 y} + \sqrt[3]{xy^2} - \sqrt[3]{x^2 y} - \sqrt[3]{xy^2} - \sqrt[3]{y^3}$$
$$= \sqrt[3]{x^3} - \sqrt[3]{y^3}$$
$$= \boxed{x - y}$$ ■

Parts **(b)** of Examples 1 and 2 illustrate that any expression that is a difference can be factored if we lift our restriction that factors be polynomials with integer coefficients. For example, $3a - 2b$ can be factored into

$$(\sqrt{3a} - \sqrt{2b})(\sqrt{3a} + \sqrt{2b})$$

as a *difference of squares*. Multiply this out and check to verify that it equals $3a - 2b$.

The last operation to cover is division of radical expressions. We begin with division by a single term.

EXAMPLE 3

Simplify. $\dfrac{\sqrt{24} - 8}{10}$

Solution

$\dfrac{\sqrt{24} - 8}{10}$ *Simplify the radical.*

$= \dfrac{\sqrt{4}\sqrt{6} - 8}{10}$

$= \dfrac{2\sqrt{6} - 8}{10}$ *Remember, we can only reduce common factors.*
              *Factor **first**. Then reduce.*

$= \dfrac{2(\sqrt{6} - 4)}{10}$

$= \boxed{\dfrac{\sqrt{6} - 4}{5}}$ ∎

In Section 7.4 we discussed rationalizing the denominator of a fraction with a single radical term in the denominator. In this section we will discuss how to rationalize the denominator of a fraction with more than one term in the denominator.

We cannot rationalize the denominator of $\dfrac{2}{3 + \sqrt{5}}$ as easily as we rationalized denominators consisting of only a single term. What shall we multiply the denominator by: $\sqrt{5}$ or $3 + \sqrt{5}$? Let's try $\sqrt{5}$ and see what happens:

$$\frac{2}{3 + \sqrt{5}} = \frac{2 \cdot \sqrt{5}}{(3 + \sqrt{5}) \cdot \sqrt{5}}$$

$$= \frac{2\sqrt{5}}{3\sqrt{5} + \sqrt{5}\sqrt{5}} = \frac{2\sqrt{5}}{3\sqrt{5} + 5}$$

Notice that we still have a radical remaining in the denominator. If we were to try $3 + \sqrt{5}$, we would again find that a radical would still remain in the denominator.

The denominator can be rationalized by another method, however. We exploit the difference of squares and multiply the numerator and denominator by a ***conjugate*** of the denominator (recall from Section 5.3 that a conjugate of $a + b$ is $a - b$):

Recall the difference of squares:
$(a + b)(a - b) = a^2 - b^2$

$\dfrac{2}{3 + \sqrt{5}} = \dfrac{2(3 - \sqrt{5})}{(3 + \sqrt{5})(3 - \sqrt{5})}$ *Multiply numerator **and** denominator by $3 - \sqrt{5}$.*

$= \dfrac{2(3 - \sqrt{5})}{(3)^2 - (\sqrt{5})^2}$ *The denominator is the difference of squares.*

$= \dfrac{2(3 - \sqrt{5})}{9 - 5}$

$= \dfrac{2(3 - \sqrt{5})}{4}$ *Then reduce.*

$= \dfrac{3 - \sqrt{5}}{2}$

EXAMPLE 4

Simplify.

(a) $\dfrac{\sqrt{a} + \sqrt{b}}{\sqrt{a} - \sqrt{b}}$ (b) $\dfrac{8\sqrt{3}}{\sqrt{7} - \sqrt{3}}$

Solution

(a) $\dfrac{\sqrt{a} + \sqrt{b}}{\sqrt{a} - \sqrt{b}}$ *Multiply the numerator and denominator by $\sqrt{a} + \sqrt{b}$, a conjugate of the denominator.*

$$= \frac{(\sqrt{a} + \sqrt{b})(\sqrt{a} + \sqrt{b})}{(\sqrt{a} - \sqrt{b})(\sqrt{a} + \sqrt{b})}$$

$$= \frac{a + \sqrt{ab} + \sqrt{ab} + b}{a - b} = \boxed{\frac{a + 2\sqrt{ab} + b}{a - b}}$$

(b) $\dfrac{8\sqrt{3}}{\sqrt{7} - \sqrt{3}}$ *Multiply the numerator and denominator by $\sqrt{7} + \sqrt{3}$, a conjugate of the denominator.*

$$= \frac{8\sqrt{3}(\sqrt{7} + \sqrt{3})}{(\sqrt{7} - \sqrt{3})(\sqrt{7} + \sqrt{3})}$$

$$= \frac{8\sqrt{3}(\sqrt{7} + \sqrt{3})}{(\sqrt{7})^2 - (\sqrt{3})^2}$$

$$= \frac{8\sqrt{3}(\sqrt{7} + \sqrt{3})}{7 - 3} = \frac{8\sqrt{3}(\sqrt{7} + \sqrt{3})}{4} \quad \textit{Now reduce.}$$

$$= 2\sqrt{3}(\sqrt{7} + \sqrt{3}) = \boxed{2\sqrt{21} + 6} \qquad \blacksquare$$

EXAMPLE 5

Perform the operations and simplify. $\dfrac{21}{3 - \sqrt{2}} - \dfrac{6}{\sqrt{2}}$

Solution

First we rationalize the denominator of each fraction:

$$\frac{21}{3 - \sqrt{2}} - \frac{6}{\sqrt{2}} = \frac{21(3 + \sqrt{2})}{(3 - \sqrt{2})(3 + \sqrt{2})} - \frac{6\sqrt{2}}{\sqrt{2}\sqrt{2}}$$

$$= \frac{21(3 + \sqrt{2})}{9 - 2} - \frac{6\sqrt{2}}{2}$$

Try finding the value of the original expression by using a calculator.

$$= \frac{21(3 + \sqrt{2})}{7} - \frac{6\sqrt{2}}{2} \qquad \textit{Reduce.}$$

$$= 3(3 + \sqrt{2}) - 3\sqrt{2} = 9 + 3\sqrt{2} - 3\sqrt{2} = \boxed{9} \qquad \blacksquare$$

EXERCISES 7.6

Perform the operations. Express your answer in simplest radical form.

1. $5(\sqrt{5} - 3)$

2. $3(\sqrt{7} + 3)$

3. $2(\sqrt{3} - \sqrt{5}) - 4(\sqrt{3} + \sqrt{5})$

4. $4(\sqrt{6} - \sqrt{2}) - 3(\sqrt{2} - \sqrt{6})$

5. $\sqrt{a}(\sqrt{a} + \sqrt{b})$

6. $\sqrt{x}(\sqrt{x} - \sqrt{y})$

7. $\sqrt{2}(\sqrt{5} + \sqrt{2})$

8. $\sqrt{3}(\sqrt{2} - \sqrt{3})$

9. $3\sqrt{5}(2\sqrt{3} - 4\sqrt{5})$

10. $5\sqrt{2}(7\sqrt{3} - 6\sqrt{2})$

11. $\sqrt{2}(\sqrt{3} + \sqrt{2}) - 3(2\sqrt{6} - 4)$

12. $2\sqrt{5}(\sqrt{3} - \sqrt{5}) + 2(\sqrt{10} - 3)$

13. $\left(\sqrt{5} - 2\right)\left(\sqrt{3} + 1\right)$

14. $\left(\sqrt{7} - 2\right)\left(\sqrt{5} + 3\right)$

15. $\left(\sqrt{5} - \sqrt{3}\right)\left(\sqrt{5} + \sqrt{3}\right)$

16. $\left(\sqrt{2} + \sqrt{5}\right)^2$

17. $\left(\sqrt{5} - \sqrt{3}\right)^2$

18. $\left(\sqrt{2} + \sqrt{5}\right)\left(\sqrt{2} - \sqrt{5}\right)$

19. $\left(2\sqrt{7} - 5\right)\left(2\sqrt{7} + 5\right)$

20. $\left(2\sqrt{5} - 7\right)\left(2\sqrt{5} + 7\right)$

21. $\left(5\sqrt{2} - 3\sqrt{5}\right)\left(5\sqrt{2} + 3\sqrt{5}\right)$

22. $\left(3\sqrt{5} - 2\sqrt{3}\right)\left(3\sqrt{5} + 2\sqrt{3}\right)$

23. $\left(2\sqrt{a} - \sqrt{b}\right)^2$

24. $\left(5\sqrt{x} - \sqrt{y}\right)^2$

25. $\left(3\sqrt{x} - 2\sqrt{y}\right)\left(3\sqrt{x} + 2\sqrt{y}\right)$

26. $\left(5\sqrt{a} - 3\sqrt{b}\right)\left(5\sqrt{a} + 3\sqrt{b}\right)$

27. $\left(\sqrt{x} - 3\right)^2$

28. $\left(\sqrt{a} + 5\right)^2$

29. $\left(\sqrt{x} - 3\right)^2$

30. $\left(\sqrt{a} + 5\right)^2$

31. $\left(\sqrt{x + 1}\right)^2 - \left(\sqrt{x} + 1\right)^2$

32. $\left(\sqrt{a} - 2\right)^2 - \left(\sqrt{a - 2}\right)^2$

33. $\left(\sqrt[3]{2} - \sqrt[3]{3}\right)\left(\sqrt[3]{4} + \sqrt[3]{6} + \sqrt[3]{9}\right)$

34. $\left(\sqrt[3]{4} + \sqrt[3]{5}\right)\left(\sqrt[3]{16} - \sqrt[3]{20} + \sqrt[3]{25}\right)$

35. $\dfrac{4\sqrt{2} - 6\sqrt{3}}{2}$

36. $\dfrac{12\sqrt{3} - 8\sqrt{2}}{4}$

37. $\dfrac{5\sqrt{8} - 2\sqrt{7}}{8}$

38. $\dfrac{2\sqrt{27} + 6\sqrt{5}}{3}$

39. $\dfrac{3\sqrt{50} + 5\sqrt{5}}{5}$

40. $\dfrac{2\sqrt{12} + 5\sqrt{8}}{12}$

41. $\dfrac{4 + \sqrt{28}}{4}$

42. $\dfrac{20 + \sqrt{60}}{4}$

43. $\dfrac{1}{\sqrt{2} - 3}$

44. $\dfrac{1}{2 - \sqrt{3}}$

45. $\dfrac{10}{\sqrt{5} + 1}$

46. $\dfrac{15}{\sqrt{6} - 1}$

47. $\dfrac{2}{\sqrt{3} - \sqrt{a}}$

48. $\dfrac{3}{\sqrt{x} - \sqrt{2}}$

49. $\dfrac{\sqrt{x}}{\sqrt{x} - \sqrt{y}}$

50. $\dfrac{\sqrt{x}}{\sqrt{x} + \sqrt{y}}$

51. $\dfrac{\sqrt{2}}{\sqrt{5} - \sqrt{2}}$

52. $\dfrac{\sqrt{5}}{\sqrt{7} + \sqrt{3}}$

53. $\dfrac{2\sqrt{2}}{2\sqrt{5} - \sqrt{2}}$

54. $\dfrac{3\sqrt{5}}{4\sqrt{3} + \sqrt{5}}$

55. $\dfrac{2\sqrt{5} - \sqrt{2}}{2\sqrt{2}}$

56. $\dfrac{4\sqrt{3} + \sqrt{5}}{3\sqrt{5}}$

57. $\dfrac{\sqrt{3} + \sqrt{2}}{\sqrt{3} - \sqrt{2}}$

58. $\dfrac{\sqrt{x} + \sqrt{y}}{\sqrt{x} - \sqrt{y}}$

59. $\dfrac{3\sqrt{5} - 2\sqrt{2}}{2\sqrt{5} - 3\sqrt{2}}$

60. $\dfrac{2\sqrt{7} + 3\sqrt{2}}{3\sqrt{7} + 2\sqrt{2}}$

61. $\dfrac{x - y}{\sqrt{x} - \sqrt{y}}$

62. $\dfrac{a^2 - b^2}{\sqrt{a} + \sqrt{b}}$

63. $\dfrac{x^2 - x - 2}{\sqrt{x} - \sqrt{2}}$

64. $\dfrac{x^2 - 3x - 4}{\sqrt{x} + 2}$

65. $\dfrac{12}{\sqrt{6} - 2} - \dfrac{36}{\sqrt{6}}$

66. $\dfrac{15}{4 + \sqrt{11}} + \dfrac{33}{\sqrt{11}}$

67. $\dfrac{20}{\sqrt{7} + \sqrt{3}} + \dfrac{28}{\sqrt{7}}$

68. $\dfrac{30}{\sqrt{10} - \sqrt{5}} - \dfrac{15}{\sqrt{5}}$

One solution to the quadratic equation $Ax^2 + Bx + C = 0$ is given by the quadratic formula, $x = \dfrac{-B + \sqrt{B^2 - 4AC}}{2A}$. In Exercises 69–74, use the quadratic formula to find and simplify x for the given values of A, B and C.

69. $A = 1$, $B = 3$, and $C = 2$

70. $A = 1$, $B = 5$, and $C = 4$

71. $A = 2$, $B = 6$, and $C = 3$

72. $A = 2$, $B = 6$, and $C = 1$

73. $A = 2$, $B = 6$, and $C = -3$

74. $A = 4$, $B = 2$, and $C = -3$

 **MINI-REVIEW**

75. Compute the value of the expressions given in Exercises 65 and 66 using a calculator. How do your answers compare to the answers found as a result of simplifying the expressions?

76. *Multiply and simplify.* $(2x - 5)^2 - (x - 10)^2$

77. *Solve.* $(2x - 1)(2x + 3) = 12$

78. Given $f(x) = \dfrac{2.4x^2 - 3.8}{5.1x - 7}$, compute $f(-1.6)$ to the nearest tenth.

79. *Factor as completely as possible.* $12x^2 - 46x + 40$

MINI-REVIEW

82. *Reduce to lowest terms.* $\dfrac{16x - 4x^2}{x^2 - 16}$

83. *Perform the indicated operations and simplify.* $\dfrac{x + 3}{x - 6} \div (x^2 - 3x - 18)$

84. *Solve for x.* $ax + 5 = 6x + 12$

85. *Find the domain of* $f(x) = \dfrac{x}{x^2 - 25}$.

CHAPTER 7 SUMMARY

After having completed this chapter you should:

1. Know the five rules of exponents and be able to use them to simplify expressions (Section 7.1).

   For example:

   $$\frac{(2x^3y^2)^5}{8(x^2y^3)^4} = \frac{2^5(x^3)^5(y^2)^5}{8(x^2)^4(y^3)^4} \qquad \text{By rule 3}$$

   $$= \frac{32x^{15}y^{10}}{8x^8y^{12}} \qquad \text{By rule 2}$$

   $$= \frac{4x^7}{y^2}$$

2. Understand the definition of zero and negative exponents (Section 7.1).

   For example:

   (a) $18^0 = 1$

   (b) $4^{-3} = \dfrac{1}{4^3} = \dfrac{1}{4 \cdot 4 \cdot 4} = \dfrac{1}{64}$

3. Be able to use the exponent rules to simplify expressions with integer exponents (Section 7.1).

   For example: Simplify and express with positive exponents only.

   (a) $\dfrac{(x^{-3}y^8)^{-2}}{(x^{-1}y^{-3})^4} = \dfrac{(x^{-3})^{-2}(y^8)^{-2}}{(x^{-1})^4(y^{-3})^4} \qquad$ *By rule 3*

   $$= \frac{x^6y^{-16}}{x^{-4}y^{-12}}$$

   $$= x^{6-(-4)}y^{-16-(-12)} \qquad \text{By rule 4}$$

   $$= x^{10}y^{-4}$$

   $$= x^{10}\left(\frac{1}{y^4}\right) \qquad \text{By definition of negative exponents}$$

   $$= \frac{x^{10}}{y^4}$$

   (b) $(x^{-2} + y^{-3})^{-1} = \left(\dfrac{1}{x^2} + \dfrac{1}{y^3}\right)^{-1} \qquad$ *Add fractions.*

   $$= \left(\frac{y^3 + x^2}{x^2y^3}\right)^{-1} \qquad \text{Take the reciprocal.}$$

   $$= \frac{x^2y^3}{y^3 + x^2}$$

4. Be able to write and compute with numbers in scientific notation (Section 7.2).

   For example:

   A *nanometer* (nm) is a unit of measurement used in microscopy where 1 nm $= 10^{-7}$ cm. If a microorganism is 1.5×10^{-4} cm long, what is its length in nanometers?

   Since 1 nm $= 10^{-7}$ cm, the length of the microorganism in nm is

   $$\frac{1.5 \times 10^{-4}}{10^{-7}} = 1.5 \times 10^3 \text{ nm} \quad \text{or} \quad 1{,}500 \text{ nm}$$

5. Understand and be able to evaluate expressions involving rational exponents (Section 7.3).

   For example:

   (a) $16^{1/2} = 4$ because $4^2 = 16$

   (b) $(-32)^{1/5} = -2$ because $(-2)^5 = -32$

   (c) $27^{-2/3} = \dfrac{1}{27^{2/3}} = \dfrac{1}{(27^{1/3})^2} = \dfrac{1}{(3)^2} = \dfrac{1}{9}$

6. Be able to simplify expressions involving rational exponents (Section 7.3).

   For example:

   (a) $\dfrac{(4x^2)^{1/2}(x^{-2/3})}{(2x)^2(x^5)^{-1/2}} = \dfrac{4^{1/2}x \cdot x^{-2/3}}{2^2x^2 \cdot x^{-5/2}} = \dfrac{2x^{1+(-2/3)}}{4x^{2+(-5/2)}}$

   $$= \dfrac{2x^{1/3}}{4x^{-1/2}} = \dfrac{x^{5/6}}{2}$$

   (b) $(x^{1/3} + x^{2/5})^2 = (x^{1/3} + x^{2/5})(x^{1/3} + x^{2/5})$

   $$= x^{1/3}x^{1/3} + 2x^{1/3}x^{2/5} + x^{2/5}x^{2/5}$$
   $$= x^{2/3} + 2x^{1/3 + 2/5} + x^{4/5}$$
   $$= x^{2/3} + 2x^{11/15} + x^{4/5}$$

7. Convert expressions from radical form to exponential form, and vice versa (Section 7.3).

   For example:

   (a) $2a^{5/4} = 2\sqrt[4]{a^5}$ or $2(\sqrt[4]{a})^5$

   (b) $\sqrt[5]{x^3y} = (x^3y)^{1/5}$ or $x^{3/5}y^{1/5}$

8. Evaluate numerical expressions given in radical or exponential form (Section 7.3).

   For example:

   (a) $\sqrt{64} = 8$ because $8^2 = 64$

   (b) $\sqrt[3]{-64} = -4$ because $(-4)^3 = -64$

   (c) $\sqrt[6]{64} = 2$ because $2^6 = 64$

9. Write radical expressions in simplest radical form (Section 7.4).

   For example:

   (a) $\sqrt{24x^5y^6} = \sqrt{(4x^4y^6)(6x)} = \sqrt{4x^4y^6}\sqrt{6x} = 2x^2y^3\sqrt{6x}$

   (b) $\sqrt[3]{24x^5y^6} = \sqrt[3]{(8x^3y^6)(3x^2)} = \sqrt[3]{8x^3y^6}\sqrt[3]{3x^2} = 2xy^2\sqrt[3]{3x^2}$

   (c) $\left(a\sqrt{3a^2}\right)\left(b\sqrt{9ab}\right) = ab\left(\sqrt{27a^3b}\right) = ab\left(\sqrt{9a^2}\sqrt{3ab}\right) = ab\left(3a\sqrt{3ab}\right) = 3a^2b\sqrt{3ab}$

   (d) $\sqrt{\dfrac{3}{x}} = \dfrac{\sqrt{3}}{\sqrt{x}} = \dfrac{\sqrt{3}\sqrt{x}}{\sqrt{x}\sqrt{x}} = \dfrac{\sqrt{3x}}{\sqrt{x^2}} = \dfrac{\sqrt{3x}}{x}$

   (e) $\dfrac{\sqrt[3]{3}}{\sqrt[3]{x^2y}} = \dfrac{\sqrt[3]{3}\sqrt[3]{xy^2}}{\sqrt[3]{x^2y}\sqrt[3]{xy^2}} = \dfrac{\sqrt[3]{3xy^2}}{\sqrt[3]{x^3y^3}} = \dfrac{\sqrt[3]{3xy^2}}{xy}$

   (f) $\sqrt[3]{3}\sqrt{3} = \sqrt[6]{3^2}\sqrt[6]{3^3} = \sqrt[6]{3^5} = \sqrt[6]{243}$

10. Combine radicals (Section 7.5).

   For example:

   (a) $2\sqrt{75} - \sqrt{12} = 2(\sqrt{25}\sqrt{3}) - \sqrt{4}\sqrt{3} = 10\sqrt{3} - 2\sqrt{3} = 8\sqrt{3}$

   (b) $\sqrt{\dfrac{3}{2}} - 5\sqrt{6} = \dfrac{\sqrt{3}}{\sqrt{2}} - 5\sqrt{6} = \dfrac{\sqrt{3}\sqrt{2}}{\sqrt{2}\sqrt{2}} - 5\sqrt{6} = \dfrac{\sqrt{6}}{2} - 5\sqrt{6}$

   $$= \dfrac{\sqrt{6}}{2} - \dfrac{10\sqrt{6}}{2} = \dfrac{-9\sqrt{6}}{2}$$

11. Find products and quotients of radicals (Section 7.6).

   For example:

   (a) $(2\sqrt{3} - 4)(3\sqrt{2} + 5) = (2\sqrt{3})(3\sqrt{2}) + 5(2\sqrt{3}) - 4(3\sqrt{2}) - 4(5)$

   $$= 6\sqrt{6} + 10\sqrt{3} - 12\sqrt{2} - 20$$

   (b) $\dfrac{18}{\sqrt{6} - \sqrt{3}} = \dfrac{18(\sqrt{6} + \sqrt{3})}{(\sqrt{6} - \sqrt{3})(\sqrt{6} + \sqrt{3})}$

   $$= \dfrac{18(\sqrt{6} + \sqrt{3})}{6 - 3}$$

   $$= \dfrac{\overset{6}{\cancel{18}}(\sqrt{6} + \sqrt{3})}{\cancel{3}}$$

   $$= 6(\sqrt{6} + \sqrt{3})$$

12. Solve radical equations (Section 7.7).

   For example:

   | Solve for x. | $\sqrt{5x - 2} = 4$ | *Square both sides.* |

   $$(\sqrt{5x - 2})^2 = 4^2$$
   $$5x - 2 = 16$$
   $$5x = 18$$
   $$x = \dfrac{18}{5}$$

   Check: $\sqrt{5\left(\dfrac{18}{5}\right) - 2} \overset{?}{=} 4$

   $$\sqrt{18 - 2} \overset{?}{=} 4$$
   $$\sqrt{16} \overset{\checkmark}{=} 4$$

13. Add, subtract, multiply, and divide complex numbers (Section 7.8).

   For example:

   (a) $(5 + 3i) + (2 - 6i) = 7 - 3i$

   (b) $(5 + 3i)(2 - 6i) = 10 - 30i + 6i - 18i^2$

   $$= 10 - 24i - 18(-1)$$
   $$= 10 - 24i + 18$$
   $$= 28 - 24i$$

   (c) $\dfrac{5 + 3i}{2 - 6i} = \dfrac{(5 + 3i)(2 + 6i)}{(2 - 6i)(2 + 6i)}$

   $$= \dfrac{10 + 36i - 18}{4 + 36}$$

   $$= \dfrac{-8 + 36i}{40} = \dfrac{-8}{40} + \dfrac{36}{40}i = -\dfrac{1}{5} + \dfrac{9}{10}i$$

CHAPTER 7   REVIEW EXERCISES

In Exercises 1–46, perform the operations and simplify; express your answers with positive exponents only. Assume all variables represent nonzero real numbers.

1. $(x^2x^5)(x^4x)$

2. $(x^5y^2)(x^6y^7)$

3. $(-3x^2y)(-2xy^4)(-x)$

4. $(-3xy^5)(-2xy)(-5x)$

5. $(a^3)^4$

6. $(b^5)^4$

7. $(a^2b^3)^7$

8. $(r^2s^3)^8$

9. $(a^2b^3)^2(a^2b)^3$

10. $(x^2y^5)^2(xy^4)^3$

11. $(a^2bc^2)^2(ab^2c)^3$

12. $(-2xy^2)(-3x^2y)^3(-3x)$

13. $\dfrac{a^5}{a^6}$

14. $\dfrac{x^7}{x^2}$

15. $\dfrac{x^2x^5}{x^4x^3}$

16. $\dfrac{y^5y^7}{y^8y^2}$

17. $\dfrac{(x^3y^2)^3}{(x^5y^4)^5}$

18. $\dfrac{(a^2b^3)^2}{(a^2b^4)^3}$

19. $\left(\dfrac{a^2b}{ab}\right)^4$

20. $\left(\dfrac{ab^2}{cb}\right)^4$

21. $\dfrac{(2ax^2)^2(3ax)^2}{(-2x)^2}$

22. $\dfrac{(-5xy)^2(-3x^2)^3}{(-15x)^2}$

23. $\left(\dfrac{-3xy}{x^2}\right)^2\left(\dfrac{-2xy^2}{x}\right)^3$

24. $\left(\dfrac{-3ab^2}{a^2b}\right)^2\left(\dfrac{-2ab}{5a^2}\right)^3$

25. $a^{-3}a^{-4}a^5$

26. $x^{-5}x^{-4}x^0$

27. $(x^{-2}y^5)^{-4}$

28. $(x^{-2}x^3)^{-4}$

29. $(-3)^{-4}(-2)^{-1}$

30. $(-2)^{-2}(-2)^2$

31. $\left(\dfrac{3x^{-5}y^2z^{-4}}{2x^{-7}y^{-4}}\right)^0$

32. $(-156,794)^0$

33. $\dfrac{x^{-3}x^{-6}}{x^{-5}x^0}$

34. $\dfrac{x^{-2}y^{-3}}{x^2y^{-4}}$

35. $\left(\dfrac{x^{-2}y^{-3}}{y^{-3}x^2}\right)^{-2}$

36. $\left(\dfrac{a^{-2}b^{-3}}{a^2b^3}\right)^{-2}$

37. $\left(\dfrac{r^{-2}s^{-3}r^{-2}}{s^{-4}}\right)^{-2}\left(\dfrac{r^{-1}}{s^{-1}}\right)^{-3}$

38. $\left(\dfrac{2r^{-1}s^{-2}}{r^{-3}s^2}\right)^{-2}\left(\dfrac{-3r^{-2}s^{-2}}{4r^{-3}s}\right)^{-1}$

39. $\left(\dfrac{2}{5}\right)^{-2}$

40. $\left(\dfrac{3}{4}\right)^{-4}$

41. $\dfrac{(2x^2y^{-1}z)^{-2}}{(3xy^2)^{-3}}$

42. $\dfrac{(3x^{-2}y^2z^4)^{-2}}{(2x^{-1}y)^{-3}}$

43. $(x^{-1}+y^{-1})(x-y)$

44. $(x^{-1}+2y^{-2})^2$

45. $\dfrac{x^{-1}+y^{-3}}{x^{-1}y^2}$

46. $\dfrac{a^{-2}+b^{-1}}{a^{-1}b^{-2}}$

In Exercises 47–50, convert to standard form.

47. 2.83×10^4

48. 6.29×10^0

49. 7.96×10^{-5}

50. 8.264×10^{-7}

In Exercises 51–54, convert to scientific notation.

51. 92.59

52. 0.00578

53. 625,897

54. 0.0000073

In Exercise 55, perform the computation by first converting the numbers to scientific notation. Express your answer in standard notation.

55. $\dfrac{(0.0014)(9,000)}{(20,000)(63,000)}$

56. A *nanometer* (nm) and a *micron* (μm) are two units of measurement used in microscopy, where 1 nm = 10^{-9}m, and 1 μm = 10^{-6}m. How many nm are in a μm?

In Exercises 57–70, perform the operations and simplify; express your answers with positive exponents only. Assume all variables represent positive real numbers only.

57. $x^{1/2}x^{1/3}$

58. $y^{1/3}y^{-1/2}$

59. $(x^{-1/2}x^{1/3})^{-6}$

60. $(y^{-1/3}y^{-1/2}y^{2/3})^{-1/2}$

61. $\dfrac{x^{1/2}x^{1/3}}{x^{2/5}}$

62. $\dfrac{r^{-1/2}s^{-1/3}}{r^{1/3}s^{-2/3}}$

63. $\left(\dfrac{a^{1/2}a^{-1/3}}{a^{1/2}b^{1/5}}\right)^{-15}$

64. $\left(\dfrac{x^{-1/2}x^{1/3}}{x^{-1/3}y^{1/2}}\right)^{-6}$

65. $\dfrac{(x^{-1/2}y^{1/2})^{-2}}{(x^{-1/3}y^{-1/3})^{-1/2}}$

66. $\dfrac{(a^{1/2}a^{1/3}a^{-2/3})^{-2}}{a^{1/3}a^{-1/2}}$

67. $\left(\dfrac{4^{-1/2}\cdot 16^{-3/4}}{8^{1/3}}\right)^{-2}$

68. $(a^{1/2} - b^{1/2})(a^{-2/3})$

69. $(a^{1/3} + b^{1/3})(a^{1/3} - b^{1/3})$

70. $(a^{-1/2} + 2b^{1/2})^2$

In Exercises 71–78, write the expression in radical form. Assume that all variables represent positive real numbers only.

71. $x^{1/2}$

72. $x^{1/3}$

73. $xy^{1/2}$

74. $(xy)^{1/2}$

75. $m^{2/3}$

76. $m^{3/2}$

77. $(5x)^{3/4}$

78. $5x^{3/4}$

In Exercises 79–84, write the expression in exponential form.

79. $\sqrt[3]{a}$

80. $\sqrt[5]{t}$

81. $-\sqrt[5]{n^4}$

82. $(\sqrt[3]{t})^5$

83. $\dfrac{1}{\sqrt[5]{t^7}}$

84. $\dfrac{1}{\sqrt[7]{t^5}}$

In Exercises 85–108, express in simplest radical form.

85. $\sqrt{54}$

86. $\sqrt[3]{54}$

87. $\sqrt{x^{60}}$

88. $\sqrt[4]{x^{60}}$

89. $\sqrt[3]{48x^4y^8}$

90. $\sqrt{28x^9y^{13}}$

91. $\sqrt{75xy}\sqrt{3x}$

92. $\sqrt{48a^2b}\sqrt{12b}$

93. $(x\sqrt{xy})(2x^2y\sqrt{xy^2})$

94. $(2x^3\sqrt{x^2})(3x^2\sqrt{x^2y^4})$

95. $\dfrac{\sqrt{28}}{\sqrt{63}}$

96. $\dfrac{\sqrt{12}}{\sqrt{27}}$

97. $\dfrac{y}{x\sqrt{y}}$

98. $\dfrac{y}{\sqrt{xy}}$

99. $\sqrt{\dfrac{48a^2b}{3a^5b^2}}$

100. $\sqrt{\dfrac{81x^3y^2}{2x^4}}$

101. $\sqrt{\dfrac{5}{a}}$

102. $\sqrt[3]{\dfrac{5}{a}}$

103. $\dfrac{4}{\sqrt[3]{2a}}$

104. $\dfrac{4}{\sqrt[3]{2a^2}}$

105. $\sqrt[6]{x^4}$

106. $\sqrt[6]{x^6}$

107. $\sqrt{2}\sqrt[3]{2}$

108. $\dfrac{\sqrt{2}}{\sqrt[3]{2}}$

In Exercises 109–126, perform the indicated operations and simplify as completely as possible.

109. $4\sqrt{2} + \sqrt{2} - 5\sqrt{2}$

110. $7\sqrt{54} + 6\sqrt{24}$

111. $6\sqrt{12} - 4\sqrt{27}$

112. $2t\sqrt{s^5t^2} - 3s\sqrt{s^2t^5}$

113. $\sqrt{\dfrac{3}{2}} + \sqrt{\dfrac{5}{3}}$

114. $\sqrt{\dfrac{5}{7}} + \sqrt{\dfrac{2}{3}}$

115. $\sqrt{3}(\sqrt{6} - \sqrt{2}) + \sqrt{2}(\sqrt{3} - 3)$

116. $\sqrt{5}(\sqrt{2} - 2) + \sqrt{10}(\sqrt{2} - 2)$

117. $(3\sqrt{7} - \sqrt{3})(\sqrt{7} - 2\sqrt{3})$

118. $(2\sqrt{x} - \sqrt{5})(3\sqrt{x} + \sqrt{4})$

119. $(\sqrt{x} - 5)^2$

120. $(\sqrt{7} - \sqrt{3})^2$

121. $(\sqrt{a + 7})^2 - (\sqrt{a} + 7)^2$

122. $(\sqrt{b} - 3)^2 - (\sqrt{b - 3})^2$

123. $\dfrac{12}{\sqrt{5} + \sqrt{3}}$

124. $\dfrac{m - n^2}{\sqrt{m} - n}$

125. $\dfrac{8x - 20y}{\sqrt{2x} - \sqrt{5y}}$

126. $\dfrac{15}{\sqrt{7} + \sqrt{2}} - \dfrac{21}{\sqrt{7}}$

In Exercises 127–136, solve the equations.

127. $\sqrt{2x - 5} = 7$

128. $\sqrt{3x} + 2 = 4$

129. $\sqrt{2x - 5} = 7$

130. $\sqrt{3x + 2} = 4$

131. $\sqrt[4]{x - 4} = 3$

132. $\sqrt[3]{x + 3} = 2$

133. $x^{1/4} + 1 = 3$

134. $(x + 1)^{1/4} = 3$

135. If $f(x) = \sqrt{3x}$, solve $f(x) = 7.25$ accurate to two decimal places.

136. If $g(x) = \sqrt{x - 2.1}$, solve $g(x) = 5.8$ accurate to two decimal places.

137. The pressure, p (in pounds per square inch or psi), of the stream from a fire hose is related to the number of gallons per minute, G, discharged from the hose, and the diameter, d, of the hose in inches according to the formula $G = 34.2d^2\sqrt{p}$. Find the pressure of the water coming out of a hose that is 3 in. in diameter and that is discharging 450 gallons per minute. Round your answer to the nearest tenth.

138. Use the formula given in Exercise 137 to find the pressure of the water coming out of a hose that is 4.5 in. in diameter and that is discharging 900 gallons per minute. Round your answer to the nearest tenth.

In Exercises 139–142, express as i, $-i$, 1, or -1.

139. i^{11}

140. i^{29}

141. $-i^{14}$

142. $(-i)^{14}$

In Exercises 143–154, perform the indicated operations with complex numbers and express your answers in complex number form.

143. $(5 + i) + (4 - 2i)$

144. $(7 - 2i) - (6 + 3i)$

145. $(7 - 2i)(2 - 3i)$

146. $(5 - 4i)(5 + 4i)$

147. $2i(3i - 4)$

148. $5i(i - 2)$

149. $(3 - 2i)^2$

150. $(2 - 3i)^2$

151. $(6 - i)^2 - 12(6 - i)$

152. $(7 - i)^2 - 2(7 - 4i)$

153. $\dfrac{4 - 3i}{3 + i}$

154. $\dfrac{2 + 3i}{-3 + 2i}$

155. Show that $1 - 2i$ is a solution for $x^2 - 2x + 5 = 0$.

156. Show that $1 + 2i$ is a solution of $x^2 - 2x + 5 = 0$.

CHAPTER 7 PRACTICE TEST

Perform the indicated operations and express your answers in simplest form with positive exponents only. Assume that all variables represent positive real numbers.

1. $(a^2b^3)(ab^4)^2$

2. $(-2x^2y)^3(-5x)^2$

3. $(-3ab^{-2})^{-1}(-2x^{-1}y)^2$

4. $\dfrac{(-2x^2y)^3}{(-6xy^4)^2}$

5. $\left(\dfrac{5r^{-1}s^{-3}}{3rs^2}\right)^{-2}$

6. $\dfrac{27^{2/3} \cdot 3^{-4}}{9^{-1/2}}$

7. $\left(\dfrac{x^{1/4}x^{-2/3}}{x^{-1}}\right)^4$

8. $\dfrac{x^{-3} + x^{-1}}{yx^{-2}}$

9. $x^{1/3}(x^{2/3} - x)$

10. Evaluate the following:

    (a) $(-125)^{1/3}$

    (b) $(-128)^{-3/7}$

11. Express $3a^{2/3}$ in radical form.

12. Compute the following by first converting the numbers to scientific notation. Express your answer in standard notation.

$$\frac{(64)(28)}{(8{,}000)(70{,}000)}$$

13. Light travels at approximately 186,000 miles per second. How far does light travel in 1 hour? (Use scientific notation to compute your answer.)

Perform the indicated operations and express the following in simplest radical form. Assume that all variables represent positive real numbers.

14. $\sqrt[3]{27x^6y^9}$

15. $\sqrt[3]{4x^2y^2}\sqrt[3]{2x}$

16. $\left(2x^2\sqrt{x}\right)\left(3x\sqrt{xy^2}\right)$

17. $\sqrt{\dfrac{5}{7}}$

18. $\sqrt[3]{\dfrac{8}{9}}$

19. $\dfrac{\left(xy\sqrt{2xy}\right)\left(3x\sqrt{y}\right)}{\sqrt{4x^3}}$

20. $\sqrt[4]{5}\sqrt{5}$

21. $\sqrt{50} - 3\sqrt{8} + 2\sqrt{18}$

22. $\left(\sqrt{x} - 3\right)^2$

23. $\dfrac{\sqrt{6}}{\sqrt{6} - 2}$

Solve the following equations.

24. $\sqrt{x - 3} + 4 = 8$

25. $\sqrt{x} - 3 = 8$

26. If $f(x) = \sqrt{5x}$, solve $f(x) = 9.3$ accurate to two decimal places.

Express the following in the form $a + bi$:

27. i^{51}

28. $(3i + 1)(i - 2)$

29. $\dfrac{2i + 3}{i - 2}$

319

In Section 5.1, we examined functions that were polynomials. In this chapter we turn our attention to polynomial functions of the *second degree*—that is, polynomial functions in which the highest degree of the variable is 2. These functions are usually called **quadratic functions** and have the form

$$f(x) = Ax^2 + Bx + C \qquad (A \neq 0)$$

where A is the coefficient of the second-degree term, B is the coefficient of the first-degree term, and C is the constant term.

In the first section of this chapter, we will discuss a few properties of quadratic functions and examine some examples of quadratic models. In subsequent sections, we will examine algebraic methods of solving quadratic equations and the graphs of quadratic functions. We will then apply methods of solving quadratic equations to more complex equations as well as to inequalities.

8.1 Quadratic Functions as Mathematical Models

In Chapter 5 we looked at the function $h(t) = 10 + 50t - 4.9t^2$, which described the height of an object, $h(t)$, above the ground (in meters) as a function of the time, t (in seconds). In that example we looked at a table of values and noted that there is a single maximum value of $f(x)$, which occurs at the turning point of the graph. We graphed the function as shown in Figure 8.1.

Figure 8.1
The graph of
$h = h(t) = 10 + 50t - 4.9t^2$

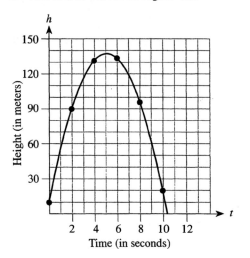

In general, the graph of a quadratic function $y = f(x) = Ax^2 + Bx + C$ (where $A \neq 0$, and $A, B,$ and C are real numbers) has an umbrella shape that is called a **parabola.** Figure 8.2 shows the graphs of two quadratic functions.

Figure 8.2

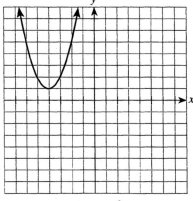

(a) The graph of $f(x) = x^2 + 8x + 17$

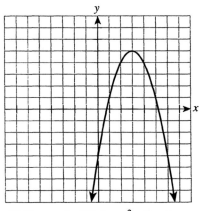

(b) The graph of $f(x) = -x^2 + 6x - 4$

320

Depending on the value of *A* (as we will see in Section 8.6), this umbrella shape opens either up or down. Note that there is only a single turning point, which is called the **vertex** of the parabola. If the parabola opens downward, the vertex is the highest point and the corresponding *y* value is called the *maximum* value of $f(x)$. If the parabola opens upward, the vertex is the lowest point and the corresponding *y* value is called the *minimum* value of $f(x)$.

Although the parabola may be stretched (appear narrower or wider) or shifted (moved up, down, right, or left), a quadratic function will always have this shape.

If we look at either a table of values or the graph of a quadratic function, we note that each *y* value is assigned to *two x* values except at the vertex: *At the vertex the y value is assigned to only one x value.* Figures 8.3a and 8.3b show an example of a table of values and the graph of the quadratic function $y = f(x) = x^2 - 2x - 2$.

Figure 8.3

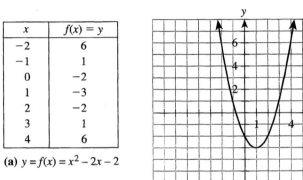

x	$f(x) = y$
−2	6
−1	1
0	−2
1	−3
2	−2
3	1
4	6

(a) $y = f(x) = x^2 - 2x - 2$

(b) $f(x) = x^2 - 2x - 2$

In Section 8.6 we will examine the graphs of quadratic functions in more detail. For now, we will use the information we have discussed thus far to further our understanding of the general behavior of quadratic models.

EXAMPLE 1

The profit in dollars, $P(x)$, made on a concert is related to the price of a ticket in dollars, *x*, in the following way:

$$P(x) = 10,000(-x^2 + 11x - 15)$$

(a) Use this function to find the profit if the ticket price is $0, $2, $4, $6, $8, and $10 per ticket, and describe what happens to the profit as the ticket price increases.

(b) Estimate the maximum profit that can be made for this concert and what ticket price will produce that maximum profit.

Solution

(a) We are looking for the value of $P(x)$ when $x = \$0, \$2, \$4, \$6, \$8,$ and $\$10$. Using function notation, this means we are looking for $P(0), P(2), P(4), P(6), P(8),$ and $P(10)$.

To find P(a), substitute x = a in $P(x) = 10,000(-x^2 + 11x - 15)$

To find P(0), substitute x = 0. $P(0) = 10,000(-0^2 + 11 \cdot 0 - 15) = -150,000$

To find P(2), substitute x = 2. $P(2) = 10,000(-2^2 + 11 \cdot 2 - 15) = 30,000$

To find P(4), substitute x = 4. $P(4) = 10,000(-4^2 + 11 \cdot 4 - 15) = 130,000$

To find P(6), substitute x = 6. $P(6) = 10,000(-6^2 + 11 \cdot 6 - 15) = 150,000$

To find P(8), substitute x = 8. $P(8) = 10,000(-8^2 + 11 \cdot 8 - 15) = 90,000$

To find P(10), substitute x = 10. $P(10) = 10,000(-10^2 + 11 \cdot 10 - 15) = -50,000$

From the values of $P(x)$ above, we can see that the profit function can be negative: We interpret this as a loss. When ticket prices are $0 (a free concert), $150,000 is lost ($P(0) = -150,000$). We see that a profit of $30,000 is realized when the ticket price is $2 ($P(2) = 30,000$); therefore, the concert begins to earn a profit somewhere between $0 and $2. As the ticket price increases, the profit rises for a while; when the ticket price exceeds $6 per ticket, the profit begins to decrease. The profit seems to reach a maximum of about $150,000 at a ticket price of $6.

As the ticket price increases beyond $6, the profit function decreases, or there is less profit. Perhaps fewer people go to the concert because the ticket prices are too expensive. Profits continue to decrease until there is a loss again, which occurs when the price of a ticket is between $8 and $10.

We can represent the data as ordered pairs $(x, P(x))$, letting P represent the dependent variable (and therefore the vertical axis), and plot the data points as shown in Figure 8.4. $P(x)$ is a quadratic function, and since we have stated that the graph of a quadratic function will give us a parabola, we can "fit" the parabola around the data points to get the rough graph of the function $P(x)$ shown in Figure 8.4.

Figure 8.4
The graph of $P(x) =$
$10,000 (-x^2 + 11x - 15)$

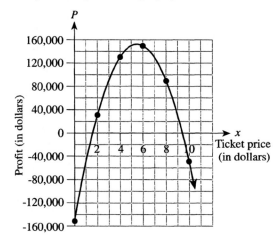

(b) We can see by the graph in part **(a)** that the maximum, or highest, profit occurs somewhere around a ticket price of $6. We are not sure how close until we examine other values around $6. We check the value of $P(x)$ for $x = 5$ to get

$$P(5) = 10,000(-5^2 + 11 \cdot 5 - 15) = 150,000$$

which is the same table value as for $x = 6$. Hence, the maximum value must lie between $x = 5$ and $x = 6$. We could improve this estimate by computing other ticket prices between $5 and $6; however, later in this chapter we will discuss methods for finding the exact values. Hence, the estimated maximum profit is around $150,000, which occurs for a ticket price between $5 and $6. ■

EXAMPLE 2

Raju wants to fence in a rectangular garden against his house. Since the house is to serve as one of the sides, he needs to fence in only three sides (see Figure 8.5). Suppose he uses 100 linear feet of fencing.

(a) Express the area of the garden as a function of x (the length of side given in Figure 8.5).

(b) Use the area function found in part **(a)** to find the area of the garden for $x = 5$, 10, 20, 30, 40, and 45 ft, and describe what happens to the area of the garden as the length x increases.

(c) Estimate the maximum area of the garden and the dimensions of the garden that would give the maximum possible area.

Figure 8.5

Solution

(a) We want to find the area of the garden in the diagram with given side x. Hence, we first write the formula for the area of the garden:

$$A = \text{(Length)(Width)}$$

Let's apply this formula to the rectangular garden in Figure 8.5:

$$A = xy$$

Now we have expressed the area of the garden as a function of two variables, but we are asked to express the area in terms of one variable, x. Let's see whether we can find a relationship between the sides x and y of the rectangle.

We know that the length of the fence used is 100 ft; hence, from the figure,

$$2x + y = 100 \qquad \textit{Solve for y.}$$
$$y = 100 - 2x$$

We have just expressed the third side, y, in terms of x. Now we can substitute into the area equation:

$$A = x \cdot y \qquad \textit{Substitute } 100 - 2x \textit{ for y.}$$
$$A = A(x) = x(100 - 2x) = 100x - 2x^2$$

This expresses the area, A, as a function of x. We note that this is a quadratic function.

(b) We make a table of values for the six values of x: 5, 10, 20, 30, 40, and 45:

x	$A(x) = 100x - 2x^2$	$=$ Area of the garden
5	$A(5) = 100(5) - 2(5)^2$	$= 450$
10	$A(10) = 100(10) - 2(10)^2$	$= 800$
20	$A(20) = 100(20) - 2(20)^2$	$= 1,200$
30	$A(30) = 100(30) - 2(30)^2$	$= 1,200$
40	$A(40) = 100(40) - 2(40)^2$	$= 800$
45	$A(45) = 100(45) - 2(45)^2$	$= 450$

From the table, we can see that the area $A(x)$ is 450 sq ft when the length x is 5 ft. As the length x increases, the area $A(x)$ increases until $A(x)$ reaches 1,200 sq ft at $x = 20$. The area is also 1,200 sq ft at $x = 30$, but then the area $A(x)$ decreases for larger values of x until it moves down to 450 sq ft again at $x = 45$.

Looking at the table, we may get the (incorrect) impression that the largest value of $A(x)$ is 1,200, occurring at $x = 20$ and $x = 30$. However, let's plot the data points (see Figure 8.6), letting A represent the vertical axis.

Since we know that $A(x)$ is a quadratic function and that the graph of a quadratic function will give us a parabola, we again "fit" the parabola around the data points to get the rough graph of the function $A(x)$ shown in Figure 8.6.

Figure 8.6
The graph of
$A = A(x) = 100x - 2x^2$

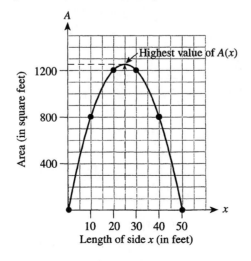

(c) We can see from the table and the graph in part **(b)** that the maximum area, or highest value of $A(x)$, occurs somewhere between $x = 20$ and $x = 30$.

We check the value $A(25)$ to get

$$A(25) = 100(25) - 2(25)^2 = 1,250$$

Later in this chapter we will be able to verify the maximum value for A(x). (See Exercise 53 in Section 8.6.)

If we check the values $A(24)$ and $A(26)$, we will find that these values will be smaller than $A(25)$. The maximum value of the area $A(x)$ is in fact 1,250 sq ft, occurring at $x = 25$ ft.

When $x = 25$, $y = 100 - 2x = 100 - 2(25) = 50$ ft. Hence we can estimate that the dimensions for the maximum area are 25 by 50 ft, where the side opposite the house is 50 ft. ∎

EXAMPLE 3

A printer manufacturing company determines that it can sell 3,000 printers at a price of $350 and that for each $25 increase in the price, 100 fewer printers will be sold. Let x represent the number of $25 increases in price. Express the total revenue from printer sales as a function of x.

Solution

The revenue is computed by multiplying the number of printers sold by the price per printer:

Revenue = (Number of printers)(Price per printer)

Before trying to write out a formula, it would be helpful to first set up a table with some numerical values for x and see whether we can identify a pattern. Let x = the number of $25 increases.

x	Price per printer	Number of printers sold	Revenue
0	350	3,000	350(3,000)
1	350 + 25	3,000 − 100	(350 + 25)(3,000 − 100)
2	350 + 2(25)	3,000 − 2(100)	(350 + 2(25))(3,000 − 2(100))
3	350 + 3(25)	3,000 − 3(100)	(350 + 3(25))(3,000 − 3(100))
⋮	⋮	⋮	⋮
x	350 + x(25)	3,000 − x(100)	(350 + x(25))(3,000 − x(100))

Thus we have

$$R(x) = (350 + 25x)(3,000 - 100x) = -2,500x^2 + 40,000x + 1,050,000 \quad ∎$$

The revenue function found in Example 3,

$$R(x) = -2,500x^2 + 40,000x + 1,050,000$$

represents the relationship between $R(x)$, the total revenue from printer sales, and x, the *number of $25 increases in price (from the original price of $350).* Figure 8.7 shows the graph of this function.

Figure 8.7

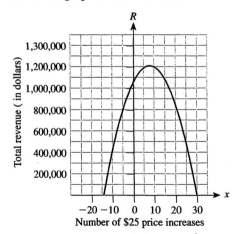

The graph of $R = R(x) = -2,500x^2 + 40,000x + 1,050,000$

Keeping in mind that x is the number of $25 increases, we see that even when x is negative (the number of $25 *decreases* in price), there is still a profit. When $x = 0$ (that is, when there is no price increase—the price of a printer is $350), the revenue is $R(x) = \$1,050,000$.

As x increases, the revenue grows until it reaches its peak. We can use the graph to estimate that the peak revenue is about $1,200,000, which occurs when $x = 8$. (Remember that $x = 8$ means that the price is increased by $25 eight times, or by $200.) Hence the highest revenue occurs when the price of the printer is $350 + 8(25) = \$550$.

As the price is increased by more than $200, the revenue drops until there is no revenue ($R(x) = 0$). This occurs when $x = 30$: Thirty $25 increases take the increase in cost to $750, so the cost of a printer is $350 + 750 = \$1,100$, which yields no revenue.

In this chapter we will continue exploring quadratic functions and will see how to construct their graphs as well as identify the values that give the function's maximum (or minimum) value, and identify other values of importance for quadratic functions.

 EXERCISES 8.1

1. A company finds that its daily profit in dollars, $P(x)$, is related to the number of items it produces daily, x, in the following way:

$$P(x) = -3.5x^2 + 600.4x$$

(a) Use this function to find the profit if the number of items produced daily is 30, 50, 70, 100, and 120, and describe what happens to the profit as the company increases its daily production of items.

(b) Estimate the maximum profit that can be made by this company and what the daily production would be for that maximum profit.

2. The daily production cost, in dollars, for a desk manufacturer is

$$C(x) = 0.3x^2 - 5.3x + 546.8$$

where x is the number of desks produced daily.

(a) Use this function to find the daily production cost if the number of desks produced daily is 4, 6, 8, 10, and 12, and describe what happens to the daily production cost as the company increases its daily production of desks.

(b) Estimate how many desks the manufacturer should produce to minimize the daily production cost. Estimate the minimum production cost.

3. Harry fires a rocket upward, which travels according to the equation

$$s(t) = -16t^2 + 725t$$

where $s(t)$ is the height (in feet) of the rocket above the ground t seconds after the rocket is fired.

(a) Use this function to find the height of the rocket at the end of 5, 10, 20, 30, 40, and 45 seconds.

(b) Estimate how many seconds it takes for the rocket to reach its maximum height. Estimate the maximum height of the rocket.

(c) Estimate how long it takes for the rocket to hit the ground.

4. A manufacturer finds that the revenue, $R(x)$, earned on the production and sale of n items is given by the function

$$R(n) = 1.82n - 0.0001n^2$$

(a) Use this function to find the revenue if the number of items produced and sold is 3,000, 6,000, 9,000, 12,000, and 15,000. Describe what happens to the revenue as the company increases its production and sales.

(b) Estimate how many items should be produced and sold to maximize the revenue. Estimate the maximum revenue.

5. A rectangular area is to be fenced in with 200 feet of fencing (see accompanying figure).

(a) Express the area of the rectangle as a function of x (the length of side x in the accompanying figure).

(b) Use the area function found in part **(a)** to find the area of the rectangle for $x = 10, 40, 60, 70$, and 90 ft, and describe what happens to the area of the rectangle as the length x increases.

(c) Estimate the maximum area of the rectangle and the dimensions of the rectangle that would give the maximum possible area.

6. For a fixed perimeter of 100 ft, estimate what dimensions will yield a rectangle with the maximum area.

7. Estimate which two numbers whose sum is 225 will yield the maximum product.

8. Estimate which two numbers whose difference is 100 will yield a minimum product.

9. Two rectangular pens are to be fenced in with 1,000 feet of fencing as illustrated in the accompanying figure.

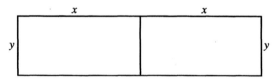

(a) Express the total area of the pens as a function of x (the length of side x in the accompanying figure).

(b) Use the area function found in part **(a)** to find the total area of the pens for $x = 50, 100, 120, 150$, and 200 ft, and describe what happens to the total area of the pens as the length x increases.

(c) Estimate the total maximum area of the pens and the values of x and y that would give the maximum possible area.

10. A rectangular pen is to be fenced in against a house with 1,000 feet of fencing as *illustrated in the accompanying figure.*

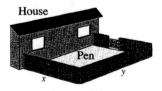

(a) Express the area of the pen as a function of x (the length of side x in the accompanying figure).

(b) Use the area function found in part **(a)** to find the area of the pen for $x = 50, 100, 200, 300$, and 400 ft, and describe what happens to the area of the pen as the length x increases.

(c) Estimate the maximum area of the pen and the dimensions of the rectangle that would give the maximum possible area.

11. In economics, the demand function for a given item indicates how the price per unit, p, is related to the number of units, x, that are sold. Suppose a company finds that the demand function for one of the items it produces is

$$p = 10 - \frac{x}{6}$$

    where p is in dollars.

    (a) How many items would be sold if the price were $6 per unit?

    (b) What should the price per unit be if 30 units were to be sold?

    (c) Sketch a graph of this function.

    (d) The revenue function, $R(x)$, is found by multiplying the price per unit, p, by the number of items sold, x (that is, $R = xp$). Find the revenue function corresponding to this demand function.

    (e) Use the revenue function found in part (d) to find the revenue if the number of items sold is 5, 15, 25, 35, and 40; describe what happens to the revenue as the company increases its sale of items.

    (f) Estimate how many items should be sold to maximize the revenue. Estimate the maximum revenue.

12. A computer company determines that it can sell 5,000 computers at a price of $800 and that for each $50 increase in price, 60 fewer computers will be sold. Let x represent the number of $50 increases in price.

    (a) Express the total revenue from computer sales as a function of x, the number of price increases.

    (b) If $R(x)$ represents the revenue function found in part (a), use $R(x)$ to find the revenue if the number of $50 price increases is 10, 20, 30, 40, and 60; describe what happens to the revenue as the company increases its price on computers.

    (c) Estimate how many price increases are needed to maximize the revenue. What computer price will produce the maximum revenue? Estimate the maximum revenue.

13. The managers of Games Inc. determined that they can sell 200,000 puzzler cubes at a price of $3.00 and that for each 25¢ increase in price, 7,250 fewer puzzler cubes will be sold. Let x represent the number of 25¢ increases in price.

    (a) Express the total revenue from puzzler cube sales as a function of x, the number of price increases.

    (b) If $R(x)$ represents the revenue function found in part (a), use $R(x)$ to find the revenue if the number of 25¢ price increases is 3, 6, 9, and 12; describe what happens to the revenue as the managers increase the price on puzzler cubes.

    (c) Estimate how many price increases are needed to maximize the revenue. What price will produce the maximum revenue? Estimate the maximum revenue.

14. A shoe manufacturer can sell 3,500 pairs of shoes for $24 each. It is determined that for each 50¢ reduction in price, 150 more pairs of shoes can be sold.

    (a) Express the revenue, R, as a function of n, where n is the number of 50¢ reductions.

    (b) If $R(n)$ represents the revenue function found in part (a), use $R(n)$ to find the revenue if the number of 50¢ price reductions is 0, 3, 6, 9, 12, and 15; describe what happens to the revenue as the manufacturer decreases its price on shoes.

    (c) Estimate how many price reductions are needed to maximize the revenue. What price will produce the maximum revenue? Estimate the maximum revenue.

◇ **MINI-REVIEW**

15. *Evaluate.* $3x^3y^2 - x^2 + y^3$ for $x = -2$ and $y = -3$

16. *Solve for x.* $|3x - 4| < 6$

17. *Solve for x.* $|5 - 2x| \geq 6$

18. A manufacturer produces two types of telephones. The more expensive model requires 1 hour to manufacture and 30 minutes to assemble. The less expensive model requires 45 minutes to manufacture and 15 minutes to assemble. If the company allocates 150 hours for manufacture and 60 hours for assembly, how many of each type can be produced?

8.2 Solving Quadratic Equations: The Factoring and Square Root Methods

A *second-degree equation* is a polynomial equation in which the highest degree of the variable is 2. In particular, a second-degree equation in one unknown is called a *quadratic equation.* We define the *standard form* of a quadratic equation as

$$Ax^2 + Bx + C = 0 \qquad (A \neq 0)$$

where A is the coefficient of the second-degree term, x^2; B is the coefficient of the first-degree term, x; and C is a numerical constant.

As with all other equations, the solutions of quadratic equations are values that, when substituted for the variable, will make the equation a true statement. The solutions to the equation $Ax^2 + Bx + C = 0$ are also called the *roots* of the equation $Ax^2 + Bx + C = 0$.

The Factoring Method

We begin by recalling the zero-product rule from Section 5.6:

The Zero–Product Rule	If $a \cdot b = 0$, then $a = 0$ or $b = 0$.

In words, if the product of two quantities is 0, then one or both of the quantities is 0.

The next example reviews the factoring method discussed in Section 5.6. You may want to review some of the simpler quadratic equations covered there before continuing in this section.

EXAMPLE 1

Solve each of the following equations.

(a) $2x^2 + 9x - 5 = 0$

(b) $(3x + 1)(x - 1) = (5x - 3)(2x - 3)$

(c) $\dfrac{x}{x - 5} - \dfrac{3}{x + 1} = \dfrac{30}{x^2 - 4x - 5}$

Solution

(a) $\quad 2x^2 + 9x - 5 = 0 \qquad$ *Factor the left side.*

$\quad (2x - 1)(x + 5) = 0 \qquad$ *Since the product is 0, set each factor equal to 0.*

$\quad 2x - 1 = 0 \quad$ or $\quad x + 5 = 0 \qquad$ *Then solve each first-degree equation.*

$$\boxed{x = \frac{1}{2}} \quad \text{or} \quad \boxed{x = -5}$$

(b) $(3x + 1)(x - 1) = (5x - 3)(2x - 3)$

To determine what type of equation we have, we must first multiply out each side.

$3x^2 - 2x - 1 = 10x^2 - 21x + 9$ *Then put in standard form.*

$0 = 7x^2 - 19x + 10$ *Factor the right side of the equation.*

$0 = (7x - 5)(x - 2)$ *Then set each factor equal to 0.*

$7x - 5 = 0$ or $x - 2 = 0$

$7x = 5$ or $x = 2$

$\boxed{x = \dfrac{5}{7}}$ or $\boxed{x = 2}$

(c) Since this equation contains fractions, we begin by clearing the denominators. First we find the LCD of the fractions, which is $(x - 5)(x + 1)$.

$$\frac{x}{x - 5} - \frac{3}{x + 1} = \frac{30}{x^2 - 4x - 5}$$ *Multiply both sides of the equation by $(x - 5)(x + 1)$.*

$$(x - 5)(x + 1)\left(\frac{x}{x - 5} - \frac{3}{x + 1}\right) = \frac{30}{(x - 5)(x + 1)}(x - 5)(x + 1)$$

$$(x - 5)(x + 1)\frac{x}{x - 5} - (x - 5)(x + 1)\frac{3}{x + 1} = \frac{30}{(x - 5)(x + 1)}(x - 5)(x + 1)$$

$x(x + 1) - 3(x - 5) = 30$

$x^2 + x - 3x + 15 = 30$ *Simplify.*

$x^2 - 2x + 15 = 30$ *Put in standard form.*

$x^2 - 2x - 15 = 0$ *Factor and solve each first-degree equation.*

$(x - 5)(x + 3) = 0$

$x - 5 = 0$ or $x + 3 = 0$

$x = 5$ or $x = -3$

Remember, you must check the solutions to rational equations to determine whether the solutions are valid.

As we pointed out in Chapter 6, we can observe at the outset that neither 5 nor −1 is an admissible value since each makes a denominator of one of the fractions 0 and therefore the fraction undefined. [Also, multiplying both sides of the equation by $(x - 5)(x + 1)$ is not valid if x is 5 or −1, since multiplying both sides by 0 does not yield an equivalent equation.] Since 5 is one of the proposed solutions, we must eliminate this value, and therefore −3 is the only solution.

Throughout the chapter, any checks not done are left to the student.

Hence, the solution is $\boxed{x = -3}$.   ■

EXAMPLE 2

The sum of a number and its reciprocal is $\frac{29}{10}$. Find the numbers.

Solution

Let $x =$ the number.

The sum of a number and its reciprocal is $\dfrac{29}{10}$

$x \quad + \quad \dfrac{1}{x} \quad = \quad \dfrac{29}{10}$

The equation is

$$x + \frac{1}{x} = \frac{29}{10}$$ *Multiply both sides of the equation by the LCD, $10x$.*

$$10x\left(x + \frac{1}{x}\right) = \left(\frac{29}{10}\right)10x \qquad \textit{Distribute 10x and reduce.}$$

$$10x(x) + 10x\left(\frac{1}{x}\right) = \frac{29}{10} \cdot \frac{10x}{1}$$

$$10x^2 + 10 = 29x \qquad \textit{Now we have a quadratic equation}$$
$$\textit{and we solve for x.}$$

$$10x^2 - 29x + 10 = 0$$
$$(5x - 2)(2x - 5) = 0$$
$$5x - 2 = 0 \quad \text{or} \quad 2x - 5 = 0$$
$$5x = 2 \qquad\qquad 2x = 5$$
$$x = \frac{2}{5} \quad \text{or} \quad x = \frac{5}{2}$$

Thus, the answers are $\boxed{\dfrac{2}{5} \text{ and } \dfrac{5}{2}}$. Notice that the two answers are reciprocals of each other. ■

Often we find that the relationship between two quantities can be expressed as a second-degree equation in two unknowns.

EXAMPLE 3   The profit in dollars, $P(x)$, on each television set made daily by AAA Television Company is related to the number of television sets, x, produced at the AAA factory as follows:

$$P(x) = -\frac{x^2}{4} + 45x - 1,625$$

(a) What is the company's profit for each TV set if it produces 90 TV sets?

(b) How many sets must be produced for the company to make a profit of $175 per set?

Solution   (a) Since profit per set is

$$P(x) = -\frac{x^2}{4} + 45x - 1,625$$

where x is the number of sets produced daily, we simply substitute the daily number of sets produced for x and find $P(90)$:

$$P(90) = -\frac{(90)^2}{4} + 45(90) - 1,625$$

$$= -\frac{8,100}{4} + 4,050 - 1,625$$

$$= -2,025 + 4,050 - 1,625$$

$$= \boxed{\$400 \text{ profit per TV set}}$$

(b) To find the number of sets to be produced to make a profit of $175 per set, we set $P(x) = 175$ and find x by solving the quadratic equation:

$$175 = -\frac{x^2}{4} + 45x - 1,625 \qquad \textit{Multiply both sides of the equation by 4.}$$

$$700 = -x^2 + 180x - 6,500 \qquad \textit{Put in standard form.}$$

$$0 = x^2 - 180x + 7,200 \qquad \textit{Solve by factoring.}$$

$$0 = (x - 60)(x - 120)$$

$$x = 60 \quad \text{or} \quad x = 120$$

Thus, for the company to make a profit of $175 per set, it must produce $\boxed{\text{either 60 TV sets or 120 TV sets daily}}$. ■

EXAMPLE 4

The rate of a stream is 4 mph. Meri rowed her boat downstream (with the current) a distance of 9 miles and then back upstream (against the current) to her starting point. If the complete trip took 10 hours, what was her rate in still water?

Solution

First we must realize that when Meri is traveling downstream, the net rate (the rate her boat is traveling relative to the land) is equal to the rate she can row in still water plus the rate of the stream. That is,

$$\text{Net rate downstream} = r_{\text{rowing}} + r_{\text{stream}}$$

On the other hand, the net rate upstream (the rate the boat travels upstream relative to the land) is the difference of the rate rowing in still water and the rate of the stream:

$$\text{Net rate upstream} = r_{\text{rowing}} - r_{\text{stream}}$$

Let's call Meri's rate rowing r. Then since the rate of the stream is 4 mph we have

$$\text{Net rate downstream} = r + 4$$
$$\text{Net rate upstream} = r - 4$$

Since distance = (rate)(time), the *time* it takes for her to go downstream is

$$\text{Time downstream} = \frac{\text{Distance}}{\text{Net rate downstream}} = \frac{9}{r + 4}$$

The *time* it takes for her to go upstream is

$$\text{Time upstream} = \frac{\text{Distance}}{\text{Net rate upstream}} = \frac{9}{r - 4}$$

Since the total time for the round trip is 10 hours, we have

$$10 = \frac{9}{r + 4} + \frac{9}{r - 4}$$

We solve for r. First multiply both sides of the equation by $(r + 4)(r - 4)$:

$$(r + 4)(r - 4) \cdot 10 = \left(\frac{9}{r + 4} + \frac{9}{r - 4}\right)(r + 4)(r - 4)$$
$$10(r + 4)(r - 4) = 9(r - 4) + 9(r + 4)$$
$$10(r^2 - 16) = 9r - 36 + 9r + 36$$
$$10r^2 - 160 = 18r$$
$$10r^2 - 18r - 160 = 0$$
$$2(5r^2 - 9r - 80) = 0 \qquad \textit{Divide both sides by 2.}$$
$$5r^2 - 9r - 80 = 0$$
$$(5r + 16)(r - 5) = 0$$
$$r = -\frac{16}{5} \quad \text{or} \quad r = 5 \qquad \textit{We eliminate the negative value.}$$

Thus, her rate in still water is $\boxed{5 \text{ mph}}$.

Check:

Going downstream takes her $\dfrac{9}{r + 4} = \dfrac{9}{5 + 4} = \dfrac{9}{9} = 1$ hour.

Going upstream takes her $\dfrac{9}{r - 4} = \dfrac{9}{5 - 4} = \dfrac{9}{1} = 9$ hours.

Total time $= 1 + 9 \overset{\checkmark}{=} 10$ hours. ■

The Square Root Method

The solutions to the equation $x^2 = d$ are numbers that, when squared, yield d. In Chapter 7 we defined $\sqrt{d}$ as the nonnegative expression that, when squared, yields d. However, since we have no information as to whether x is positive or negative, we must take into account the negative square root as well. For example, in solving $x^2 = 4$, since $(+2)^2 = 4$ and $(-2)^2 = (-2)(-2) = 4$, both $+2$ *and* -2 are solutions. Hence, if $x^2 = d$, then $x = +\sqrt{d}$ or $x = -\sqrt{d}$.

A shorter way to write a quantity and its opposite would be to write "$\pm$" in front of the quantity to symbolize both answers. Thus, the answers to $x^2 = 4$ can be written as $x = \pm 2$ rather than $x = +2$ or $x = -2$.

THEOREM	If $x^2 = d$, then $x = \pm\sqrt{d}$.

The square root method of solving quadratic equations is used mainly when there is no x term in the standard form of the quadratic equation—that is, when $B = 0$ in $Ax^2 + Bx + C = 0$.

The square root method requires us to isolate x^2 on one side of the equation and then apply the theorem. When we use this theorem we will say that we are *taking square roots*. For example:

Solve for x if $x^2 + 5 = 8$.

We proceed as follows:

$$x^2 + 5 = 8 \qquad \textit{Isolate } x^2.$$
$$x^2 = 3 \qquad \textit{Take square roots.}$$
$$x = \pm\sqrt{3} \qquad \textit{This means that } x = +\sqrt{3} \textit{ or } x = -\sqrt{3}.$$

EXAMPLE 5

Solve each of the following equations.

(a) $x^2 + 2 = 5 - 2x^2$ (b) $2x^2 + 15 = 7$

Solution

(a) $x^2 + 2 = 5 - 2x^2$ *First isolate x^2 on the left side of the equation.*

$$3x^2 = 3$$
$$x^2 = 1 \qquad \textit{Then take the square roots.}$$
$$x = \pm\sqrt{1} \qquad \textit{Do not forget the negative root.}$$
$$\boxed{x = \pm 1}$$

(b) $2x^2 + 15 = 7$ *Isolate x^2.*

$$2x^2 = -8$$
$$x^2 = \frac{-8}{2} = -4 \qquad \textit{Take the square roots.}$$
$$x = \pm\sqrt{-4}$$

This means there are no *real* solutions, but if we use complex numbers, then

$$x = \pm\sqrt{-4} = \pm i\sqrt{4} = \boxed{\pm 2i}$$

Let's check the solutions:

Check: $x = +2i$:

$$2x^2 + 15 = 7$$
$$2(2i)^2 + 15 \overset{?}{=} 7$$
$$2(4i^2) + 15 \overset{?}{=} 7$$
$$8i^2 + 15 \overset{?}{=} 7$$
$$-8 + 15 \overset{\checkmark}{=} 7 \qquad \textit{Since } i^2 = -1$$

Check: $x = -2i$:

$$2x^2 + 15 = 7$$
$$2(-2i)^2 + 15 \overset{?}{=} 7$$
$$2(4i^2) + 15 \overset{?}{=} 7$$
$$8i^2 + 15 \overset{?}{=} 7$$
$$-8 + 15 \overset{\checkmark}{=} 7$$

∎

EXAMPLE 6 If $f(x) = 3x^2 - 2$, find the value of x for which $f(x) = 6$.

Solution Since $f(x) = 3x^2 - 2$, we are in effect being asked to solve $3x^2 - 2 = 6$.

$$f(x) = 6 \qquad \textit{Substitute } f(x) = 3x^2 - 2 \textit{ to get}$$
$$3x^2 - 2 = 6 \qquad \textit{Isolate } x^2 \textit{ (add +2 to both sides of the equation).}$$
$$3x^2 = 8 \qquad \textit{Divide both sides of the equation by 3.}$$
$$x^2 = \frac{8}{3} \qquad \textit{Take square roots.}$$
$$x = \pm\sqrt{\frac{8}{3}} \qquad \textit{Simplify your answers: rationalize the denominator.}$$
$$x = \frac{\pm\sqrt{8}}{\sqrt{3}} = \frac{\pm\sqrt{8}\sqrt{3}}{\sqrt{3}\sqrt{3}} = \frac{\pm\sqrt{24}}{3} \quad \frac{\pm 2\sqrt{6}}{3}$$

If you are asked to estimate $\sqrt{\dfrac{8}{3}}$ using a calculator, you do not need to simplify first.

Recall that this means the solutions are $\boxed{\dfrac{2\sqrt{6}}{3} \text{ and } \dfrac{-2\sqrt{6}}{3}}$. ∎

We can solve literal quadratic equations by the same methods.

EXAMPLE 7 Solve the following explicitly for x: $9x^2 + a = b$

Solution
$$9x^2 + a = b \qquad \textit{Isolate } x^2.$$
$$9x^2 = b - a$$
$$\frac{9x^2}{9} = \frac{b - a}{9}$$
$$x^2 = \frac{b - a}{9} \qquad \textit{Take the square roots.}$$
$$x = \pm\sqrt{\frac{b - a}{9}} \qquad \textit{Simplify.}$$
$$\boxed{x = \pm\frac{\sqrt{b - a}}{3}}$$

∎

We mentioned that the square root method is used mainly when the standard form of a quadratic equation has no first-degree term. The square root method can also be used immediately if we have the square of a binomial equal to a constant. For example, consider solving the following equation for x:

$$(x - 5)^2 = 7$$

If we tried to solve this equation by first putting it in standard form, we would square $x - 5$ to get $x^2 - 10x + 25 = 7$, which becomes

$$x^2 - 10x + 18 = 0$$

Note that $x^2 - 10x + 18$ does not factor (with integer coefficients), so we do not use the factoring method. In addition, we cannot use the square root method on the equation in standard form since there is a first-degree term.

We can, however, take advantage of the given form of the equation and "take square roots" as our *first* step in solving the equation.

If $(x - 5)^2 = 7$ then $x - 5$ must be either $\sqrt{7}$ or $-\sqrt{7}$.

$$(x - 5)^2 = 7 \qquad \textit{Take square roots.}$$
$$x - 5 = \pm\sqrt{7} \qquad \textit{Now isolate } x \textit{ by adding 5 to both sides of the equation.}$$
$$x = 5 \pm\sqrt{7}$$

The two solutions are $5 + \sqrt{7}$ and $5 - \sqrt{7}$.

EXAMPLE 8

Solve for x if $(x - 3)^2 = 4$.

Solution

$$(x - 3)^2 = 4 \qquad \textit{Take square roots.}$$
$$(x - 3) = \pm\sqrt{4}$$
$$x - 3 = \pm2 \qquad \textit{Then add 3 to both sides of the equation.}$$
$$x = \pm2 + 3$$

Then,

$$x = 2 + 3 = 5 \quad \text{or} \quad x = -2 + 3 = 1$$

Hence, $\boxed{x = 5 \quad \text{or} \quad x = 1}$. ∎

The Pythagorean Theorem

A *right triangle* is a triangle with a right (90°) angle. The sides forming the right angle in a right triangle are called the *legs* of the right triangle. The side opposite the right angle is called the *hypotenuse* (see Figure 8.8).

Figure 8.8
Right triangle

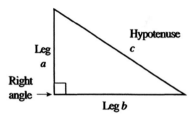

The Pythagorean Theorem	Given a right triangle with legs of length a and b and hypotenuse c, we have the following relationship: $$a^2 + b^2 = c^2$$

In other words, the sum of the squares of the legs of a right triangle is equal to the square of the hypotenuse. This is called the **Pythagorean theorem.** The converse is also true; that is, if the sum of the squares of two sides of a triangle is equal to the square of the third side, then the triangle is a right triangle.

EXAMPLE 9

Given a right triangle with one leg equal to 9 in. and the hypotenuse equal to 15 in., find the other leg.

Solution

Let $a = 9$ in. and $c = 15$ in. (the hypotenuse) and use the Pythagorean theorem to find the other leg (see Figure 8.9).

$$a^2 + b^2 = c^2$$
$$9^2 + b^2 = 15^2$$
$$81 + b^2 = 225$$
$$b^2 = 144$$
$$b = \pm\sqrt{144} = \pm12 \qquad \textit{Eliminate the negative answer.}$$

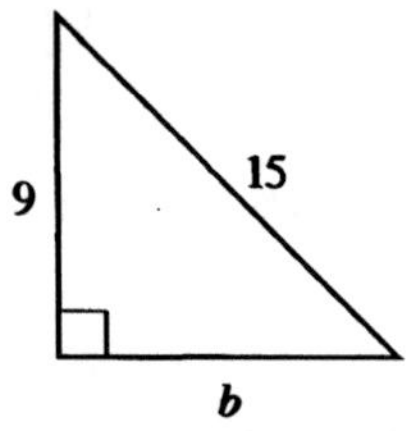

Figure 8.9
Diagram for Example 9

Thus, the other leg is $\boxed{12 \text{ in}}$. ∎

EXAMPLE 10

Find the side of a square with diagonal 10 in.

Solution

We draw a diagram and label the diagonal as shown in Figure 8.10.

Figure 8.10
Diagram for Example 10

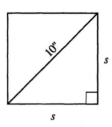

A square has all right angles and so its diagonal will cut the square into two right triangles. Since a square has equal sides, the legs of the right triangles will be equal. The hypotenuse is 10 in. since the hypotenuse of the right triangle is the diagonal of the square.

Using the Pythagorean theorem with each leg equal to s and hypotenuse equal to 10 in., we have

$$s^2 + s^2 = 10^2$$
$$2s^2 = 100$$
$$s^2 = \frac{100}{2} = 50$$
$$s = \pm\sqrt{50} = \pm5\sqrt{2}$$

The length of the sides of the square is $\boxed{5\sqrt{2} \text{ in.} \approx 7.07 \text{ in.}}$ ■

EXERCISES 8.2

In Exercises 1–58, solve the equation using the factoring or square root method where appropriate.

1. $(x + 2)(x - 3) = 0$

2. $(a - 5)(a + 7) = 0$

3. $x^2 = 25$

4. $a^2 = 81$

5. $x(x - 4) = 0$

6. $y(y + 3) = 0$

7. $12 = x(x - 4)$

8. $15 = y(y + 2)$

9. $5y(y - 7) = 0$

10. $3x(x + 2) = 0$

11. $x^2 - 16 = 0$

12. $a^2 - 225 = 0$

13. $0 = 9c^2 - 16$

14. $0 = 25x^2 - 4$

15. $8a^2 - 18 = 0$

16. $2x^2 = 32$

17. $0 = x^2 - x - 6$

18. $0 = a^2 + 2a - 8$

19. $2y^2 - 3y + 1 = 0$

20. $5a^2 - 14a - 3 = 0$

21. If $f(x) = 4x^2 - 24$, solve the equation $f(x) = 0$.

22. If $g(x) = 5x^2$, solve the equation $g(x) = 65$.

23. If $g(x) = 7x^2$, find the value(s) of x for which $g(x) = 19$.

24. If $f(x) = 6x^2 - 25$, find the value(s) of x for which $f(x) = 0$.

25. $10 = x^2 - 3x$

26. $1 - 2x = 3x^2$

27. $6a^2 + 3a - 1 = 4a$

28. $9a^2 + 4 = 12a^2$

29. $3y^2 - 5y + 8 = 9y^2 - 10y + 2$

30. $5y^2 + 15y + 4 = 2y + 10$

31. $0 = 3x^2 + 5$

32. $0 = 2x^2 + 7$

33. $(2s - 3)(3s + 1) = 7$

34. $x(x - 2) = -1$

35. $(x + 2)^2 = 25$

36. $(y - 15)^2 = 36$

37. $(x - 2)(3x - 1) = (2x - 3)(x + 1)$

38. $(x + 5)(2x - 3) = (x - 1)(3x + 1)$

39. $(x + 3)^2 = x(x + 5)$

40. $(2x + 1)^2 = 4x(x - 3)$

41. $x^2 + 3 = 1$

42. $x^2 - 7 = -12$

43. $8 = (x - 8)^2$

44. $12 = (x + 12)^2$

45. $(y - 5)^2 = -16$

46. $(y + 3)^2 = -4$

47. $\dfrac{2}{x - 1} + x = 4$

48. $\dfrac{6}{x - 3} + x = 8$

49. $2a - 5 = \dfrac{3(a + 2)}{a + 4}$

50. $3a - 4 = \dfrac{a + 2}{a}$

51. $\dfrac{x}{x + 2} - \dfrac{3}{x} = \dfrac{x + 1}{x}$

52. $\dfrac{x}{x - 1} + \dfrac{4}{x} = \dfrac{x + 2}{x}$

53. $\dfrac{1}{x} + x = 2$

54. $2x - \dfrac{5}{x} = 9$

55. $\dfrac{3}{x - 2} + \dfrac{7}{x + 2} = \dfrac{x + 1}{x - 2}$

56. $\dfrac{3}{a + 4} + \dfrac{2}{a - 2} = \dfrac{4a + 5}{a + 4}$

57. $\dfrac{2}{x - 1} + \dfrac{3x}{x + 2} = \dfrac{2(5x + 9)}{x^2 + x - 2}$

58. $\dfrac{3}{y - 1} + \dfrac{2}{y + 1} = \dfrac{2y + 3}{3(y - 1)}$

In Exercises 59–68, solve explicitly for the given variable using the factoring or square root method.

59. $8a^2 + 3b = 5b$ for a

60. $5r^2 - 8a = 2a - 3r^2$ for r

61. $5x^2 + 7y^2 = 9$ for y

62. $14a^2 + 3b^2 = c$ for b

63. $V = \dfrac{2}{3}\pi r^2$ for $r > 0$

64. $K = \dfrac{2gm}{s^2}$ for $s > 0$

65. $a^2 - 4b^2 = 0$ for a

66. $x^2 - 9y^2 = 0$ for x

67. $x^2 - xy - 6y^2 = 0$ for x

68. $a^2 + 3ab - 10b^2 = 0$ for a

Solve each of the following problems algebraically.

69. Five less than the square of a positive number is 1 more than 5 times the number. Find the number.

70. Seven more than the square of a positive number is 1 less than 6 times the number. Find the number(s).

71. The sum of the squares of two positive numbers is 68. If one of the numbers is 8, find the other number.

72. The sum of the squares of two negative numbers is 30. If one of the numbers is -5, find the other number.

73. Find the numbers such that the square of the sum of the number and 6 is 169.

74. Find the numbers such that the square of the sum of the number and 3 is 100.

75. The sum of a number and its reciprocal is $\frac{13}{6}$. Find the number(s).

76. The sum of a number and twice its reciprocal is 3. Find the number(s).

77. The profit in dollars (P) made on a concert is related to the price in dollars (d) of a ticket in the following way:

$$P(d) = 10,000(-d^2 + 12d - 35)$$

   (a) How much profit is made by selling tickets for $5?

   (b) What must the price of a ticket be to make a profit of $10,000?

78. The daily cost in dollars (C) of producing items in a factory is related to the number of items (x) produced in the following way:

$$C(x) = -\frac{x^2}{10} + 100x - 24,000$$

   (a) How much does it cost to produce 450 items?

   (b) How many items must be produced so that the daily cost is $1,000?

79. A man jumps off a diving board into a pool. The equation

$$h(t) = -16t^2 + 40$$

gives the height h (in feet) the man is above the pool t seconds after he jumps.

   (a) How high above the pool is the diver after the first second?

   (b) How long does it take for him to hit the water?

   (c) How high is the diving board? [*Hint:* Let $t = 0$.]

80. Alex throws a ball straight up into the air. The equation

$$h(t) = -16t^2 + 80t + 44$$

gives the height h (in feet) the ball is above the ground t seconds after he throws it.

   (a) How high is the ball at $t = 2$ seconds?

   (b) How long does it take for the ball to hit the ground?

81. Find the dimensions of a rectangle whose area is 80 sq ft and whose length is 2 feet more than its width.

82. Find the dimensions of a rectangle whose area is 108 sq ft and whose length is 3 feet more than its width.

83. Find the dimensions of a square with area 60 sq in.

84. Find the dimensions of a square with area 75 sq in.

85. The product of two numbers is 120. What are the numbers if one number is 2 less than the other?

86. The sum of two numbers is 20. Find the numbers if their product is 96.

87. The product of two numbers is 85. What are the numbers if one number is 2 more than 3 times the other?

88. The sum of two numbers is 25. Find the numbers if their product is 144.

89. In a right triangle, a leg is 4″ and the hypotenuse is 7″. Find the length of the other leg.

90. A leg of a right triangle is 7″ and the hypotenuse is 15″. Find the length of the other leg.

91. Find the lengths of the sides of the right triangle shown in the accompanying figure.

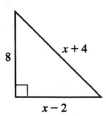

92. The lengths of the sides of the right triangle are shown in the figure below. Find x.

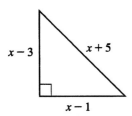

93. Find the length of the diagonals of a 7″ by 12″ rectangle.

94. Find the length of the diagonals of a 4″ by 5″ rectangle.

95. Harold leans a 30′ ladder against a building. If the base of the ladder is 8′ from the building, how high up the building does the ladder reach? (See the accompanying figure.)

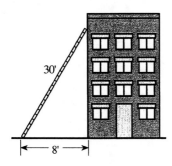

96. Harold leans a 30′ ladder against a building. If the base of the ladder is 4′ from the building, how high up the building does the ladder reach?

97. Find the area of a square if its diagonal is 8″.

98. Find the area of a square if its diagonal is 9″.

99. Find the area of a rectangle with diagonal 12″ and width 5″.

100. Find the area of a rectangle with diagonal 15″ and width 3″.

101. Find the value(s) of n so that the line passing through the points $(1, n)$ and $(3, n^2)$ is parallel to the line passing through the points $(-6, 0)$ and $(-5, 6)$.

102. Find the value(s) of a so that the line passing through the points $(-1, a)$ and $(2, a^2)$ is perpendicular to the line passing through the points $(0, 2)$ and $(2, 1)$.

103. A rectangular picture has a 1-inch (uniform-width) frame as its border. If the length of the picture is twice its width and the total area of the picture and frame is 60 sq in., find the dimensions of the picture.

104. A 7″ by 10″ rectangular picture has a frame of uniform width. If the area of the frame is 60 sq in., how wide is the frame?

105. A boat travels upstream for 20 km against a current of 5 kph, then it travels downstream for 10 km with the same current. If the 30-km trip took $1\frac{1}{3}$ hours, how fast was the boat traveling in still water?

106. An airplane heads into the wind to get to its destination 200 miles away and returns traveling with the wind to its starting point. If the wind currents were at a constant 20 mph and the total round trip took $2\frac{1}{4}$ hours, find the speed of the airplane.

QUESTIONS FOR THOUGHT

107. On what property of real numbers is the factoring method based?

108. Discuss what is *wrong* (and why) with the solutions to the following equations:

(a) *Problem:* Solve $(x - 3)(x - 4) = 7$.

Solution: $x - 3 = 7$ or $x - 4 = 7$
$x = 10$ or $x = 11$

(b) *Problem:* Solve $3x(x - 2) = 0$.

Solution: $x = 3$, $x = 0$, or $x = 2$

(c) *Problem:* Solve $(x - 4) + (x + 3) = 0$.

Solution: $x = 4$ or $x = -3$

109. Discuss the differences between the solutions of
$$x^2 = 36 \quad \text{and} \quad x = \sqrt{36}$$

110. Solve each of the following by the factoring method *and* the square root method.

(a) $x^2 = 9$ (b) $9x^2 - 16 = 0$

(c) $7x^2 - 5 = 3x^2 + 4$

111. Look at the solution of the following problem. See whether you can justify each step.

Problem: $x^2 + 4x - 7 = 0$

Solution: 1. $x^2 + 4x - 7 = 0$

2. $x^2 + 4x = 7$

3. $x^2 + 4x + 4 = 7 + 4$

4. $x^2 + 4x + 4 = 11$

5. $(x + 2)^2 = 11$

6. $x + 2 = \pm\sqrt{11}$

7. $x = -2 \pm \sqrt{11}$

112. Check that $2 + \sqrt{3}$ is a solution to the equation $x^2 - 4x + 1 = 0$ by substituting $2 + \sqrt{3}$ for x in the equation. Check to see whether $2 - \sqrt{3}$ is also a solution of the same equation.

8.3 Solving Quadratic Equations: Completing the Square

Thus far we have discussed the factoring and square root methods for solving quadratic equations algebraically. However, those methods cannot be applied to an equation such as $x^2 + 3x - 5 = 0$ because the expression $x^2 + 3x - 5$ is not factorable using integer coefficients and is not in the form appropriate to the square root method (there *is* a first-degree term).

Our interest in this section is to find a method for solving quadratic equations that can be applied to all cases.

If we can take any equation and put it in the form $(x + p)^2 = d$, where p and d are constants, then all that remains is to apply the square root method—that is, take square roots, solve for x, and simplify the answer. But can all quadratic equations be put in the form $(x + p)^2 = d$, where p and d are constants?

To answer this, we first examine the squares of binomials of the form $(x + p)$, where p is a constant. When the squares are multiplied out, we call them **perfect squares.**

First we will square binomials of the form $x + p$ and look at the relationship between the x coefficient and the numerical term. Observe the following:

	Coefficient of the x term	The numerical term
$(x - 3)^2 = x^2 - 6x + 9$	-6	$+9$
$(x + 5)^2 = x^2 + 10x + 25$	$+10$	$+25$
$(x + 4)^2 = x^2 + 8x + 16$	$+8$	$+16$

Let's examine what happens when we square $(x + p)$:

Square of second term in the binomial

$$(x + p)^2 = x^2 + 2px + p^2$$

— *Twice the product of the terms in the binomial*

Square of first term in the binomial

Given that p is a constant and x is a variable, the middle (first-degree) term *coefficient* will be $2p$, and the numerical term will be p^2. What is the relationship between the middle-term coefficient, $2p$, and the numerical term, p^2?

If you take half of $2p$ and square it, you will get p^2:

$$\left[\frac{1}{2}(2p)\right]^2 = \left(\frac{2p}{2}\right)^2 = p^2$$

The square of half of $2p$ is p^2

Thus, if you square the binomial $(x + p)$, *the square of one-half the middle-term coefficient will yield the numerical term.*

We now return to our examples:

$$(x - 3)^2 = x^2 - 6x + 9 \qquad\qquad (x + 5)^2 = x^2 + 10x + 25$$

1. Take half of -6 to get -3.

2. Square -3 to get the numerical term, $+9$.

1. Take half of 10 to get 5.

2. Square 5 to get the numerical term, 25.

Now we will demonstrate how we can take any second-degree equation and put it in the form $(x + p)^2 = d$, where p and d are constants. Suppose we have an equation such as

$$x^2 + 6x - 8 = 0$$

To make it clearer how to make the left side into a perfect square, we first add 8 to both sides of the equation:

$$x^2 + 6x - 8 = 0 \qquad \textit{Add 8 to both sides of the equation.}$$
$$x^2 + 6x = 8$$

Now what is missing to make the left side a perfect square? Take half the middle-term coefficient, 6, and square it:

$$\left[\frac{1}{2}(6)\right]^2 = (3)^2 = 9$$

Thus, 9 must be added to make the left side a perfect square. But since we are dealing with equations, we must add 9 to *both sides* of the equation:

$$x^2 + 6x + 9 = 8 + 9$$
$$x^2 + 6x + 9 = 17 \qquad \textit{Write the left side as a perfect square}$$
$$(x + 3)^2 = 17 \qquad \textit{in factored form.}$$

The only difference between the equation $x^2 + 6x = 8$ and the perfect square version $x^2 + 6x + 9 = 17$ is that 9 was added to both sides. Why 9? To make the left side a perfect square so that it could be written in factored form. This process of adding a number to make a perfect square is called ***completing the square.***

Now we can solve this equation by the square root method, as demonstrated in Section 8.2.

$$(x + 3)^2 = 17 \qquad \textit{Take square roots.}$$
$$x + 3 = \pm\sqrt{17} \qquad \textit{Then isolate x by adding -3 to both sides of the}$$
$$\qquad\qquad\qquad \textit{equation.}$$
$$x = -3 \pm\sqrt{17}$$

Similarly, *any* quadratic equation can be put in the form $(x + p)^2 = d$, where p and d are constants.

EXAMPLE 1 Solve the following by completing the square: $x^2 + 8x - 4 = 0$

Solution

1. Add $+4$ to both sides of the equation. $\qquad x^2 + 8x = 4$

2. Take one-half the middle-term coefficient and square it: $[\frac{1}{2}(8)]^2 = 4^2 = 16$.

3. Add result of step 2 to both sides of the equation. $\qquad x^2 + 8x\ \boxed{+ 16} = 4\ \boxed{+ 16}$

$$x^2 + 8x + 16 = 20$$

4. Factor the left side as a perfect square. $\qquad (x + 4)^2 = 20$

5. Take square roots. $\qquad x + 4 = \pm\sqrt{20}$

6. Isolate x by adding -4 to both sides of the equation. $\qquad x = -4 \pm \sqrt{20}$

7. Simplify the radical. $\qquad x = -4 \pm 2\sqrt{5}$

The solutions are $\boxed{-4 + 2\sqrt{5} \text{ and } -4 - 2\sqrt{5}}$. ∎

EXAMPLE 2 Solve $2x^2 - 6x + 5 = 0$ by completing the square.

Solution Keep in mind that the number we add to a quadratic expression to make it a perfect square is found by exploiting the relationship between coefficients in $x^2 + 2px + p^2$, when x^2 has a coefficient of 1. However, in this example, the coefficient of x^2 is not 1. Thus, the relationship between the x-term coefficient and the numerical coefficient (being the square of half the x-term coefficient) does not apply yet. We must first divide both sides of the equation by 2, so that the leading (highest-degree) term has a coefficient of 1.

1. Divide both sides of the equation by the leading-term coefficient, 2.

$$\frac{2x^2}{2} - \frac{6x}{2} + \frac{5}{2} = \frac{0}{2}$$

$$x^2 - 3x + \frac{5}{2} = 0$$

2. Add $-\frac{5}{2}$ to both sides of equation.

$$x^2 - 3x = -\frac{5}{2}$$

3. Take half the middle-term coefficient, square it, and add the result to both sides of the equation.

$$\left[\frac{1}{2}(-3)\right]^2 = \left(\frac{-3}{2}\right)^2 = \frac{9}{4} \qquad x^2 - 3x + \frac{9}{4} = -\frac{5}{2} + \frac{9}{4}$$

4. Factor the left side as a perfect square and simplify the right side.

$$\left(x - \frac{3}{2}\right)^2 = -\frac{10}{4} + \frac{9}{4} = -\frac{1}{4}$$

5. Take square roots.

$$x - \frac{3}{2} = \pm\sqrt{-\frac{1}{4}}$$

This equation has *no real solutions,* but if we use complex numbers,

6. Isolate x by adding $\frac{3}{2}$ to both sides.

$$x = \frac{3}{2} \pm \sqrt{-\frac{1}{4}}$$

7. Simplify.

$$\boxed{x = \frac{3}{2} \pm \frac{i}{2}}$$ ∎

In general, we solve quadratic equations by completing the square as indicated in the following example:

Solve: $3x^2 - 5 = -12x$

1. Simplify to standard quadratic form.

$$3x^2 + 12x - 5 = 0$$

2. Divide both sides of the equation by the leading coefficient (if not 1).

$$\frac{3x^2}{3} + \frac{12x}{3} - \frac{5}{3} = \frac{0}{3}$$

$$x^2 + 4x - \frac{5}{3} = 0$$

3. Put the numerical term on the other side of the equation by adding its opposite to both sides of the equation.

$$x^2 + 4x = \frac{5}{3}$$

4. Take half the middle-term coefficient, square it, and add this result to both sides of the equation.

$$\left[\frac{1}{2}(4)\right]^2 = 2^2 = 4 \qquad x^2 + 4x + 4 = \frac{5}{3} + 4$$

Add 4 to both sides of the equation.

5. Factor the left side as a perfect square and simplify the right side.

$$(x + 2)^2 = \frac{5}{3} + \frac{12}{3} = \frac{17}{3}$$

6. Take square roots.

$$x + 2 = \pm\sqrt{\frac{17}{3}}$$

7. Isolate x.

$$x = -2 \pm \sqrt{\frac{17}{3}}$$

8. Express your answer in simplest radical form.

$$x = -2 \pm \frac{\sqrt{17}}{\sqrt{3}} \quad \textit{Rationalize the denominator.}$$

$$= -2 \pm \frac{\sqrt{17}\sqrt{3}}{\sqrt{3}\sqrt{3}} = \boxed{-2 \pm \frac{\sqrt{51}}{3}}$$

or $\boxed{\dfrac{-6 \pm \sqrt{51}}{3}}$

 EXERCISES 8.3

Solve the following by completing the square only.

1. $x^2 - 6x - 1 = 0$

2. $s^2 - 2s - 15 = 0$

3. $0 = c^2 - 2c - 5$

4. $0 = a^2 - 2a - 4$

5. $y^2 + 5y - 2 = 0$

6. $x^2 + 3x - 2 = 0$

7. $2x^2 + 3x - 1 = x^2 - 2$

8. $y^2 - 3y - 2 = 2y - 3$

9. $(a - 2)(a + 1) = 2$

10. $(2b + 3)(b - 4) = 3b$

11. $10 = 5a^2 + 10a + 20$

12. $y + 1 = (y + 2)(y + 3)$

13. $3x^2 + 3x = x^2 - 5x + 4$

14. $3x^2 - 7x - 4 = 2x^2 - 3x + 1$

15. $(a - 2)(a + 1) = 6$

16. $(c - 3)(2c + 1) = c(c - 1)$

17. $2x - 7 = x^2 - 3x + 4$

18. $2t - 4 = t^2 - 3$

19. $5x^2 + 10x - 14 = 20$

20. $2a^2 - 4a - 14 = 0$

21. $2t^2 + 3t - 4 = 2t - 1$

22. $3s^2 + 12s + 4 = 0$

23. $(2x + 5)(x - 3) = (x + 4)(x - 1)$

24. $(3x - 2)(x - 1) = (2x - 1)(x - 4)$

25. $\dfrac{2x}{2x - 3} = \dfrac{3x - 1}{x + 1}$

26. $\dfrac{x + 1}{2x + 3} = \dfrac{3x + 2}{x + 2}$

27. $a^2 - a + 1 = 0$

28. $a^2 + a + 1 = 0$

29. $0 = 2y^2 + 2y + 5$

30. $0 = 2y^2 + 2y - 5$

31. $5n^2 - 3n = 2n^2 - 6$

32. $(3n - 1)(n - 2) = n + 8$

33. $(3t + 5)(t + 1) = (t + 4)(t + 2)$

34. $(2z - 1)(z + 3) = (3z - 2)(2z + 1)$

35. $\dfrac{3}{x + 2} - \dfrac{2}{x - 1} = 5$

36. $\dfrac{2y + 1}{y + 1} - \dfrac{2}{y + 4} = 7$

 QUESTIONS FOR THOUGHT

37. Verbally state the relationship between the middle-term coefficient and the numerical term of a perfect square.

38. Solve the equation $3x^2 + 11x = 4$ by completing the square. What does the fact that the answers are rational tell you? Solve the same equation by factoring. Which method was easier?

39. Solve for x in the equation $x^2 + rx + q = 0$ by completing the square; that is, solve for x in terms of r and q.

40. Solve for x in the equation $Ax^2 + Bx + C = 0$ (where $A > 0$) by completing the square.

 MINI-REVIEW

41. *Solve for x and y.* $\begin{cases} 0.3x + 0.4y = 15 \\ 0.5x + 0.6y = 24 \end{cases}$

42. *Simplify.* $(3x^2)^3(x^{-1}y)^4$

43. Evaluate $5n^0 + n^{-1} + 6n^{-2}$ for $n = 3$.

44. Write an equation of the line that crosses the x-axis at 4 and is parallel to the line whose equation is $7x - 2y = 12$.

8.4 Solving Quadratic Equations: The Quadratic Formula

Completing the square is a useful algebraic technique that will be needed elsewhere in intermediate algebra, as well as in precalculus and calculus. It is the most powerful of the methods for solving quadratic equations covered so far because, unlike the previous methods, completing the square works for *all* quadratic equations. It can be, however, a tedious method.

What we would like is a method that works for all quadratic equations without the effort required in completing the square. Algebraically, we can derive a formula that will allow us to produce the solutions to the "general" quadratic equation.

To derive the formula, we start with the general equation $Ax^2 + Bx + C = 0$ and solve it for x by the method of completing the square. (We start by assuming $A > 0$.)

Start with the equation $Ax^2 + Bx + C = 0$.

1. Divide both sides of the equation by A.

$$\frac{Ax^2}{A} + \frac{Bx}{A} + \frac{C}{A} = \frac{0}{A}$$

$$x^2 + \frac{Bx}{A} + \frac{C}{A} = 0$$

2. Subtract $\frac{C}{A}$ from both sides of the equation.

$$x^2 + \frac{B}{A}x = -\frac{C}{A}$$

3. Take half the middle-term coefficient, square it,

$$\left[\frac{1}{2} \cdot \frac{B}{A}\right]^2 = \left(\frac{B}{2A}\right)^2 = \frac{B^2}{4A^2}$$

and add the result to both sides of the equation.

$$x^2 + \frac{B}{A}x + \frac{B^2}{4A^2} = \frac{B^2}{4A^2} - \frac{C}{A}$$

4. Factor the left side as a perfect square and simplify the right side.

$$\left(x + \frac{B}{2A}\right)^2 = \frac{B^2}{4A^2} - \frac{4AC}{4A^2}$$

$$\left(x + \frac{B}{2A}\right)^2 = \frac{B^2 - 4AC}{4A^2}$$

5. Take square roots.

$$x + \frac{B}{2A} = \pm\sqrt{\frac{B^2 - 4AC}{4A^2}}$$

6. Isolate x.

$$x = -\frac{B}{2A} \pm \sqrt{\frac{B^2 - 4AC}{4A^2}}$$

7. Simplify the solution.

$$x = \frac{-B}{2A} \pm \frac{\sqrt{B^2 - 4AC}}{\sqrt{4A^2}}$$

Note: Since $A > 0$, $\sqrt{4A^2} = 2A$.

$$x = \frac{-B}{2A} \pm \frac{\sqrt{B^2 - 4AC}}{2A}$$

$$x = \frac{-B \pm \sqrt{B^2 - 4AC}}{2A}$$

This solution is known as the **quadratic formula.** A similar proof applies where $A < 0$.

The Quadratic Formula	The solutions to the equation $Ax^2 + Bx + C = 0$, $A \neq 0$, are given by $$x = \frac{-B \pm \sqrt{B^2 - 4AC}}{2A}$$

As long as we can put an expression in standard quadratic form, we can identify A (the coefficient of x^2), B (the coefficient of x), and C (the constant). Once we have identified A, B, and C, we substitute the numbers into the quadratic formula and find the solutions to the equation.

EXAMPLE 1

Solve each of the following equations by using the quadratic formula.

(a) $y^2 - 4y - 3 = 0$ (b) $\dfrac{2}{z + 2} + \dfrac{1}{z} = 1$ (c) $(x + 4)(x - 1) = -8$

Solution

(a) The equation $y^2 - 4y - 3 = 0$ is already in standard form, so we can identify A, B, and C:

$$A = 1 \quad \text{(the coefficient of } y^2)$$
$$B = -4 \quad \text{(the coefficient of } y)$$
$$C = -3 \quad \text{(the constant)}$$

We now find y using the quadratic formula:

$$y = \frac{-B \pm \sqrt{B^2 - 4AC}}{2A} = \frac{-(-4) \pm \sqrt{(-4)^2 - 4(1)(-3)}}{2(1)}$$

$$= \frac{4 \pm \sqrt{16 + 12}}{2}$$

$$= \frac{4 \pm \sqrt{28}}{2} = \frac{4 \pm 2\sqrt{7}}{2} = \frac{2(2 \pm \sqrt{7})}{2}$$

$$= \frac{\cancel{2}(2 \pm \sqrt{7})}{\cancel{2}} = \boxed{2 \pm \sqrt{7}}$$

Notice that we must factor the numerator first before reducing.

We will check these solutions:

Check: $y = 2 + \sqrt{7}$:

$$y^2 - 4y - 3 = 0$$
$$(2 + \sqrt{7})^2 - 4(2 + \sqrt{7}) - 3 \stackrel{?}{=} 0$$
$$4 + 4\sqrt{7} + 7 - 4(2 + \sqrt{7}) - 3 \stackrel{?}{=} 0$$
$$4 + 4\sqrt{7} + 7 - 8 - 4\sqrt{7} - 3 \stackrel{\checkmark}{=} 0$$

Check: $y = 2 - \sqrt{7}$:

$$y^2 - 4y - 3 = 0$$
$$(2 - \sqrt{7})^2 - 4(2 - \sqrt{7}) - 3 \stackrel{?}{=} 0$$
$$4 - 4\sqrt{7} + 7 - 4(2 - \sqrt{7}) - 3 \stackrel{?}{=} 0$$
$$4 - 4\sqrt{7} + 7 - 8 + 4\sqrt{7} - 3 \stackrel{\checkmark}{=} 0$$

(b)
$$\frac{2}{z + 2} + \frac{1}{z} = 1$$

First put the equation in standard form. Multiply both sides by $z(z + 2)$.

$$z(z + 2)\left(\frac{2}{z + 2} + \frac{1}{z}\right) = 1 \cdot z(z + 2)$$
$$2z + (z + 2) = z(z + 2)$$
$$3z + 2 = z^2 + 2z$$
$$0 = z^2 - z - 2$$

Now identify A, B, and C:

$$A = 1, \quad B = -1, \quad C = -2$$

Solve for z using the quadratic formula:

$$z = \frac{-B \pm \sqrt{B^2 - 4AC}}{2A} = \frac{-(-1) \pm \sqrt{(-1)^2 - 4(1)(-2)}}{2(1)}$$
$$= \frac{1 \pm \sqrt{1 + 8}}{2}$$
$$= \frac{1 \pm \sqrt{9}}{2} = \frac{1 \pm 3}{2}$$

Thus,

$$z = \frac{1 + 3}{2} = \frac{4}{2} = 2 \quad \text{or} \quad z = \frac{1 - 3}{2} = \frac{-2}{2} = -1$$

The solutions are $\boxed{2 \text{ and } -1}$. *Since the solutions are rational, we could have solved the equation by the factoring method. Try it for yourself.*

You should check these solutions to see that both are valid.

(c) $(x + 4)(x - 1) = -8$ *We put the equation in standard form.*
$$x^2 + 3x - 4 = -8$$
$$x^2 + 3x + 4 = 0 \qquad \textit{Now we identify } A, B, \textit{ and } C.$$
$$A = 1, \quad B = 3, \quad C = 4$$

Solve for x by the quadratic formula:

$$x = \frac{-B \pm \sqrt{B^2 - 4AC}}{2A} = \frac{-3 \pm \sqrt{(3)^2 - 4(1)(4)}}{2(1)}$$

$$= \frac{-3 \pm \sqrt{9 - 16}}{2}$$

$$= \frac{-3 \pm \sqrt{-7}}{2}$$

Hence, there are *no real solutions*. The complex number solutions are

$$\boxed{\frac{-3 + i\sqrt{7}}{2} \quad \text{and} \quad \frac{-3 - i\sqrt{7}}{2}}$$

Here are a few things to be careful about when you use the quadratic formula:

1. If B is a negative number, remember that $-B$ will be positive [see parts **(a)** and **(b)** of Example 1].

2. If C is negative (and A is positive), then you will end up *adding* the expressions under the radical [see parts **(a)** and **(b)** of Example 1].

3. Do not forget that $2A$ is in the denominator of the *entire expression:*

$$\frac{-B \pm \sqrt{B^2 - 4AC}}{2A}$$

The Discriminant

Let us further examine the quadratic formula; in particular, let's look at the radical portion of the quadratic formula: $\sqrt{B^2 - 4AC}$. Note that if we solve a quadratic equation and the quantity $B^2 - 4AC$ is negative [that is, if $B^2 - 4AC < 0$, as in part **(c)** of Example 1], then we have the square root of a negative number. As we discussed in Chapter 7, the square root of a negative number is not a real number. Thus, if $B^2 - 4AC < 0$, then the two solutions or roots

$$x = \frac{-B + \sqrt{B^2 - 4AC}}{2A} \quad \text{and} \quad x = \frac{-B - \sqrt{B^2 - 4AC}}{2A}$$

are not real.

On the other hand, if $B^2 - 4AC = 0$, then $\sqrt{B^2 - 4AC} = \sqrt{0} = 0$. Thus, the two roots

$$x = \frac{-B + \sqrt{0}}{2A} = \frac{-B}{2A} \quad \text{and} \quad x = \frac{-B - \sqrt{0}}{2A} = \frac{-B}{2A}$$

are equal. They are also real, since the quotient of two real numbers yields a real number.

Finally, if $B^2 - 4AC$ is positive (that is, $B^2 - 4AC > 0$), then the two roots are real and distinct (unequal):

$$x = \frac{-B + \sqrt{B^2 - 4AC}}{2A} \quad \text{and} \quad x = \frac{-B - \sqrt{B^2 - 4AC}}{2A}$$

We call $B^2 - 4AC$ the **discriminant** of the equation $Ax^2 + Bx + C = 0$. The above discussion is summarized in the box.

In Section 8.6 we will see how the discriminant relates to the graph of a quadratic function.

For the equation $Ax^2 + Bx + C = 0$ $(A \neq 0)$:

If $B^2 - 4AC < 0$, the roots are not real.

If $B^2 - 4AC = 0$, the roots are real and equal.

If $B^2 - 4AC > 0$, the roots are real and distinct.

EXAMPLE 2 | Without solving the given equation, determine the nature of the roots of

$$3x^2 - 2x + 5 = 0$$

Solution | Identify A, B, and C:

$$A = 3, \quad B = -2, \quad C = 5$$

The discriminant is $B^2 - 4AC = (-2)^2 - 4(3)(5) = 4 - 60 = -56 < 0$.

Thus, | the roots are not real | . ∎

Choosing a Method for Solving Quadratic Equations

In this chapter we have discussed a variety of methods for solving quadratic equations. The methods of completing the square and using the quadratic formula will work for all quadratic equations, but both methods can be a bit messy computationally. The factoring and square root methods are often easiest, but do not always work. In general, we recommend the following:

Unless the equation is in the form $(x + a)^2 = b$ or $(ax + b)(cx + d) = 0$, put the equation in the standard form $Ax^2 + Bx + C = 0$.

If there is no x term (that is, if $B = 0$), then use the square root method.

If there is an x term, try the factoring method.

If the quadratic expression does not factor easily, then use either the quadratic formula or completing the square.

EXERCISES 8.4

In Exercises 1–12, solve using the quadratic formula only.

1. $x^2 - 4x - 5 = 0$

2. $a^2 + 4a - 5 = 0$

3. $2a^2 - 3a - 4 = 0$

4. $5x^2 + x - 2 = 0$

5. $(3y - 1)(2y - 3) = y$

6. $(5s + 2)(s - 1) = 2s + 1$

7. $y^2 - 3y + 4 = 2y^2 + 4y - 3$

8. $2a^2 - 4a - 9 = 0$

9. $3a^2 + a + 2 = 0$

10. $2y^2 - 3y = -4$

11. $(s - 3)(s + 4) = (2s - 1)(s + 2)$

12. $\dfrac{2x}{x + 1} + \dfrac{1}{x} = 1$

In Exercises 13–20, use the discriminant to determine the nature of the roots.

13. $3a^2 - 2a + 5 = 0$

14. $(2z - 3)(z + 4) = z - 2$

15. $(3y + 5)(2y - 8) = (y - 4)(y + 1)$

16. $\dfrac{3a - 2}{2a + 1} = \dfrac{1}{a - 2}$

17. $2a^2 + 4a = 0$

18. $(5s + 3)(2s + 1) = s^2 - s - 1$

19. $(2y + 3)(y - 1) = y + 5$

20. $\dfrac{2}{2x + 1} + \dfrac{3x}{x - 2} = 4$

In Exercises 21–60, solve by any method. Answer to the nearest hundredth where necessary.

21. $a^2 - 3a - 4 = 0$

22. $x^2 - 5x + 4 = 0$

23. $8y^2 = 3$

24. $12y^2 = 5$

25. $(5x - 4)(2x - 3) = 0$

26. $(2z - 3)(3z + 1) = 0$

27. $(5x - 4) + (2x - 3) = 0$

28. $(2z - 3) + (3z + 1) = 0$

29. $(5x - 4)(2x - 3) = 17$

30. $(2z - 3)(3z + 1) = 17$

31. $(a - 1)(a + 2) = -2$

32. $(5x - 1)(x + 2) = 2x^2 - 3x + 10$

33. $2.4x^2 - 12.72x + 3.6 = 0$

34. $2.3x^2 - 13.11x + 8.05 = 0$

35. $x^2 - 3x + 5 = 0$

36. $3z^2 - 5z - 4 = -4z - 3$

37. $2s^2 - 5s - 12 = -5s$

38. $5a^2 - 2a + 4 = 8 - 2a$

39. $3x^2 - 2x + 9 = 2x^2 - 3x - 1$

40. $(3z - 2)(2z + 1) = 2z - 3$

41. $x^2 + 3x - 8 = x^2 - x + 11$

42. $t^2 - 6t + 1 = t^2 - 5t + 3$

43. $3x^2 + 2.7x = 14.58$

44. $x^2 + 1.1x - 2.1 = 3.2x + 2.8$

45. $3a^2 - 4a + 2 = 0$

46. $x^2 - 2x + 4 = 0$

47. $(x - 4)(2x + 3) = x^2 - 4$

48. $(a - 5)(a + 2) = (2a - 3)(a - 1)$

49. $(a + 1)(a - 3) = (3a + 1)(a - 2)$

50. $(2y + 3)(y + 5) = (y - 1)(y + 4)$

51. $(z + 3)(z - 1) = (z - 2)^2$

52. $(w - 3)^2 = (w + 4)(w - 2)$

53. $\dfrac{y}{y - 2} = \dfrac{y - 3}{y}$

54. $\dfrac{x - 4}{3} = \dfrac{2}{x + 5}$

55. $0.001x^2 - 2x = 0.1$

56. $0.35x - \dfrac{4}{x} = 0.8$

57. $\dfrac{3a}{a + 1} + \dfrac{2}{a - 2} = 5$

58. $\dfrac{3x}{2} + \dfrac{2}{x + 1} = 4$

59. $\dfrac{3}{a + 2} - \dfrac{5}{a - 2} = 2$

60. $\dfrac{2}{a + 4} - \dfrac{3}{a + 1} = 4$

61. The product of two numbers is 40. Find the numbers if the difference between the two numbers is 3.

62. The product of two numbers is 72. Find the numbers if the difference between the two numbers is 1.

63. In a right triangle, the legs are 3″ and 8″. Find the hypotenuse.

64. In a right triangle, the legs are 5″ and 7″. Find the hypotenuse.

65. Find the length of the diagonals of a square with a side equal to 5″.

66. Find the length of the diagonals of a square with a side equal to 12″.

67. Find the length of the side of a square with the diagonal equal to 8″.

68. Find the length of a rectangle if the width is 3″ and the diagonal is 18″.

69. Find the value(s) of c so that the line passing through the points $(0, 1)$ and (c, c) is perpendicular to the line passing through the points $(0, 2)$ and (c, c).

70. Find the value(s) of t so that the line passing through the points $(-2, t)$ and $(-t, 1)$ is parallel to the line passing through the points $(-4, t)$ and $(-t, 3)$.

71. A company determines that the profit, P, earned on the sale of w items is given by the formula

$$P(w) = 20w - w^2$$

Determine the number of items sold if the company loses $2,400.

72. If a line segment (called an *edge*) is drawn from each vertex of a polygon of n sides to every other vertex of the polygon, we obtain a *complete graph* on n vertices. A complete graph on 5 vertices is illustrated in the accompanying figure. The number, E, of edges in a complete graph of n vertices is given by the formula $E = \dfrac{n(n-1)}{2}$.

A complete graph on 5 vertices

   (a) How many edges are there in a complete graph on 8 vertices?

   (b) If a complete graph on a polygon has 15 edges, how many vertices are there?

73. A circular garden is surrounded by a path of uniform width. If the path has area 44π sq ft and the radius of the garden is 10 ft, find the width of the path. [*Hint:* See Section 5.2, Example 6.]

74. A circular garden is surrounded by a path of uniform width. If the path has area 57π sq ft and the radius of the garden is 8 ft, find the width of the path.

75. A discount wallpaper store has a policy of setting a fixed price on all rolls of wallpaper in the store. During a certain week $10,000 worth of wallpaper was sold. The next week the price was reduced by $2 per roll and another $10,000 dollars worth of wallpaper was sold. If a total of 2,250 rolls were sold during the two weeks, what was the price per roll during each week?

76. The Books-R-Us discount bookstore charges the same price for all the books in the store. During a certain week $1,000 worth of books were sold. The next week the price was reduced by $2 per book and another $1,000 worth of books were sold. If a total of 1,500 books were sold during the two weeks, what was the price per book during each week?

? QUESTIONS FOR THOUGHT

77. Compare and contrast the various methods for solving quadratic equations.

78. Discuss what is **wrong** (if anything) with the solutions to the following problems:

   (a) *Solve* $x^2 - 3x + 1 = 0$.

   Solution: $x \stackrel{?}{=} \dfrac{-3 \pm \sqrt{9 - 4(1)}}{2} \stackrel{?}{=} \dfrac{-3 \pm \sqrt{5}}{2}$

   (b) *Solve* $x^2 - 5x - 3 = 0$.

   Solution: $x \stackrel{?}{=} \dfrac{5 \pm \sqrt{25 - 12}}{2} \stackrel{?}{=} \dfrac{5 \pm \sqrt{13}}{2}$

   (c) *Solve* $x^2 - 3x + 2 = 0$.

   Solution: $x \stackrel{?}{=} -3 \pm \dfrac{\sqrt{9 - 8}}{2} \stackrel{?}{=} -3 \pm \dfrac{\sqrt{1}}{2} \stackrel{?}{=} -3 \pm \dfrac{1}{2}$

(d) *Solve* $x^2 - 6x - 3 = 0.$

Solution: $x \stackrel{?}{=} \dfrac{6 \pm \sqrt{36 + 12}}{2} \stackrel{?}{=} \dfrac{6 \pm \sqrt{48}}{2} \stackrel{?}{=} \dfrac{6 \pm 4\sqrt{3}}{2}$

$$\stackrel{?}{=} \dfrac{6 \pm \overset{2}{\cancel{4}}\sqrt{3}}{\cancel{2}} \stackrel{?}{=} 6 \pm 2\sqrt{3}$$

79. Write an equation with the following roots:

   (a) 3 and 4   **(b)** -4 and $+5$ **(c)** $\dfrac{3}{5}$ and -2 **(d)** $3i$ and $-3i$

MINI-REVIEW

80. Given $f(x) = \dfrac{2x - 1}{1 - x}$, find and simplify $f\left(\tfrac{2}{3}\right)$.

81. *Evaluate.* $(-27)^{-2/3}$

82. *Combine and simplify.* $\dfrac{7}{x^2 + x - 12} - \dfrac{4}{x^2 + 4x} + \dfrac{3}{x^2 - 3x}$

83. A person invests a certain amount of money, part at 8% and the remainder at 10%, yielding a total of $730 in annual interest. Had the amounts invested been reversed, the annual interest would have been $710. How much was invested altogether?

8.5 Equations Reducible to Quadratic Form (and More Radical Equations)

Radical Equations

In Chapter 7, we solved radical equations by first isolating the radical and then squaring both sides of the equation to eliminate the radical where possible.

    In this chapter we employ the same techniques to solve radical equations, except, unlike the radical equations we covered in Chapter 7, the radical equations we will solve in this section may give rise to quadratic equations.

EXAMPLE 1   Solve for x. $x - \sqrt{2x} = 0$

Solution   Keep in mind that simply squaring both sides of an equation containing a radical does not necessarily eliminate the radical. We should isolate the radical first.

$$x - \sqrt{2x} = 0 \qquad \text{\textit{Isolate the radical.}}$$
$$x = \sqrt{2x} \qquad \text{\textit{Square both sides of the equation.}}$$
$$(x^2) = \left(\sqrt{2x}\right)^2$$
$$x^2 = 2x \qquad \text{\textit{Now we have a quadratic equation that}}$$
$$x^2 - 2x = 0 \qquad \text{\textit{we can solve by factoring.}}$$
$$x(x - 2) = 0$$
$$x = 0 \quad \text{or} \quad x - 2 = 0$$
$$x = 2$$

351

As usual, we check the solutions to all radical equations to ensure that all our solutions are valid.

Check: $x = 0$: $x - \sqrt{2x} = 0$ **Check:** $x = 2$: $x - \sqrt{2x} = 0$

$0 - \sqrt{2(0)} \overset{\checkmark}{=} 0$ $2 - \sqrt{2(2)} \overset{?}{=} 0$

$2 - \sqrt{4} \overset{\checkmark}{=} 0$

Therefore, the solutions are $\boxed{x = 0 \text{ and } x = 2}$. ∎

EXAMPLE 2

Solve for z. $\sqrt{z + 3} + 2z = 0$

Solution

$\sqrt{z + 3} + 2z = 0$ *First isolate the radical.*

$\sqrt{z + 3} = -2z$ *Next, square both sides to eliminate the radical.*

$\left(\sqrt{z + 3}\right)^2 = (-2z)^2$

$z + 3 = 4z^2$ *Now we have a quadratic equation to solve. Put it in standard form.*

$0 = 4z^2 - z - 3$ *Solve for z.*

$0 = (4z + 3)(z - 1)$

$0 = 4z + 3 \quad \text{or} \quad 0 = z - 1$

$z = -\dfrac{3}{4} \quad \text{or} \quad z = 1$

Now we must check both solutions in the original equation.

Check: $z = 1$: $\sqrt{z + 3} + 2z = 0$

$\sqrt{1 + 3} + 2(1) \overset{?}{=} 0$

$\sqrt{4} + 2 \overset{?}{=} 0$

$2 + 2 \neq 0$

Thus, $z = 1$ is an extraneous root.

Check: $z = -\dfrac{3}{4}$: $\sqrt{z + 3} + 2z \overset{?}{=} 0$

$\sqrt{\dfrac{-3}{4} + 3} + 2\left(\dfrac{-3}{4}\right) \overset{?}{=} 0$

$\sqrt{\dfrac{9}{4}} + \dfrac{-3}{2} \overset{?}{=} 0$

$\dfrac{3}{2} + \dfrac{-3}{2} \overset{\checkmark}{=} 0$

Hence the *only* solution is $\boxed{z = -\dfrac{3}{4}}$. ∎

When we are confronted with two radicals in an equation, the algebra is more complicated. For example, the process of squaring $\sqrt{5a} - \sqrt{2a - 1}$ can be messy. It is usually less trouble to *first isolate the more complicated radical and then square both sides of the equation,* as demonstrated in the next example.

EXAMPLE 3 Solve for a. $\sqrt{5a} - \sqrt{2a - 1} = 2$

Solution

$\sqrt{5a} - \sqrt{2a - 1} = 2$	*Isolate $\sqrt{2a - 1}$.*
$\sqrt{5a} - 2 = \sqrt{2a - 1}$	*Square both sides of the equation.*
$(\sqrt{5a} - 2)^2 = (\sqrt{2a - 1})^2$	
$5a - 4\sqrt{5a} + 4 = 2a - 1$	*Note how each side is squared differently. Isolate $4\sqrt{5a}$.*
$3a + 5 = 4\sqrt{5a}$	*Square both sides of the equation again.*
$(3a + 5)^2 = (4\sqrt{5a})^2$	
$9a^2 + 30a + 25 = 16(5a)$	*Simplify.*
$9a^2 + 30a + 25 = 80a$	
$9a^2 - 50a + 25 = 0$	*Solve for a by factoring.*
$(9a - 5)(a - 5) = 0$	
$a = \dfrac{5}{9}$ or $a = 5$	

Check for extraneous solutions.

Check: $a = \dfrac{5}{9}$:

$$\sqrt{5a} - \sqrt{2a - 1} = 2$$

$$\sqrt{5\left(\frac{5}{9}\right)} - \sqrt{2\left(\frac{5}{9}\right) - 1} \overset{?}{=} 2$$

$$\sqrt{\frac{25}{9}} - \sqrt{\frac{10}{9} - 1} \overset{?}{=} 2$$

$$\sqrt{\frac{25}{9}} - \sqrt{\frac{1}{9}} \overset{?}{=} 2$$

$$\frac{5}{3} - \frac{1}{3} \neq 2$$

Thus, $\dfrac{5}{9}$ is extraneous.

The solution is $\boxed{a = 5}$.

Check: $a = 5$:

$$\sqrt{5a} - \sqrt{2a - 1} = 2$$

$$\sqrt{5 \cdot 5} - \sqrt{2 \cdot 5 - 1} \overset{?}{=} 2$$

$$\sqrt{25} - \sqrt{9} \overset{?}{=} 2$$

$$5 - 3 \overset{\checkmark}{=} 2$$

∎

We follow the same principles in solving literal equations, as demonstrated in Example 4.

EXAMPLE 4 Solve for a. $\sqrt{ab + c} - b = d$

Solution

$\sqrt{ab + c} - b = d$	*Isolate the radical.*
$\sqrt{ab + c} = d + b$	*Square both sides of the equation.*
$(\sqrt{ab + c})^2 = (d + b)^2$	*Isolate a: Subtract c from both sides of the equation.*
$ab + c = d^2 + 2bd + b^2$	
$ab = d^2 + 2bd + b^2 - c$	*Divide both sides of the equation by b.*
$\boxed{a = \dfrac{d^2 + 2bd + b^2 - c}{b}}$	

∎

Miscellaneous Equations

As we saw in Sections 5.6 and 8.2, we can apply the factoring method to any higher-degree equation that can be factored into first-degree factors. For example:

$$x^4 - 13x^2 + 36 = 0 \qquad \textit{We factor the left-hand expression.}$$

$$(x^2 - 4)(x^2 - 9) = 0 \qquad \textit{This can be factored further.}$$

$$(x - 2)(x + 2)(x - 3)(x + 3) = 0 \qquad \textit{Then set each factor equal to 0.}$$

$$x - 2 = 0 \quad \text{or} \quad x + 2 = 0 \quad \text{or} \quad x - 3 = 0 \quad \text{or} \quad x + 3 = 0 \qquad \textit{Solve each first-degree equation.}$$

$$x = 2 \quad \text{or} \quad x = -2 \quad \text{or} \quad x = 3 \quad \text{or} \quad x = -3 \qquad \textit{Check these solutions in the original equation.}$$

By applying our knowledge of solving quadratic equations, we can also solve equations that have second-degree factors that cannot be factored using integer coefficients. For example:

$$x^3 - 5x = 0 \qquad \textit{We factor the left side.}$$

$$x(x^2 - 5) = 0 \qquad \textit{Set each factor equal to 0.}$$

$$x = 0 \quad \text{or} \quad x^2 - 5 = 0$$

The first equation is a simple linear equation, $x = 0$. The second equation is a quadratic equation that factors no further with integer coefficients, but we can solve it using the square root method as follows:

$$x^2 - 5 = 0$$
$$x^2 = 5$$
$$x = \pm\sqrt{5}$$

Therefore, the solutions are $x = 0$, $-\sqrt{5}$, and $+\sqrt{5}$.

EXAMPLE 5

Solve for y. $y^4 - 15y^2 = 16$

Solution

$$y^4 - 15y^2 = 16 \qquad \textit{Rewrite the equation so that one side of the equation is 0.}$$

$$y^4 - 15y^2 - 16 = 0 \qquad \textit{Factor.}$$

$$(y^2 - 16)(y^2 + 1) = 0$$

$$(y - 4)(y + 4)(y^2 + 1) = 0 \qquad \textit{Set each factor equal to 0, and solve each equation.}$$

$$y - 4 = 0 \quad \text{or} \quad y + 4 = 0 \quad \text{or} \quad y^2 + 1 = 0$$

$$y = 4 \quad \text{or} \quad y = -4 \quad \text{or} \quad y^2 = -1 \qquad \textit{This equation has no real solutions.}$$

Note that two of the solutions are real and two are not. If we use complex numbers, we solve $y^2 = -1$ to get:

$$y = \pm\sqrt{-1} = \pm i$$

The solutions are $\boxed{-4,\ 4,\ -i,\ \text{and}\ i}$.

The student should check to see that the answers are correct. ∎

Let's reexamine how we solved the equation $x^4 - 13x^2 + 36 = 0$ previously. To begin with, this is a fourth-degree equation, and at this point our only method of solving an equation of degree greater than 2 is by the factoring method. Although $x^4 - 13x^2 + 36$ is not a quadratic expression, we initially factored it as though it were. That is,

We factored $x^4 - 13x^2 + 36$ into $(x^2 - 9)(x^2 - 4)$ as though we were factoring the quadratic $u^2 - 13u + 36$ into $(u - 9)(u - 4)$ where u would equal x^2.

Thus, although $x^4 - 13x^2 + 36 = 0$ is not a quadratic equation, it does have the form of a quadratic equation, which is why we call it **an equation in quadratic form.**

Having examined how we originally solved the equation, now let's approach it in a slightly different way.

Suppose we let $u = x^2$. [Then $u^2 = (x^2)^2 = x^4$.] Now let's substitute u for x^2 and u^2 for x^4 in the original equation. Then

$$x^4 - 13x^2 + 36 = 0 \quad \text{becomes} \quad u^2 - 13u + 36 = 0$$

Now let's solve for u:

$$u^2 - 13u + 36 = 0$$
$$(u - 9)(u - 4) = 0$$
$$u = 9 \quad \text{or} \quad u = 4$$

Since we were asked originally to solve for x, we substitute x^2 back for u:

$u = 9$	or	$u = 4$	*Substitute x^2 for u.*
$x^2 = 9$	or	$x^2 = 4$	*Now we solve for x. Take square roots.*
$x = \pm\sqrt{9}$	or	$x = \pm\sqrt{4}$	
$x = \pm 3$	or	$x = \pm 2$	*Note that we get the same solutions.*

We used this example to illustrate the method of **substitution of variables.** We are substituting a single variable for a more complex expression in the equation to help us determine whether the equation is in quadratic form.

You may be able to factor $x^4 - 13x^2 + 36$ by recognizing that it is in quadratic form, and therefore the substitution of variables method may seem to be an unnecessary complication. However, the method can help us in solving more complicated equations, such as in Example 6.

EXAMPLE 6   Solve the following: $2a^{1/2} + 3a^{1/4} - 2 = 0$.

Solution   The given equation is not a quadratic equation (for that matter, it is not even a polynomial equation), but it is an equation in quadratic form. Let's examine

$$2a^{1/2} + 3a^{1/4} - 2 = 0$$

Is it obvious that we can solve this equation by factoring? It is probably not obvious that

$$2a^{1/2} + 3a^{1/4} - 2 \quad \text{factors into} \quad (2a^{1/4} - 1)(a^{1/4} + 2)$$

Let's see what happens when we make the appropriate substitution of variables. Let $u = a^{1/4}$. [Then $u^2 = (a^{1/4})^2 = a^{2/4} = a^{1/2}$.] Then

$$2a^{1/2} + 3a^{1/4} - 2 = 0 \quad \text{becomes} \quad 2u^2 + 3u - 2 = 0$$

We can solve for u by factoring:

$$(2u - 1)(u + 2) = 0$$
$$2u - 1 = 0 \quad \text{or} \quad u + 2 = 0$$
$$\text{Hence,} \quad u = \frac{1}{2} \quad \text{or} \quad u = -2.$$

We found the values of *u*, but we are looking for the values of *a*, so we substitute $a^{1/4}$ back in for *u*:

$$a^{1/4} = \frac{1}{2} \quad \text{or} \quad a^{1/4} = -2 \qquad \textit{Since } a^{1/4} = u$$

We can discard the equation on the right as $a^{1/4} = -2$ has no solution. The remaining equation above is similar to the equations we solved in Chapter 7. Raise both sides of the equation to the fourth power:

$$(a^{1/4})^4 = \left(\frac{1}{2}\right)^4$$

$$a = \frac{1}{16}$$

Now we must check for extraneous roots:

Check: $a = \dfrac{1}{16}$:

$$2a^{1/2} + 3a^{1/4} - 2 = 0$$

$$2\left(\frac{1}{16}\right)^{1/2} + 3\left(\frac{1}{16}\right)^{1/4} - 2 \stackrel{?}{=} 0$$

$$2\left(\frac{1}{4}\right) + 3\left(\frac{1}{2}\right) - 2 \stackrel{?}{=} 0$$

$$\frac{1}{2} + \frac{3}{2} - 2 \stackrel{?}{=} 0$$

$$2 - 2 \stackrel{\checkmark}{=} 0$$

The solution is $\boxed{a = \dfrac{1}{16}}$. ∎

How do we know an equation is in quadratic form? How do we know what or where to substitute? To begin with, we observe that an equation in standard quadratic form should look like

$$Ax^2 + Bx + C = 0$$

But *x* can represent any expression. For example,

$$5(3a + 2)^2 + 7(3a + 2) + 8 = 0 \quad \text{and} \quad 5(y^{1/3})^2 + 7y^{1/3} + 8 = 0$$

are expressions in quadratic form. The important condition is that, ignoring the coefficients, the expression with the higher power should be the square of the expression with the lower power. (The reverse is true if the exponents are negative.)

The following are more examples of equations in quadratic form:

$$a^6 - 7a^3 - 8 = 0 \qquad a^6 \textit{ is the square of } a^3.$$
$$2x^{2/3} + x^{1/3} - 15 = 0 \qquad x^{2/3} \textit{ is the square of } x^{1/3}.$$
$$a^{-4} - 6a^{-2} - 7 = 0 \qquad a^{-4} \textit{ is the square of } a^{-2}.$$

We let *u* equal the middle-term literal expression. Note that we always find u^2 to make sure it checks out. For example, suppose in $2x^{2/3} - 7x^{1/3} + 3 = 0$, we let $u = x^{2/3}$. Then $u^2 = (x^{2/3})^2 = x^{4/3}$. Since $x^{4/3}$ is not in the equation, we reason that we chose the wrong variable for substituting *u*. Therefore, if the equation *is* in quadratic form, then *u must be* $x^{1/3}$.

 EXERCISES 8.5

In Exercises 1–20, solve the equation.

1. $\sqrt{x} + 3 = 2x$

2. $\sqrt{a} - 2 = a - 4$

3. $\sqrt{x + 5} = 7 - x$

4. $\sqrt{y - 2} = 22 - y$

5. $\sqrt{5a - 1} + 5 = a$

6. $\sqrt{7a + 4} - 2 = a$

7. $\sqrt{a + 1} + a = 11$

8. $\sqrt{3a + 1} + a = 9$

9. $\sqrt{3x + 1} + 3 = x$

10. $5a - \sqrt{2a - 3} = 4a + 9$

11. $5a - 2\sqrt{a + 3} = 2a - 1$

12. $6a - 3\sqrt{a + 5} = 4a - 1$

13. $\sqrt{y + 3} = 1 + \sqrt{y}$

14. $\sqrt{3x + 4} = 2 + \sqrt{x}$

15. $\sqrt{a + 7} = 1 + \sqrt{2a}$

16. $\sqrt{2r - 1} = \sqrt{5r} - 2$

17. $\sqrt{7s + 1} - 2\sqrt{s} = 2$

18. $\sqrt{3s + 4} - \sqrt{s} = 2$

19. $\sqrt{7 - a} - \sqrt{3 + a} = 2$

20. $\sqrt{3 - 2a} - \sqrt{3 - 3a} = -1$

In Exercises 21–28, solve for the given variable.

21. $\sqrt{x} + a = b$ for x

22. $\sqrt{3a} - x = b$ for a

23. $\dfrac{\sqrt{\pi L}}{g} = T$ for L

24. $K = \sqrt{\dfrac{2gs}{l}}$ for s

25. $\sqrt{5x + b} = 6 + b$ for x

26. $\sqrt{3x + y} = 5 - y$ for x

27. $t = \dfrac{\overline{X} - a}{\dfrac{s}{\sqrt{n}}}$ for n

28. $s_e = s_y\sqrt{1 - r^2}$ for r

In Exercises 29–68, solve the equation.

29. $x^3 - 2x^2 - 15x = 0$

30. $x^3 + x^2 - 20x = 0$

31. $6a^3 - a^2 - 2a = 0$

32. $2s^4 - 7s^3 + 3s^2 = 0$

33. $y^4 - 17y^2 + 16 = 0$

34. $2t^4 - 34t^2 = -32$

35. $3a^4 + 24 = 18a^2$

36. $a^4 + 45 = 14a^2$

37. $b^4 + 112 = 23b^2$

38. $b^4 + 75 = 28b^2$

39. $9 - \dfrac{8}{x^2} = x^2$

40. $3 - \dfrac{1}{x^2} = 2x^2$

41. $x^3 + x^2 - x - 1 = 0$

42. $a^3 - 2a^2 - 4a + 8 = 0$

43. $x^{2/3} - 4 = 0$

44. $a^{2/3} = 9$

45. $x + x^{1/2} - 6 = 0$ [*Hint:* Let $u = x^{1/2}$.]

46. $x - 5x^{1/2} + 6 = 0$

47. $y^{2/3} - 4y^{1/3} - 5 = 0$

48. $b^{2/3} - 4b^{1/3} = -3$

49. $x^{1/2} + 8x^{1/4} + 7 = 0$

50. $x^{1/2} + 3x^{1/4} - 10 = 0$

51. $x^{-2} - 5x^{-1} + 6 = 0$ [*Hint:* Let $u = x^{-1}$.]

52. $x^{-2} - 2x^{-1} - 15 = 0$

53. $6x^{-2} + x^{-1} - 1 = 0$

54. $15x^{-2} + 7x^{-1} - 2 = 0$

55. $x^{-4} - 13x^{-2} + 36 = 0$

56. $x^{-4} - 3x^{-2} = 4$ [*Hint:* Let $u = x^{-2}$.]

57. $\sqrt{a} - \sqrt[4]{a} - 6 = 0$
   [*Hint:* Change radicals to rational exponents.]

58. $\sqrt{b} + 2\sqrt[4]{b} = 3$

59. $\sqrt{x} - 4\sqrt[4]{x} = 5$

60. $\sqrt{x} - 2\sqrt[4]{x} = 8$

61. $(a + 4)^2 + 6(a + 4) + 9 = 0$

62. $(a - 1)^2 - 3(a - 1) = 10$

63. $2(3x + 1)^2 - 5(3x + 1) - 3 = 0$

64. $3(2x - 1)^2 - 1 = 0$

65. $(x^2 + x)^2 - 4 = 0$

66. $(x^2 - 4x)^2 - 25 = 0$

67. $\left(a - \dfrac{10}{a}\right)^2 - 12\left(a - \dfrac{10}{a}\right) + 27 = 0$

68. $\left(y + \dfrac{12}{y}\right)^2 - 15\left(y + \dfrac{12}{y}\right) + 56 = 0$

69. Given $s_e = s_y\sqrt{1 - r^2}$, if $s_e = 1.4$ and $s_y = 2.2$, compute r to two decimal places.

70. Given $t = \dfrac{\overline{X} - a}{\dfrac{s}{\sqrt{n}}}$, compute the nearest whole number n for $t = 2.2$, $s = 3.4$, $\overline{X} = 68$, and $a = 66$.

 **QUESTION FOR THOUGHT**

71. Discuss what is **wrong** (if anything) with solving the equation $\sqrt{3x - 2} - \sqrt{x} = 2$ in the following way:

$$\sqrt{3x - 2} - \sqrt{x} = 2$$
$$(\sqrt{3x - 2} - \sqrt{x})^2 = 2^2$$
$$3x - 2 - x = 4$$
$$2x - 2 = 4$$
$$2x = 6$$
$$x = 3$$

MINI-REVIEW

72. *Solve.* $(x - 2)^2 = (x + 1)^2 - 15$

73. Find the slope of the line whose equation is $2x + 5y - 8 = 0$.

74. *Solve for a.* $\dfrac{3}{a} = \dfrac{r}{1 - a}$

75. In a Senate race, the two candidates received votes in the ratio of 8 to 5. If the winner received 875,400 votes, how many votes were cast altogether?

CHAPTER 8 REVIEW EXERCISES

1. Suppose that a motor vehicle consumer ratings service finds that the distance, d, in miles that a certain car can travel on one (15-gallon) tank of gasoline depends on its speed, v, in miles per hour, according to the function

$$d = d(v) = 18v - \left(\frac{v}{2.3}\right)^2 \quad \text{for } 10 \leq v \leq 90$$

   (a) To the nearest tenth of a mile, determine the distance the car can travel on a tank of gas at a constant speed of 30 mph, 40 mph, 50 mph, and 60 mph.

   (b) Estimate the constant speed that must be maintained for the car to travel 400 miles on one tank (to the nearest mile per hour).

2. To encourage the use of mass transit, a local transit authority projects that 36,000 people will use buses if the fare is $4, and that for each $0.25 decrease in fare, 3,000 additional passengers will take the bus rather than drive.

   (a) Express the total revenue from bus fares, $R(x)$, as a function of the number of $0.25 fare decreases, x.

   (b) Using $R(x)$ found in part (a), predict the revenue if the fare is $3.50.

Solve Exercises 3–18 by factoring or the square root method.

3. $2y^2 - y - 1 = 0$

4. $3a^2 - 13a - 10 = 0$

5. $3x^2 - 17x = 28$

6. $10a^2 - 3a = 1$

7. $81 = a^2$

8. $0 = y^2 - 65$

9. $z^2 + 7 = 2$

10. $3r^2 + 5 = r^2$

11. $4x^2 + 36 = 24x$

12. $5a^2 - 5a = 10$

13. $(a + 7)(a + 3) = (3a + 1)(a + 1)$

14. $(y + 2)(y + 1) = (3y + 1)(y - 1)$

15. $x - 2 = \dfrac{1}{x + 2}$

16. $a - 5 = \dfrac{1}{a - 5}$

17. $\dfrac{2}{x - 2} - \dfrac{5}{x + 2} = 1$

18. $\dfrac{3}{x + 4} + \dfrac{5}{x + 2} = 6$

Solve Exercises 19–26 by completing the square.

19. $x^2 + 2x - 4 = 0$

20. $x^2 - 2x - 4 = 0$

21. $2y^2 + 4y - 3 = 0$

22. $2y^2 + 4y + 3 = 0$

23. $3a^2 + 6a - 5 = 0$

24. $3a^2 - 6a + 5 = 0$

25. $\dfrac{1}{a - 5} + \dfrac{3}{a + 2} = 4$

26. $\dfrac{3}{a - 1} - \dfrac{1}{a + 2} = 2$

Solve Exercises 27–48 by any method.

27. $6a^2 - 13a = 5$

28. $5x^2 - 18x = 8$

29. $3.2a^2 - 5.8a + 4 = 9.6$

30. $2y^2 + 5y = 7$

31. $5a^2 - 3a = 3 - 3a + 2a^2$

32. $5a^2 + 6a - 4 = 3a^2 + 10a + 26$

33. $(x - 4)(x + 1) = x - 2$

34. $(y + 5)(y - 7) = 3$

35. $(t + 3)(t - 4) = t(t + 2)$

36. $(u - 5)(u + 1) = (u - 3)(u + 5)$

37. $8x^2 = 12$

38. $3x^2 - 14 = 5$

39. $3x^2 - 2x + 5 = 7x^2 - 2x + 5$

40. $7.4x^2 - 3.8x = -5.4$

41. $(x + 2)(x - 4) = 2x - 10$

42. $2.8x^2 - 1.4x - 8.7 = 1.3$

43. $\dfrac{1}{z + 2} = z - 4$

44. $\dfrac{3}{z - 2} = z$

45. $\dfrac{1}{x + 4} - \dfrac{3}{x + 2} = 5$

46. $\dfrac{2}{x - 1} - \dfrac{3}{x + 4} = 2$

47. $\dfrac{3}{x - 4} + \dfrac{2x}{x - 5} = \dfrac{3}{x - 5}$

48. $\dfrac{2}{x - 6} - \dfrac{x}{x + 6} = \dfrac{3}{x^2 - 36}$

In Exercises 49–52, solve for the given variable.

49. $A = \pi r^2 h$ for $r > 0$

50. $l = \dfrac{gt^2}{2}$ for $t > 0$

51. $2x^2 + xy - 3y^2 = 0$ for x

52. $5x^2 + 4xy - y^2 = 0$ for y

In Exercises 53–60, solve the equation.

53. $\sqrt{2a + 3} = a$

54. $\sqrt{5a - 4} = a$

55. $\sqrt{3a + 1} + 1 = a$

56. $\sqrt{7y + 4} - 2 = y$

57. $\sqrt{2x + 1} - \sqrt{x - 3} = 4$

58. $\sqrt{3x + 1} - \sqrt{x - 1} = 2$

59. $\sqrt{3x + 4} - \sqrt{x - 3} = 3$

60. $\sqrt{2x - 1} - \sqrt{9 - x} = 1$

In Exercises 61–64, solve for y.

61. $\sqrt{3y + z} = x$

62. $\sqrt{5y - z} = x$

63. $\sqrt{3y} + z = x$

64. $\sqrt{5y} - z = x$

In Exercises 65–82, solve the equation.

65. $x^3 - 2x^2 - 15x = 0$

66. $x^4 - 2x^3 = 35x^2$

67. $4x^3 - 10x^2 - 6x = 0$

68. $9x^3 + 3x^2 - 6x = 0$

69. $a^4 - 17a^2 = -16$

70. $y^4 - 18y^2 = -81$

71. $y^4 - 3y^2 = 4$

72. $a^4 - 5a^2 = 36$

73. $z^4 = 6z^2 - 5$

74. $z^4 = 11z^2 - 18$

75. $a^{1/2} - a^{1/4} - 6 = 0$

76. $a^{2/3} - a^{1/3} - 6 = 0$

77. $2x^{2/3} = 5x^{1/3} + 3$

78. $2x^{1/2} = 5x^{1/4} + 3$

79. $\sqrt{x} + 2\sqrt[4]{x} - 35 = 0$

80. $\sqrt{x} - 5\sqrt[4]{x} + 6 = 0$

81. $3x^{-2} + x^{-1} - 2 = 0$

82. $5x^{-2} - 2x^{-1} - 3 = 0$

In Exercises 83–86, sketch a graph and identify the vertex and axis of symmetry.

83. $y = (x - 2)^2 + 1$

84. $y = -(x - 4)^2 + 5$

85. $y = -3(x - 2)^2 - 4$

86. $y = 2(x + 3)^2 - 6$

Answers

ANSWERS TO SELECTED EXERCISES

This answer section contains the answers to all odd-numbered exercises as well as the answers to all exercises in the Mini-Reviews, Chapter Reviews, Chapter Tests, Cumulative Reviews, and Cumulative Tests.

EXERCISES 1.1

1. $\{3, 4, 5, 6, 7, 8, 9, 10, 11\}$
3. $\varnothing$ 5. $\{41, 43, 47\}$
7. $\{0, 7, 14, 21, \ldots\}$
9. $\{1, 2, 3, 6, 9, 18, 27, 54\}$
11. $\{0, 3, 6\}$
13. $\{0, 1, 2, 3, 4, 5, 6, 9, 12, 15, 18, 21, 24, 27, 30, 33\}$
15. $\{0, 1, 2, 3, 4, 5, 6, 7, 8, 9, 10, 11, 12, 13\}$
17. $2 \cdot 3 \cdot 11$
19. $2 \cdot 2 \cdot 2 \cdot 2 \cdot 2 \cdot 2 \cdot 2$
21. Prime number   23. $7 \cdot 13$
25. True   27. True   29. True
31. False   33. False   35. True
37. $>, \geq, \neq$ 39. $<, \leq, \neq$
41.
43.
45.
47.
49.
51.
53. No solution
55.
57. $C \cup D = \{x \mid -4 \leq x < 9, x \in Z\}$
59. $A \cap D = \{x \mid 1 \leq x < 9, x \in Z\}$
61. $A \cup B = \{x \mid x \in R\}$
63. $C \cap D = \{x \mid 1 \leq x \leq 6\}$
65. $A \cup C = \{x \mid x \geq -4\}$
67. Associative property of addition
69. Commutative property of addition
71. Distributive property   73. False
75. Distributive property   77. False
79. Associative property of multiplication
81. Multiplicative inverse property
83. Additive inverse property

85. Commutative property of addition
87. Distributive property
89. Closure property of multiplication
91. False

EXERCISES 1.2

1. 5   3. -11 5. 24   7. 6.481
9. -12 11. -23 13. -60
15. -27 17. -11 19. 3
21. -16 23. 0.87   25. 4   27. $\frac{16}{5}$
29. 8   31. 4   33. 1   35. -12
37. -4 39. -3 41. 45   43. 17
45. 10   47. -16 49. 2   51. 2
53. -8 55. 36   57. 29   59. 50
61. -81 63. -40 65. -360
67. -46 69. $\frac{50}{7}$ 71. -13
73. 111   75. -6 77. 10   79. 24
81. -4 83. \$1,230.42   85. 30,335 ft
87. (a) $\frac{-9}{49}$ (b) -0.18 89. 0   91. 30
93. 6   95. 1   97. Undefined
99. 1.55   101. (a) 0.070   (b) 0.110
103. (a) 240 million   (b) 9 million
105. (a) \$330 million, \$347 million, \$363 million, \$380 million
   (b) 5.2%, 94–95; 4.6%, 95–96; 4.7%, 96–97

EXERCISES 1.3

1. $8x$ 3. $12x^2$ 5. $-4x$ 7. $-12x^2$
9. $-6m$ 11. $60m^3$ 13. $-9t^2$
15. $-24t^6$ 17. $2x + 3y + 5z$
19. $30xyz$ 21. $x^3 + x^2 + 2x$
23. $2x^6$ 25. $-17x^2y$ 27. $30x^4y^2$
29. $x^2 + 2x - 6$ 31. $11x^2y - 7xy^2$
33. $9m + 12n$ 35. $2a - 16b$
37. $6c - 16d$ 39. $x^2 - 2xy + y^2$
41. 0   43. $40a^3b^4c^3$ 45. $72x^5$
47. $18x^5$ 49. $-32x^{11}$ 51. 0
53. $-16x^3$ 55. $-b + 10$
57. $17t + 12$ 59. $13a - 64$
61. $4x^2 - 8x$ 63. $10x - 7y$
65. $-8y^3 + 2xy^2 + 2xy + 3x$
67. $12s^2$ 69. -131.31 71. -73.38
73. (a) $P = 16.75t - 32,701.5$
   (b) 765 million
75. $96 - 3x$ 77. $x^2 + 3x$

EXERCISES 1.4

1. Let x = number; $x + 8$
3. Let x = number; $2x - 3$
5. Let x = number; $3x + 4 = x - 7$
7. Let x and y be the two numbers; $x + y = xy + 1$

9. Let the smaller number be x; the larger number = $2x + 5$
11. Let x = smallest number; the other two numbers are $3x$ and $3x + 12$
13. x and $x + 1$ 15. $x, x + 2, x + 4$
17. $x^3 + (x + 1)^3$
19. Let x = one number; the other number is $40 - x$
21. Let x = first number; second number = $2x$; third number = $100 - 3x$
23. Let x = width; area = $(x)(3x) = 3x^2$; perimeter = $2x + 2(3x) = 8x$
25. Let x = second side; perimeter = $2x + x + x + 4 = 4x + 4$
27. (a) 31 coins
   (b) Value of coins = \$4
29. (a) Number of coins = $n + d + q$
   (b) Value of coins (in cents) = $5n + 10d + 25q$ cents
31. (a) $2w$ meters   (b) $4w$ dollars
   (c) $6w$ (d) $30w$ dollars
   (e) $34w$ dollars
33. Let x = nickels, then $20 - x$ = dimes; value of coins (in cents) = $5x + 10(20 - x) = 200 - 5x$ cents
35. (a) \$1,590   (b) \$1,685.40
   (c) $A = 1,500(1.06)^n$ (d) $A = 1,500(1.06)^{15} = \$3,594.84$
37. (a) 2 hr: \$12, Standard; \$16.20, Saver. 1 hr: \$6.00, Standard; \$12.60, Saver
   (b) Standard: $P = 0.10t$; Saver: $P = 0.06t + 9$. Standard Plan is cheaper for $t < 225$ min; Saver Plan is cheaper for $t > 225$ min.
39. (a) \$984.38
   (b) $0.75x + 0.05(0.75x) = 0.7875x$
41. (a) \$2,100
   (b) $0.5x + 0.5(0.5x) = 0.75x$

EXERCISES 1.5

1. 3 satisfies; 0 and 5 do not
3. 2 satisfies; -3 and 0 do not
5. -1 and 5 satisfy; 2 does not
7. 1 satisfies; -1 and 3 do not
9. $x = 6$ 11. $y = -\frac{3}{4}$ 13. $m = 0$
15. $t = 4$ 17. $y = -9$ 19. $s = -\frac{9}{2}$
21. $x = -\frac{11}{9} \approx -1.22$ 23. $x = \frac{7}{8}$

25. $x = 4$ 27. $x = 0$ 29. $t = 2$
31. $x = 5$ 33. $x = \frac{3}{2}$
35. $x = 10{,}500$ 37. $x = 12$
39. $x = -12$ 41. $x = \frac{8}{57}$ 43. $x = \frac{8}{105}$
45. $x = -\frac{5}{33}$ 47. $x = \frac{22}{3}$ 49. $x = \frac{1}{3}$
51. (a) $141{,}000
   (b) In 1995 (1995.8)
53. $x = \dfrac{4 - 7y}{5}$ 55. $y = \dfrac{2x - 11}{9}$
57. $x = -2y - 4$
59. $x > -\frac{3}{5}$

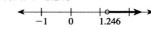

61. $x < \frac{17}{3}$

63. $x > 4$

65. $x \geq \frac{1}{3}$

67. $x \leq 2$

69. $x \geq \frac{26}{23}$

Chapter 1 Review Exercises

1. $A = \{1, 2, 3, 4\}$
2. $B = \{6, 7, 8, 9, \ldots\}$
3. $C \cap D = \{b\}$
4. $C \cup D = \{a, b, c, e, f, g, r, s\}$
5. $A \cup B = \{0, 1, 2, 3, 4, 6, 7, \ldots\}$
   or $A \cup B = \{x \mid x \in N, x \neq 5\}$
6. $\varnothing$ 7. $A = \{1, 2, 3, 4, 6, 12\}$
8. $B = \{0, 12, 24, 36, 48, \ldots\}$
9. $A \cap B = \{12\}$
10. $A \cup B = \{0, 1, 2, 3, 4, 6, 12, 24,$
    $36, 48, 60, \ldots, 12n, \ldots\}$,
    $n = 6, 7, 8, \ldots$
11. $B \cap C = \{x \mid x \in W \text{ and } x \text{ is a}$
    multiple of $12\} = \{0, 12, 24, 36, \ldots\}$
12. $A \cap C = \{6, 12\}$
13. $A \cap B = \{r \mid 3 \leq r \leq 4, r \in Z\}$
    $= \{3, 4\}$
14. $A \cup B = \{-1, 0, 1, 2, 3, 4, 5, 6, 7,$
    $8, 9, 10, 11, 12\}$
15.
16.
17.
18.

19.

20.

21. False 22. True 23. True
24. True 25. False 26. True
27. True 28. False
29. Commutative property of addition
30. Commutative property of
    multiplication
31. Distributive property
32. Distributive property
33. Multiplicative inverse property
34. Additive identity property
35. False 36. False 37. -6
38. -11 39. -8 40. -9 41. -30
42. -210 43. 64 44. -64 45. -11
46. 3 47. 63 48. -15 49. -34
50. 16 51. -61 52. -136 53. -17
54. Undefined 55. 1 56. 11 57. 0
58. 4 59. Not defined 60. 0
61. 3.86 62. 0.09
63. $-6x^3y - 3x^2y^2$ 64. $-36a^3b^4$
65. $36x^4y^4$ 66. $54r^8s^6$ 67. $3y - 4x$
68. $-8a - 2b$ 69. $-5r^2s + rs^2$
70. $-3x^2y^3 - 2xy^2$ 71. -1
72. $3a^2 - 3ab + 3ac$
73. $10r^2s + 15rs^2$ 74. $-x + 12$
75. $7y - 18x - 9$ 76. $4a - 9$
77. $-2r - 3s + 36$ 78. $-6x + 30$
79. $-21y + 31$
80. (a) $C = 4.695t - 9230.375$
    (b) $126,760
81. Let the two numbers be x and y;
    $xy - 5 = x + y + 3$
82. Let $x =$ number;
    $2x + 8 = x^2 - 3$
83. Let $x =$ first odd integer;
    $x + (x + 2) = (x + 4) - 5$
84. Let $x =$ first even integer;
    $(x + 2)(x + 4) = 10x + 8$
85. Let width $= x$;
    area $= (4x - 5)x = 4x^2 - 5x$;
    perimeter $= 2x + 2(4x - 5) =$
    $10x - 10$
86. Let $w =$ width;
    area $= (3w + 5)(w) = 3w^2 + 5w$;
    perimeter $= 2(3w + 5) + 2w =$
    $8w + 10$
87. Let x and y be the numbers;
    $x^2 + y^2 = xy + 8$
88. Let x and y be the two numbers;
    $(x + y)^2 = xy + 8$
89. Let $x =$ number of dimes,
    then $40 - x =$ number of nickels;
    value (in cents) $= 10x + 5(40 - x)$
    $= 5x + 200$ cents
90. $18x + 10(30 - x) =$
    $8x + 300$ dollars
91. $x = 0$ 92. $x = 4$

93. $x = 11$ 94. $y = \frac{4}{5}$
95. $x = -1$ 96. $x = -2$
97. $a = \frac{7}{3}$ 98. $b = -\frac{1}{2}$
99. No solution 100. All reals
101. $x = 0$ 102. $a = 0$
103. $x = -\frac{14}{3}$ 104. $x = \frac{5}{4}$
105. $x = -2$ 106. $y = \frac{5}{6}$
107. $x = -12$
108. (a) 714,750 physicians
     (b) 1988
109. $y = \dfrac{22 - 7x}{8}$
110. $a = \dfrac{5b + 2}{2}$
111. $y = \dfrac{7x - 2}{8}$
112. $a = \dfrac{10b + 2}{5}$
113. $x < -21$

114. $x \geq 1$

115. $x < \frac{27}{5}$

116. $x \geq -\frac{33}{17}$

117. $x \geq 0.713$

118. $x > 1.246$

Chapter 1 Practice Test

1. (a) $A \cap B = \{2, 3, 5, 7\}$
   (b) $A \cup B = \{2, 3, 5, 7, 11, 13,$
       $17, 19, 23\}$
2. (a) False (b) True (c) False
3. (a)

   (b)

4. (a) False
   (b) Commutative property
       of addition
5. (a) 8 (b) 85 (c) 1 (d) 6
6. (a) 1 (b) $\dfrac{5}{17}$
7. (a) $10x^6y^5$ (b) $-rs^2 - 5r^2s - 7rs$
   (c) 0 (d) $9r - 6s - 3$
8. Let $x =$ width; perimeter $=$
   $2x + 2(3x - 8) = 8x - 16$
9. Number of nickels $= 34 - x$;
   value of coins (in cents) $=$
   $10x + 5(34 - x) = 5x + 170$

10. (a) $x = -5$ (b) $x = -\frac{1}{3}$

(c) $x = -\frac{1}{8}$ (d) $x \geq -1$

(e) $x < -\frac{1}{32}$

11. $t = \dfrac{3s + 4}{7}$

EXERCISES 2.1

1. Let G = the course grade, f = the final exam grade. We can use the equation $G = 0.75(82) + 0.25f$
   (a) 74
   (b) She would need a score of at least 114 on the final exam. Assuming a final exam based on 100 points, it would be impossible for her to get a 90 course grade.

3. Let G = the course grade, f = the final exam grade. We can use the equation $G = 0.75(78) + 0.25f$. She would need a score of at least 86 to get a course grade of 80.

5. Let C = weekly commission, G = gross sales. We can use the equation $C = 0.09G$. Weekly sales of around \$6,700 (exact, \$6,666.67) would be needed.

7. Let u = U.S. dollars and x = eurodollar; $0.8702x = u$; $0.8702(300) = \$261.06$

9. Let x = British pounds and u = U.S. dollars; $1.4388x = u$; $(1.4388)400 = \$575.52$

11. Let P = weekly pay, G = gross sales. The strictly commission equation is $P = 0.09G$. The base salary plus commission equation is $P = 120 + 0.06G$. For gross sales greater than \$4,000, the strictly commission plan is better. For gross sales less than \$4,000, the salary plus commission plan is better.

13. Let P = perimeter, w = width, and $3w + 1$ = length. We have $P = 2w + 2(3w + 1)$. The rectangle must be around 10″ by 30″ (exact, 9.75 in. by 30.25 in.).

15. Let I = interest earned, x = the amount invested. We have $I = 0.083x$. She should invest around \$12,000 (exact, \$12,048.19).

17. Let I = interest earned, x = the amount invested at 8%. Then $12,500 - x$ = the amount invested at 5%. The interest earned is $I = 0.08x + 0.05(12,500 - x) = 0.03x + 625$. If $x = 0$ (no money invested in the long-term certificate), then the total interest is \$625 (the minimum amount). If all the money is put into the long-term certificate ($x = \$12,500$), the total amount of interest would be \$1,000 (the maximum amount of interest).

19. Let I = interest earned, x = the amount invested at 4.2%, and $24,000 - x$ = the amount invested at 7.8%. The interest earned is $I = 0.042x + 0.078(24,000 - x)$. The maximum interest is \$1,872; the minimum interest is \$1,008. To earn \$1,200 in total interest, about \$18,000 to \$19,000 must be invested at 4.2% (exact, \$18,666.67) and about \$5,000 to \$6,000 must be invested at 7.8% (exact, \$5,333.33).

21. Let n = total number of copies printed, t = the number of minutes the faster printer works, $t - 5$ = the number of minutes the slower printer works. The total number of copies produced by both printers working together is $n = 9t + 4(t - 5)$; it takes approximately 12.5 minutes to print 142 pages.

23. Let x = number of \$850 computers sold, $58 - x$ = the number of \$600 computers sold. The total C collected on the sale of all the computers is $C = 850x + 600(58 - x)$; twenty-two \$850 computers were sold.

25. Let x = the value of the stock yesterday; the value of the stock today = $\frac{47}{61}x$; $\frac{47}{61}x = 2,500$; $x = \$3,244.69$

27. Let h = number of hours Lewis works, $h - \frac{1}{2}$ = number of hours Arthur works. The total number n of forms they can process is $n = 200h + 300(h - \frac{1}{2})$. It takes 6–7 hours (6.3, exact) to process 3,000 forms from the time Lewis starts.

29. Let x = number of AM radios, $24 - x$ = number of AM/FM radios. The total cost C is $C = 35x + 50(24 - x) + 70$; there are 18 AM radios and 6 AM/FM radios.

EXERCISES 2.2

1. Contradiction 3. Identity

5. Identity 7. Contradiction

9. $x = -0.8, 0$ do not satisfy; $x = 5$ satisfies

11. $x = -5, -\frac{1}{2}$ do not satisfy; $x = 5$ satisfies

13. $x = 4$ 15. All reals

17. $t = 6$ 19. No solution

21. No solution 23. $t = \frac{5}{7}$

25. No solution 27. All reals

29. $x = 0$ 31. $x = -\frac{2}{11}$

33. $t = -\frac{1}{2}$ 35. $x = -40$

37. $y = \frac{32}{5}$ 39. $y = \frac{11}{2}$ 41. $a = \frac{19}{15}$

43. Let x = first number; $x + (2x + 5) = 23$; 6 and 17

45. Let x = first number; $x + (x + 1) + (x + 2) + (x + 3) = (x + 2) + 1$; $-1, 0, 1, 2$

47. Let u = number of U.S. dollars; $u = 0.864(500)$; \$432

49. Let x = stock value on Jan. 4; $1.25(0.75x) = 2,500$; \$2,666.67

51. Let x = width; $2x + 2(2x) = 42$; 7m by 14m

53. Let x = second side; $33 = (x - 5) + x + 2(x - 5)$; sides are 7, 12, 14 cm

55. Let x = original width; $2(x + 2) + 2[2(3x + 1)] = 5(3x + 1) - 3$; original width = 6; original length = 19

57. Let x = weekly gross sales; $0.08x = 600$; $x = \$7,500$

59. Let x = final exam grade; $0.45x + 0.55(72) = 80$; $x = 89.8$

61. Let x = number of \$5 bills; $1[25 - (2x + 1)] + 5x + 10(x + 1) = 164$; four \$1 bills, ten \$5 bills, eleven \$10 bills

63. Let x = number of 20-lb packages; $20x + 25(50 - x) = 1,075$; number of 20-lb packages = 35; number of 25-lb packages = 15

65. Let x = number of pairs of shoes sold; $368 = 200 + 3(70 - x) + 2x$; 42 pairs of shoes

67. Let x = quantity of \$2/lb coffee; $2x + 30(3) = 2.6(x + 30)$; 20 lb of \$2/lb coffee

69. Let x = number of orchestra seats; $96x + 76(56 - x) = 5,016$; 38 orchestra seats

71. Let x = number of hours the plumber worked; $32x + 16(x + 2) = 320$; the plumber worked 6 hours

73. Let t = hours until they meet; $345 = 55t + 60t$; $t = 3$; at 6:00 P.M.

75. $595 = 35t + 50t$ where t = time of travel; 7 hours

77. $17t = 7(t + 3)$ where t = time it takes to overtake; $t = 2.1$ hours (2 hours and 6 minutes)

79. Let t = length of time to go to convention; $48t = 54(17 - t)$; $t = 9$ hours; distance to convention = $48 \cdot 9 = 432$ km

48. $2 \leq x \leq \frac{21}{5}$

49. $a < -3$;

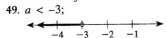

50. No solution   **51.** No solution

52. $x > \frac{2}{3}$;

53. $q \leq \frac{12}{5}$;

54. $x > -2$;

55. $-4 < x < 4$;

56. $x < -4$ or $x > 4$;

57. $s \leq -5$ or $s \geq 5$;

58. $-5 \leq x \leq 5$;

59. No solution

60. $t = 0$;

61. $-1 < t < 3$;

62. $t < -1$ or $t > 3$;

63. $a \leq 3$ or $a \geq 9$;

64. $3 \leq a \leq 9$;

65. $-13 \leq r \leq -5$;

66. $r \leq 5$ or $r \geq 13$;

67. $x \leq -\frac{1}{2}$ or $x \geq \frac{3}{2}$;

68. $x < -\frac{1}{2}$ or $x > \frac{3}{2}$;

69. $-\frac{2}{3} < x < 2$;

70. $x < -\frac{2}{3}$ or $x > 2$;

71. $-1 \leq x \leq 4$ **72.** $x \geq 4$ or $x \leq -1$

73. $x > 0$ or $x < -\frac{10}{3}$

74. $-\frac{10}{3} < x < 0$ **75.** No solution

76. $-\frac{9}{2} \leq x \leq \frac{15}{2}$

77. Let $x =$ number;
$3x = 4x - 4$; $x = 4$

78. Let $x =$ number;
$5(x + 6) = x - 2$; $x = -8$

79. Let $u =$ U.S. dollars;
yen $= 114.05u$;
$114.05(800) = 91,240$ yen

80. Let $x =$ value of stock on April 5;
$0.85x + 0.2(0.85x) = 4,500$;
$4,411.76

81. Let $G =$ gross sales; $650 = 0.09G$;
$G = \$7,222.22$

82. Let $G =$ gross sales;
$600 = 100 + 0.05G$; $G = \$10,000$

83. Let $f =$ final exam grade;
$(0.60)(74) + 0.40f = 80$; $f = 89$

84. Let $f =$ final exam grade;
$(0.55)(78) + 0.45f = 80$; $f = 82.4$

85. Let $x =$ number of packages
weighing 8 lb each;
$8x + 5(30 - x) = 186$; twelve
8-lb packages and eighteen
5-lb packages

86. Let $x =$ number of packages
weighing 8 lb; $8x + 5(45 - x) = 276$;
seventeen 8-lb packages and twenty-
eight 5-lb packages

87. Let $x =$ number of single beds;
$10x + 15(23 - x) = 295$;
10 single beds and 13 larger beds

88. Let $x =$ number of hours the
plumber worked;
$25x + 10(7 - x) + 27 = 134.50$;
plumber worked 2.5 hours; assistant
worked 4.5 hours

89. Let $x =$ number of hours of tutoring;
$12(30 - x) + 20x \geq 456$; at least
12 hours

90. Let $x =$ number of hours tutoring;
$20x + 12(40 - x) \leq 680$;
no more than 25 hours tutoring

Chapter 2 Practice Test

1. Let $x =$ amount in savings account;
$I = 0.035x + 0.06(5,000 - x)$
$3,200 in savings

2. $x = \frac{11}{2}$ **3.** No solution

4. $a = -9$ **5.** $x \geq 4$

6. $x < \frac{1}{5}$ **7.** $\frac{1}{2} < x < 4$

8. $x = 7$ or $x = 0$;

9. $-\frac{1}{3} < x < 3$;

10. $x \leq 1$ or $x \geq \frac{9}{5}$;

11. Let $u =$ U.S. dollars;
$\frac{d}{0.9105} = 500$; $455.25

12. Let $x =$ number of boxes weighing
35 kg; $35x + 45(93 - x) = 3,465$;
seventy-two 35-kg boxes and twenty-
one 45-kg boxes

13. $8x = 3(x + 2)$, where $x =$ time
of jogger; $x = \frac{6}{5} = 1\frac{1}{5}$ hours to
catch up

14. Let $x =$ number of dimes;
$10x + 5(32 - x) \geq 265$; at least
21 dimes

EXERCISES 3.1

1. No   **3.** No   **5.** Yes

7. Yes   **9.** Yes

11. $(-1, 9)$, $(0, 8)$, $(1, 7)$, $(10, -2)$,
$(8, 0)$, $(4, 4)$

13. $(-2, \frac{15}{2})$, $(0, 5)$, $(4, 0)$, $(8, -5)$,
$(4, 0)$, $(\frac{4}{5}, 4)$

15. $(-3, 8)$, $(0, 4)$, $(3, 0)$, $(6, -4)$,
$(3, 0)$, $(0, 4)$

17. x-intercept: 6; y-intercept: 6

19. x-intercept: 6; y-intercept: -6

21. x-intercept: -6; y-intercept: 6

23. x-intercept: 6; y-intercept: 3

25. x-intercept: 3; y-intercept: 4

27. x-intercept: 5; y-intercept: -3

29. x-intercept: $-\frac{7}{3}$; y-intercept: $\frac{7}{2}$

31.

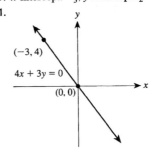

33.

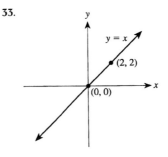

35.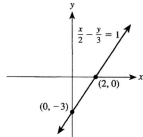

37.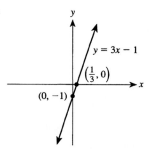

39.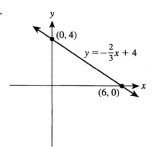

41.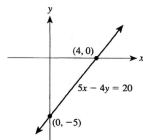

43.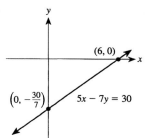

45.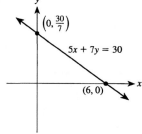

47.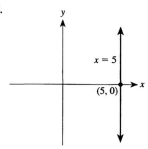

49.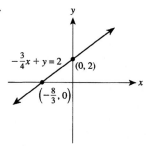

51.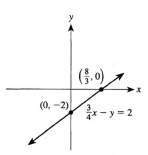

53.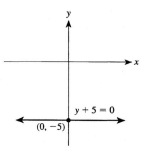

55.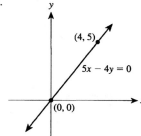

57.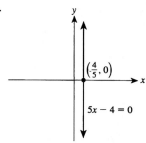

59.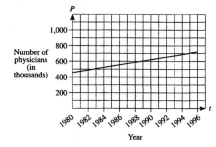

61. (a) $S = 0.05v + 220$
(b)

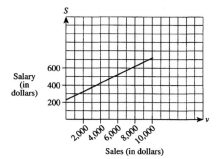

63. (a) $d = 260 + 52t$
(b)

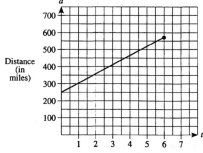

65. (a) $C = 29 + 0.14n$
(b)

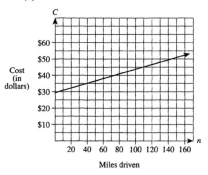

Cost (in dollars) vs. Miles driven

EXERCISES 3.2

1. (a) $y = -3$ when $x = -4$;
  $y = 1$ when $x = 4$
  (b) $x = 6$ when $y = 2$
3. (a) $y = -4$ when $x = -3$;
  $y = -4, 0$, and 3 when $x = 2$
  (b) $x = 1$ when $y = 2$; $x = 0$ and -2
  when $y = -6$
5. $y = -1$ **7.** $x = 3, x = -1$
9. (a) $(3, -3)$ (b) $(-4, 4)$
  (c) $(3, -3)$ and $(-2, -3)$
  (d) $(5, 4)$ and $(-4, 4)$
11. (a) $y = -3$ and 3
  (b) $x = -2$ and 2
13. (a) y-intercept $= 4$
  (b) x-intercept $= 8$
15. (a) y-intercept $= 2$
  (b) x-intercept $= -4$
  (c) Smallest x is -4; no largest x
  (d) Smallest y is 0; no largest y
17. (a) Smallest x is -3; no largest x
  (b) Largest y is 3; no smallest y
19. (a)

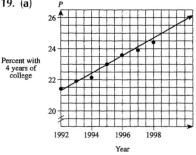

Percent with 4 years of college vs. Year

21. (a) $C = 0.10g$
  (b)

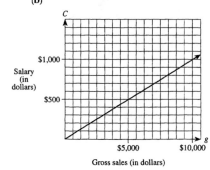

Salary (in dollars) vs. Gross sales (in dollars)

(c) $400
(d) $8,500
23. (a) $C = 10 + 0.25n$
  (b)

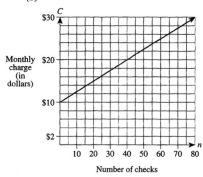

Monthly charge (in dollars) vs. Number of checks

(c) $22 to $23
(d) 20 checks

EXERCISES 3.3

1. $\{(3, 9), (3, 7), (8, 2), (7, 2)\}$
3. $\{(3, a), (3, b), (8, b), (-1, b), (-1, c)\}$
5. Domain: $\{3, 4, 5\}$; range: $\{2, 3\}$
7. Domain: $\{-2, 3, 4\}$; range: $\{-2, -1, 3\}$
9. $\{x \mid x \neq 0\}$ **11.** All reals
13. $\{x \mid x \neq -\frac{3}{2}\}$ **15.** All reals
17. $\{x \mid x \geq 4\}$ **19.** $\{x \mid x \leq \frac{5}{4}\}$
21. $\{x \mid x \geq 0\}$ **23.** $\{x \mid x > 3\}$
25. Function **27.** Not a function
29. Function **31.** Not a function
33. Function **35.** Function
37. Not a function **39.** Function
41. Not a function **43.** Not a function
45. Function **47.** Not a Function
49. Function **51.** Not a function **53.** 0
55. $(7, -6)$ **57.** Three; $x = -6, -2, 4$
59. One **61.** $\{x \mid -7 \leq x \leq 7\}$
63. 3 **65.** $(7, -3)$
67. Three: $x = -3, 2, 6$
69. One: $y = 2$ **71.** $\{x \mid -5 \leq x \leq 7\}$
73. Domain $= \{x \mid -4 \leq x \leq 5\}$;
  range $= \{y \mid -4 \leq y \leq 6\}$
75. Domain $= \{x \mid 0 \leq x \leq 4\}$;
  range $= \{y \mid -3 \leq y \leq 3\}$
77. Domain $= \{x \mid -5 \leq x \leq -2$ or
  $1 \leq x \leq 5\}$;
  range $= \{y \mid -3 \leq y \leq 1$ or
  $3 \leq y \leq 4\}$
79. $A = s^2$ **81.** $A = 2a^2 - 15; a \geq 3$
83. $C = 116 + 0.12m$
85. $C = 22d + 60$
87. $20,200; $30,800; $65,000; $130,000
89. (a) $C = 29.95 + 0.33m$
  (b) $54.70; $89.35; $128.95
91. (a) Yes
  (b) Domain: The rent varies
  between $200 and $400;
  Range: The profit varies
  between $35,000 and $50,000.
  (c) $300; $50,000

EXERCISES 3.4

1. -3 **3.** 11 **5.** 15
7. $\sqrt{8} = 2\sqrt{2}$ **9.** $\sqrt{2}$
11. $\sqrt{a + 5}$ **13.** 33 **15.** 6
17. $2x + 1$ **19.** $4x^2 + 2$
21. $6x + 1$ **23.** 4 **25.** 9
27. $x^2 + 2x - 7$ **29.** $x^2 + 2x - 24$
31. $9x^2 + 6x - 3$ **33.** $3x^2 + 6x - 9$
35. $-\frac{3}{2}$ **37.** $\frac{1}{21}$ **39.** $\frac{x + 5}{x + 10}$
41. (a) 1 (b) -1 (c) -2
  (d) $-\frac{1}{2}$ (e) 2
43. (a) 3 (b) 5 (c) 0
  (d) $x = -5, -3, 5$ (e) Two
45. $C = 87 + 0.14m$
47. $A = 3L^2 - 12L$
49. $C = 30x + 24(600 - x)$
51. $N = 20m + 22(m + 35)$
53. $A = 45h + 25(h - 2)$
55. $I = 10t + 6.35(15 - t)$

EXERCISES 3.5

1. (a) 7,500 (b) 4 A.M. (c) 30,000
  (d) Between 4 P.M. and 4 A.M.
  (e) Between 10 A.M. and 4 P.M.
  (f) Between 10 A.M. and 4 P.M.
3. (a) Consumed: 80 quadrillion Btu;
  produced: 65 quadrillion Btu;
  imported: 15 quadrillion Btu
  (b) Production: There was a slight
  decrease in production between
  1982 and 1983, followed by an
  increase beween 1983 and 1984.
  Production then slightly increased
  over the years 1984–1998.
  Consumption: There was a
  decrease in consumption from
  1980 to 1983, then a relatively
  steady increase from 1983 to
  1998. Imports: There was a
  decrease from 1980 to 1982
  and then a relatively steady
  increase from 1982 to 1998.
5. (a) The graph shows that the
  temperature does *not* drop
  steadily as altitude increases.
  (b) Between 0 and 10 kilometers,
  and between 50 and
  80 kilometers
  (c) Starting at 45 kilometers, the
  temperature increases until it
  reaches approximately 10°C at
  an altitude of 50 kilometers,
  then the temperature decreases.
7. (a) Approximately 30%
  (b) About 2 days
  (c) As time passes material is forgotten. Material is forgotten rapidly
  during the first 3 hours of the
  given time period (more than half
  the material is forgotten during

this time), then the rate of forgetting slows down. Only about 18–20% of the material is remembered by the 6th day.

9. (a) 14 trials   (b) 3 trials
   (c) Performance with spaced practice is superior to performance with massed practice. Learning with spaced practice occurs more rapidly than with massed practice.

11. Starting at home, Kyle starts his trip by traveling 90 miles away during the first 2 hours of the day. His average rate of speed during the first hour was 50 mph, and during the second hour was 40 mph. For the next 2 hours Kyle did not travel. Then Kyle traveled closer to his home between hours 4 and 5. He was traveling an average of 30 mph during this time. Kyle stopped again for about 1 hour, and then drove home in $1\frac{1}{2}$ hours at an average rate of 40 mph.

13. The graph shows that children assigned to each group had approximately the same number of aggressive behaviors before treatment. By the end of the treatment period, however, treatments A and C seemed to be the most effective in reducing these aggressive behaviors, whereas treatment C reduced their behaviors most quickly.

    After the treatment period, however, the children in treatment C reverted back to their aggressive behavior. Hence treatment C ends up being the least effective at the end of the time period given following treatment.

    The children in treatment B slowly reduced their aggressive behaviors even after the treatment ended. Although it seemed the least effective at the end of the treatment, it actually is shown to be the most effective of the three at the end of the time period given following treatment.

Chapter 3 Review Exercises

1.

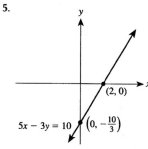

2.

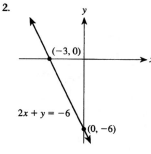

3.

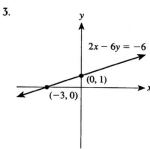

4.

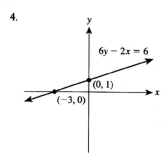

5.

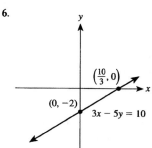

6.

7.

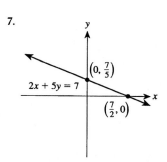

8.

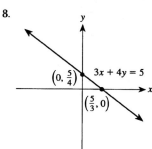

9.

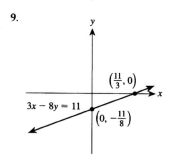

10.

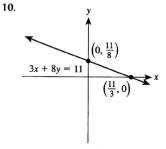

11.

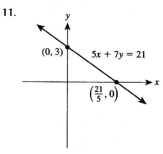

12.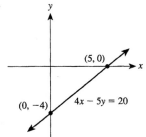

13.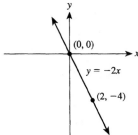

14.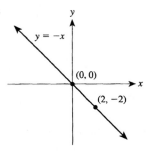

15.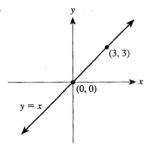

16.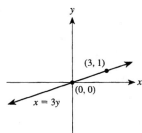

17.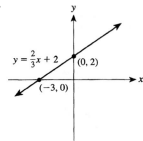

18.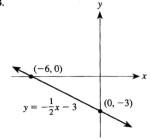

19.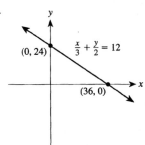

20.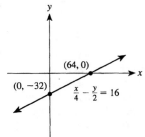

21.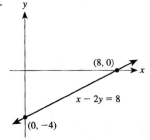

22.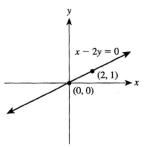

23.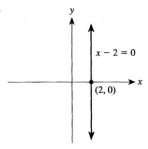

24.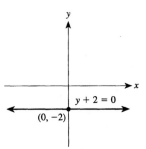

25.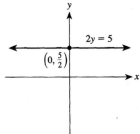

26.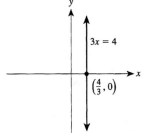

27. (a) $y = 3$ when $x = -2$;
  $y = -1$ when $x = 2$
  (b) $x = 1$ and $x = -2$ when $y = 3$
28. (a) $y = 4$ and $y = -2$ when $x = -3$
  (b) $x = 3$ when $y = 2$;
    $x = 2$ when $y = -5$
29. $y = 6$

30. (a) $(5, 4)$ (b) $(5, 4)$ and $(-1, 4)$
31. x-intercepts $= 1$ and 3
32. y-intercept $= 2$
33. $y = -4$ and 4
34. $x = -2$ and 2
35. (a) $I = 150 + 0.05g$

(b)

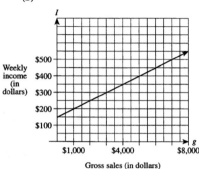

(c) $400
(d) $12,000
36. (a) $C = 30 + 0.20m$

(b)

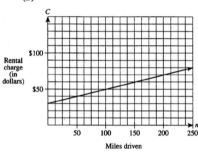

(c) $70
(d) 175 miles
37. All reals   38. All reals
39. $\{x \mid x \leq 4\}$ 40. $\{x \mid x \geq -3\}$
41. $\{x \mid x \neq -2\}$ 42. $\{x \mid x \neq -\frac{1}{2}\}$
43. Function   44. Not a function
45. Not a function   46. Function
47. Function   48. Function
49. Function   50. Not a function
51. Function   52. Function
53. Not a function   54. Function
55. Domain $= \{-2, 0, 3, 5\}$;
range $= \{3, 4, 5, 7\}$; function
56. Domain $= \{-3, 0, 2\}$;
range $= \{-8, 0, 7, 10\}$; not a function
57. Domain $= \{1, 4, 6, 8\}$;
range $= \{9\}$; function
58. Domain $= \{6\}$;
range $= \{-5, -3, 0, 2\}$; not a function
59. Domain $= \{x \mid -5 \leq x \leq 6\}$;
range $= \{y \mid -2 \leq y \leq 5\}$; function
60. Domain $=$ all real numbers;
range $= \{y \mid y \geq -3\}$; function

61. Domain $= \{x \mid -3 \leq x \leq 3\}$;
range $= \{y \mid -4 \leq y \leq 4\}$;
not a function
62. Domain $=$ all real numbers;
range $=$ all real numbers; function
63. $2, 5, 8, 11$ 64. $9, 5, 1, -3$
65. $7, 2, 1, 4$ 66. $-8, -3, 2, 25$
67. $1, 0, h(4)$ is not a real number
[4 not in the domain of $h(x)$]
68. $\sqrt{2}, g(2)$ is not a real number
[2 not in the domain of $g(x)$],
$\sqrt{8} = 2\sqrt{2}$
69. $0, \frac{1}{3}$, undefined [-3 not in the domain of $h(x)$]
70. 0, undefined [0 not in the domain of $h(x)$], $\frac{5}{4}$
71. $2a^2 + 4a - 1, 2z^2 + 4z - 1$
72. $2x^2 - 4x + 2, 2z^2 - 4z + 2$
73. $5x + 12$ 74. $5x + 17$
75. $5x + 4$ 76. $5x + 5$
77. $5x + 14$ 78. $5x + 19$
79. $4 - x$ 80. $3 - x$
81. $6 - 2x$ 82. $6 - 3x$
83. $12 - 2x$ 84. $18 - 3x$
85. (a) 0 (b) 2 (c) -2 (d) -3
(e) $f(5)$ (f) $x = -6, -2, 5$
86. (a) 5 (b) 1 (c) 3 (d) -1
(e) 2 (f) $x = 3, 5$
87. Rasheed starts his trip by traveling 90 miles away from his home during the first 2 hours of the day. His average rate of speed for the first hour was 40 mph; during the second hour his average rate was 50 mph. During the next hour Rasheed did not travel. Then Rasheed drove closer to his home between hours 3 and 4. He was traveling an average of 60 mph during this time. Rasheed drove another 20 miles away from his home, traveling at 20 mph between the 4th and 5th hour. Finally, during the last hour, Rasheed drove home at a rate of 50 mph.
88. If you look carefully at the distance it travels (the vertical change) for each half-second interval (horizontal change), you see that the distance it falls is getting longer for each progressive half-second. If you compute the speed, you can see that the longer the ball stays in the air, the faster it travels; that is, its speed is increasing with time.
89. $C = 30 + 42n$
90. $M = 5,000 + 2,500s$

Chapter 3 Practice Test

1. (a)

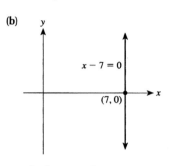

(b)

$x - 7 = 0$

$(7, 0)$

2. $y = 3$ when $x = 5$
3. (a) Domain $= \{2, 3, 4\}$;
range $= \{-3, 5, 6\}$
(b) Domain $= \{x \mid -4 \leq x \leq 5\}$;
range $= \{y \mid -3 \leq y \leq 6\}$
4. (a) $\{x \mid x \geq 4\}$ (b) $\{x \mid x \neq \frac{4}{3}\}$
5. (a) Not a function (b) Function
(c) Not a function (d) Function
6. (a) $\sqrt{5}$ (b) 23 (c) $5x - 13$
(d) $3x^4 - 4$ (e) $3x^2 - 75$
7. (a) 2 (b) -2 (c) 0 (d) 2
(e) $f(-4)$ (f) $x = 0, 5$
8. (a) 30 minutes (b) 8 mg
(c) Between 10 and 20 minutes; 3 mg

**CHAPTERS 1–3
CUMULATIVE REVIEW**

The number in parentheses after the answer indicates the section in which the material is discussed.
1. $\{11, 13, 17, 19, 23, 29, 31, 37\}$ (§1.1)
2. $\varnothing$ (§1.1) 3. $\varnothing$ (§1.1)
4. $\{10, 11, 13, 15, 17, 19, 20, 23, 25, 29, 30, 31, 35, 37\}$ (§1.1)
5. True (§1.2) 6. False (§1.2)
7. (§1.2):

8. (§1.2):

9. Closure property for addition (§1.3)
10. Multiplicative inverse property (§1.3)

80. (§3.1):

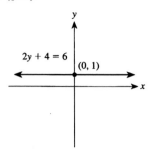

$2y + 4 = 6$
$(0, 1)$

81. (a) Approx. 40,000   (b) Approx. 4.7 hr
(c) Between 3.5 and 5.5 hr
(d) After approx. 7.5 hr (§3.5)

82. $I = 275 + 0.025s$ (§3.3)

83. $C = 350 + 75h$ (§3.3)

84. Domain = $\{x \mid -3 \le x \le 5\}$;
range = $\{y \mid -1 \le y \le 4\}$ (§3.3)

85. Domain = all real numbers;
range = $\{y \mid y \ge -3\}$ (§3.3)

86. (a) -3 (b) -3 (c) 5   (d) -4
(e) $f(1)$ (f) $-6, -1, 5$ (§3.4)

87. Let h = the number of hours Jonas
grades homework papers, and I =
the total amount of money he makes;
$I = 15h + 25(20 - h) = 500 - 10h$;
he makes $450 grading 5 hours; to
make $380, he should be grading
homework for 12 hours. (§3.1):

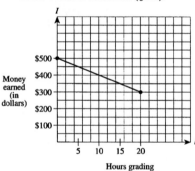

Money earned (in dollars)

Hours grading

CHAPTERS 1–3
CUMULATIVE PRACTICE TEST

1. (a) $\{4, 8, 12, 16, 20\} = A$
(b) $\{2, 4, 6, 8, 10, 12, 14, 16, 18, 20, 22\} = B$

2. Distributive property

3. (a) -4 (b) -18 **4.** 6

5. (a) $x = -3$ (b) No solution
(c) $x = 11, -5$

6. (a) $x > \frac{9}{4}$:

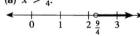

(b) $-1 < x < \frac{7}{3}$:

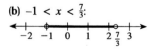

(c) $x \le 1$ or $x \ge \frac{3}{2}$:

---

7. Let p = number of packages weighing 30 lb; $30p + 10(170 - p) = 3{,}140$; seventy-two 30-lb packages, ninety-eight 10-lb packages

8. Let t = time the faster car travels;
$55t = 40(t + 1)$; $2\frac{2}{3}$ hours

9. Evan starts his trip by traveling
50 miles away from his home during
the first hour of the day; his average
rate of speed for the first hour was
50 mph. During the next 2 hours Evan
did not travel. Then Evan drove closer
to his home between hours 3 and 4.
He was traveling an average of 40 mph
during this time, and ended up only
10 miles from his home. Evan drove
another 60 miles away from his home
traveling at 60 mph between the 4th
and 5th hour, and stopped traveling
for an hour. Finally, during the last
hour and a half, Evan drove home
at a rate of 47 mph.

10.

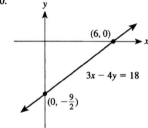

$(6, 0)$
$3x - 4y = 18$
$(0, -\frac{9}{2})$

11. The x-intercepts are -4 and 4.

12. (a) $\{x \mid x \ne 9\}$ (b) $\left\{x \mid x \ge \frac{3}{2}\right\}$

13. (a) $\frac{7}{4}$ (b) $4x^2 - 1$
(c) $\frac{x}{x + 3}$ (d) $\frac{x - 2}{x + 1} + 2$
(e) $20x - 1$ (f) $20x - 5$
(g) Undefined   (h) -9

14. (a) 2   (b) -2 (c) 0   (d) 3
(e) $f(-3)$ (f) 0 and 5
(g) Domain = $\{x \mid -6 \le x \le 7\}$;
range = $\{y \mid -2 \le y \le 3\}$

15. Let g = his gross sales, and S = his
weekly salary; $S = 200 + 0.10g$; he
would need about $4,000 in gross
sales to make $600 a week.

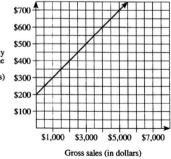

Weekly income (in dollars)

Gross sales (in dollars)

EXERCISES 4.1

1.

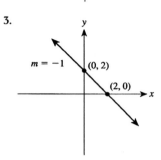

$m = -\frac{3}{4}$
$(-3, 1)$
$(1, -2)$

3.

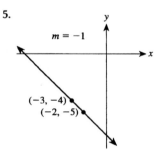

$m = -1$ $(0, 2)$
$(2, 0)$

5.

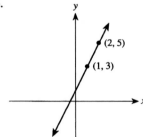

$m = -1$
$(-3, -4)$
$(-2, -5)$

7. Slope = 0   **9.** Undefined

11. 1   **13.** $\frac{b^2 - a^2}{b - a} = b + a$

15. -0.531 (to 3 places)

17. -20.412 (to 3 places)

19. 1.5   **21.** 3.5   **23.** $\frac{3}{5}$

25.

$(2, 5)$
$(1, 3)$

27.

$(0, 5)$
$(1, 3)$

29.

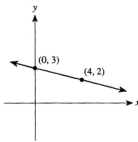

31.

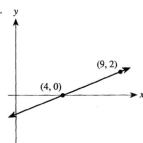

33.

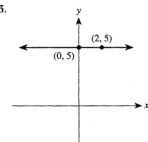

35.

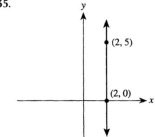

37. $m = 2$ **39.** $m = -0.4$
41. $m = 1.5$ **43.** Parallel
45. Neither   **47.** Perpendicular
49. $h = 13$
51. The slopes of the parallel sides are $\frac{1}{2}$ and $-\frac{5}{2}$.
53. The slope of one side is $-\frac{1}{2}$ and of another side is 2. Hence the two sides are perpendicular to each other.
55. 160 meters $= 0.16$ km
57. Approximately 10,417 ft
59. Sprinter runs 10.8 m/sec.
61. The slope represents the average change in °F per hour. In this case, the temperature *falls* an average of 3.5°F per hour.

63. The slope gives the change in profit per change in wholesale price. Choosing points (100, 40) and (135, 100) on the line, we obtain a slope of $\frac{12}{7}$. This means the profit increases by $12,000 for every $7 increase in wholesale price (or a $1,714 increase in profit for every dollar increase in wholesale price).

Mini-Review

70. $54x^{11}$ **71.** $-6x^2y - 16xy^2$
72. 3   **73.** $t = 21$

EXERCISES 4.2

1. $y = 5x - 8$ **3.** $y = -3x - 13$
5. $y = \frac{2}{3}x - 3$ **7.** $y = -\frac{1}{2}x + 2$
9. $y = \frac{3}{4}x + 5$ **11.** $y = -4$
13. $x = -4$ **15.** $y = \frac{4}{3}x + \frac{1}{3}$
17. $y = 4x + 7$ **19.** $y = -x + 5$
21. $y = 4x + 6$ **23.** $y = -2x - 6$
25. $y = 3$ **27.** $x = -2$
29. $y = \frac{2}{3}x + 2$ **31.** $y = 3x - 4$
33. $y = \frac{3}{2}x + \frac{13}{2}$ **35.** $y = -x$
37. $y = \frac{3}{2}x - \frac{1}{2}$ **39.** $y = -\frac{3}{4}x - \frac{9}{4}$
41. $y = -\frac{5}{8}x - 4$ **43.** $y = -2x + 4$
45. $y = 3$ **47.** $x = -1$ **49.** $y = \frac{3}{2}x$
51. $y = \frac{7}{2}x - 7$
53. (a) $H = 55t - 108,700$
   (b) 1,245 billion
55. Parallel   **57.** Neither
59. Perpendicular   **61.** Parallel
63. $C = 0.12n + 29; m = 0.12$
65. $B = 0.825n + 23; m = 0.825$
67. $P = 30x - 340;$ if $x = 200,$ $P = \$5,660$
69. Test B score: 85
71. $V = -1,000E + 105,000;$ $E = 90$ when $V = 15,000$

Mini-Review

75. -6 **76.** $x \geq -1$ **77.** $\{x \mid x \neq \frac{5}{4}\}$
78. $y = \frac{8x - 12}{3}$

EXERCISES 4.3

1. $x = 5, y = 2$ **3.** $x = 4, y = 3$
5. $x = 1, y = 3$ **7.** $x = 6, y = 2$
9. $x = 5, y = -4$ **11.** Dependent
13. Inconsistent   **15.** $x = 5, y = 0$
17. $x = -1, y = 1$
19. $a = \frac{13}{27}, b = \frac{17}{27}$ **21.** $s = \frac{5}{2}, t = \frac{5}{2}$
23. $m = \frac{8}{7}, n = -\frac{16}{7}$
25. $p = 3, q = 1$ **27.** $u = \frac{27}{5}, v = \frac{4}{5}$
29. $w = 12, z = 6$ **31.** $x = 3, y = 2$
33. $x = 2, y = 6$ **35.** $x = 3, y = 7$
37. $x = \frac{1}{2}, y = 2$

39. Let $x =$ amount invested at 5% and $y =$ amount at 8%; $x + y = 14,000,$ $0.05x + 0.08y = 835;$ $9,500 at 5% and $4,500 at 8%
41. Let $x =$ amount at 8% and $y =$ amount at 10%; $x + y = 10,000, 0.08x = 0.10y;$ $5,555.56 at 8% and $4,444.44 at 10%
43. Let $L =$ length and $W =$ width; $L = W + 2, 2L + 2W = 36;$ 8 cm by 10 cm
45. Let $T =$ cost of 35-mm roll and $M =$ cost of movie roll; $5T + 3M = 35.60, 3T + 5M = 43.60;$ cost of movie roll $=$ $6.95 each; cost of 35-mm roll $=$ $2.95 each
47. Let $c =$ cost of cream-filled donut and $j =$ cost of jelly donut; $7c + 5j = 3.16, 4c + 8j = 3.04;$ single cream donut $=$ 28¢; single jelly donut $=$ 24¢
49. Let $E =$ # of expensive models and $L =$ # of less expensive models; $6E + 5L = 730, 3E + 2L = 340;$ 80 of the more expensive type and 50 of the less expensive type
51. Let $y =$ cost of the plan, $x =$ total annual medical expenses; $y = 1,680 + 0.10x, y = 1,200 + 0.25x;$ plans are equal at $3,200 in annual medical expenses.
53. Let $C =$ cost of rental, $n =$ number of miles driven; $C = 29 + 0.12n,$ $C = 22 + 0.15n;$ costs are equal if 233.3 miles are driven.
55. The break-even point is 14,400 units
57. Let $C =$ cost per month, $n =$ number of calls per month; $C = 18 + 0.11n,$ $C = 24 + 0.09(n - 50);$ plans are equal at 75 calls per month.
59. Let $f =$ # of five-dollar bills and $t =$ # of ten-dollar bills; $f + t = 43, 5f + 10t = 340;$ eighteen $5 bills and twenty-five $10 bills
61. Let $f =$ flat rate and $r =$ mileage rate; $f + 85r = 44.30, f + 125r = 51.50;$ $29 flat rate and 18¢ per mile
63. Let $x =$ speed of plane and $y =$ wind speed; $6(x + y) = 2,310, 6(x - y) = 1,530;$ speed of plane $=$ 320 mph, speed of wind $=$ 65 mph

65. $\frac{y - 3}{x - 2} = -1; \frac{y + 2}{x - 1} = 2;$ $x = 3, y = 2$
67. 1994

Mini-Review

71. $x = 8$ **72.** $x = 24$
73. $f(-4) = 57; f(a) = 3a^2 - 2a + 1$

Mini-Review

61. 0   62. $x \geq \frac{-7}{3}$
63. Distributive property
64. $x = 0$ or $x = 5$
65. Let t = the time Bobby was running;
   $6t = 5(t + 1)$; it takes Bobby 5 hours
66. Let t = the number of minutes it
   takes for both to complete the job;
   $32t + 40t = 3,960$; it takes
   55 minutes

Chapter 4 Review Exercises

1. $-\frac{1}{2}$ 2. $-\frac{3}{5}$ 3. 3 4. $\frac{2}{3}$ 5. $\frac{3}{4}$ 6. $\frac{1}{3}$
7. $\frac{1}{2}$ 8. $-\frac{4}{3}$ 9. 0 10. -2 11. 0
12. Undefined 13. 3 14. $-\frac{1}{5}$
15. $-\frac{3}{5}$ 16. $\frac{3}{2}$ 17. Undefined
18. 0 19. $a = 14$ 20. $a = 0$
21. $a = \frac{21}{10}$ 22. $a = \frac{25}{7}$
23. $y = -\frac{7}{3}x - \frac{5}{3}$ 24. $y = 2x - 2$
25. $y = \frac{5}{3}x$ 26. $y = -3x$
27. $y = \frac{2}{5}x + \frac{21}{5}$ 28. $y = -4x + 4$
29. $y = 5x - 13$ 30. $y = -\frac{3}{4}x + \frac{41}{4}$
31. $y = 5x + 3$ 32. $y = -3x - 4$
33. $y = 3$ 34. $y = -4$ 35. $y = \frac{3}{2}x$
36. $y = \frac{1}{5}x + \frac{3}{5}$ 37. $y = -\frac{2}{5}x + 6$
38. $y = \frac{6}{7}x + \frac{5}{7}$ 39. $y = \frac{5}{3}x$
40. $y = -\frac{3}{5}x$ 41. $y = \frac{5}{3}x - 5$
42. $y = -\frac{8}{5}x + 8$ 43. $y = \frac{3}{2}x + \frac{3}{5}$
44. $y = -\frac{2}{5}x - 2$
45. $P = 160x - 28,000$; $P = \$36,000$
   when $x = 400$ gadgets
46. Jake's score on test B: 86;
   Charles' score on test A: 37
47. (a) $P = 16.67t - 32,533$
   (b) 790,000 physicians
48. (a) $D = 4.4545t - 8,685$
   (b) 220,000 dentists
49. $x = 5, y = 1$ 50. $x = 3, y = -2$
51. $x = 8, y = 0$ 52. $x = \frac{1}{2}, y = \frac{1}{3}$
53. Dependent 54. Inconsistent
55. $x = -\frac{1}{5}, y = \frac{7}{5}$
56. $s = \frac{64}{23}, t = -\frac{2}{23}$
57. Let $\$x$ be deposited at 4.75% and
   $\$y$ be deposited at 6.65%;
   $0.0475x + 0.0665y = 512.05$,
   $x + y = 8,500$; $\$5,700$ at 6.65%
   and $\$2,800$ at 4.75%
58. Let price per lb of bread = $\$x$
   and price per lb of cookies = $\$y$;
   $3x + 5y = 22.02$, $2x + 3y =$
   13.43; $x = \$1.09$/lb, $y = \$3.75$/lb

59.
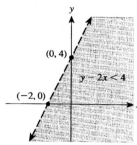

60.
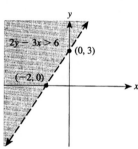

61.
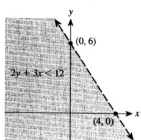

62.
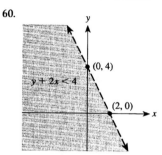

63.
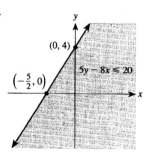

64.
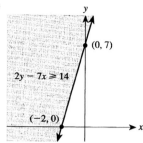

65.
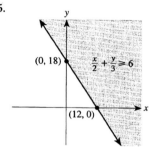

66.
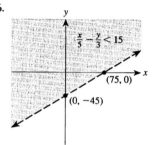

67.
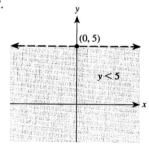

68.
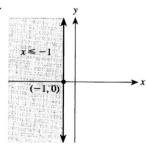

69. $2x + 2y > 100$;

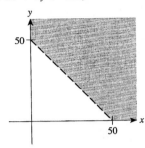

70. $9t + 6b \leq 72$;

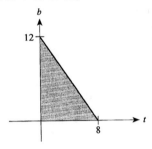

Chapter 4 Practice Test

1. (a)

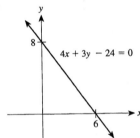

$4x + 3y - 24 = 0$

(b)

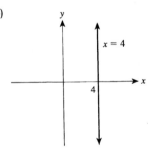

$x = 4$

(c)

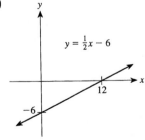

$y = \frac{1}{2}x - 6$

---

2. (a) 1 **(b)** $\frac{3}{2}$ **3.** $a = \frac{1}{2}$
4. (a) $y = 8x - 19$
   (b) $y = -4x + 4$
   (c) $y = x + 3$
   (d) $y = -\frac{x}{3} - \frac{7}{3}$
   (e) $y = 3x - 9$
   (f) $y = -1$
5. 165 on test B   **6.** $y = \frac{1}{2}x + \frac{3}{2}$
7. (a) $x = 8, y = -5$
   (b) $a = -3, b = 6$
8. Let x = amount invested at $8\frac{1}{2}\%$
   and y = amount invested at 9%;
   $x + y = 3,500, 0.085x + 0.09y$
   $= 309$; \$1,200 at $8\frac{1}{2}\%$, \$2,300 at 9%
9.

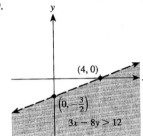

$(4, 0)$

$\left(0, -\frac{3}{2}\right)$

$3x - 8y > 12$

10. $315c + 425s \leq 7,200$

EXERCISES 5.1

1. 2 terms; degree 2; 1 variable;
   coefficients are 5 and 4
3. 1 term; degree 0; no variables;
   coefficient is 59
5. Not a polynomial
7. 1 term; degree 11; 3 variables;
   coefficient is -4
9. Not a polynomial
11. 4 terms; degree 3; 1 variable;
   coefficients are 4, -1, -2, and 1
13. 1970: 32.6; 1975: 35.4;
   1980: 39.9; 1985: 46.2;
   1990: 54.2; 1995: 64.0
15. (a) $R(d) = 4,300d - 10d^3$
   (b) $R(8) = 29,280$; $R(10) =$
   $33,000$; $R(12) = 34,320$;
   $R(14) = 32,760$
17. (a) $R(n) = 2n + 0.45n^2 - 0.001n^3$
   (b) $R(100) = 3,700$; $R(200) =$
   $10,400$; $R(300) = 14,100$ at
   prices \$37, \$52, and \$47,
   respectively
19. $S(w) = 14w^2 - 48w$;
   $S(20) = 4,640$ sq in.;
   $S(26) = 8,216$ sq in.;
   $S(42) = 22,680$ sq in.
21. (a) $(0, 0)$, $(5, 8.7)$, $(10, 21.8)$,
   $(15, 24.5)$, $(20, 1.6)$, $(25, 0)$, $(30, 0)$
   (b) Approximately 13 minutes
   after the medication is taken

Mini-Review

23. 4   **24.** -6
25. First side is 34 in.;
   second side is 17 in.
26. 4.5 hr

EXERCISES 5.2

1. $5x^2 - 9x + 9$
3. $-x^2 - 3xy - 4y^2 + 3x - 2$
5. $6a^2 - 5ab + 3b^2$
7. $ab + 5b^2$ **9.** $-5b^2 - ab$
11. $-5y^2 + 3xy - 3y + 4$
13. $-11x^2 - 3xy + 2y^2$
15. $-5a^2 + ab - 4b^2$
17. $3x^4y - 2x^3y^2 + 2x^2y^3$
19. $3x^4y - 2x^3y^2 + 2x^2y^3$
21. $x^2 + 7x + 12$
23. $6x^2 + x - 1$
25. $6x^2 - x - 1$
27. $3a^2 + 2ab - b^2$
29. $4r^2 - 4rs + s^2$ **31.** $4r^2 - s^2$
33. $9x^2 - 4y^2$
35. $9x^2 - 12xy + 4y^2$
37. $ax - bx - ay + by$
39. $4ar + 6br + 6as + 9bs$
41. $2y^4 - y^2 - 3$
43. $5x^3 + 12x^2 - 5x + 12$
45. $27a^3 + 18a^2 - 12a - 5$
47. $a^3 + b^3$
49. $x^2 + y^2 + z^2 - 2xy - 2xz + 2yz$
51. $x^3 + 8$
53. $a^2 + b^2 + 2ab + ac + ad$
   $+ bc + bd$
55. $P = 2w + 2(3w + 5)$
   $= 8w + 10$;
   $A = w(3w + 5) = 3w^2 + 5w$
57. $A = \pi(8 + x)^2 - \pi(8)^2$
   $= \pi x^2 + 16\pi x$ sq. ft
59. $A = (20 + 2x)(60 + 2x)$
   $- (20)(60)$
   $= 4x^2 + 160x$ sq. ft
61. $-3x^2 + 7x - 5$
63. $x^3 + 3x^2 - 8x + 5$
65. $6x^3 - 19x^2 + 19x - 6$
67. $3x^5 - 3x^4 - 4x^3 + 3x^2 + x$
69. $3x^2 - 5x + 6$
71. $3x^2 + 7x + 4$
73. $x^3 - x - 1$

Mini-Review

77. $\frac{19}{7}$
78. 36 30-lb packages;
   24 25-lb packages
79. $-1 \leq x \leq 4$ **80.** No solution

EXERCISES 5.3

1. $x^2 + 9x + 20$ **3.** $x^2 - 4x - 21$
5. $x^2 - 19x + 88$ **7.** $x^2 - x - 30$

9. $6x - 30$ 11. -3
13. $2x^2 - 7x - 4$ 15. $25a^2 - 16$
17. $9z^2 + 30z + 25$
19. $9z^2 - 30z + 25$ 21. $9z^2 - 25$
23. $15r^3 + 25r^2s + 9rs + 15s^2$
25. $9s^2 - 12sy + 4y^2$
27. $9y^2 + 60yz + 100z^2$
29. $9y^2 - 100z^2$
31. $9a^2 + 18ab + 8b^2$
33. $64a^2 - 16a + 1$
35. $25r^2 - 20rs + 4s^2$
37. $56x^2 - 113x + 56$
39. $25t^2 - 15s^2t + 15st - 9s^3$
41. $9y^6 - 24xy^3 + 16x^2$
43. $9y^6 - 16x^2$
45. $4r^2s^2t^2 - 28rstxyz + 49x^2y^2z^2$
47. $-9x^2 - 5x - 5$ 49. $-4ab$
51. $-30a^3 - 5a^2 + 10a$
53. $-10a^2 + 8a + 2$ 55. $3rs^2$
57. $-y^2 + 19y - 7$
59. $125a^3 - 225a^2b + 135ab^2 - 27b^3$
61. $-2x^3 - x^2 + x$
63. $a^2 + 2ab + b^2 - 1$
65. $a^2 - 4ab + 4b^2 + 10az$
$\qquad\qquad - 20bz + 25z^2$
67. $a^2 - 4ab + 4b^2 - 25z^2$
69. $a^2 + 2ab + b^2 - 4x^2 - 4x - 1$
71. $a^{2n} - 9$ 73. $3x^2 + 10x + 9$
75. $3x^2 - 2x + 10$
77. $12x^2 - 4x + 1$
79. $6x^2 - 4x + 2$
81. $7x^2 - 6x + 11$
83. $V = 4x^3 - 4x^2 + x$
85. $2x^2 - 30$ 87. $36x + 138$

Mini-Review

93. $x < -1$ or $x > \frac{7}{3}$
94. 3 hours 15 minutes
95. 2.8 in. by 18 in.
96. (a)

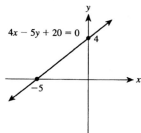

(b)

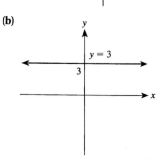

EXERCISES 5.4

1. $2x(2x + 1)$ 3. $x(x + 1)$
5. $3xy^2(1 - 2xy)$
7. $3x^2(2x^2 + 3x - 7)$
9. $5x^2y^3z(7x^2y - 3xy^2 + 2z)$
11. $6r^2s^3(4rs - 3rs^2 - 1)$
13. $7ab(5ab^2 - 3a^2b + 1)$
15. $(3x + 5)(x + 2)$
17. $(3x - 5)(x + 2)$
19. $(2x + 5y)(x + 3y)$
21. $(x + 4y)(3x - 5y)$
23. $2(r + 3)(a - 2)$
25. $2(a - 3)^2(x + 1)$
27. $4a(b - 4)(4ab - 16a - 1)$
29. $(2x + 3)(x - 4)$
31. $(3x + 5y)(x - 4y)$
33. $(7x + 3y)(a - b)$
35. $(7x - 3y)(a + b)$
37. $(7x - 3y)(a - b)$
39. Not factorable
41. $(2r - s)(r + s)$
43. Not factorable
45. $(5a - 2b)(a - b)$
47. $(3a - 1)(a - 2)$
49. $(3a + 1)(a - 2)$
51. $(3a - 1)(a + 2)$
53. $(a + 2)(a^2 + 4)$

Mini-Review

58. $a = \frac{1}{2}$
59. $1 \leq a \leq 5$ 60. $a \leq 1$ or $a \geq 5$
61.

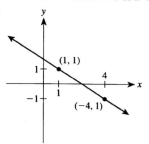

EXERCISES 5.5

1. $(x + 9)(x - 5)$
3. $(y - 5)(y + 2)$
5. $(x - 5y)(x + 3y)$
7. $(r + 9)(r - 9)$
9. $(x - 3y)(x + 2y)$
11. Not factorable
13. $(r - 3s)(r - 4s)$
15. $(r - 4s)(r + 3s)$
17. $(3x + 7y)(3x - 7y)$
19. $(5x + 4)(3x + 1)$
21. $(5x + 3y)(3x - 2y)$
23. $(5x - 3y)(3x + 2y)$
25. $(3x - 5y)(x + 5y)$
27. $(5a - 2b)(2a + 5b)$
29. $(5 + y)(5 - 2y)$
31. Not factorable

33. $2x(x + 4)(x - 2)$
35. $x(x + 7)(x - 4)$
37. $(x - 2)(3x + 1)$
39. $3ab(2 - 3x)(3 + 2x)$
41. $6y^2(5y - 3)(3y - 2)$
43. $(2r^2 + 1)(3r^2 - 2)$
45. $3(x + 3)(x - 3)$
47. $2xy(10y^4 + xy^2 - 4x^2)$
49. $3xy(6x - y^2)(6x + 5y^2)$
51. $ab(3a^3 - 2)(4a^3 + 3)$
53. $(5a^4 - 2)(3a^4 + 5)$
55. $(4x + 3y)(4x - 3y)$
57. $(x + 2y)^2$ 59. $(x - 2y)^2$
61. Not factorable
63. $(3xy - 1)(2xy - 1)$
65. $(9rs - 4)(9rs + 4)$
67. $(3xy + 2z)(3xy - 2z)$
69. $a^2(5 - 2b)(5 + 2b)$
71. $(1 - 7a)^2$
73. $(2a - b)(4a^2 + 2ab + b^2)$
75. $(x + 5y)(x^2 - 5xy + 25y^2)$
77. Not factorable
79. $2(2y^2 - 10y + 5)$
81. $3ac(2a + 3c)^2$
83. $(2x^2 + 9y^2)(2x^2 - 9y^2)$
85. $(5a^3 + b)^2$ 87. $3y^2(4y^4 + 9)$
89. $(a + b + 2)(a + b - 2)$
91. $(a - b + 4)(a - b - 4)$
93. $(x + 3 + r)(x + 3 - r)$
95. $(a + 1)(a + 2)(a - 2)$
97. $(x + 1)(x - 1)(x^2 + x + 1)$
99. $n(n - 2)(n - 1)$

Mini-Review

110. $m = 11$
111. $y = -6x + 31$
112.

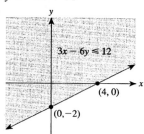

113. Let $s = $ # of pairs of sandals and
    $F = $ the weekly temperature in °F;
    $s = 2F - 128$; at 90°, 52 pairs will
    be sold.

EXERCISES 5.6

1. $x = -2, 3$ 3. $y = \frac{1}{2}, 4$
5. $x = \pm 5$ 7. $x = 0, 4$
9. $x = 6, -2$ 11. $y = 0, 7$
13. $x = \pm 4$ 15. $c = \pm \frac{4}{3}$
17. $a = \pm \frac{3}{2}$ 19. $x = 3, -2$
21. $y = 1, \frac{1}{2}$ 23. $x = \frac{7}{2}, -4$
25. $x = 0, -3, 2$ 27. $t = 0, -1$

29. $m = 0, -\frac{1}{2}, \frac{1}{2}$ 31. $x = \frac{10}{3}$
33. $t = 5$ 35. $t = -5, 2$
37. $x = -10, -2$ 39. $x = -\frac{2}{3}, \frac{2}{3}$
41. $x = 3, -2$ 43. $x = -10$
45. (a) $x = -3, 5$; (b) $x = -4, 6$
47. Let x = number; $x^2 - 5 = 5x + 1$;
$\quad x = 6$
49. Let x = number; $x^2 + 64 = 68$;
$\quad x = 2$
51. Let x = number; $(x + 6)^2 = 169$;
$\quad x = -19$ or $x = 7$
53. Let x = number; $x + \frac{1}{x} = \frac{13}{6}$;
$\quad x = \frac{2}{3}$ or $x = \frac{3}{2}$
55. Let x = number; $x + \frac{2}{x} = 3$; $x = 2$
$\quad$ or $x = 1$
57. (a) Profit = \$0 (b) Price = \$6
59. (a) $s = 48$ ft (b) $t = 2$ sec
$\quad$ (c) 64 ft
61. Let x = width; $(x + 2)(x) = 80$;
$\quad$ length = 10 ft, width = 8 ft
63. Let x = width of walkway;
$\quad (20 + 2x)(55 + 2x) - (20)(55)$
$\quad = 400$; width of walkway is $2\frac{1}{2}$ ft

Mini-Review

67. Let h = # of hours it takes 52-mph
$\quad$ car to catch up; $52h = 40(h + 1)$;
$\quad$ 3 hours 20 minutes
68. $-\frac{2}{3} \le x < \frac{7}{3}$;

$\quad -\frac{2}{3} \qquad \frac{7}{3}$

69. $m = \frac{3}{2}$ 70. $y = \frac{5}{4}x + 5$

EXERCISES 5.7

Note: R stands for remainder.

1. $x + 4$ 3. $a + 2$
5. $7z - 2, R -14$
7. $a^2 + 2a + 3, R -5$
9. $3x^2 + x - 1, R 8$
11. $2z - 3, R -6$
13. $x^3 + 3x^2 + 2x + 1$
15. $3y^3 - 2y^2 + 5, R -5$
17. $2a^3 - 5, R 16$
19. $y^2 - y + 1, R -2$
21. $4a^2 + 2a + 1, R 2$
23. $2y^3 - 3y^2 - 2y + 2, R 3y + 2$
25. $3z^3 - 6z^2 + 11z - 25$,
$\quad R 73z - 35$
27. $7x^4 - 3, R x - 5$

Mini-Review

29. $f(4) = 70$;
$\quad f(x^2) = 5x^4 - 3x^2 + 2$

Chapter 5 Review Exercises

1. $2x^3 - 7x^2 + 3x - 5$
2. $6x^2 - 8x + 15$
3. $6x^3y - 9x^2y + 3x^2$
4. $15r^3s^3 - 10r^2s^4 - 15rs^2$
5. $-ab^2$ 6. $-4x^2y - 11xy^2 + 18xy$
7. $-2x + 16$ 8. $21x - 28$
9. $x^2 - x - 6$ 10. $x^2 - 13x + 40$
11. $6y^2 - 7y + 2$ 12. $25y^2 - 9a^2$
13. $9x^2 - 24xy + 16y^2$
14. $5a^2 - 7ab - 6b^2$
15. $16x^4 - 40x^2y + 25y^2$
16. $16a^2 - 9b^4$ 17. $49x^4 - 25y^6$
18. $6x^3 - 19x^2 + 12x - 5$
19. $10y^3 - 21y^2 + 23y - 21$
20. $21x^3 - 5x^2y - 12xy^2 + 4y^3$
21. $4x^2 + 12xy + 9y^2 - 2x - 3y - 20$
22. $a^2 + 2ab + b^2 - x^2 + 2xy - y^2$
23. $x^2 - 2xy + y^2 + 10x - 10y + 25$
24. $x^2 - 6x + 9 - y^2$
25. $a^2 + 2ab + b^2 - 8a - 8b + 16$
26. $x^2 + 2xy + y^2 + 10x + 10y + 25$
27. $3xy(2x - 4y + 3)$
28. $5ab^2(3a - 2b^2 + 1)$
29. $(3x - 2)(a + b)$
30. $(y - 1)(5y + 3)$
31. $(a - b)(2a - 2b + 3)$
32. $(a - b)(4a - 4b + 7)$
33. $(x - 1)(5a + 3b)$
34. $(a + b)(2x + 3)$
35. $(5y + 3)(y - 1)$
36. $(2a - b)(7a + 3b)$
37. $2a(a - 5)$ 38. $t(t + 3)(t - 2)$
39. Not factorable 40. Not factorable
41. $(x - 7)(x + 5)$
42. $(a + 9)(a - 4)$
43. $(a + 7b)(a - 2b)$
44. $(y^2 + 3x^2)(y^2 - 2x^2)$
45. $(7a + 2b)(5a + b)$
46. $(x - 3y)^2$ 47. $(a - 3b^2)^2$
48. $2x(x^2 + 3x - 27)$
49. $3a(a - 5)(a - 2)$
50. $5ab(a + 3b)(a - 2b)$
51. $2x(x + 5y)(x - 5y)$
52. $3y(y + 4)^2$
53. $(3x - 2)(2x + 3)$
54. $(5y - 4)(5y + 3)$
55. $(2x + 5y)(4x^2 - 10xy + 25y^2)$
56. $(x - 3)(x^2 + 3x + 9)$
57. $(6a + b)(a - 3b)$
58. $(6x + 5y^2)(2x + y^2)$
59. $(7a^2 + 2b^2)(3a^2 + 5b^2)$
60. $2a(3a - 2b)(9a^2 + 6ab + 4b^2)$
61. $(5x^2 - 4y^2)^2$
62. $3x(2x + 3y)(3x - 2y)$
63. $5xy(2x - 3y)^2$
64. $(2a^2 + 3b^2)(2a^2 - 3b^2)$
65. $2a^2b(3a + 2b)(a - 2b)$
66. $7x^2y(2x + 3y)(2x - 3y)$
67. $2x(x^2 - 2)(3x^2 + 1)$
68. $5xy(3x^2 - y)(2x^2 - 5y)$
69. $(a - b + 2)(a - b - 2)$
70. $(3x + 5y + 1)(3x - 5y - 5)$
71. $(3y + 5 + 3x)(3y + 5 - 3x)$
72. $(5x^2 + y + 4)(5x^2 - y - 4)$
73. $3x^2 + 2x + 11, R 17$
74. $x^3 - x^2 + x - 2, R 1$
75. $4a^2 + 6a + 9$ 76. $y^4 + y, R 1$
77. $x = 0, -5, \frac{4}{3}$ 78. $x = -2, 10$
79. $x = 0, \pm 5$ 80. $x = 0, -12, 2$
81. $x = -\frac{5}{3}, -2$ 82. $x = -3, x = -10$
83. $6x^3 - 17x^2 + 14x - 3$
84. $2x^2 - 2x + 2$ 85. $2x^2 - x$
86. $3x - 6$ 87. $\frac{1}{6}n(2n + 1)(n + 1)$
88. $\frac{1}{4}n^2(n + 1)^2$
89. (a) $R(c) = 20,000c - 1,000c^3$
$\quad$ (b) $R(1) = \$19,000$;
$\qquad R(2) = \$32,000$;
$\qquad R(4) = \$16,000$
90. (a) \$6,000 (b) \$4 or \$7

Chapter 5 Practice Test

1. $27a^3 - 8b^3$ 2. $6x - 18$
3. $x^2 - 2xy + y^2 - 4$
4. $9x^2 + 6xy^2 + y^4$
5. $2xy(5x^2y - 3xy^2 + 1)$
6. $(3a - b)(2x + 5)$
7. $(x + 15y)(x - 4y)$
8. $(5x + 2)(2x - 3)$
9. Not factorable
10. $3ab(a + b)(a - b)$
11. $rs(r - 5s)^2$
12. $(2a - 1)(4a^2 + 2a + 1)$
13. $(2x + y + 8)(2x + y - 8)$
14. $(a + 4)(a + 1)(a - 1)$
15. $x^2 + 3x + 16, R 40$
16. (a) $x = 0, -6, 2$ (b) $x = 1, 5$
17. (a) 48 ft (b) 3 seconds
18. (a) $f(5) = 12$;
$\quad$ (b) $f(x + 5) = x^2 + 7x + 12$

EXERCISES 6.1

1. $x \ne 2$
3. x and y can be any number
5. $x \ne 0$ 7. $3x \ne y$
9. $\{x \mid x \ne 8\}$
11. $\left\{x \mid x \ne \frac{8}{5}\right\}$
13. $\{x \mid x \ne 5, -5\}$
15. $\{x \mid x \ne -2, 3\}$
17. (a) Let w = width. $L(w) = \frac{20}{w}$
$\quad$ (b) $L(0.5) = 40; L(1) = 20$;
$\qquad L(2) = 10; L(4) = 5$;
$\qquad L(5) = 4; L(10) = 2$;
$\qquad L(20) = 1.$
$\quad$ The larger the width, the
$\quad$ smaller the length.
19. (a) $A(5) = \$1,600.40$;
$\qquad A(10) = \$800.40$;
$\qquad A(50) = \$160.40$;
$\qquad A(100) = \$80.40$;
$\qquad A(200) = \$40.40$;
$\qquad A(300) = \$27.07$;
$\quad$ The larger the width, the
$\quad$ smaller the length.

(b)

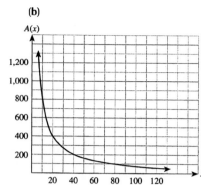

$A(x)$

21. (a) $n(1) = 5$; $n(10) = 33$;
$n(50) = 71$; $n(100) = 83$

(b)

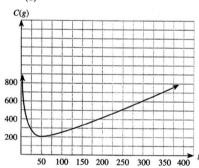

$n(a)$

23. (a) $g > 0$
(b) $C(1) = \$5,002$;
$C(5) = \$1,010$;
$C(10) = \$520$;
$C(20) = \$290$;
$C(40) = \$205$;
$C(100) = \$250$;
$C(200) = \$425$;
$C(300) = \$616.67$

(c)

$C(g)$

EXERCISES 6.2

1. $\dfrac{x}{5}$ 3. $\dfrac{8x}{9ya^2}$ 5. $\dfrac{x-5}{x-3}$

7. $\dfrac{(2x-3)(x-5)}{(2x+3)(x+3)}$ 9. -1

11. $\dfrac{x-1}{2(x+3)}$ 13. $\dfrac{x+3}{x-3}$

15. $\dfrac{(w-7z)(w-z)}{(w+7z)(w+z)}$ 17. $x+4$

---

19. $-(x+4)$ 21. $\dfrac{a-6}{5a+1}$

23. $\dfrac{2(x-3)(x+2)}{3(x-2)}$ 25. $\dfrac{2x^2}{3(x^2-2)}$

27. $-\dfrac{3a+2}{1+2a}$ 29. -1

31. $\dfrac{a^2-ab+b^2}{(a+b)^2}$ 33. $-\dfrac{a+b}{2x}$

35. $a+b-x-y$ 37. $6x^3$
39. $25a^2b$ 41. $3x(x+5)$
43. $(a-b)(x+y)$
45. $-(y-2)(y+4)$
47. $(x-y)(x+y)$

Mini-Review

51. $x = 40$ 52. $y = -\frac{5}{4}x - \frac{13}{4}$
53. $2x^6 - x^4 + 3$

EXERCISES 6.3

1. $\dfrac{6y}{a^2b^6}$ 3. $\dfrac{b^3}{4}$ 5. $\dfrac{128x^3ab^4}{3}$

7. $\dfrac{12r^2s^5}{a^2}$ 9. $\dfrac{16r^2s}{27a^2b^2}$

11. $\dfrac{2(x+1)^2(x-2)}{3(x+3)^2}$ 13. $\dfrac{3(x-2)}{2}$

15. $\dfrac{5a(a-b)}{3}$ 17. $\dfrac{5a(a-b)}{3(a+b)^2}$

19. -1 21. $\dfrac{2a+3}{a+1}$ 23. $\dfrac{1}{x-y}$

25. $3x$ 27. $\dfrac{2(1-x)}{(x+1)^2}$ 29. 1

31. $\dfrac{1}{5m(m+5)}$ 33. $\dfrac{2t+1}{2t-1}$

35. $\dfrac{1}{3a+1}$ 37. 1 39. $\dfrac{-1}{xy(x+y)^2}$

41. $2(x+2)^2$ 43. $\dfrac{1}{2(x-3)^2}$

45. $\dfrac{2(x-3)^2}{3x(x+2)}$

Mini-Review

47. $x = \frac{1}{2}, y = -2$
48. $x^2 + 8x - 15$
49. Degree is 3
50. $x = -7, -\frac{1}{5}$

EXERCISES 6.4

1. 2 3. 10 5. $\dfrac{1}{a+1}$

7. $\dfrac{x-y}{x+y}$ 9. $\dfrac{12(x+1)}{x+3}$

11. $\dfrac{27x-8x^2y}{18y^2}$ 13. $\dfrac{21y^3-16x^4}{18x^2y^2}$

---

15. $\dfrac{28}{27y}$ 17. $\dfrac{252a^2c^2 + 168b - 3bc^2}{7b^2c^3}$

19. $\dfrac{x^2+3x+6}{x(x+2)}$ 21. $\dfrac{a^2-ab+b^2}{a(a-b)}$

23. $\dfrac{3x-29}{(x+7)(x-3)}$

25. $\dfrac{3(x^2-6x-1)}{(x-7)(x+2)}$

27. $\dfrac{r^2+6rs-s^2}{(r-s)(r+s)}$ 29. -1

31. 1 33. $\dfrac{a^2+ab-b}{a^2-b^2}$

35. $\dfrac{a(a+b)}{b}$

37. $\dfrac{y^3+10y^2+19y+3}{(y+2)(y+3)}$

39. $\dfrac{5x+3}{x+2}$ 41. $\dfrac{5x+1}{2}$

43. $\dfrac{2x^2-4x-3}{x(x-3)^2}$

45. $\dfrac{2a^2+4a+9}{(a+4)(a-3)}$ 47. $\dfrac{-1}{y-3}$

49. $\dfrac{(3x+4)(x-2)}{(x-5)(x+2)}$

51. $\dfrac{2a^2-15a-2}{(a-2)(a+3)(a-5)}$

53. $\dfrac{75a^3+51a^2+2a-3}{(3a-1)(5a+2)}$

55. $2+x$ 57. $\dfrac{1}{r-s}$

59. $\dfrac{3s^2-3st+2s+t}{s^3-t^3}$

61. (a) $\dfrac{x+4}{4}$ (b) $\dfrac{x}{4}+1$

63. (a) $3x-2y$ (b) $3x-2y$

65. (a) $\dfrac{6m-4m^2n-9}{15n}$

(b) $\dfrac{2m}{5n} - \dfrac{4m^2}{15} - \dfrac{3}{5n}$

67. $\dfrac{x^2-2x+4}{(x+2)(x-2)}$ 69. $\dfrac{x}{x+2}$

71. $\dfrac{x^2+4x}{x^2-4}$ 73. $\dfrac{x+2}{2}$

75. $\dfrac{-3h}{x(x+h)}$

77. $\dfrac{-3h}{(x+h-3)(x-3)}$

Mini-Review

80. $x = 48$ 81. $m = -\dfrac{4}{9}$ 82. $-12x$

83.

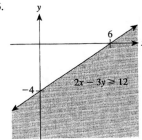

$2x - 3y \geq 12$

EXERCISES 6.5

1. $\dfrac{x}{5y}$ 3. $\dfrac{9}{(x-y)^2}$ 5. $\dfrac{a}{3a+1}$

7. $\dfrac{x^3+2}{x(2x+1)}$ 9. $x+2$

11. $\dfrac{1}{y+8}$ 13. $z(z-2)$

15. $\dfrac{2x-3y}{2x+3y}$ 17. $\dfrac{2x+5y}{y(3x-y)}$

19. $\dfrac{x-5}{4x}$ 21. $\dfrac{3t-5}{2t}$

23. $\dfrac{1}{x(x-3)}$ 25. $\dfrac{-h}{h^2-1}$

27. $\dfrac{6x-2}{11x-5}$ 29. $-\dfrac{4}{x(x+3)}$

31. $-\dfrac{4}{7}$ 33. $-\dfrac{x}{2}$

35. $-\dfrac{6}{x(x-3)}$ 37. $\dfrac{2}{x(x-2)}$

39. $\dfrac{2x^2-x+3}{(x-3)(x+2)}$ 41. $\dfrac{x-1}{x+2}$

43. $\dfrac{x^2+x+6}{3x^2-9x}$

Mini-Review

45. $x=5$ 46. $x=-5,2$

47. $y=\dfrac{3}{2}x+11$

48. $4x-20$

EXERCISES 6.6

1. $x=12$ 3. $t<-30$ 5. $a=4$
7. $y=7$ 9. $y\leq 17$ 11. $x=-17$
13. $x\leq -17$ 15. $x=-3$
17. $x>-\dfrac{177}{11}$ 19. $x=4$
21. $\dfrac{75-2x}{10x}$ 23. $t=\dfrac{3}{4}$ 25. $a=5$
27. No solution   29. $y=\dfrac{38}{13}$

31. No solution   33. $\dfrac{3y^2+y+6}{6y(y+3)}$

35. $x=2$ 37. $x=1$ 39. $x=\dfrac{22}{7}$

41. $\dfrac{13(x+1)}{(x+2)(x-2)}$ 43. $x=3$

45. No solution

47. $\dfrac{3n^2-8n+2}{(3n+2)(3n-2)}$

49. $\left\{n \mid n \neq \dfrac{4}{3}, -\dfrac{4}{3}\right\}$ 51. $x=-\dfrac{5}{8}$

53. $x=2,3$ 55. $x=0,3$

57. $x=-1,2$ 59. $x=-1,\dfrac{5}{2}$

61. No solution   63. $x=-\dfrac{7}{2}$

65. $x=-\dfrac{22}{3}$ 67. $x=0,3$

69. $x=\dfrac{5}{18}$ 71. $\dfrac{x^2+6x-9}{(x-2)^2}$

73. $\dfrac{-3x^2-3x+32}{(x-2)^2}$

75. $\dfrac{3x+1}{(x-2)(x+5)}$

Mini-Review

77. $6x^5y^3$ 78. $6x^5y+3x^2y^3$

79. $f(x)=x^2$ 80. $\left\{x \mid x > \dfrac{5}{3}\right\}$

EXERCISES 6.7

1. $x=\dfrac{4-7y}{5}$ 3. $y=\dfrac{2x-11}{9}$

5. $w=5z-4$ 7. $r>\dfrac{15}{2}t$

9. $n=\dfrac{3m+4p+8}{9}$

11. $a=\dfrac{-5b}{9}$ 13. $x=\dfrac{21}{19}y$

15. $x=\dfrac{d-b}{a-c}$

17. $x=\dfrac{by-2y+6}{3-a}$

19. $x=\dfrac{a}{y+7}-3=\dfrac{a-3y-21}{y+7}$

21. $u=\dfrac{-y-1}{y-1}$

23. $t=\dfrac{2x-3}{3x-2}$ 25. $b=\dfrac{2A}{h}$

27. $b_1=\dfrac{2A}{h}-b_2$ 29. $r=\dfrac{A-P}{Pt}$

31. $F=\dfrac{9}{5}C+32$ 33. $P_2=\dfrac{P_1V_1}{V_1}$

35. $g=\dfrac{2}{t^2}(S-s_0-v_0t)$

37. $x<\mu+1.96s$

39. $f_1=\dfrac{ff_2}{f_2-f}$

41. $h=\dfrac{S-2\pi r^2}{2\pi r}$

Mini-Review

43. $x=1,5$
44. $x^3-6x^2+12x-8$
45. 4 heavy-duty, 14 regular

46. Domain $=\{x \mid -4 \leq x \leq 3\}$;
range $=\{y \mid -3 \leq y \leq 2\}$;
$f(-3)=2$

EXERCISES 6.8

1. Let $x=$ number; $\dfrac{3}{4}x=\dfrac{2}{5}x-7$;
$x=-20$

3. Let $x=$ # of men; $\dfrac{7}{9}=\dfrac{x}{810}$;
630 men

5. Let $x=$ the larger number;
$\dfrac{5}{12}=\dfrac{x-21}{x}$; two numbers are
36 and 15

7. Let $x=$ # inches in 52 cm;
$\dfrac{1}{2.54}=\dfrac{x}{52}$; 20.47 in.

9. Let $x=$ # of dribbles;
$\dfrac{x}{28}=\dfrac{25}{7}\cdot\dfrac{4}{5}$; 80 dribbles

11. Let $x=$ second side;
$P=22=\dfrac{1}{2}x+x+x+2$;
lengths are 4, 8, and 10 cm

13. Let $x=$ width; $50=2(2.5x+x)$;
$x=\dfrac{50}{7}$cm (width), length $=\dfrac{125}{7}$cm

15. Let $x=$ distance from home;
$\dfrac{3x}{4}=6$; 8 miles

17. Let $x=$ distance from home to
school; $x-\dfrac{1}{5}x-\dfrac{1}{4}\left(\dfrac{4}{5}x\right)=2$;
$3\dfrac{1}{3}$ blocks

19. $\dfrac{4}{5}=\dfrac{1}{2}+\dfrac{1}{5}+\dfrac{1}{R_3}$; $R_3=10$ ohms

21. Let $\$x$ be invested in bond;
$0.10x+0.06(x+3,000)=580$;
$\$2,500$ in bond; $\$5,500$ in CD

23. Let $\$x$ be invested at $5\dfrac{1}{2}\%$;
$0.055x+0.07(25,000-x)=1,465$;
$\$19,000$ at $5\dfrac{1}{2}\%$, $\$6,000$ at 7%

25. Let $\$x$ be invested at $8\dfrac{1}{2}\%$;
$0.085x+0.11(18,000-x)=$
$0.10(18,000)$; $\$7,200$ at $8\dfrac{1}{2}\%$,
$\$10,800$ at 11%

27. Let $x=$ number of hours working
together; $\dfrac{x}{3}+\dfrac{x}{5}=1$; $1\dfrac{7}{8}$ hours

29. Let $x=$ number of hours working
together; $\dfrac{x}{30}+\dfrac{x}{20}=1$; 12 hours

31. Let $x=$ time working together;
$\dfrac{x}{2\frac{2}{3}}+\dfrac{x}{5}=1$; $1\dfrac{17}{23}$ days

33. Let $x=$ # hours for the
Super-Quickie Service to finish
cleaning; $\dfrac{10}{30}+\dfrac{x}{20}=1$; $x=\dfrac{40}{3}$;
Total time $=23\dfrac{1}{3}$ hours

35. Let x = number of minutes to overflow; $\dfrac{x}{10} - \dfrac{x}{15} = 1$; 30 minutes

37. Let x = # hours they work together; $\dfrac{3}{10} + \dfrac{x}{10} + \dfrac{x}{8} = 1$; $x = 3.11$, at 6:07 P.M.

39. Let x = the number of hours it takes Megan to do the job herself; $\dfrac{1}{6} + \dfrac{2}{6} + \dfrac{2}{x} = 1$; 4 hours

41. Let x = Bill's rate; $\dfrac{10}{x} = \dfrac{15}{x + 10}$; 20 kph

43. Let x = number of miles at slow speed; $\dfrac{600 - x}{50} + \dfrac{x}{20} = 14$; $66\frac{2}{3}$ miles

45. Let x = number of ounces of 20% alcohol; $0.20x + 0.50(5) = 0.30(x + 5)$; 10 ounces of 20% alcohol

47. Let x = number of ml of 30% solution; $0.30x + 0.75(80 - x) = 0.50(80)$; $44\frac{4}{9} \approx 44.44$ ml of 30% solution, $35\frac{5}{9} \approx 35.56$ ml of 75% solution

49. Let x = number of tons of 40% iron; $0.40x + 0.60(80 - x) = 0.55(80)$; $x = 20$ tons of 40% iron; 60 tons of 60% iron

51. Let x = number of liters of pure alcohol; $0.60(2) + 1(x) = 0.80(x + 2)$; 2 liters of pure alcohol

53. Let x = number of gallons drained off = water added; $0.30(3 - x) + 0(x) = 0.20(3)$; 1 gallon

55. Let x = number of advance tickets sold; $25x + 30.50(3{,}600 - x) = 97{,}700$; 2,200 advance tickets

57. Let x = number of nickels; $0.05x + 0.10(x + 5) + 0.25(2x) = 20.00$; 30 nickels, 35 dimes, 60 quarters

59. Let x = number of orchestra tickets; $25x + 16(2x) + 20.5(900 - 3x) = 17{,}325$; 250 orchestra seats, 500 general admission, 150 balcony

61. Let x = score on final exam; $0.20(85) + 0.20(65) + 0.20(72) + 0.40(x) \geq 80$; he needs at least an 89

63. Let x = amount invested in high-risk bond; $0.082x + 0.039(20{,}000 - x) \geq 1{,}000$; $x \approx 5{,}116.28$; at least \$5,116.28 invested in high-risk bond

65. Let x = score on the final exam; $0.20(85) + 0.20(92) + 0.20(86) + 0.40x \geq 90$; $x \geq 93.5$; at least 93.5

67. (a) 6 ohms

(b) $\dfrac{6A}{6 - A}$

69. (a) 61 ($x = 60.12$)

(b) $\dfrac{6{,}000}{T - 0.2}$

Mini-Review

72. $-5x + 23$ 73. $3xy(x - y)^2$

74. $(x - a - 3)(x - a + 3)$

75. $-9 \leq x \leq 1$

Chapter 6 Review Exercises

1. $\{x \mid x \neq -5\}$ 2. $\left\{x \mid x \neq -\frac{4}{3}\right\}$

3. $\left\{x \mid x \neq -\frac{1}{3}, 4\right\}$ 4. $\left\{x \mid x \neq -7, \frac{1}{2}\right\}$

5. $\dfrac{x}{4y^2}$ 6. $\dfrac{3b^3}{4a^3c^2}$ 7. $\dfrac{x + 4}{x + 5}$

8. $\dfrac{3x + 1}{2x - 3}$ 9. $x^2 - 2x + 3$

10. $\dfrac{6a^2b^4 - 8b^3 + 9}{2ab}$

11. $\dfrac{5x - 7}{3x - 2}$ 12. $2a - b$ 13. $\dfrac{xy^3z^2}{2}$

14. $\dfrac{2xz^2}{9y^5}$ 15. $\dfrac{2}{x^2y}$ 16. 0

17. $\dfrac{3(x + 1)}{x - 1}$ 18. 2   19. 2   20. 3

21. $\dfrac{20b^3 - 21a}{12a^2b^4}$ 22. $\dfrac{4y + 35}{15xy^2}$

23. $\dfrac{-6x^2 + 19x + 5}{10x^2}$

24. $\dfrac{14x^2 + 3x + 2}{6x^2}$

25. $\dfrac{2(x + 5)}{x - 5}$ 26. $\dfrac{a - 2}{a - 4}$

27. $2x$ 28. $\dfrac{a - 3}{2}$

29. $\dfrac{1}{a - b}$ 30. $\dfrac{r + s}{3}$

31. $\dfrac{3x^2 - 22x - 15}{(2x + 3)(x - 4)}$

32. $\dfrac{13a^2 + 2a}{(a - 1)(2a + 1)}$

33. $\dfrac{16x^2 - 44x - 8}{(2x - 7)(2x - 3)}$

34. $\dfrac{5x^2 - 22x - 11}{(x - 2)(x + 3)}$

35. $\dfrac{10a^3 + 10a^2 + a - 3}{2a^2(a + 1)(a - 3)}$

36. $\dfrac{-2x - 17}{(x + 4)(x - 2)(x + 1)}$

37. $\dfrac{8x + 4}{(x - 2)^2(x + 2)}$

38. $\dfrac{-2a + 24}{(a + 3)(a - 3)^2}$

39. $\dfrac{x(x + 3)}{7(x - 3)(x + 1)}$

40. $\dfrac{5x + 5y - 3}{x^2 - y^2}$

41. $\dfrac{8x^2 + 2x - 3}{x^2 - 4}$

42. $\dfrac{-x^2 + 26x + 1}{x^2 - 25}$ 43. $\dfrac{1}{y}$ 44. b^2

45. $\dfrac{3(x^2 + 5x + 5)}{(x + 3)(x - 2)(x + 1)}$

46. $\dfrac{x^2 - 9x + 2}{(2x + 3)(x + 5)(x - 3)}$

47. $\dfrac{5x + 3}{(x - 2)(x + 1)}$

48. $\dfrac{2r^2 + 2s^2 + 3r - 6s}{(r - 2s)(r + s)(r - s)}$

49. $\dfrac{3x}{2x - 3}$ 50. $\dfrac{3x}{2x + 3}$

51. $\dfrac{2x + 3y}{2}$ 52. $\dfrac{2}{2x + 3y}$

53. $\dfrac{(x^2 + 6)(x + 1)}{2x^2}$ 54. xy

55. $\dfrac{8axy}{3b}$ 56. $\dfrac{x}{y}$ 57. $\dfrac{1}{5}$ 58. $\dfrac{1}{2 - x}$

59. $\dfrac{(b - 1)(2b + 5)}{b^3 + b + 2}$

60. $\dfrac{z^2 + 2z - 2}{3z}$

61. $\dfrac{x^2 - 2x - 10}{(x - 2)(x - 4)}$

62. $\dfrac{-h}{(x + h - 4)(x - 4)}$

63. $-\frac{3}{10}$ 64. $-\frac{18}{7}$ 65. $x = 2$
66. $x = 5$ 67. $x > -5$ 68. $x \geq 5$
69. $x = 4$ 70. $x = \frac{11}{10}$ 71. $x < -22$
72. $x \geq -\frac{28}{3}$ 73. $x = \frac{1}{2}$ 74. $x = \frac{3}{2}$
75. $x = 7$ 76. $x = 4$ 77. $x > \frac{8}{3}$
78. $x \leq \frac{6}{11}$ 79. No solution
80. No solution   81. $x = 4$
82. No solution

83. $x = \dfrac{10y}{3}$ 84. $y = \dfrac{3x}{10}$

85. $y = \dfrac{4}{x}$ 86. $b = \dfrac{a}{a - 1}$

87. $y = \dfrac{2x + 1}{x}$ 88. $a = \dfrac{b}{c - x}$

89. $x = \dfrac{dy - b}{a - cy}$ 90. $s = \dfrac{3 + 2r}{3r - 2}$

91. $b = \dfrac{adc}{ac - cd - ad}$

92. $c = \dfrac{ad}{b + de}$

93. Let x = # of inches in 1 cm;
$\dfrac{2.54 \text{ cm}}{1 \text{ in.}} = \dfrac{1}{x}, x = \dfrac{1}{254} \approx 0.39$ in.

94. Let x = # of Democrats;
$\dfrac{4}{3} = \dfrac{x}{1{,}890 - x}$; 1,080 Democrats

95. Let total distance = x;
$\dfrac{1}{2}x + \dfrac{1}{3}\left(\dfrac{1}{2}x\right) + \dfrac{3}{2} = x$; 4.5 miles

96. Let r = Carlos' rate; $\dfrac{3}{r - 5} = \dfrac{5}{r}$;
$12\dfrac{1}{2}$ mph

97. Let x = number of days required
by both; $\dfrac{x}{2\frac{1}{3}} + \dfrac{x}{2\frac{1}{3}} = 1$; $1\dfrac{6}{29}$ days

98. Let x = amount of time to clean
kitchen together; $\dfrac{x}{\frac{1}{3}} + \dfrac{x}{\frac{2}{3}} = 1$;
$\dfrac{2}{9}$ hour

99. Let x = # hours it takes John to
complete the job alone; $\dfrac{2}{6} + \dfrac{3}{x}$
$= 1$; $4\dfrac{1}{2}$ hours

100. Let x = # hours it takes for the other
to complete the job;
$\dfrac{3}{8} + \dfrac{3}{x} = 1$; $4\dfrac{4}{5}$ hours

101. Let x = amount of 35% alcohol;
$0.70(5) + 0.35x = 0.60(x + 5)$;
2 liters

102. Let x = quantity of pure water;
$0(x) + 0.65(3) = 0.30(x + 3)$;
$x = 3.5$ liters

103. Let x = number of children's tickets;
$3.50x + 6.25(980 - x) = 4{,}970.00$;
420 children's tickets, 560 adult
tickets

104. Let x = number of dimes;
$0.05(4x) + 0.10x$
$\qquad + 0.01(82 - 5x) = 3.32$;
40 nickels, 10 dimes, and 32 pennies

105. (a) $c(0.25) = 3.68$;
$c(0.5) = 6.76$; $c(1) = 10.13$;
$c(2) = 10.13$; $c(4) = 6.76$;
$c(10) = 2.98$

(b)

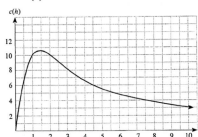

106. (a) 205 items

(b) $\dfrac{2{,}500}{A - 0.3}$ items

Chapter 6 Practice Test

1. $\left\{x \mid x \neq \dfrac{5}{2}\right\}$

2. (a) $\dfrac{3y^3}{8x}$ (b) $\dfrac{x + 3}{x - 3}$

(c) $\dfrac{3(2x + 1)}{5x}$

3. (a) $\dfrac{3}{4x^3y^2ab^4}$ (b) $\dfrac{4x^3 + 15y}{24x^2y^2}$

(c) $2(r + s)$ (d) 2

(e) $\dfrac{x^2 - x + 8}{(x + 2)(x - 2)(x - 3)}$

(f) $\dfrac{x + 3}{x}$

4. $\dfrac{x(1 - 2x)}{(x + 1)(x + 5)}$ 5. $-\dfrac{4}{17}$

6. (a) $x > \dfrac{-15}{4}$ (b) No solution
(c) $x = 2$

7. $x = \dfrac{-y - 2}{2y - 1}$

8. Let x = amount of 30% alcohol
solution; $0.30(x) + 0.45(8) =$
$0.42(x + 8)$; 2 liters

9. Let x = time required working
together; $\dfrac{x}{3\frac{1}{2}} + \dfrac{x}{2} = 1$;
$x = 1\dfrac{3}{11}$ hours

10. 180 items

CHAPTERS 4–6 CUMULATIVE REVIEW

1. (§4.1)

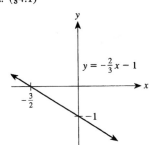

2. (§4.1)

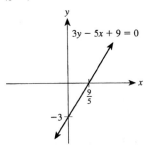

3. (§4.1)

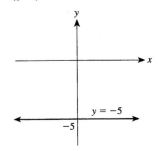

4. (§4.1)

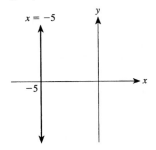

5. (§4.1)

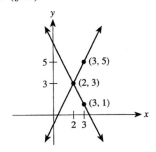

6. (§4.1)

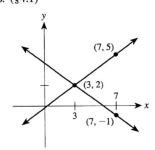

7. $m = 8$ (§4.1) 8. $m = -1$ (§4.1)

9. $m = 5$ (§4.1) 10. $m = \dfrac{3}{2}$ (§4.1)

11. $m = \dfrac{5}{4}$ (§4.1) 12. $m = -\dfrac{2}{5}$ (§4.1)

13. $a = 1$ (§4.1) 14. $a = \dfrac{1}{2}$ (§4.1)

15. $y = 3x + 13$ (§4.2)

16. $y = -2x + 9$ (§4.2)

17. $y = -6x + 19$ (§4.2)

18. $y = 5$ (§4.2)

19. $y = 4x + 2$ (§4.2)

20. $y = -x + 3$ (§4.2)

21. $y = -\dfrac{3}{5}x - \dfrac{9}{5}$ (§4.2)

22. $y = -\dfrac{1}{2}x - 2$ (§4.2)

ANSWERS TO SELECTED EXERCISES

23. $y = \frac{3}{2}x + 1$ (§4.2)

24. $P = \frac{125}{6}T - \frac{4,025}{3}$; \$533.33 (§4.2)

25. $x = 2, y = -1$ (§4.3)

26. $x = \frac{1}{2}, y = 0$ (§4.3)

27. $u = 4, v = -1$ (§4.3)

28. $s = \frac{1}{4}, t = -\frac{1}{2}$ (§4.3)

29. Inconsistent (§4.3)

30. Dependent (§4.3)

31. $x = 8, y = 15$ (§4.3)

32. $x = 3, y = -2$ (§4.3)

33. (§4.4)

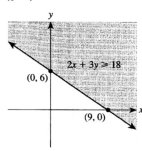

34. (§4.4)

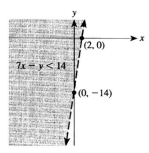

35. (§4.4)

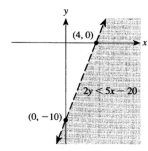

36. (§4.4)

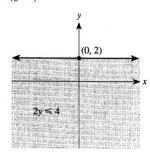

37. 5 (§5.1) 38. 0 (§5.1)

39. $x^2 + 5x - 9$ (§5.2)

40. $-6x^2 + 15xy - 12x$ (§5.2)

41. $x^2 - 4xy + 3y^2$ (§5.2)

42. $3x^2 - 5xy + 2y^2$ (§5.2)

43. $x^2 + 2xy + y^2 - 2x - 2y$ (§5.2)

44. $8a^3 + b^3$ (§5.2)

45. $9x^2 - 30xy + 25y^2$ (§5.3)

46. $4m^2 - 9n^2$ (§5.3)

47. $9x^2 - 25y^2$ (§5.3)

48. $4m^2 + 12mn + 9n^2$ (§5.3)

49. $4x^2 + 4xy + y^2 - 9$ (§5.3)

50. $x^2 - 4xy + 4y^2 + 6x - 12y + 9$ (§5.3)

51. $(x - 8)(x + 3)$ (§5.5)

52. $(y - 2x)(y + 2x)$ (§5.5)

53. $(y - 7x)(y - 5x)$ (§5.5)

54. $(5a + b)(2a - b)$ (§5.5)

55. $(2y + 3z)(2y + 5z)$ (§5.5)

56. $(3x - 5z)(3x + 5z)$ (§5.5)

57. $(5a + 2b)^2$ (§5.5)

58. Not factorable (§5.5)

59. $9(2x - 1)(2x + 1)$ (§5.5)

60. $(5x - 3z)^2$ (§5.5)

61. Not factorable (§5.5)

62. $y(6y + 1)(2y - 3)$ (§5.5)

63. $y(3y - 1)(y + 2)$ (§5.5)

64. $(5a^2 - 2b^2)(5a^2 + 4b^2)$ (§5.5)

65. $(7a^2 - 3z)(7a^2 + z)$ (§5.5)

66. $ab(6a^2 + b)(3a^2 - 2b)$ (§5.5)

67. $(x - y - 4)(x - y + 4)$ (§5.5)

68. $(a - 2b - 5)(a - 2b + 5)$ (§5.5)

69. $(4a^2 + b^2)(2a - b)(2a + b)$ (§5.5)

70. $(x + y + 2)(x + y + 1)$ (§5.5)

71. $(2a + 5b)(4a^2 - 10ab + 25b^2)$ (§5.5)

72. $(x - 1)(x + 5)(x - 5)$ (§5.5)

73. $x = -3, 4$ (§5.6)

74. $t = 1, \frac{5}{2}$ (§5.6)

75. $a = -4, 6$ (§5.6)

76. $c = -\frac{1}{8}$ (§5.6)

77. $r = 2, -10$ (§5.6)

78. $x = 0, \frac{5}{3}$ (§5.6)

79. $x = 1, 4$ 80. $x = 0, 5$

81. $x - 2, R\, 11$ (§5.7)

82. $x + 3, R\, -4$ (§5.7)

83. $2x^2 - 3x + 6, R\, -17$ (§5.7)

84. $x^2 - 2x + 3, R\, -4x - 1$ (§5.7)

85. $\left\{x \mid x \neq -\frac{3}{2}\right\}$ (§6.1)

86. $\left\{x \mid x \neq -\frac{1}{3}, 2\right\}$ (§6.1)

87. $\frac{9b}{8a^2}$ (§6.2) 88. $\frac{x + 3y}{x - 3y}$ (§6.2)

89. $\frac{2a + b}{a(a + b)}$ (§6.2)

90. $\frac{3x - y}{2}$ (§6.2)

91. $\frac{5yb^2}{7a^2x^2}$ (§§6.3–6.4)

92. $(2x + y)(x - y)$ (§§6.3–6.4)

93. $\frac{9x^2 + 4y^2}{6xy}$ (§§6.3–6.4)

94. -3 (§§6.3–6.4)

95. $\frac{x - 4}{2}$ (§§6.3–6.4)

96. $3a - b$ (§§6.3–6.4)

97. $\frac{-x + 11}{(x - 5)(x - 2)}$ (§§6.3–6.4)

98. $\frac{-7x - 2y}{(x - 3y)(x + y)(2x + y)}$ (§§6.3–6.4)

99. $\frac{x}{x + 3y}$ (§§6.3–6.4)

100. $\frac{x - 2y}{x - 5y}$ (§§6.3–6.4)

101. $\frac{2x^2 - 4}{x - 2x^2}$ (§6.5)

102. $\frac{(x - 2y)(x + 2y)}{(2x - y)(x + 4y)}$ (§6.5)

103. 2 (§6.5)

104. $\frac{-3h}{(x + h + 1)(x + 1)}$ (§6.5)

105. $x = \frac{6}{5}$ (§6.6) 106. $x = -2$ (§6.6)

107. $x > 6$ (§6.6)

108. No solution (§6.6)

109. $x = 1$ (§6.6) 110. $x \geq -\frac{1}{5}$ (§6.6)

111. $a = \frac{b}{3}$ (§6.7)

112. $y = \frac{5x}{3x - 5}$ (§6.7)

113. $y = \frac{x}{x + 1}$ (§6.7)

114. $x = \frac{2y + 3}{y - 2}$ (§6.7)

115. Let x = total # of cars; $\frac{5}{6} = \frac{x - 1,200}{1,200}$; 2,200 cars (§6.8)

116. Let x = amount of 20% solution; $0.20x + 0.35(8) = 0.30(8 + x)$; 4 liters (§6.8)

117. Let t = time they would take to work together; $\frac{t}{4} + \frac{t}{4\frac{1}{2}} = 1$; $2\frac{2}{17}$ hours (§6.8)

118. Let x = # hours it takes Jason to complete the job alone; $\frac{2}{5} + \frac{1}{5} + \frac{1}{x} = 1$; $2\frac{1}{2}$ hours

119. Let x = number of general admission tickets sold; $3.50x + 4.25(505 - x) = 1,861.25$; 380 general admission tickets, 125 reserved seat tickets (§6.8)

120. (a) $C(5) = 355$;
$C(10) = 332.5$;
$C(50) = 325.3$;
$C(100) = 325.08$;
$C(300) = 325.0083$;
$C(500) = 325.003$;
$C(1,000) = 325.00075$ (§6.1)

384

(b)

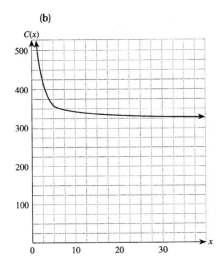

CHAPTERS 4–6
CUMULATIVE PRACTICE TEST

1. (a) $-3x^2 - xy + 3y^2$
   (b) $15a^2 - ab - 6b^2$
   (c) $4x^4 - y^2$
   (d) $9y^2 - 12yz + 4z^2$
   (e) $x^2 + 2xy + y^2 - 6x - 6y + 9$
2. (a) $(a - 7)(a - 2)$
   (b) $(3r + 2s)(2r - 3s)$
   (c) $(5a^2 + 3y)(2a^2 - 3y)$
   (d) $(2a^2 - 3b^2)^2$
   (e) $(a + 2b - 5)(a + 2b + 5)$
   (f) $(5x - 1)(25x^2 + 5x + 1)$
3. $x = -9, 3$
4. (a) $x = -2, \frac{1}{2}$
   (b) $x = -5, 4$
5. $2x^2 - 4x + 14, R\,-23$
6. $\left\{x \mid x \neq -1, \frac{2}{3}\right\}$
7. (a) $5x + 3y$
   (b) -2
   (c) $\dfrac{(3x - 14)(x - 1)}{(x - 5)(x - 3)(x - 7)}$
8. $\dfrac{-2x^2 - x + 1}{3x^2 + 4x}$
9. $\dfrac{h}{(2x + 2h + 1)(2x + 1)}$
10. (a) $x = \frac{9}{7}$
    (b) $x < \frac{45}{2}$
    (c) No solution
11. $a = \dfrac{y}{1 - y}$
12. Let t = time it takes to process 80 forms together; $\dfrac{t}{6} + \dfrac{t}{5\frac{1}{2}} = 1$; $2\frac{20}{23}$ hours

13.

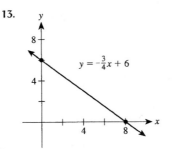

$y = -\frac{3}{4}x + 6$

14. $m = -1$
15. (a) $y = \frac{2}{3}x - \frac{13}{3}$ (b) $y = -\frac{3}{2}x$
16. $B = 28$ 17. $x = 2, y = -3$
18.

$3x + 6y > 18$

$(0, 3)$ $(6, 0)$

EXERCISES 7.1

1. x^{11} 3. $-6a^7b^{10}$ 5. a^{10} 7. $\frac{4}{9}$
9. $x^2 + 2xy^3 + y^6$ 11. x^2y^6
13. $2^6 \cdot 3^4$ 15. $x^{26}y^{19}$
17. $-8a^{10}b^8$ 19. $16r^{10}s^{11}t^7$
21. x^3 23. $\dfrac{x^2}{y^2}$ 25. $\frac{1}{4}$ 27. $\dfrac{ab^8}{c^4}$
29. $-\dfrac{1}{y}$ 31. $\frac{1}{18}$ 33. $\dfrac{1}{y^9}$ 35. y^{15}
37. $\dfrac{4r^8s^9}{3}$ 39. $\dfrac{x^5y^4}{2}$
41. $-1,728a^3b^9$ 43. $216a^3b^6x^3y^6$
45. $r^{26}s^{28}$ 47. 0.000003
49. 7.984000 51. $\dfrac{1}{x}$ 53. $\dfrac{x^2}{y^2}$
55. 3^6 57. $\dfrac{1}{a^4b^6}$ 59. $\dfrac{r^6}{s^8}$ 61. $-\dfrac{1}{4}$
63. $\frac{1}{9}$ 65. $\dfrac{2^6}{3^6}$ 67. $\dfrac{s^{18}}{3^{12}}$ 69. x^6
71. y^2x^2 73. 2 75. $-\dfrac{125}{27}$ 77. $\dfrac{1}{x^4}$
79. $\dfrac{a^5}{b^4}$ 81. x^6 83. 81 85. $\dfrac{4y^6}{9x^6}$
87. $\dfrac{1}{x^6y^9}$ 89. $\dfrac{9b^3}{a^4}$ 91. $\dfrac{y^3}{x^2}$
93. $\dfrac{y^3}{x^2y^3 + 1}$ 95. $\dfrac{x^4y^4}{(x^2 + y^2)^2}$ 97. 1
99. $\dfrac{x + y}{x^2}$ 101. $\dfrac{s(s + r^2)}{r(s^2 + r)}$
103. $\dfrac{a(2b^2 + a)}{b^2(1 + a^2b)}$

Mini-Review

111. $-3 < x \leq \frac{7}{2}$
112. $28w^2 - 70w$ dollars
113. $y = \frac{2}{3}x - 4$
114. $f(3) + f(2) = -1; f(5) = 24$

EXERCISES 7.2

1. $1,000$ 3. $1,000,000,000$
5. 10 7. 0.000001 9. $1,000,000$
11. 16.2 13. $760,000,000$
15. 0.000000851 17. $6,000$
19. 8.24×10^2 21. 5.0×10^0
23. 9.3×10^{-3} 25. 8.27546×10^8
27. 7.2×10^{-7} 29. 7.932×10^1
31. $0.16\overline{6}$ or 0.17 33. 0.000001
35. Red: 5×10^6; White: 7.5×10^3
37. $\dfrac{2,000}{3}$ 39. 5 hr 28 min 51 sec
41. 6.048×10^{13} tons in one day, 2.20752×10^{16} tons in one year
43. 10^4 Å in 1 micron
45. 0.66×10^{-8} cm $= 6.6 \times 10^{-9}$ cm
47. $\dfrac{1 \text{ mile}}{1.6 \text{ km}} = \dfrac{5.86 \times 10^{12} \text{ miles}}{x \text{ km}};$ 9.376×10^{12} km
49. 60×10^{-4} cm $= 6.0 \times 10^{-3}$ cm
51. 10^{23} atoms   53. 240 cm
55. Approximately 63,011 AU

Mini-Review

59. $2x^2 - 18x$ 60. $\dfrac{2x + 2}{x}$
61. -17 62. Approx. 11:42 A.M.

EXERCISES 7.3

1. 2 3. -2 5. -10 7. 4
9. 3 11. Not a real number
13. 1 15. -7 17. -6 19. 2
21. 5 23. -8 25. $\frac{1}{2}$ 27. $-\frac{1}{2}$
29. $-\frac{1}{9}$ 31. $\frac{1}{16}$ 33. 16
35. Not a real number   37. -16
39. 9 41. $\frac{4}{3}$ 43. $\frac{2}{3}$ 45. 16 47. $x^{7/6}$
49. $a^{3/8}$ 51. 1 53. $\dfrac{r^{1/3}}{s}$ 55. $\dfrac{r}{s^{1/3}}$
57. $\dfrac{1}{x^{1/6}}$ 59. $\dfrac{b^{2/15}}{a^{3/4}}$ 61. x^5 63. $-\frac{1}{2}$
65. $\dfrac{1}{x^6y^{47/12}}$ 67. $x + x^{3/2}$
69. $\dfrac{x^2 - 4x + 4}{x}$
71. $(xy)^{1/3}$ 73. $(x^2 + y^2)^{1/2}$
75. $(5a^2b^3)^{1/5}$ 77. $2(3xyz^4)^{1/3}$
79. $5(x - y)^{2/3}$ 81. $(x^n - y^n)^{1/n}$
83. $(x^{5n+1}y^{2n-1})^{1/n}$
85. $\sqrt[3]{x}$ 87. $m\sqrt[3]{n}$

89. $\sqrt[3]{(-a)^2}$ 91. $-\sqrt[3]{a^2}$

93. $\sqrt[3]{a^2b}$ 95. $\sqrt{x^2 + y^2}$

97. $\sqrt{x^n - y^n}$

99. 0.1667   101. 2.8856

Mini-Review

110. $x = 0, \frac{3}{2}$

111. **(a)** -3 **(b)** -6 **(c)** 3
     (d) 0 **(e)** $-1, 2, 5$

112. $\frac{-x + 24}{6}$ 113. $x = -24$

EXERCISES 7.4

1. $2\sqrt{14}$ 3. $4\sqrt{3}$ 5. $2\sqrt[5]{2}$

7. 12 9. $8x^4$ 11. $3x^3$

13. $8x^{30}\sqrt{2}$ 15. $2x^{15}\sqrt[4]{8}$

17. $2x^{12}\sqrt[3]{4}$ 19. xy^2

21. $4ab^2\sqrt{2}$ 23. a^7b^{15} 25. x^2y^2

27. $\frac{\sqrt{2}}{2}$ 29. $\frac{\sqrt{5x}}{5}$ 31. $\frac{3\sqrt{5}}{2}$

33. $\frac{\sqrt{3}}{15}$ 35. $8x^2y^4\sqrt{x}$

37. $3x^2y^2\sqrt[3]{3x^2y}$ 39. $6y\sqrt[4]{2y^2}$

41. $x + y^2$ 43. $\sqrt[4]{x^4 - y^4}$

45. $30st\sqrt{2st}$ 47. $12a^3b^2$

49. $\frac{xy^2}{2}$ 51. $\frac{2x^2\sqrt[4]{2x}}{y^3}$ 53. $3\sqrt{3}$

55. $\frac{y^4}{x^3}$ 57. $\frac{\sqrt{15x}}{5x}$ 59. $\frac{\sqrt{3xy}}{xy^2}$

61. $\frac{\sqrt[3]{12}}{2}$ 63. $\frac{\sqrt[3]{18}}{2}$ 65. $\frac{\sqrt{6}}{2}$

67. $\frac{3y}{2x}\sqrt[3]{12x^2}$ 69. $\frac{x^2}{3a^5}$

71. $-\frac{6s^3\sqrt{sr}}{r}$ 73. $\sqrt{a}$

75. $x^{12}\sqrt{x}$ 77. $\sqrt[6]{a}$ 79. x^5y^3

Mini-Review

82. $(2x - 3)(x + 5)$

83. $x^2 - 4x + 14, R -53$

EXERCISES 7.5

1. $4\sqrt{3}$ 3. $-3\sqrt{5}$

5. $4\sqrt{3} + 2\sqrt{6}$ 7. $\sqrt{3} - \sqrt{5}$

9. 0 11. $(7a - 3a^3)\sqrt{b}$

13. $(3x + 4)\sqrt[4]{x^2}$ 15. $1 - 2\sqrt[3]{a}$

17. $-\sqrt{3}$ 19. $5\sqrt{6} - 3\sqrt{3}$

21. $6\sqrt{3} - 36$ 23. $5\sqrt{6} - 20\sqrt{3}$

25. $6\sqrt[3]{3} - 11\sqrt[6]{6}$

27. $2ab\sqrt{a} - 3ab\sqrt{b} - ab\sqrt{ab}$

29. 0 31. $4x^4y^4\sqrt{5x}$

33. $9x\sqrt[3]{9x^2} - 3x\sqrt[3]{x^2}$

35. $(8 - 4x)\sqrt[4]{x}$ 37. $\frac{\sqrt{5} + 10}{5}$

39. 0 41. $\frac{3\sqrt{2}}{2}$ 43. $\frac{7\sqrt{10}}{10}$

45. $\frac{5\sqrt{7} - 21\sqrt{5}}{35}$ 47. $-\frac{11\sqrt[3]{4}}{2}$

49. $\frac{y\sqrt{x} + x\sqrt{y}}{xy}$ 51. $\frac{\sqrt[3]{3} - 3\sqrt[3]{9}}{3}$

53. $\frac{3\sqrt{2} + 21\sqrt{7}}{7}$ 55. $\frac{14\sqrt{10}}{5}$

57. $4\sqrt[3]{25}$ 59. $\frac{(2x - 1)\sqrt{x - 1}}{2(x - 1)}$

Mini-Review

61. **(a)** $\{x \mid -4 \leq x \leq 6\}$
    (b) $\{y \mid -1 \leq y \leq 5\}$
    (c) $\{x \mid -4 \leq x \leq -2$ and
        $3 \leq x \leq 6\}$
    (d) $\{x \mid -2 \leq x \leq 3\}$

62. $3x(x + 5)(x - 5)$

63.

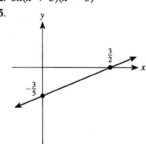

EXERCISES 7.6

1. $5\sqrt{5} - 15$ 3. $-2\sqrt{3} - 6\sqrt{5}$

5. $a + \sqrt{ab}$ 7. $\sqrt{10} + 2$

9. $6\sqrt{15} - 60$ 11. $-5\sqrt{6} + 14$

13. $\sqrt{15} + \sqrt{5} - 2\sqrt{3} - 2$

15. 2 17. $8 - 2\sqrt{15}$ 19. 3

21. 5 23. $4a - 4\sqrt{ab} + b$

25. $9x - 4y$ 27. $x - 6\sqrt{x} + 9$

29. $x - 3$ 31. $-2\sqrt{x}$ 33. -1

35. $2\sqrt{2} - 3\sqrt{3}$ 37. $\frac{5\sqrt{2} - \sqrt{7}}{4}$

39. $3\sqrt{2} + \sqrt{5}$ 41. $\frac{2 + \sqrt{7}}{2}$

43. $-\frac{\sqrt{2} + 3}{7}$ 45. $\frac{5\sqrt{5} - 5}{2}$

47. $\frac{2\sqrt{3} + 2\sqrt{a}}{3 - a}$ 49. $\frac{x + \sqrt{xy}}{x - y}$

51. $\frac{\sqrt{10} + 2}{3}$ 53. $\frac{2\sqrt{10} + 2}{9}$

55. $\frac{\sqrt{10} - 1}{2}$ 57. $5 + 2\sqrt{6}$

59. $\frac{18 + 5\sqrt{10}}{2}$ 61. $\sqrt{x} + \sqrt{y}$

63. $(x + 1)(\sqrt{x} + \sqrt{2})$ 65. 12

67. $9\sqrt{7} - 5\sqrt{3}$ 69. $x = -1$

71. $x = \frac{-3 + \sqrt{3}}{2}$

73. $x = \frac{-3 + \sqrt{15}}{2}$

Mini-Review

75. 12; 12; answers are identical

76. $3x^2 - 75$ 77. $x = -\frac{5}{2}, \frac{3}{2}$

78. -0.2 79. $2(3x - 4)(2x - 5)$

EXERCISES 7.7

1. $a = 49$ 3. $a = 31$

5. $x = \frac{26}{3}$ 7. $y = 116$

9. $x = \frac{10}{3}$ 11. $x = 16$

13. $a = 8.90$ 15. No solution

17. $x = 8$ 19. $x = -1$

21. $x = 64$ 23. $s = -243$

25. $y = -32$ 27. $x = 125$

29. $x = -8$ 31. $x = 118$

33. $x = \frac{1}{256}$ 35. $x = -11$

37. $x = 60.84$ 39. $x = 92.28$

41. $x = 9.49$ 43. $x = 8.60$

45. $x = 11$ 47. $x = 512$

49. $a = \frac{25}{3}$ 51. $x = 22$

53. $y = 53.76$ 55. $x = 2.88$

57. $x = -2$ 59. 151.25 ft

61. $L = 1,588.7$ cm   63. 2.9 in.

Mini-Review

66. $x = -2, 8$ 67. $x = 3$

68. $\frac{11x - 73}{20}$

EXERCISES 7.8

1. $-i$ 3. $-i$ 5. $-i$ 7. 1

9. $-i$ 11. -1 13. $i\sqrt{5}$

15. $3 - i\sqrt{2}$ 17. $-2\sqrt{7} + 4i$

19. $\frac{3}{5} - i\frac{\sqrt{2}}{5}$ 21. $2 - i\frac{\sqrt{3}}{3}$

23. $1 - i$ 25. 4 27. $15 - 35i$

29. $-4 + 2i$ 31. -15 33. -9

35. $-4 + 6i$ 37. $10 + 6i$

39. 0 41. $25 - 5i$ 43. 10

45. 53   47. $2i$ 49. -5

51. -1 53. $2 - \frac{5}{3}i$

55. $-1 - 3i$ 57. $-1 - \frac{5}{2}i$

59. $-\frac{4}{29} + \frac{10}{29}i$ 61. $\frac{10}{29} + \frac{4}{29}i$

63. $\frac{3}{5} + \frac{4}{5}i$ 65. $-\frac{21}{29} - \frac{20}{29}i$

67. $\frac{1}{29} - \frac{41}{29}i$ 69. $\frac{5}{34} - \frac{31}{34}i$

71. $x = -2 + i$

73. $x = -1 + i\dfrac{\sqrt{6}}{2}$

75. $x^2 + 4 = 0$
Substitute $x = 2i$.
$(2i)^2 + 4 \overset{?}{=} 0$
$4i^2 + 4 \overset{?}{=} 0$
$4(-1) + 4 \overset{\checkmark}{=} 0$

77. $x^2 - 4x + 5 = 0$
Substitute $x = 2 - i$.
$(2 - i)^2 - 4(2 - i) + 5 \overset{?}{=} 0$
$4 - 4i + i^2 - 8 + 4i + 5 \overset{?}{=} 0$
$4 - 4i - 1 - 8 + 4i + 5 \overset{\checkmark}{=} 0$

Mini-Review

82. $\dfrac{-4x}{x + 4}$ 83. $\dfrac{1}{(x - 6)^2}$

84. $x = \dfrac{7}{a - 6}$ 85. $\{x \mid x \neq \pm 5\}$

Chapter 7 Review Exercises

1. x^{12} 2. $x^{11}y^9$ 3. $-6x^4y^5$

4. $-30x^3y^6$ 5. a^{12} 6. b^{20}

7. $a^{14}b^{21}$ 8. $r^{16}s^{24}$ 9. $a^{10}b^9$

10. x^7y^{22} 11. $a^7b^8c^7$ 12. $-162x^8y^5$

13. $\dfrac{1}{a}$ 14. x^5 15. 1   16. y^2

17. $\dfrac{1}{x^{16}y^{14}}$ 18. $\dfrac{1}{a^2b^6}$ 19. a^4

20. $\dfrac{a^4b^4}{c^4}$ 21. $9a^4x^4$ 22. $-3x^6y^2$

23. $\dfrac{-72y^8}{x^2}$ 24. $\dfrac{-72b^5}{125a^5}$ 25. $\dfrac{1}{a^2}$

26. $\dfrac{1}{x^9}$ 27. $\dfrac{x^8}{y^{20}}$ 28. $\dfrac{1}{x^4}$

29. $-\dfrac{1}{162}$ 30. 1   31. 1   32. 1

33. $\dfrac{1}{x^4}$ 34. $\dfrac{y}{x^4}$ 35. x^8 36. a^8b^{12}

37. $\dfrac{r^{11}}{s^5}$ 38. $-\dfrac{s^{11}}{3r^5}$ 39. $\dfrac{25}{4}$ 40. $\dfrac{256}{81}$

41. $\dfrac{27y^8}{4xz^2}$ 42. $\dfrac{8x}{9yz^8}$ 43. $\dfrac{x^2 - y^2}{xy}$

44. $\dfrac{y^4 + 4xy^2 + 4x^2}{x^2y^4}$ 45. $\dfrac{y^3 + x}{y^5}$

46. $\dfrac{b(b + a^2)}{a}$ 47. 28,300   48. 6.29

49. 0.0000796   50. 0.0000008264

51. 9.259×10^1 52. 5.78×10^{-3}

53. 6.25897×10^5 54. 7.3×10^{-6}

55. 0.00000001   56. 1,000

57. $x^{5/6}$ 58. $\dfrac{1}{y^{1/6}}$ 59. x 60. $y^{1/12}$

61. $x^{13/30}$ 62. $\dfrac{s^{1/3}}{r^{5/6}}$ 63. a^5b^3

64. $\dfrac{y^3}{x}$ 65. $\dfrac{x^{5/6}}{y^{7/6}}$ 66. $\dfrac{1}{a^{1/6}}$ 67. 2^{10}

68. $\dfrac{1}{a^{1/6}} - \dfrac{b^{1/2}}{a^{2/3}} = \dfrac{a^{1/2} - b^{1/2}}{a^{2/3}}$

69. $a^{2/3} - b^{2/3}$ 70. $\dfrac{1}{a} + \dfrac{4b^{1/2}}{a^{1/2}} + 4b$

71. $\sqrt{x}$ 72. $\sqrt[3]{x}$ 73. $x\sqrt{y}$

74. $\sqrt{xy}$ 75. $\sqrt[3]{m^2}$ 76. $\sqrt{m^3}$

77. $\sqrt[4]{(5x)^3}$ 78. $5\sqrt[4]{x^3}$ 79. $a^{1/3}$

80. $t^{1/5}$ 81. $-n^{4/5}$ 82. $t^{5/3}$ 83. $t^{-7/5}$

84. $t^{-5/7}$ 85. 36   86. $3\sqrt[3]{2}$

87. x^{30} 88. x^{15} 89. $2xy^2\sqrt[3]{6xy^2}$

90. $2x^4y^6\sqrt{7xy}$ 91. $15x\sqrt{y}$

92. $24ab$ 93. $2x^4y^2\sqrt{y}$ 94. $6x^7y^2$

95. $\dfrac{2}{3}$ 96. $\dfrac{2}{3}$ 97. $\dfrac{\sqrt{y}}{x}$ 98. $\dfrac{\sqrt{xy}}{x}$

99. $\dfrac{4\sqrt{ab}}{a^2b}$ 100. $\dfrac{9y\sqrt{2x}}{2x}$ 101. $\dfrac{\sqrt{5a}}{a}$

102. $\dfrac{\sqrt[3]{5a^2}}{a}$ 103. $\dfrac{2\sqrt[3]{4a^2}}{a}$

104. $\dfrac{2\sqrt[3]{4a}}{a}$ 105. $\sqrt[3]{x^2}$ 106. $\sqrt[8]{x^3}$

107. $\sqrt[6]{2^5}$ 108. $\sqrt[6]{2}$ 109. 0

110. $33\sqrt{6}$ 111. 0

112. $2s^2t^2\sqrt{s} - 3s^2t^2\sqrt{t}$

113. $\dfrac{3\sqrt{6} + 2\sqrt{15}}{6}$

114. $\dfrac{3\sqrt{35} + 7\sqrt{6}}{21}$

115. 0   116. $-\sqrt{10}$ 117. $27 - 7\sqrt{21}$

118. $6x + 4\sqrt{x} - 3\sqrt{5x} - 2\sqrt{5}$

119. $x - 10\sqrt{x} + 25$

120. $10 - 2\sqrt{21}$ 121. $-14\sqrt{a} - 42$

122. $12 - 6\sqrt{b}$ 123. $6\sqrt{5} - 6\sqrt{3}$

124. $\sqrt{m} + n$ 125. $4\sqrt{2x} + 4\sqrt{5y}$

126. $-3\sqrt{2}$ 127. $x = 27$ 128. $x = \dfrac{4}{3}$

129. $x = 27$ 130. $x = \dfrac{14}{3}$

131. $x = 85$ 132. $x = 5$

133. $x = 16$ 134. $x = 80$

135. $x = 17.5$ 136. $x = 35.7$

137. 2.1 psi   138. 1.7 psi

139. $-i$ 140. i 141. 1   142. -1

143. $9 - i$ 144. $1 - 5i$

145. $8 - 25i$ 146. 41

147. $-6 - 8i$ 148. $-5 - 10i$

149. $5 - 12i$ 150. $-5 - 12i$

151. -37 152. $34 - 6i$

153. $\dfrac{9}{10} - \dfrac{13}{10}i$ 154. $-i$

Chapter 7 Practice Test

1. a^4b^{11} 2. $-200x^8y^3$

3. $-\dfrac{4b^2y^2}{3ax^2}$ 4. $-\dfrac{2x^4}{9y^5}$ 5. $\dfrac{9r^4s^{10}}{25}$

6. $\dfrac{1}{3}$ 7. $x^{7/3}$ 8. $\dfrac{1 + x^2}{xy}$

9. $x - x^{4/3}$ 10. (a) -5 (b) $-\dfrac{1}{8}$

11. $3\sqrt[3]{a^2}$ 12. 0.0000032

13. In one hour it travels
$186{,}000 \times 60 \times 60 =$
6.696×10^8 miles.

14. $3x^2y^3$ 15. $2x\sqrt[3]{y^2}$ 16. $6x^4y$

17. $\dfrac{\sqrt{35}}{7}$ 18. $\dfrac{2\sqrt{3}}{3}$ 19. $\dfrac{3xy^2\sqrt{2}}{2}$

20. $\sqrt[6]{5^3}$ 21. $5\sqrt{2}$

22. $x - 6\sqrt{x} + 9$ 23. $3 + \sqrt{6}$

24. $x = 19$ 25. $x = 121$

26. $x = 17.30$ 27. $-i$ 28. $-5 - 5i$

29. $-\dfrac{4}{5} - \dfrac{7}{5}i$

EXERCISES 8.1

1. (a) $P(30) = 14{,}862$;
$P(50) = 21{,}270$;
$P(70) = 24{,}878$;
$P(100) = 25{,}040$;
$P(120) = 21{,}648$ dollars. As the
number of items, x, increases,
profit rises for a while, and when
the number of items exceeds \$100,
the profit begins to decrease.

(b) The profit seems to reach a
maximum of \$25,700 occurring
between 85 and 86 items.

3. (a) $s(5) = 3{,}225$; $s(10) = 5{,}650$;
$s(20) = 8{,}100$; $s(30) = 7{,}350$;
$s(40) = 3{,}400$; $s(45) = 225$

(b) The maximum height is about
8,200 ft, occurring at
20–25 seconds.

(c) The rocket hits the ground
somewhere between 45 and
46 seconds.

5. (a) $A(x) = 100x - x^2$
   (b) $A(10) = 900; A(40) = 2,400;$
   $A(60) = 2,400; A(70) = 2,100;$
   $A(90) = 900$ sq ft.
   As the length, x, increases, the area increases until the length x is a value between 40 and 60 feet. The area then decreases as the length exceeds that value.
   (c) The maximum area occurs at 50 ft, so the dimensions are $50' \times 50'$, and the maximum area is 2,500 sq feet for these dimensions.

7. Let $x =$ the first number, then the other number is $225 - x$. Their product is $A = x(225 - x)$. A will be a maximum when x is between 112 and 113, and hence the other number will be between 112 and 113 (exact values are 112.5 for each number).

9. (a) $A(x) = 2x\left(\frac{1,000 - 4x}{3}\right) = \frac{2,000x - 8x^2}{3}$
   (b) $A(50) = 26,666.67;$
   $A(100) = 40,000;$
   $A(120) = 41,600;$
   $A(150) = 40,000;$
   $A(200) = 26,666.67$ sq ft.
   As the length, x, increases, the area increases until the length x is a value around 120 ft. The area then decreases as the length exceeds that value.
   (c) The maximum area occurs at about 125 ft, and the area for $x = 125$ is about 41,667 sq ft where $y = 166.7$ ft.

11. (a) 24 items   (b) $5 per item
   (c)

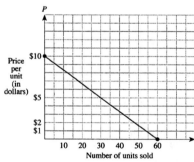

   (d) $R(x) = x\left(10 - \frac{x}{6}\right)$
   (e) $R(5) = 45.83; R(15) = 112.5;$
   $R(25) = 145.83; R(35) = 145.83;$
   $R(40) = 133.33$ dollars.
   As the number of units sold, x, increases, the revenue increases until the number of units sold is a value between 25 and 45. Then the revenue decreases as the number of units sold exceeds that value.

(f) The maximum revenue occurs at 30 units sold, and the maximum revenue is $150.

13. (a) $R(x) = (200,000 - 7,250x)(3 + 0.25x)$
   (b) $R(3) = 668,437.50;$
   $R(6) = 704,250;$
   $R(9) = 707,437.50;$
   $R(12) = 678,000$ dollars.
   As the number of 25¢ price increases rises, the revenue increases until the number of increases reaches about 8. The revenue then decreases as the number of increases exceeds that value.
   (c) The maximum revenue occurs at $x \approx 8$, so the price is $3 + 0.25(8) = \$5$. The revenue at $x = 8$ is $710,000.

Mini-Review

15. -247 16. $-\frac{2}{3} < x < \frac{10}{3}$

17. $x \leq -\frac{1}{2}$ or $x \geq \frac{11}{2}$

18. Let $x =$ # of more expensive models, $y =$ # of less expensive models; $x + 0.75y = 150, 0.5x + 0.25y = 60;$ 60 more expensive models, 120 less expensive models

EXERCISES 8.2

1. $x = -2, 3$ 3. $x = \pm 5$
5. $x = 0, 4$ 7. $x = 6, -2$
9. $y = 0, 7$ 11. $x = \pm 4$
13. $c = \pm\frac{4}{3}$ 15. $a = \pm\frac{3}{2}$
17. $x = 3, -2$ 19. $y = 1, \frac{1}{2}$
21. $x = \pm\sqrt{6}$ 23. $x = \pm\frac{\sqrt{133}}{7}$
25. $x = 5, -2$ 27. $a = -\frac{1}{3}, \frac{1}{2}$
29. $y = \frac{3}{2}, -\frac{2}{3}$ 31. $x = \pm\frac{i\sqrt{15}}{3}$
33. $s = -\frac{5}{6}, 2$ 35. $x = 3, -7$
37. $x = 5, 1$ 39. $x = -9$
41. $x = \pm i\sqrt{2}$ 43. $x = 8 \pm 2\sqrt{2}$
45. $y = 5 \pm 4i$ 47. $x = 2, 3$
49. $a = \pm\sqrt{13}$ 51. $x = -\frac{4}{3}$
53. $x = 1$ 55. $x = 5$
57. $x = \frac{14}{3}, -1$ 59. $a = \pm\frac{\sqrt{b}}{2}$
61. $y = \pm\frac{\sqrt{63 - 35x^2}}{7}$
63. $r = \frac{\sqrt{6V\pi}}{2\pi}$ 65. $a = \pm 2b$
67. $x = 3y, -2y$
69. Let $x =$ number; $x^2 - 5 = 5x + 1; x = 6$

71. Let $x =$ number; $x^2 + 64 = 68;$ $x = 2$
73. Let $x =$ number; $(x + 6)^2 = 169;$ $x = -19$ or $x = 7$
75. Let $x =$ number; $x + \frac{1}{x} = \frac{13}{6};$ $x = \frac{2}{3}$ or $x = \frac{3}{2}$
77. (a) Profit $= \$0$ (b) Price $= \$6$
79. (a) $h(1) = 24$ ft
   (b) $t = \frac{\sqrt{10}}{2}$ sec ≈ 1.58 sec
   (c) 40 ft
81. Let $x =$ width; $(x + 2)(x) = 80;$ length $= 10$ ft, width $= 8$ ft
83. Let side of square $= x$ inches; $x^2 = 60; 2\sqrt{15} \approx 7.75$ inches (each side)
85. Let $x =$ large number; $(x)(x - 2) = 120; x = 12$ or $x = -10;$ two sets of numbers: 12 and 10; -12 and -10
87. Let $x =$ one number; $x(3x + 2) = 85;$ two sets of numbers: 5 and 17, $-\frac{17}{3}$ and -15
89. Length of other leg $= \sqrt{33} \approx 5.74''$
91. Dimensions are 8, $2\frac{1}{3}$, and $8\frac{1}{3}$
93. Length of diagonal $= \sqrt{193} \approx 13.9''$
95. It reaches $2\sqrt{209} \approx 28.9$ ft high
97. Area $= 32$ sq in.
99. Area $= 5\sqrt{119} \approx 54.54$ sq in.
101. $n = -3, 4$
103. Let $x =$ width of picture; $(x + 2)(2x + 2) = 60;$ dimensions of picture are 4 in. by 8 in.
105. Let $r =$ speed of boat in still water; $\frac{20}{r - 5} + \frac{10}{r + 5} = \frac{4}{3};$ 25 kph

EXERCISES 8.3

1. $x = 3 \pm \sqrt{10}$ 3. $c = 1 \pm \sqrt{6}$
5. $y = \frac{-5 \pm \sqrt{33}}{2}$
7. $x = \frac{-3 \pm \sqrt{5}}{2}$
9. $a = \frac{1 \pm \sqrt{17}}{2}$ 11. $a = -1 \pm i$
13. $x = -2 \pm \sqrt{6}$
15. $a = \frac{1 \pm \sqrt{33}}{2}$
17. $x = \frac{5 \pm i\sqrt{19}}{2}$
19. $x = \frac{-5 \pm \sqrt{195}}{5}$

21. $t = -\frac{3}{2}, 1$ **23.** $x = 2 \pm \sqrt{15}$

25. $x = \frac{1}{4}, 3$ **27.** $a = \frac{1 \pm i\sqrt{3}}{2}$

29. $y = \frac{-1 \pm 3i}{2}$ **31.** $n = \frac{1 \pm i\sqrt{7}}{2}$

33. $t = \frac{-1 \pm i\sqrt{7}}{2}$

35. $x = \frac{-2 \pm \sqrt{19}}{5}$

Mini-Review

41. $x = 30, y = 15$ **42.** $27x^2y^4$

43. 6 **44.** $y = \frac{7}{2}x - 14$

EXERCISES 8.4

1. $x = 5, -1$ **3.** $a = \frac{3 \pm \sqrt{41}}{4}$

5. $y = \frac{2 \pm \sqrt{2}}{2}$

7. $y = \frac{-7 \pm \sqrt{77}}{2}$

9. $a = \frac{-1 \pm i\sqrt{23}}{6}$

11. $s = -1 \pm 3i$
13. Roots are not real.
15. Roots are real and distinct.
17. Roots are real and distinct.
19. Roots are real and distinct.

21. $a = 4, -1$ **23.** $y = \pm\frac{\sqrt{6}}{4}$

25. $x = \frac{4}{5}, \frac{3}{2}$ **27.** $x = 1$

29. $x = \frac{5}{2}, -\frac{1}{5}$ **31.** $a = 0, -1$

33. $x = 0.3, 5$ **35.** $x = \frac{3 \pm i\sqrt{11}}{2}$

37. $s = \pm\sqrt{6}$ **39.** $x = \frac{-1 \pm i\sqrt{39}}{2}$

41. $x = \frac{19}{4}$ **43.** $x = -2.7, 1.8$

45. $a = \frac{2 \pm i\sqrt{2}}{3}$

47. $x = \frac{5 \pm \sqrt{57}}{2}$

49. $a = 1, \frac{1}{2}$ **51.** $z = \frac{7}{6}$ **53.** $y = \frac{6}{5}$
55. $x = -0.05, 2,000.05$

57. $a = \frac{1 \pm \sqrt{97}}{4}$

59. $a = \frac{-1 \pm i\sqrt{15}}{2}$

61. Let x = number; $x(x - 3) = 40$;
two sets of numbers: 8 and 5,
-5 and -8

63. Hypotenuse = $\sqrt{73} \approx 8.54''$

65. Length of diagonal = $5\sqrt{2} \approx 7.07''$

67. Length of side = $4\sqrt{2} \approx 5.66''$

69. $\frac{c - 1}{c} = -\frac{c}{c - 2}; c = \frac{3 \pm i\sqrt{7}}{4};$
since c is not real, no solution.

71. 60 items
73. Let x = width of path;
$\pi(10 + x)^2 - \pi(10)^2 = 44\pi$;
width of path is 2 ft.
75. Let x = price per roll the first
week, $x - 2$ = price per roll the
second week;

$$(x - 2)\left(2,250 - \frac{10,000}{x}\right) = 10,000;$$

$10 per roll and $8 per roll

Mini-Review

80. 1 **81.** $\frac{1}{9}$ **82.** $\frac{6}{x(x - 3)}$

83. Let x = amount invested at 8%,
y = amount invested at 10%;
$0.08x + 0.10y = 730$,
$0.10x + 0.08y = 710$;
$8,000 altogether

EXERCISES 8.5

1. $x = \frac{9}{4}$ **3.** $x = 4$ **5.** $a = 13$
7. $a = 8$ **9.** $x = 8$ **11.** $a = 1$
13. $y = 1$ **15.** $a = 2$ **17.** $s = 9$
19. $a = -2$ **21.** $x = (b - a)^2$

23. $L = \frac{g^2T^2}{\pi}$

25. $x = \frac{b^2 + 11b + 36}{5}$

27. $n = \left(\frac{ts}{\overline{X} - a}\right)^2$ **29.** $x = 0, 5, -3$

31. $a = 0, \frac{2}{3}, -\frac{1}{2}$ **33.** $y = \pm 4, \pm 1$

35. $a = \pm 2, \pm\sqrt{2}$

37. $b = \pm 4, \pm\sqrt{7}$

39. $x = \pm 2\sqrt{2}, \pm 1$

41. $x = \pm 1$ **43.** $x = \pm 8$ **45.** $x = 4$

47. $y = 125, y = -1$

49. No solution **51.** $x = \frac{1}{2}, \frac{1}{3}$

53. $x = -2, 3$ **55.** $x = \pm\frac{1}{3}, \pm\frac{1}{2}$
57. $a = 81$ **59.** $x = 625$
61. $a = -7$ **63.** $x = \frac{2}{3}, -\frac{1}{2}$

65. $x = -2, 1, \frac{-1 \pm i\sqrt{7}}{2}$

67. $a = 10, -1, 5, -2$ **69.** 0.77

Mini-Review

72. $x = 3$ **73.** $m = -\frac{2}{5}$

74. $a = \frac{3}{r + 3}$ **75.** 1,422,525

EXERCISES 8.6

1.

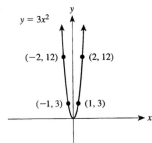

3.

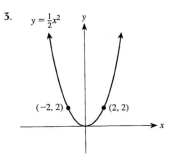

5.

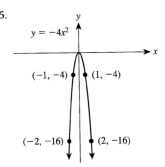

7.

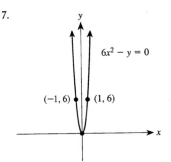

9.

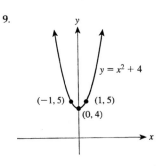

69.

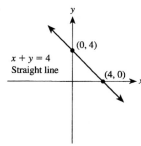

$x + y = 4$
Straight line

71. $(x - 1)^2 + \left(y - \dfrac{3}{2}\right)^2 = \dfrac{205}{4}$

73. $(x - 3)^2 + (y + 5)^2 = 122$

75. $C = 4\pi\sqrt{17}$

77. $(x - 3)^2 + (y + 2)^2 = 4$

79. $(x - 3)^2 + (y + 3)^2 = 9$

Mini-Review

83. 10^7 **84.** $\dfrac{y^2 + x}{x^2 y}$

85. $2\sqrt{x} - \sqrt[3]{25x^2}$ **86.** 16

Chapter 8 Review Exercises

1. (a) $d(30) = 369.9,$
$d(40) = 417.5,$
$d(50) = 427.4,$
$d(60) = 399.5$
(b) Approx. 35 mph and 60 mph

2. (a) $R(x) =$
$(36,000 + 3,000x)(4 - 0.25x) =$
$144,000 + 3,000x - 750x^2$
(b) At fare $= 3.50, x = 2$ and
the revenue is \$147,000.

3. $y = -\dfrac{1}{2}, 1$ **4.** $a = -\dfrac{2}{3}, 5$

5. $x = -\dfrac{4}{3}, 7$ **6.** $a = \dfrac{1}{2}, -\dfrac{1}{5}$

7. $a = \pm 9$ **8.** $y = \pm\sqrt{65}$

9. $z = \pm i\sqrt{5}$ **10.** $r = \pm\dfrac{i\sqrt{10}}{2}$

11. $x = 3$ **12.** $a = 2, -1$

13. $a = 5, -2$ **14.** $y = 3, -\dfrac{1}{2}$

15. $x = \pm\sqrt{5}$ **16.** $a = 6, 4$

17. $x = -6, 3$ **18.** $x = -1, -\dfrac{11}{3}$

19. $x = -1 \pm \sqrt{5}$ **20.** $x = 1 \pm \sqrt{5}$

21. $y = \dfrac{-2 \pm \sqrt{10}}{2}$

22. $y = \dfrac{-2 \pm i\sqrt{2}}{2}$

23. $a = \dfrac{-3 \pm 2\sqrt{6}}{3}$

24. $a = \dfrac{3 \pm i\sqrt{6}}{3}$

25. $a = \dfrac{4 \pm \sqrt{43}}{2}$

26. $a = \pm\dfrac{\sqrt{22}}{2}$

27. $a = -\dfrac{1}{3}, \dfrac{5}{2}$ **28.** $x = 4, -\dfrac{2}{5}$

29. $a \approx -0.7, 2.5$ **30.** $y = 1, -\dfrac{7}{2}$

31. $a = \pm 1$ **32.** $a = 5, -3$

33. $x = 2 \pm \sqrt{6}$ **34.** $y = 1 \pm \sqrt{39}$

35. $t = -4$ **36.** $u = \dfrac{5}{3}$

37. $x = \pm\dfrac{\sqrt{6}}{2}$ **38.** $x = \pm\dfrac{\sqrt{57}}{3}$

39. $x = 0$ **40.** $x = \dfrac{3.8 \pm i\sqrt{145.4}}{14.8}$

41. $x = 2 \pm \sqrt{2}$

42. $x \approx -1.66, 2.16$

43. $z = 1 \pm \sqrt{10}$ **44.** $z = 3, -1$

45. $x = \dfrac{-16 \pm \sqrt{6}}{5}$

46. $x = \dfrac{-7 \pm \sqrt{201}}{4}$

47. $x = \dfrac{4 \pm \sqrt{22}}{2}$ **48.** $x = 9, -1$

49. $r = \dfrac{\sqrt{\pi A h}}{\pi h}$ **50.** $t = \dfrac{\sqrt{2lg}}{g}$

51. $x = \dfrac{-3y}{2}, x = y$

52. $y = 5x, y = -x$

53. $a = 3$ **54.** $a = 4, 1$

55. $a = 5$ **56.** $y = 0, 3$

57. $x \approx 44.8$ **58.** $x = 16$

59. $x = 7, 4$ **60.** $x = 5$

61. $y = \dfrac{x^2 - z}{3}$ **62.** $y = \dfrac{x^2 + z}{5}$

63. $y = \dfrac{(x - z)^2}{3}$ **64.** $y = \dfrac{(x + z)^2}{5}$

65. $x = 0, 5, -3$ **66.** $x = 0, 7, -5$

67. $x = 0, 3, -\dfrac{1}{2}$ **68.** $x = 0, -1, \dfrac{2}{3}$

69. $a = \pm 4, \pm 1$ **70.** $y = \pm 3$

71. $y = \pm 2, \pm i$ **72.** $a = \pm 3, \pm 2i$

73. $z = \pm\sqrt{5}, \pm 1$ **74.** $z = \pm 3, \pm\sqrt{2}$

75. $a = 81$ **76.** $a = 27, -8$

77. $x = 27, -\dfrac{1}{8}$ **78.** $x = 81$

79. $x = 625$ **80.** $x = 16, 81$

81. $x = -1, \dfrac{3}{2}$ **82.** $x = -\dfrac{5}{3}, 1$

83.

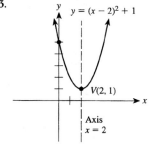

$y = (x - 2)^2 + 1$

$V(2, 1)$

Axis
$x = 2$

84.

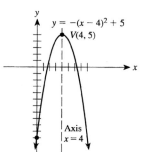

$y = -(x - 4)^2 + 5$
$V(4, 5)$

Axis
$x = 4$

85.

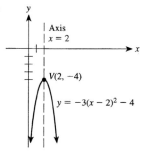

Axis
$x = 2$

$V(2, -4)$

$y = -3(x - 2)^2 - 4$

86.

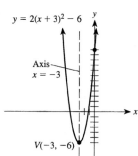

$y = 2(x + 3)^2 - 6$

Axis
$x = -3$

$V(-3, -6)$

87. $y = 2(x - 3)^2 - 14;$
vertex: $(3, -14)$; axis: $x = 3$

88. $y = 2\left(x - \dfrac{3}{2}\right)^2 - \dfrac{7}{2};$
vertex: $\left(\dfrac{3}{2}, -\dfrac{7}{2}\right)$; axis: $x = \dfrac{3}{2}$

89. $y = -(x - 2)^2 - 8;$
vertex: $(2, -8)$; axis: $x = 2$

90. $y = -(x + 3)^2 + 9;$
vertex: $(-3, 9)$; axis: $x = -3$

91.

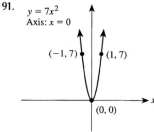

$y = 7x^2$
Axis: $x = 0$

$(-1, 7)$ $(1, 7)$

$(0, 0)$